Physical Education: Theory and Practice

Physical Education: Theory and Practice

Damien Davis, Dip.Phys. Ed., B. Ed., G.D.S.S., MDA Noosa Grammar School, Queensland
Tom Kimmet, Cert.Ed. (Human Movt), Marcellin College, Victoria
Margaret Auty, B.A., Dip. Ed., B.App.Sci. (Human Movt), McLeod High School, Victoria

AUTHOR'S DEDICATIONS:
DAMIEN DAVIS
- Dedicated to Gerry, Luke and Emma.
TOM KIMMET
- Dedicated to Eileen, Jenny and Thomas.
MARGARET AUTY
- Dedicated to Glen, Philip and my parents.

First published 1986 by
MACMILLAN EDUCATION AUSTRALIA PTY LTD
107 Moray Street, South Melbourne 3205
Reprinted 1986, 1987 (twice), 1988 (twice), 1989 (twice),
1990, 1991, 1992, 1993 (twice), 1995 (twice)

Associated companies and representatives
throughout the world.

National Library of Australia
cataloguing in publication data.

Davis, Damien
Physical education.

Bibliography.
Includes index.
ISBN 0 333 43021 2.

1. Physical fitness. 2. Physical education and
training. I. Kimmet, Tom. II. Auty, Margaret. III.
Title.

613.7

Set in Plantin by
Graphicraft Typesetters Ltd, Hong Kong
Printed in Malaysia by
Chee Leong Press Sdn Bhd, Ipoh.

Contents

Preface

Senior Secondary Physical Education is now an established academic subject, with one of the highest growth rates of any subject area in Australia. Unfortunately, until now the many teachers and students who have taken the subject at Years 11 and 12 have had to battle through many unsuitable textbooks to find all the material included in the syllabus. *Physical Education: Theory and Practice* includes all the relevant material for any Year 11 or 12 Physical Education course, and is pitched at a level that is appropriate to Senior Secondary students. Both teachers and students now have a textbook written by experienced and practising Physical Education teachers.

Physical Education: Theory and Practice covers all the sub-disciplines of Physical Education — anatomy, physiology, exercise physiology, biomechanics, motor learning (skill acquisition), history and sociology. Each chapter is followed by worksheets and laboratories designed to reinforce the theory, assist with student revision and reduce the burden of teacher preparation. The aim of this book is to make the learning of Senior Physical Education the relevant and enjoyable experience it should be.

Acknowledgements

The authors and publishers are grateful to the following for permission to reproduce copyright material:

The *Age* for the newspaper articles on pp. 342, 370–1, 372–3, 375–6, 379–81, 391–3, 402, 403, 403–4; Australian Government Publishing Service for Figures 1.1, 8.12, 9.2, 18.6, 19.8, 19.9, adapted from *Towards Better Coaching*, Pyke, 1980, and for the extract on pp. 428–9 from *The Way We P(l)ay*, 1983; Burgess International Group Inc. for Figures 31.7, 31.8, adapted from *Motor Learning Principles and Practices*, J. N. Drowatzky, 1981; CBS College Publishing for Figures 4.12, 4.13, 6.1, 8.11, 8.16, 18.1, 18.4, 19.3, 19.4, 19.5, 20.5, 20.6, adapted from *The Physiological Basis of Physical Education and Athletics*, 3/e, Edward L. Fox and Donald K. Mathews, copyright © 1981 by CBS College Publishing, Copyright © 1971 & 1976 by W. B. Saunders Company, for Figures 6.3, 6.4, 6.5, 8.1, 8.10, 8.13, 8.15, 18.3, 20.1, 20.2, adapted from *Sports Physiology*, 2/e, Edward L. Fox, copyright © 1984 by CBS College Publishing. Copyright 1979 by W. B. Saunders Company, and for some of the exercises in Part 3, adapted from *Concepts in Kinesiology*, 2/e, Richard Groves and David N. Camaione, copyright © 1983 by CBS College Publishing. Copyright 1975 by W. B. Saunders Company; Professors D. W. Edington and V. R. Edington for Figures 6.2, 6.12, 7.3, 18.7, adapted from *The Biology of Physical Activity*, Edington and Edington, Houghton Mifflin Company, 1976; Robert V. Hockey for Figures 13.8, 13.9, 13.10, 13.12, 13.13, 13.14, 13.15, 13.16, and the extract 'Risko: How to assess cardiovascular disease risk' on pp. 106–7, adapted from *Physical Fitness: The pathway to healthful living*, 4/e, R. V. Hockey, The C. V. Mosby Co.; Human Kinetics Publishers for Figure 29.8, adapted from *Motor Control and Learing*, R. A. Schmidt, 1982, Human Kinetics Publishers, Champaign, I1.; Jonathan Cape for the extract on p. 374 from *The Soccer Tribe* by Desmond Morris; Macmillan Publishing Company, New York, for Figures 32.3, 33.1, 33.2, adapted from *Motor Learning and Human Performance*, 2/e, Robert N. Singer © 1975; *The New York Times* for the newspaper article on pp. 415–16; Prentice-Hall Inc. for Figures 23.10, 27.12, 27.23, adapted from *The Biomechanics of Sports Techniques*, 2/e, © 1978, Prentice-Hall, Inc., Englewood Cliffs, New Jersey, and for Figures, 29.11, 31.2, adapted from *The Dynamics of Motor-Skill Acquisition*, Margaret D. Robb, © 1972, Prentice-Hall, Inc., Englewood Cliffs, New Jersey; *Sports Coach* for the articles on pp. 396–8, 406–8, 420–4, and 424–6; Michael Garnett and Richard Hall of The Melbourne Royal Tennis Club for Figure 40.8, and the extracts on pp. 351, 352.

Photographs: The *Age*, Figures 42.1, 42.2, 45.2, 45.3, 47.4, 50.1, 50.2; The Herald and Weekly Times Ltd, Figures 49.1, 49.2.

Whilst every care has been taken to trace and acknowledge copyright, the publishers tender their apologies for any accidental infringement where copyright has proved untraceable. They would be please to come to a suitable arrangement with the rightful owner in each case.

Cover by Jan Schmoeger.
Interior illustrations and diagrams by Joseph Szabo,
Anneke Veenstra, Sylvia Isaac and Randy Glusac.

Part One:
Anatomy, physiology and health in society

1. The skeletal system

Functions of the skeleton

The skeleton provides four basic functions:

(1) It *supports* the organs and tissues of the body. Without this support they would collapse under their own weight.

(2) It provides *protection* for internal organs. For example, the cranium protects the brain, the orbits protect the eyes, and the rib cage protects the heart and lungs.

(3) It provides a base for the attachment of muscles, and so allows *movement*, with the bones acting as levers.

(4) The bones are a source of *supply* of blood cells and a *store* for minerals required for body functions. For example, both red and white blood cells are produced in the bone marrow.

Structure of the skeleton

There are about 206 bones in the skeleton (see Figure 1.1), and they are divided into two main groups:

(1) The **axial** skeleton

(2) The **appendicular** skeleton.

The axial skeleton

The axial skeleton consists of the skull, the spine and the rib cage (thorax), and forms the basic structure by which the rest of the skeleton is supported.

(1) The skull

All together, the **cranium** consists of eight bones fused together, while the **face** has fourteen bones. Some are fused together while others, like the lower jaw (**mandible**), can move independently.

(2) The spine

The spine consists of seven **cervical**, twelve **thoracic** and five **lumbar vertebrae**. The bottom nine bones (five in the **sacrum** and four in the **coccyx**) are fused together to form one solid bone.

The first cervical vertebra is the **atlas**. The second cervical vertebra is the **axis**. The coccyx is said to be the remnants of a tail.

(3) The thorax

The thorax consists of twelve pairs of **ribs**, which join the thoracic vertebrae. The top ten pairs are joined to the **sternum** at the front by **cartilage**. The remaining two pairs have 'free' ends.

The appendicular skeleton

The appendicular skeleton consists of the limbs joined together by the girdles of the pelvis and shoulders.

(1) The shoulder girdle

The shoulder girdle consists of the **clavicle** joined to the top of the sternum at one end, and holding the **scapula** away from the rib cage at the other. There is a cavity on the scapula (the glenoid fossa) for the joint with the **humerus**.

(2) The arm

The humerus joins the **ulna** and the **radius** at the elbow and, in turn, these are joined to a highly mobile wrist and hand.

(3) The wrist

The ulnar and the radius join two rows of four **carpal bones** at the wrist.

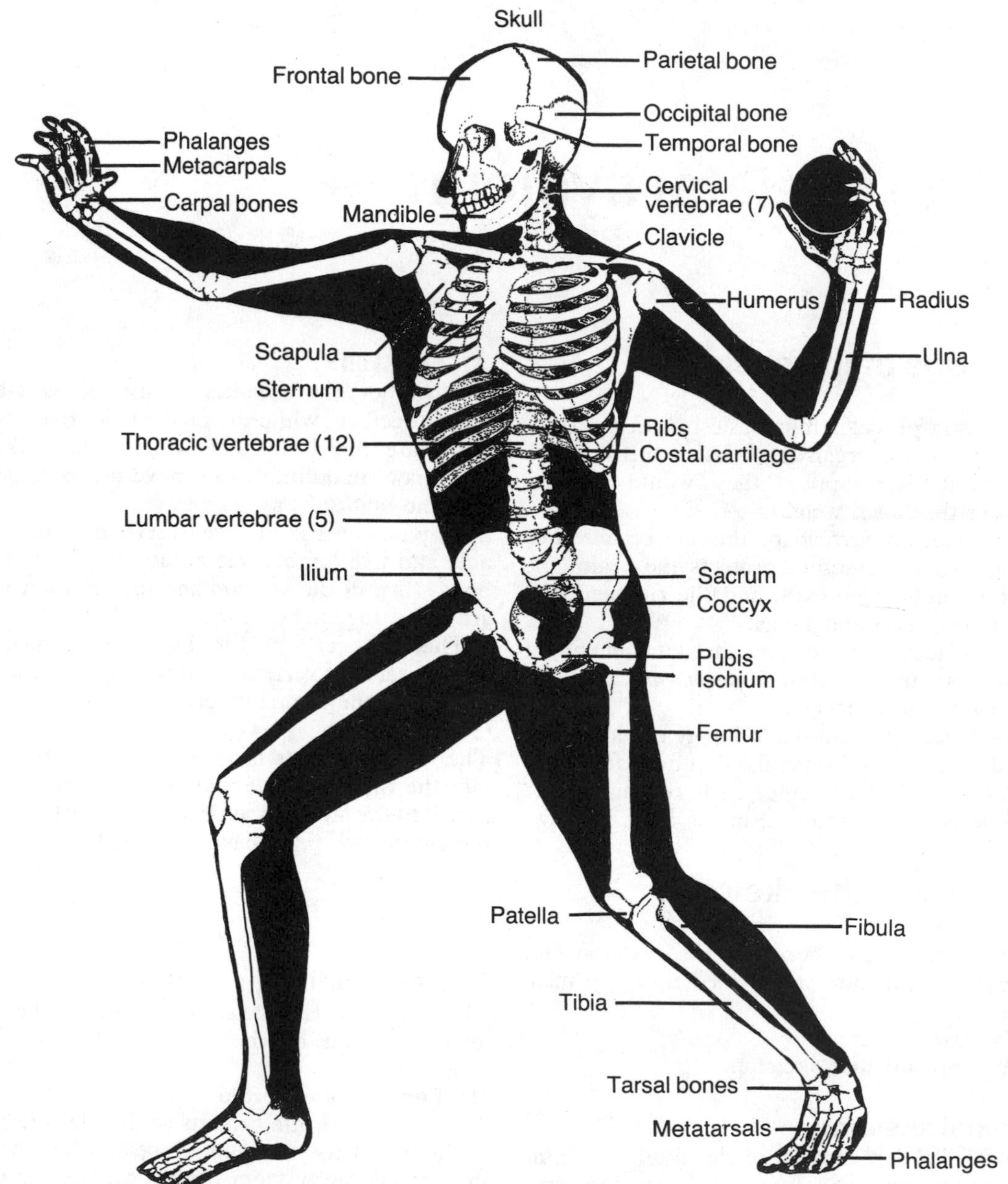

Figure 1.1 Skeletal framework of man.

(4) The hand

The palm of the hand consists of five **metacarpal bones**, which join with the phalanges of the thumb and fingers.

(5) The leg

The **femur** is the longest, heaviest and strongest bone in the body. It bears the weight of the body and the shocks caused by movement.

The femur fits into a socket (the **acetabulum**) in the pelvis and, at the other end, joins the **tibia** to form the knee joint. The **patella**, in front, protects this joint. The **fibula** acts as a support to the ankle and to the muscles of the lower leg.

(6) The foot

The seven **tarsals** and five **metatarsals** support the body weight. The fourteen **phalanges** are much smaller than in the hand, as they have little active function.

Types of bone tissue

The main types of bone tissue are:

(1) Compact tissue

Compact tissue is heavy, dense and strong bone tissue. Compact bone has an ivory appearance, and covers the complete bone. It is thickest at the centre of the shaft, that is, at the bone's weakest point. (See Figure 1.3.)

(2) Cancellous tissue

Cancellous tissue is also called spongy bone because of its honeycombed appearance. Cancellous tissue is strong and hard, and allows increased size without increased weight. Cancellous tissue is found mainly in the ends of bones where they flare out to form joints. This increases the surface area for more stable joints. (See Figure 1.3.)

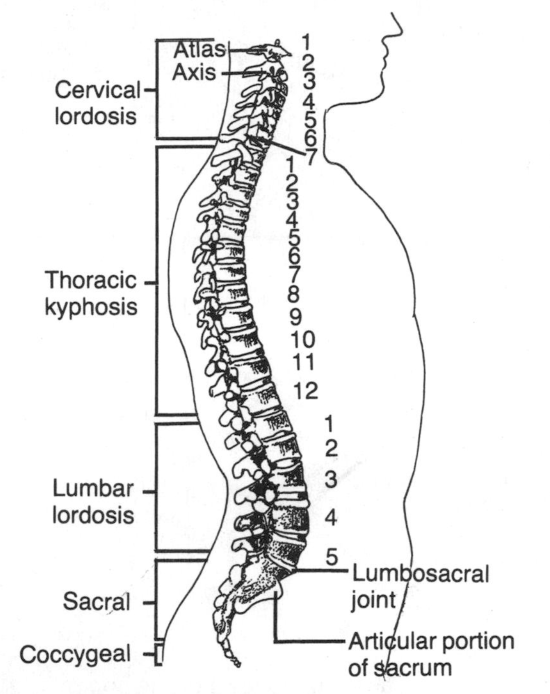

Cervical vertebrae—Allow movement of the head and bending and twisting of the neck

Thoracic vertebrae—Support the rib cage and allow some bending and rotation of the trunk

Lumbar vertebrae—Allow bending and rotation of the trunk

Sacral vertebrae—Transmit weight of body to hips and legs

In general the vertebral column:
(1) Protects the spinal cord
(2) Absorbs any shocks transmitted up the body
(3) Increases the range of trunk movements.

Figure 1.2 Regions, curves and functions of the vertebral column.

Types of bones

Bones are classified according to their shape:

(1) **Long bones**, such as the humerus, tibia, radius and phalanges. (See Figure 1.3.)
(2) **Short bones**, such as the carpals and tarsals.
(3) **Flat bones**, such as the skull, ribs, pelvis or shoulder blades. Flat bones give protection of the internal organs or an attachment for the large muscles.
(4) **Irregular bones**, such as the face and the vertebrae.

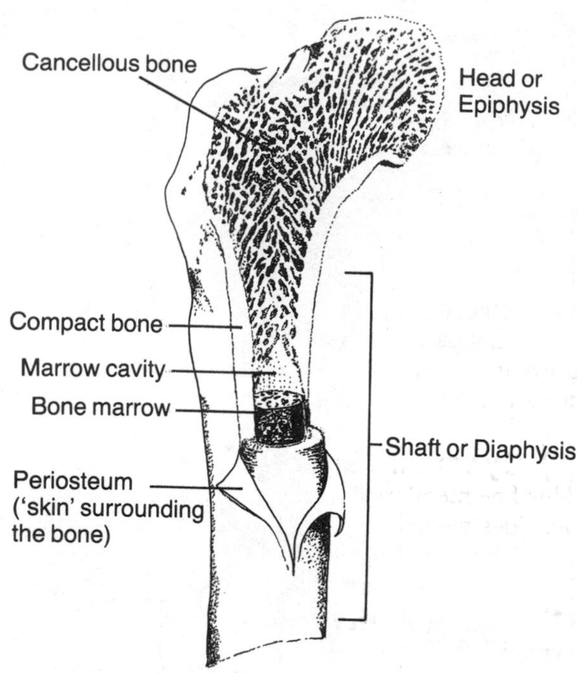

Figure 1.3 The structure of the long bone.

Laboratory exercise 1: Structure of a bone

Purpose

To examine the structure of a bone.

Materials

- A long bone that has been sectioned longitudinally (sawn in half lengthways) by a butcher
- A probe.

Procedure

(1) Use your probe (gently) to find where the bone ends and the marrow cavity begins.

(2) Examine the structure of the bone of the shaft. This bone is continuous with the outer layer of bone at each end. It is called **compact bone**, and is very hard, dense and strong.

(3) Examine the structure of the bone forming the 'swellings' at both ends of the shaft. The bone inside the 'swellings' is called **cancellous bone**, because it has an open meshwork structure. It is strong but light in weight.

(4) **The bone marrow** is found throughout the bone — in the marrow cavity and in the spaces of the cancellous bone.

- (a) Describe the colour of the bone marrow. Explain the function of red bone marrow. Is all bone marrow red?
- (b) Draw and label a diagram of the sectioned bone. Include: the shaft, marrow cavity, bone marrow, compact bone, cancellous bone.

(5) Examine the bone for the presence of cartilage. Can you find any?

- (a) Explain where you expect to find cartilage on the outer surface of the bone.
- (b) Describe the feel of the cartilage.
- (c) Explain the function of this cartilage.

Worksheet 1: Anatomical landmarks

Using a skeleton, partner and the necessary diagrams, answer the following questions in your notebook:

(1) Draw a vertebra from the side and the back
(2) Are all vertebrae the same shape?
(3) What is the function of the clavicles?
(4) How are the scapulae attached to the ribs?
(5) What is the most important function of the radius?
(6) Why is the hip a more stable joint than the shoulder?
(7) What are malleoli?
(8) What do you sit on?
(9) Where is your coracoid process?
(10) Locate the sterno-clavicular joint
(11) Locate the sacro-iliac joint
(12) What is your olecranon?
(13) What are false ribs?
(14) What is the bump above your shoulder joint?
(15) What is your heel?
(16) What is a knuckle?
(17) What is the real name for your hips?
(18) Locate your seventh cervical vertebra
(19) To what are your ribs attached?

2. The articular system

This chapter gives some of the elements of **arthrology**, which is the study of the joints of the body.

An **articulation** is the place of union between two or more bones.

Types of joint

Joints are of three categories, according to the degree of movement that each permits:

(1) Fibrous joints

Fibrous joints occur where bones are united by intervening fibrous tissue. Examples include the skull bones and the pelvic bones.

(2) Cartilagenous joints

Cartilagenous joints occur where bones are united by intervening cartilage, such as in the vertebral column, the pubic bones, and the diaphysis and epiphysis.

(3) Synovial joints

The main feature of the synovial joints is their mobility, along with a series of common features, described below.

Common characteristics of synovial joints

(1) Hyaline cartilage

The articular surfaces of the bones are covered with hyaline cartilage, which forms a smooth, white, shiny mass on the surface, looking rather like marble. This protects the bone tissue, and helps to reduce friction between the bones.

(2) Articular capsule

The articular capsule is a strong, fibrous tissue envelope surrounding the joint, and attached to the bones near the edge of the articular surfaces. The capsule blends with the periosteum of the bones, and is perforated only by blood vessels and nerves. The capsule adds stability to a joint, and stops unwanted material from entering the joint. Capsules are reinforced by ligaments.

(3) Synovial membrane

This fine membrane lines the inside of the capsule, but does not cover the hyaline cartilage. Its role is to produce synovial fluid.

(4) Synovial fluid

Synovial fluid is a yellowish oily fluid that:

- Lubricates the articulating surfaces
- Forms a fluid cushion between surfaces
- Provides nutrient for the hyaline cartilage
- Absorbs debris produced by friction between joint surfaces.

Synovial fluid becomes more viscous in cold weather, which is why some people have a feeling of stiff joints.

If the synovial membrane becomes inflamed (a condition called synovitis) because of injury or disease, the feeding capillaries become more permeable and fluid rushes into the joint. This causes such conditions as fluid on the knee.

(5) Ligaments

The ligaments are strong fibrous bands, such as the cruciate ligaments of the knee, that unite articular surfaces. They control movement and the stability of joints.

(6) Articular discs (menisci)

They lie between the articular surfaces, and are attached to the capsule at the outer edge of the joint. Their function is to absorb shock, maintain joint stability and protect the bone surfaces.

(7) Pads of fat

These pads fill the crevices in and around the joints, and form protective cushions for vital joint structures.

(8) Bursae

The bursae are closed sacs filled with synovial fluid, and are located wherever friction may develop, such as between the tendons and the bones.

Bursitis is the inflammation of the bursae as a result of overuse. It can cause pain and restricted movement. Common sites of bursitis are the knees, elbows and the Achilles tendon.

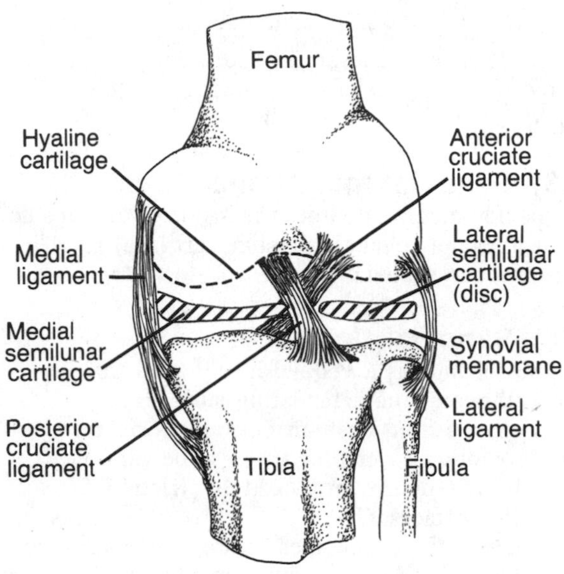

Figure 2.1 The knee joint (a typical synovial joint).

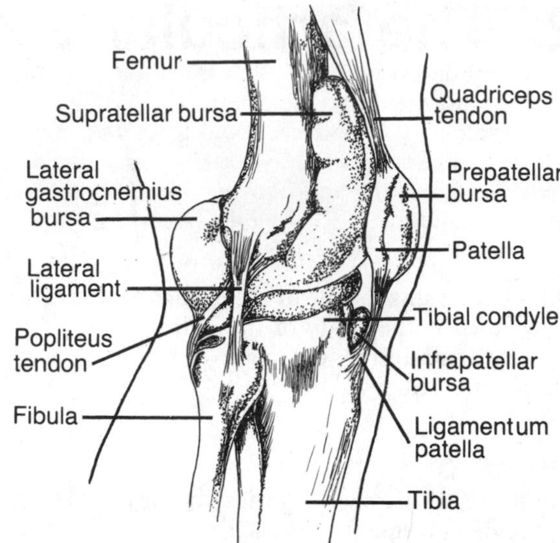

Figure 2.2 Lateral view of the right knee joint. The bursae have been expanded to show them more clearly.

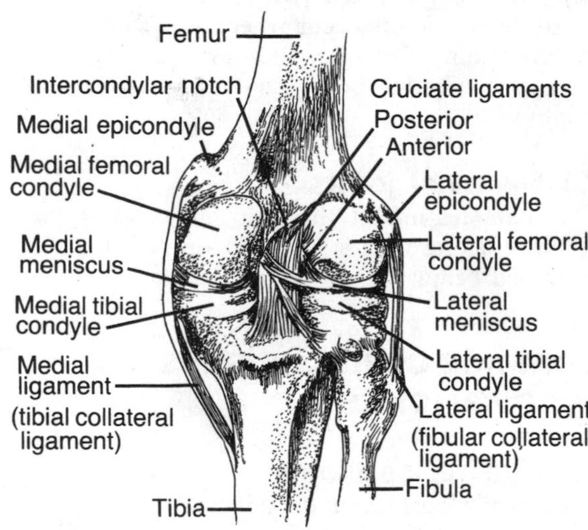

Figure 2.3 Posterior view of the right knee joint.

Types of synovial joints

There are six types of synovial joint:

(1) The hinge joint

The hinge joint allows only back-and-forth movement, such bending and straightening — for example, at the knee, knuckle, ankle and elbow. It is **uniaxial**.

(2) The pivot joint

The pivot joint allows rotation only (also uniaxial) — such as between the atlas and the axis, and between the radius and the humerus.

(3) The ovoid (ellipsoid) joint

The ovoid joint permits back-and-forth and side-to-side movement, and therefore is called a **biaxial** joint. It does not allow rotation. Such joints occur between the carpals (wrist) and the radius; and between the metacarpal and the phalange (between the finger and the palm).

(4) The gliding (plane) joint

The gliding joint occurs where two bones with flat surfaces slide on each other, but are restricted to limited movement by the ligaments. Such joints permit side-to-side and back-and-forth movement (biaxial) — for example, between the carpals; between the tarsals; and between the ribs and the thoracic vertebrae.

(5) The saddle joint

The saddle joint, which is biaxial, permits side-to-side and back-and-forth movements, but no rotation; for example, at the joint between the carpal and the metacarpal bones of the thumb. It is this joint that allows the thumb to be placed across the palm.

(6) The ball and socket joint

The ball and socket joint permits side-to-side, back-and-forth and rotational movement (and is therefore **triaxial**). In the hip and shoulder joints, the head of the femur/humerus fits snugly into the cavity in the pelvis/scapula, and is held in place by ligaments. The shoulder joint is the weaker of the two, and has a much shallower socket. Therefore it is much more likely than other joints to be dislocated.

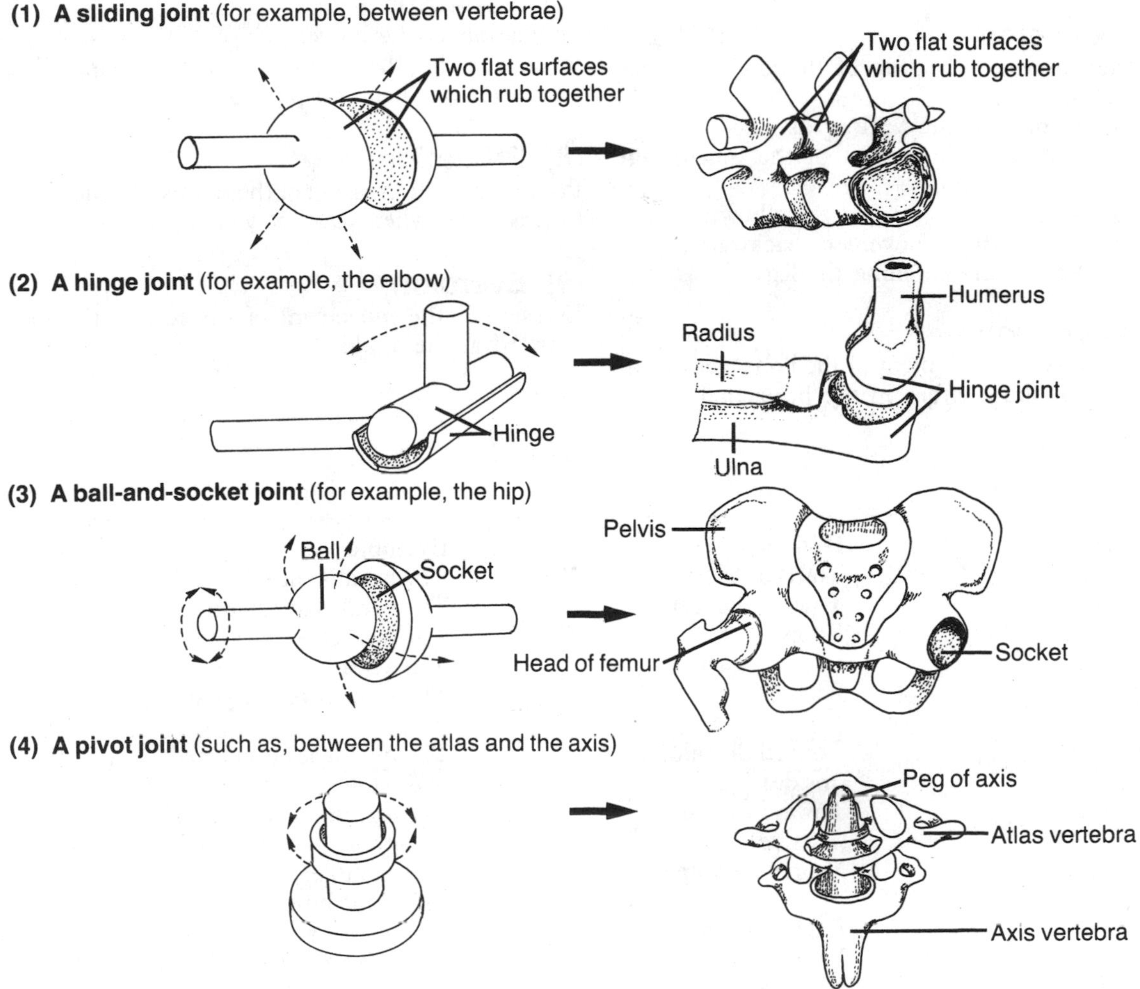

Figure 2.4 The type of movement possible at a joint depends upon the shape of the bones where they rub together. This diagram shows some examples.

Movements allowed by synovial joints

(1) Flexion

Flexion is bending — decreasing the angle between two bones:

(a) The trunk
- Bending forwards
- Bending sideways (this is called **lateral flexion**).

(b) The shoulder: movement of the arm or the shoulders forwards.
(c) In the arm: bending the elbow.
(d) At the hip: the thigh moves forwards.
(e) The knee: bending the leg.

(2) Extension

Extension is the increasing of the angle between two bones:

(a) The trunk bending backwards.
(b) The shoulder: movement of the arm or the shoulder backwards.
(c) The arm: straightening at the elbow.
(d) At the hip, thigh movement backwards.
(e) The knees: straightening the leg.

(3) Abduction

Abduction is the movement of the bone away from the body midline, either in the horizontal or the vertical plane.

(4) Adduction

Adduction is the movement of the bone towards the body midline, in either the horizontal or the vertical plane.

(5) Circumduction

Circumduction is the movement of the bone so that the end describes a circle, and the bone makes the shape of a cone as it moves around.

(6) Rotation

Rotation is the movement of a bone around a central axis. For instance, the arm has both internal and external rotation.

(7) Supination

Supination is the movement of the bones of the forearm so that the radius and the ulna are parallel; for instance, when you put your palms up.

(8) Pronation

Pronation is the crossing of the radius and the ulna, for instance, when you put your palms down.

(9) Eversion

Eversion is the movement of the sole of the foot outward at the ankle.

Term	Definition	Example
Superior	Toward the head	The head is superior to the trunk
Inferior	Toward the feet	The hand is inferior to the elbow
Anterior (Ventral)	Front	The nose is on the anterior aspect of the head
Posterior (Dorsal)	Back	The spine is on the posterior trunk
Medial	Toward the midline (inside)	The big toe is on the medial aspect of the foot
Lateral	Toward the side (outside)	The ears are on the lateral head
Proximal	Nearer the trunk	The shoulder is at the proximal end of the humerus
Distal	Further from the trunk	The fingers are distal to the wrist
Prone	Face down	Push up position
Supine	Face up	Beginning a sit up

Figure 2.5 Terms of reference.

(10) Inversion
Inversion is the movement of the sole of the foot inward at the ankle.

(11) Dorsiflexion
Dorsiflexion is the raising of the toes and the foot towards the tibia.

(12) Plantarflexion
Plantarflexion is the pointing of the toes.

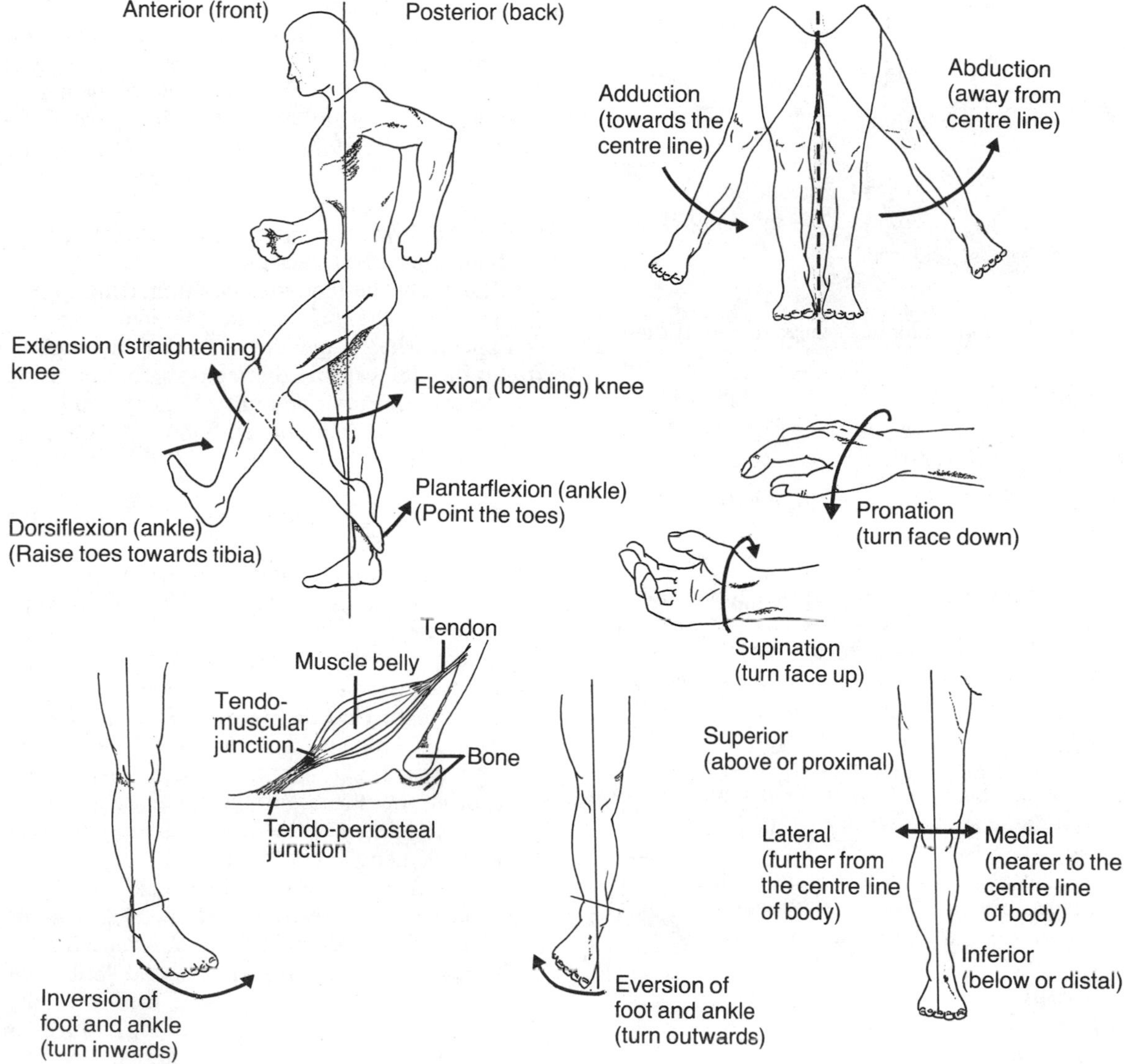

Figure 2.6 Anatomical and biomechanical terms.

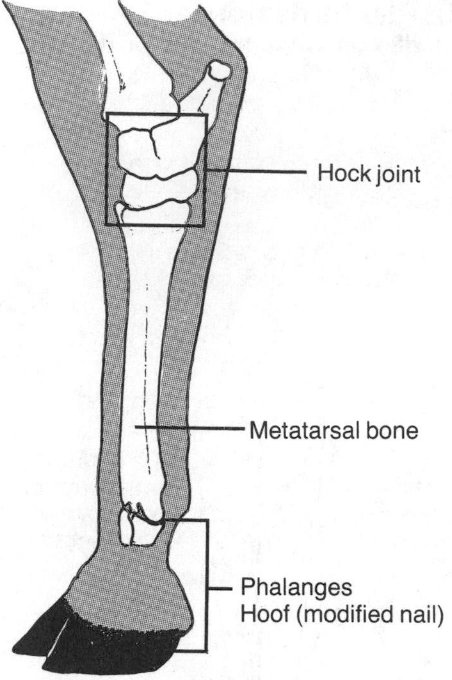

Figure 2.7 Bones of a hock viewed from the side.

Laboratory work 2: Structure of a synovial joint

Purpose

- To examine the structure of a synovial joint
- To examine the tissues that form a joint
- To find out how movement occurs at a joint
- To work out the factors that make joints stable.

You will observe and dissect the 'hock' of a sheep or bullock during this examination. The hock joint on the hindlimb is the equivalent of our ankle joint, but because sheep and other quadrupeds walk on their **phalanges** (see Figure 2.7), it is raised off the ground.

You may dissect the hock joint itself or, if your specimen does not have one, examine one of the other joints below the hock joint.

Materials

- Hock
- Dissecting board
- Scalpel
- Scissors
- Forceps
- Probes.

Procedure

(1) Select a joint that you will dissect by hand. Move it, and compare this movement with the movement possible *after* you have dissected the joint.

(2) Using scissors, remove the skin from the hock. Can you find any blood vessels or nerves? Identify the muscles, tendons, supporting tissues and bones on the hock.

(3) Using a scalpel and forceps, slit open the sheath around one or more tendons. Pull on a tendon. Can you make the joint move? Can you find another tendon and make the joint move in the opposite direction? Notice how easily the tendon slides in its sheath. Follow the tendon to where it attaches to the bone.

(4) Explain how the contraction of muscle brings about movement at a joint.

(5) Clear away the tendons and supporting tissues to expose the bones and the joint capsule. Explain what is meant by a **joint capsule.**

(6) Cut into the capsule, between the bones, using a scalpel. A small amount of sticky fluid may leak out from the joint cavity between the ends of the bones. Rub this fluid between your fingers.
   (a) What is the name of the fluid found in the joint cavity?
   (b) Explain its feel and its function.
   (c) Where did you find cartilage in the hock joint?
   (d) Explain its function.

(7) Find the cartilage of one of the bones. Feel how smooth it is. Feel the inner surface of the joint capsule. This is the synovial membrane. Explain the function of the synovial membrane.

(8) Look at the shapes of the bones where they form the joint. Do they fit together well? Test the movement of the joint again.
   (a) From your observations, explain what factors may restrict movement at a joint. Which tissues help to stabilize a joint?
   (b) Compare the hock joint and your own ankle joint. Look at such factors as the bones that make up the joint, range of movement and the attachment of the muscles.

Worksheet 2: The skeletal and articular systems

Answer these questions in your notebook:

(1) What are the two types of bone tissue, and what purpose has each?

(2) List the bones that articulate in the following joints:
- **(a)** Shoulder
- **(b)** Elbow
- **(c)** Spinal column
- **(d)** Hip
- **(e)** Knee.

(3) What is a joint capsule?

(4) List five characteristics of synovial joints.

(5) Why are hinge joints and ball-and-socket joints important?

(6) **(a)** What is a cartilage?
- **(b)** What is its function?
- **(c)** List one example of a cartilage.

(7) Where do the red blood cells originate, and how are they introduced into the bloodstream?

(8) Which bone forms the bony point of the elbow?

(9) Which bone forms the bony knob on the inside of the ankle?

(10) What type of joint is the knee joint?

(11) Why are the cruciate ligaments given that name?

(12) Why is the knee joint injured easily?

(13) Which four bones meet at the knee?

(14) What shape are the knee cartilages?

(15) What is the function of the patella?

(16) Fill in the missing words:
- **(a)** The big toe is on the .... side of the foot. (lateral/medial)
- **(b)** The lateral bone of the leg is the .... (tibia/fibula)
- **(c)** The side of the body containing the scapula is called the .... (anterior/posterior)
- **(d)** The hand is .... to the elbow. (distal/proximal)
- **(e)** The muscle, with its attachments to the radius and humerus, has its distal attachment on the .... (radius/humerus)
- **(f)** The femur is .... to the tibia. (inferior/superior)
- **(g)** The carpal bones are located .... to the radius. (inferior/superior)
- **(h)** The junction between two bones or between a bone and the cartilage is called an articulation or ....
- **(i)** The three primary types of joints in the human body are ....
 ....
- **(j)** The type of joint that is most important for human motion is the ....
- **(k)** What *type* of joint is each of these?
  - **(i)** Hip and shoulder joints ....
  - **(ii)** The elbow ....
  - **(iii)** The joints of the pelvis ....
  - **(iv)** The joints of the skull ....
  - **(v)** The joints between the ribs and the sternum ....
  - **(vi)** The atlas/axis joint ....

(17) Copy into your notebook the statement that is correct:
- **(a)** The patella is
  - **(i)** inferior to the foot
  - **(ii)** anterior to the knee
  - **(iii)** medial to the midline of the femur
  - **(iv)** near the distal end of the femur.
- **(b)** The sternum is
  - **(i)** inferior to the hips
  - **(ii)** on the anterior side of the body
  - **(iii)** medial to the shoulder
  - **(iv)** inferior to the skull.

(18) What is the movement performed at each key joint for the following actions? You might find diagrams useful to answer this question. The first example is done for you.
- **(a)** Kicking a football:
  - Hip: flexion
  - Knees: extension
- **(b)** Push up:
  - Elbows
- **(c)** Hanging pull up to chin over bar:
  - Elbows
  - Shoulders
- **(d)** Tennis serve (contact phase):
  - Elbows
  - Shoulder
- **(e)** Sit up (effort phase):
  - Trunk
  - Hip
- **(f)** Netball goal-shooting:
  - Elbow
  - Shoulder
  - Knees

(**g**) Toe-touching from standing:
- Trunk
- Hips
- Knees

(**h**) Vertical jump (upward phase):
- Hip
- Trunk
- Knees
- Shoulders
- Elbows
- Ankles

(**i**) Overarm throw:
- Elbow
- Shoulder

(**j**) Tennis backhand (forward swing):
- Elbow
- Shoulder

(**k**) Jogging:
- Shoulder
- Hip
- Knee.

3. The skeletal muscles of the body

Muscle action and control

Muscles produce movement by *pulling* bones in different directions, depending on the type of joint. Muscles work singly or in groups on joints to produce movement.

All muscles are attached to bones, at either end, by tendons. The end that is relatively fixed is called the **origin**, and the end that moves most is the **insertion**. The main body of the muscle is its **belly**.

Action of the muscle

When a muscle contracts, the origin and the insertion are drawn together; that is, the muscle shortens in length. The bones attached to the muscle are pulled in the direction of the shortening. This produces movement in a specific direction. This movement is the muscle's **action**.

For instance, elbow flexion is caused by the contraction of the biceps, which is attached at the origin to the scapula, and at the insertion to the radius.

For any movement in one direction caused by a muscle or a group of muscles at a specific joint, an opposite muscle or group of muscles can cause an opposite movement at the same joint.

Reciprocal inhibition

Skeletal muscles usually work in pairs. The muscle that causes movement is the **agonist**. As the agonist contracts, the other muscle in the pair relaxes and lengthens. This muscle is called the **antagonist**.

For instance, when your elbow extends, the triceps contracts (origin at the scapula and the humerus, and insertion at the ulna). The triceps is the agonist; since the biceps relaxes, it is the antagonist.

For the triceps to cause extension, the biceps must not contract and cause flexion. The process of one muscle contracting, and its opposite or antagonist relaxing, is called **reciprocal inhibition**.

Some people, such as those with cerebral palsy, lack reciprocal inhibition. Therefore their movements become jerky and disjointed because the antagonist contracts before the agonist has completed its action.

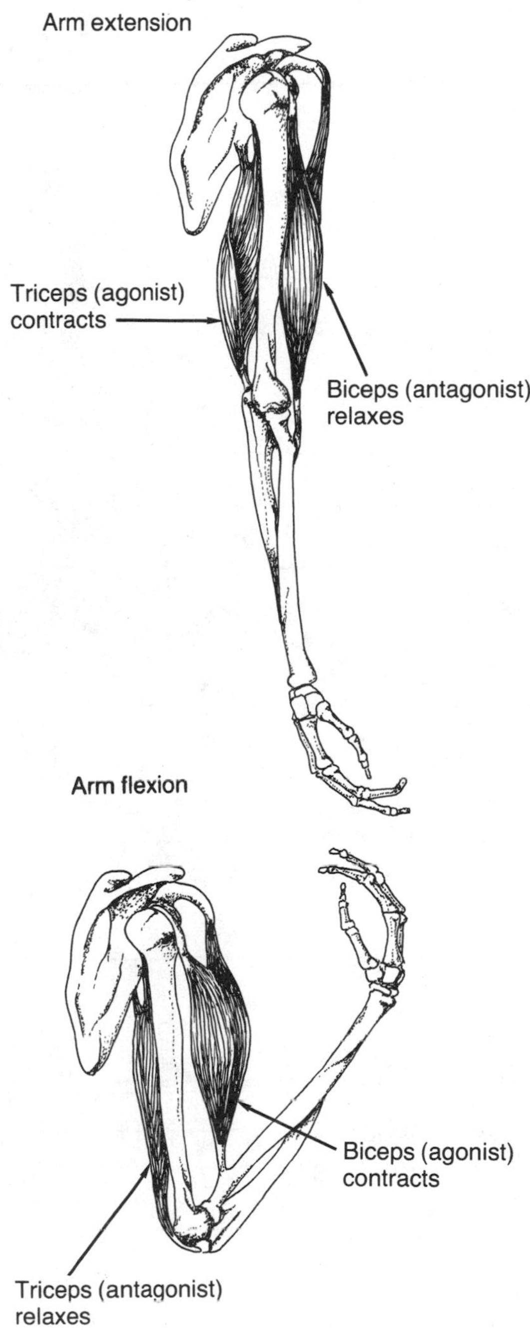

Figure 3.1 Muscle control of the elbow joint.

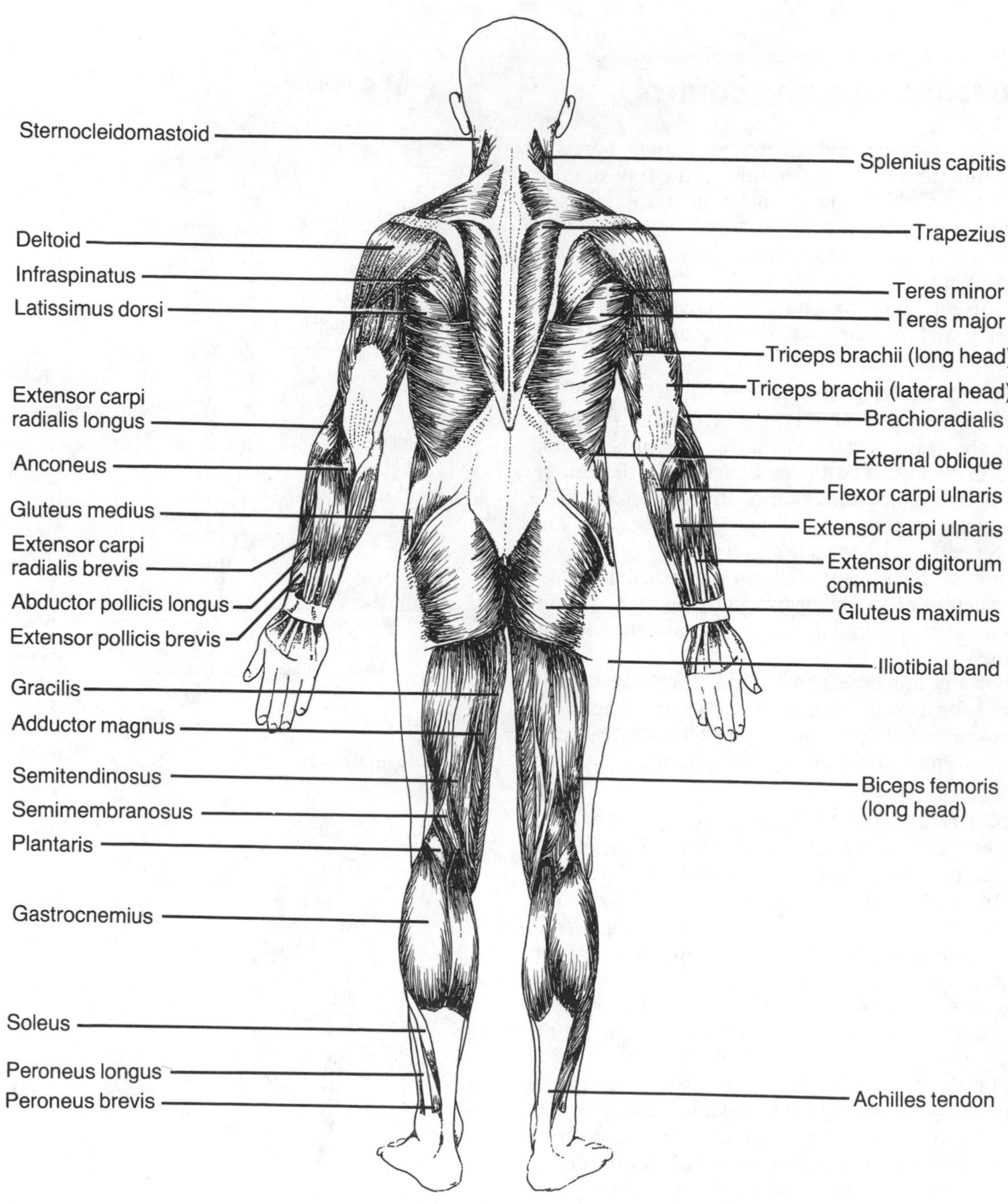

Figure 3.2 Muscles of the human body—major muscles exposed.

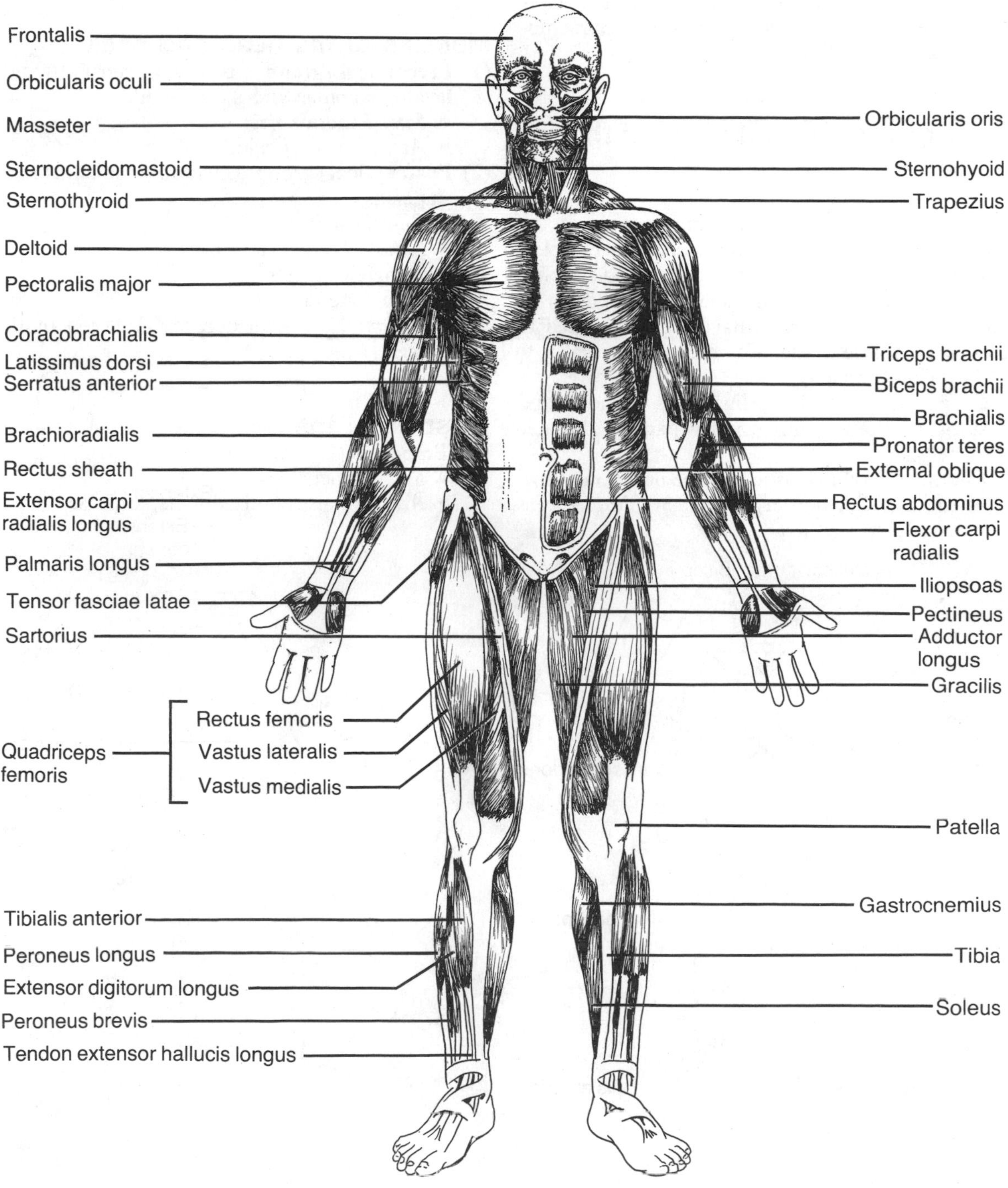
Frontalis
Orbicularis oculi
Masseter
Sternocleidomastoid
Sternothyroid
Deltoid
Pectoralis major
Coracobrachialis
Latissimus dorsi
Serratus anterior
Brachioradialis
Rectus sheath
Extensor carpi radialis longus
Palmaris longus
Tensor fasciae latae
Sartorius
Quadriceps femoris
Rectus femoris
Vastus lateralis
Vastus medialis
Tibialis anterior
Peroneus longus
Extensor digitorum longus
Peroneus brevis
Tendon extensor hallucis longus
Orbicularis oris
Sternohyoid
Trapezius
Triceps brachii
Biceps brachii
Brachialis
Pronator teres
External oblique
Rectus abdominus
Flexor carpi radialis
Iliopsoas
Pectineus
Adductor longus
Gracilis
Patella
Gastrocnemius
Tibia
Soleus

Synergists

Synergists are muscles that assist agonists and antagonists in producing particular joint movements. For instance, in elbow flexion, the agonist is the biceps assisted by the synergists, the brachioradialis and the brachialis.

Describing the muscles of the body

When describing the location of a muscle in the body, it is correct procedure to give the muscle's **origin, insertion** and **action**. However, to simplify the learning of the major muscles mentioned in this book, origin and insertion have been combined to give each muscle a **site**. For example:

- **Trapezius muscle**
  Origin: Base of skull, ligaments of neck and spine of the seventh cervical and all thoracic vertebrae.
  Insertion: Posterior aspect of the outer one-third of the clavicle; border of the acromion process and upper border of the spine of the scapula. This is more easily given as:
  Site: Upper back.

Muscles of the head and neck

(1) **Precervical group** (including sternothyroid, levator scapulae and sternohyoid)
- *Site:* Anterior neck
- *Action:* Neck flexion.

(2) **Postcervical group** (including splenius and trapezius)
- *Site:* Posterior neck
- *Action:* Neck extension.

(3) **Sternocleidomastoid**
- *Site:* Lateral neck
- *Action:* Lateral flexion and rotation of the neck.

Muscles of the back

(1) **Trapezius**
- *Site:* Upper back
- *Action:* Raises and adducts scapulae.

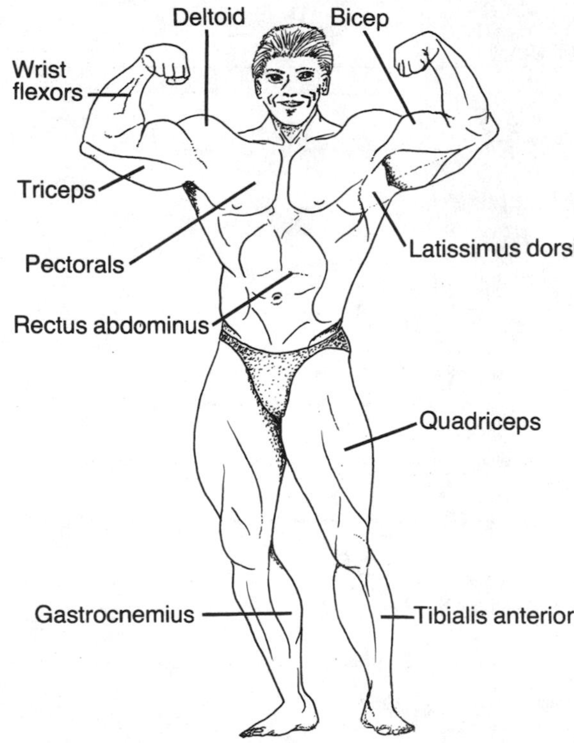

Figure 3.3 Major external muscles: anterior view.

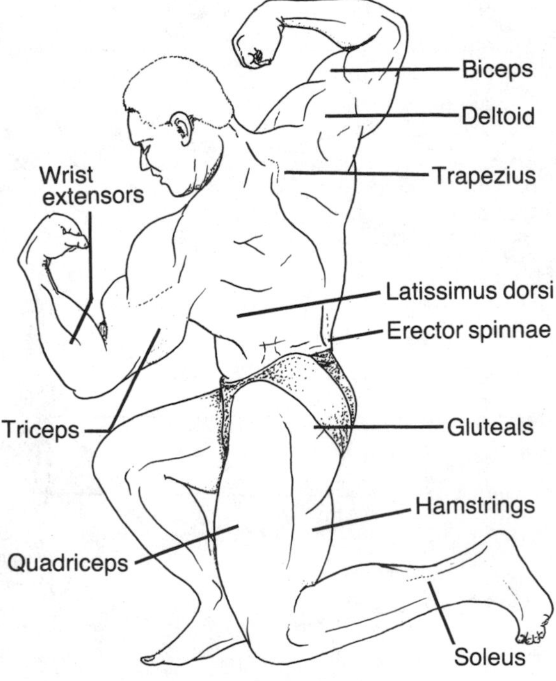

Figure 3.4 Major external muscles: posterior view.

(2) **Rhomboids** (major and minor)
- *Site:* Beneath trapezius
- *Action:* Adduct scapulae.

(3) **Latissimus dorsi**
- *Site:* Lower back (forms back of armpit)
- *Action:* Extension, internal rotation and adduction of shoulder.

(4) **Quadratus lumborum**
- *Site:* Beneath latissimus dorsi
- *Action:* Extension and lateral trunk flexion.

(5) **Erector spinae group**
- *Site:* Lower back (medial)
- *Action:* Trunk extension.

Muscles of the chest

(1) **Pectoral group** (major and minor)
- *Site:* Upper chest
- *Action:* Flexion, internal rotation and adduction of shoulder.

(2) **Serratus anterior**
- *Site:* Lateral chest
- *Action:* Abducts shoulder blades.

(3) **Intercostals** (external and internal)
- *Site:* Between the ribs
- *Action:* Raising and lowering the ribs.

Muscles of the abdomen

(1) **Rectus abdominus**
- *Site:* Medial abdomen
- *Action:* Trunk flexion and lateral flexion.

(2) **Oblique abdominals** (external and internal)
- *Site:* Lateral abdomen
- *Action:* Trunk flexion and rotation.

(3) **Transverse abdominal**
- *Site:* Across the abdomen
- *Action:* Forced expiration by increasing abdominal pressure.

Muscles of the arm and shoulder

(1) **Deltoid**
- *Site:* Above shoulder joint
- *Action:* Flexion, extension, rotation and *abduction* of the shoulder.

(2) **Biceps brachii**
- *Site:* Anterior arm
- *Action:* Supination of the forearm and elbow flexion.

(3) **Brachialis**
- *Site:* Beneath the biceps
- *Action:* True elbow flexion.

(4) **Triceps brachii**
- *Site:* Posterior arm
- *Action:* Extension of the elbow.

(5) **Wrist flexors**
- *Site:* Anterior (assuming anatomical position) forearm
- *Action:* Flexion of wrist and fingers.

(6) **Wrist extensors**
- *Site:* Posterior forearm
- *Action:* Extension of wrist and fingers.

Muscles of the hip and leg

(1) **Iliopsoas** (includes iliacus, psoas major and psoas minor)
- *Site:* From lower lumbar vertebrae and pelvis to upper femur
- *Action:* Hip flexion.

(2) **Gluteals** (includes maximus, medius and minimus)
- *Site:* Posterior hip
- *Action:* Hip extension, external rotation and abduction.

(3) **Adductors** (includes brevis, longus and magnus)
- *Site:* Medial thigh
- *Action:* Hip adduction.

(4) **Quadriceps** (includes the rectus femoris, vastus lateralis, vastus medialis and vastus intermedius)
- *Site:* Anterior thigh
- *Action:* Hip flexion, *knee extension.*

(5) **Hamstrings** (includes the biceps femoris, semimembranosus and semitendonosus)
- *Site:* Posterior thigh
- *Action:* Hip extension, *knee flexion.*

(6) **Tibialis anterior**
- *Site:* Anterior lower leg
- *Action:* Dorsiflexion and inversion.

(7) **Gastrocnemius** (calf)
- *Site:* Posterior lower leg
- *Action:* *Plantarflexion* and knee flexion.

(8) **Soleus**
- *Site:* Beneath gastrocnemius
- *Action:* Plantarflexion.

(9) **Tibialis posterior**
- *Site:* Beneath soleus
- *Action:* Plantarflexion and inversion.

(10) **Peroneus** (includes longus and brevis)
- *Site:* Lateral lower leg
- *Action:* Plantarflexion and eversion.

Worksheet 3: The major skeletal muscles

(1) How and where do you palpate the following muscles? (Note that 'how' means 'you resist its primary movement'; 'where' means 'the location or site of the muscle'.)
- **(a)** Pectorals
- **(b)** Trapezius
- **(c)** Deltoid
- **(d)** Latissimus dorsi
- **(e)** Biceps
- **(f)** Triceps
- **(g)** Quadriceps
- **(h)** Hamstrings
- **(i)** Gluteals
- **(j)** Tibialis anterior.

(2) List the muscles *primarily* responsible for:
- **(a)** Shoulder adduction
- **(b)** Shoulder extension
- **(c)** Shoulder elevation
- **(d)** Elbow flexion
- **(e)** Hip adduction
- **(f)** Knee flexion
- **(g)** Ankle dorsiflexion.

(3) Name the muscles used in:
- **(a)** Batting in softball (the swing)
- **(b)** Sitting up straight (back against the chair)
- **(c)** A sit up
- **(d)** A push up
- **(e)** A vertical jump
- **(f)** Running: the push-off phase.

(4) Copy Figure 3.5 into your notebook. On it, pencil in the outline of the following muscles:
- **(a)** Trapezius
- **(b)** Triceps
- **(c)** Hamstrings
- **(d)** Gluteals
- **(e)** Latissimus dorsi.

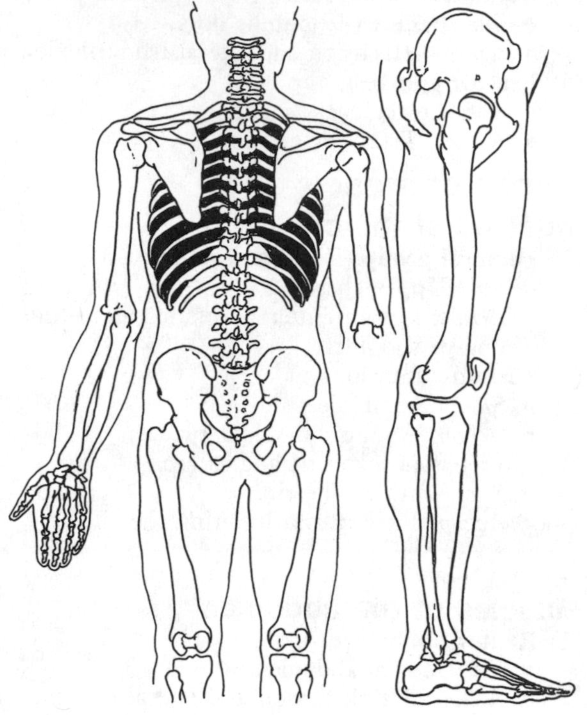

Figure 3.5

4. The muscular system

Myology is the study of the muscles:

- Muscle constitutes 50 per cent of total body weight
- Muscle tissue weighs more than fat tissue
- Muscle consists of 30 per cent protein and 70 per cent salt solution.

Types of muscle

Muscles can be described as either

- **Voluntary** (over which we have direct control)

or

- **Involuntary** (over which we have no direct control).

The main types of muscle are:

(1) Smooth muscle

Smooth muscle, such as that found in the blood vessel and intestinal walls, is usually internal, involuntary muscle, which is made up of spindle-shaped cells (see Figure 4.1).

(2) Cardiac muscle

Cardiac muscle is muscle found only in the wall of the heart. This is involuntary muscle, whose branched fibres give it a striped appearance (see Figure 4.2).

(3) Striped, striated or skeletal muscle

These are external, voluntary muscles, such as the deltoid, quadriceps and biceps.

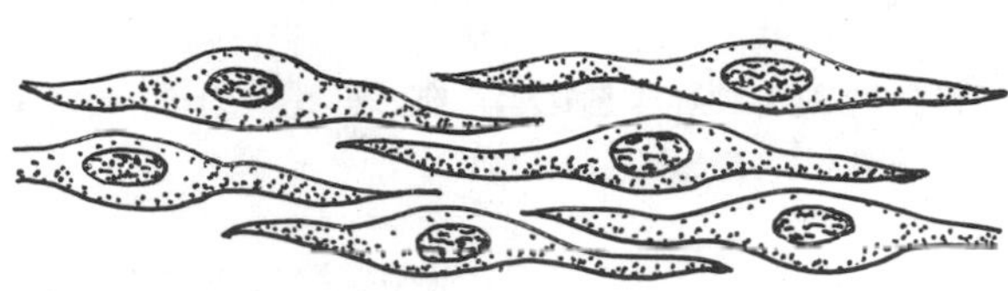

Figure 4.1 Smooth muscle fibres.

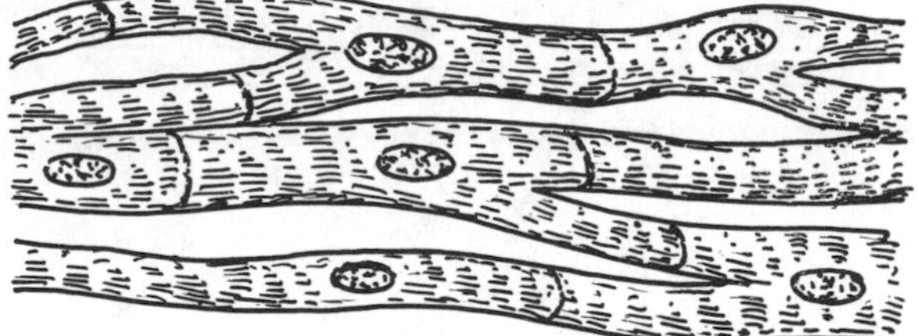

Figure 4.2 Cardiac muscle fibres.

Main features of all muscles

All three types of muscle tissue:

(1) Are controlled by nerve stimuli.
(2) Can contract, or shorten, thus becoming thicker. This is called **contractility**.
(3) Can stretch with the application of force. This is called **extensibility**.
(4) Can return to their original size and shape after being stretched or contracted. This is called **elasticity**.
(5) Will **atrophy** (waste) if not enough blood is supplied to them.
(6) Will **hypertrophy** (enlarge) in response to increased work.
(7) Are fed from the circulatory system by capillaries (small blood vessels) that penetrate the fibres.

The structure of striped muscle

In general, muscles consist of a muscle **belly**, with a fibrous **tendon** at either end which plugs into the bonc.

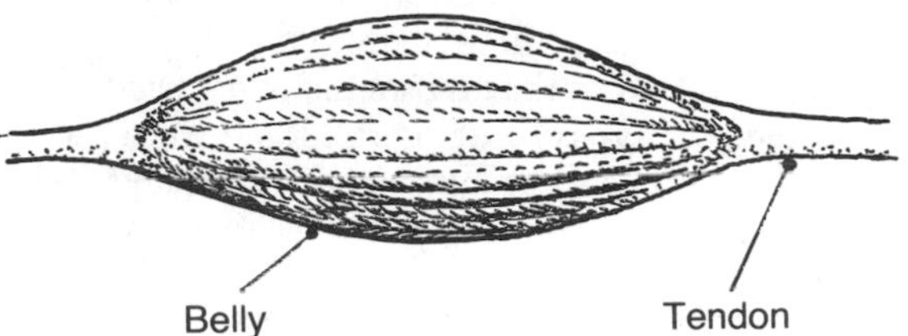

Fiugre 4.3 Skeletal muscle.

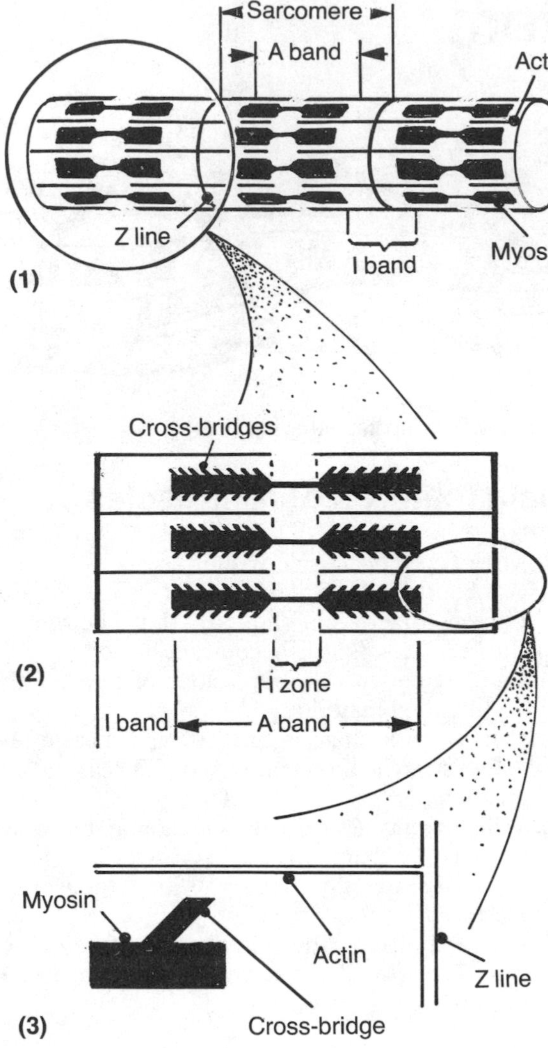

Figure 4.4 Myofibril—the contractile unit of skeletal muscle.
(1) Note that the A band is composed of two protein filaments (actin and myosin). The I band contains actin filaments only.
(2) A closer look at the myosin filament, which projects in cross-bridging fashion toward the actin filament. The H zone (in the middle of the A band) is a result of the absence of actin filaments.
(3) A magnified view of a single myosin cross-bridge as it projects toward a single actin filament.

The muscle belly consists of thousands of muscle **fibres** (cells), arranged in bundles that run the length of the muscle. Each muscle fibre consists of many contractile units called **myofibrils**, which run the length of the fibre, and have characteristic dark and light bands.

Each myofibril consists of units called **sarcomeres**. Each sarcomere contains two protein filaments: a thick filament called **myosin**, and a thin filament called **actin**. The overlapping of these two filaments creates the striped appearance.

The myosin filaments have tiny protein projections that extend towards the actin filaments. They are called **cross-bridges**, and are very important for muscle contraction (see Figure 4.4).

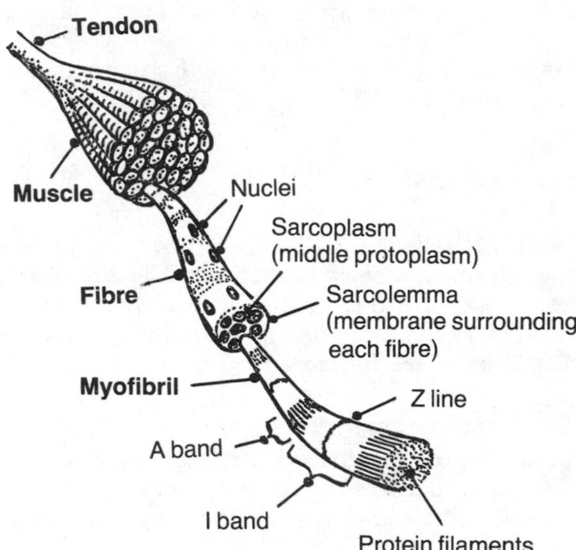

Figure 4.5 Skeletal muscle showing microscopic delineation of fibre and myofibril. Note the striations in both the fibre and the myofibril; these alternating light and dark bands are caused by the geometric arrangement of the protein filaments.

The nervous system and the muscular system

To understand how the muscle knows when to contract, we need a basic understanding of the nervous system.

Nervous system
= **Central nervous system**
that is, the brain and the spinal cord
+ **Peripheral nervous system**
that is, nerves branching out into the body from the spinal cord.

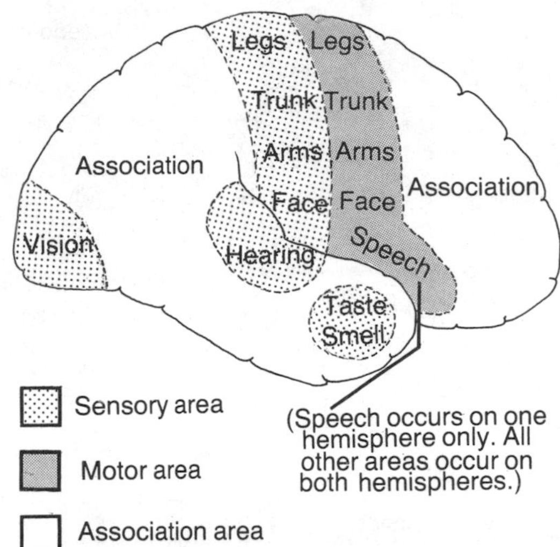

Figure 4.7 A map of half of the cerebrum. Sensory areas receive impulses from sense organs. Motor areas control voluntary muscles. Association areas are connected with thought, memory and emotion.

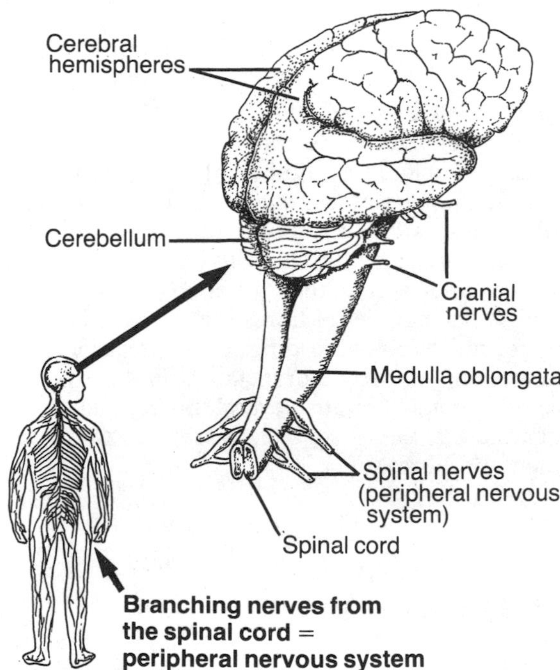

Figure 4.6 Parts of the nervous system.

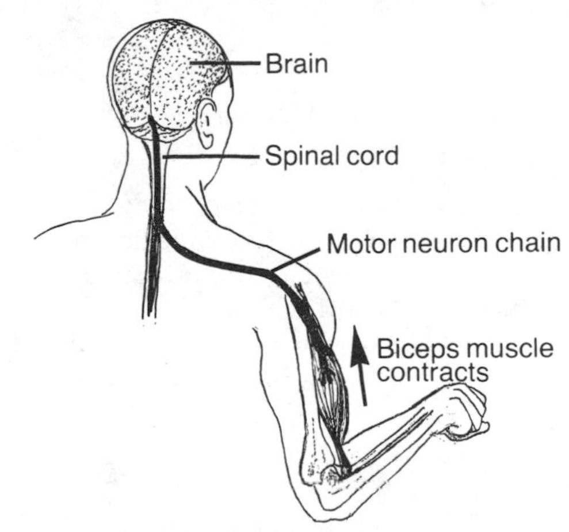

Figure 4.8 The neuron chain.

The muscle is stimulated to contract by a chemically created electric impulse, whose path from the brain to the muscle can be followed in Figure 4.8.

Neurons

The electrical impulse begins at the brain (in the **motor cortex**) and passes down the vertebral column and across to the particular muscle. The impulse is transmitted by nerve cells called **neurons** (see Figure 4.9).

The neuron is made up three main parts:

- The cell body (**soma**), which directs the activities of the neuron
- **Dendrites**, which pick up the impulses
- The **axon**, which transmits the impulse away from the cell body.

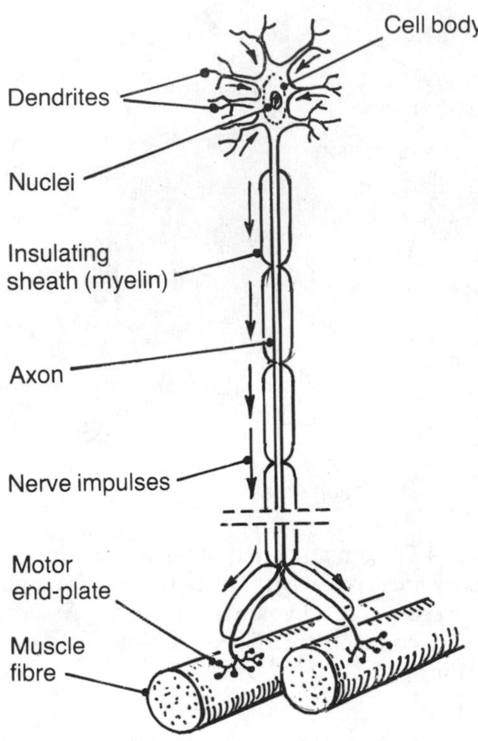

Figure 4.9 A typical motor neuron.

Types of neurons

There are two main types of neuron:

- **Sensory neurons**, which conduct impulses from a sensory organ or receptor, such as pain receptors, toward the brain.
- **Motor neurons**, which conduct impulses from the brain to effectors, such as the muscles or the glands.

Neural chains

Because of the large distances between the brain and the muscles or receptors in various parts of the body, several neurons link together to transmit messages over long distances. They are called **neural chains**.

Synapses

A **synapse** is the junction between the dendrite of one neuron and the axon of another. The junction between an axon and a muscle is called a **neuromuscular synapse**.

Structure of the neuromuscular synapse

As the impulse reaches the end of the axon, it triggers the release of a transmitter substance, **ACh (acetylcholine)**, which travels across the **synaptic cleft** (space between the end of the axon and the surface of the muscle) and stimulates an electrical impulse in the muscle, causing contraction (see Figure 4.11).

Motor unit

One motor neuron does not stimulate the whole muscle, but only a number of fibres within that muscle. The motor neuron, plus the fibres it stimulates, is called a **motor unit**.

Therefore any muscle will have a number of motor units stimulating different sections of its fibres. The number of fibres innervated by a single motor unit varies according to the precision of the movement required. For instance, in the eye, there is one motor unit to several fibres, but in the quadriceps there is one motor unit to each thousand fibres.

The all-or-none law

The all-or-none law states that, until the electrical impulse reaches a certain threshold level of intensity, it will not cause a stimulation of muscle fibres. However, once it reaches that threshold level, all the fibres of that motor unit contract at the same time, and they contract to the maximum posssible extent.

However, there may be differences in the force exerted with each contraction of a specific muscle. These variations are caused by:

- The *number* of motor units stimulated by the brain in order to carry out a particular action, not any variation in the force exerted by specific motor units. In other words, the greater the strength required, the greater the number of motor units that contract (see Figure 4.12).
- The *frequency* at which stimuli arrive at the fibres of a motor unit. That is, the greater the frequency of arrival of stimuli, the greater the tension developed by the muscle.

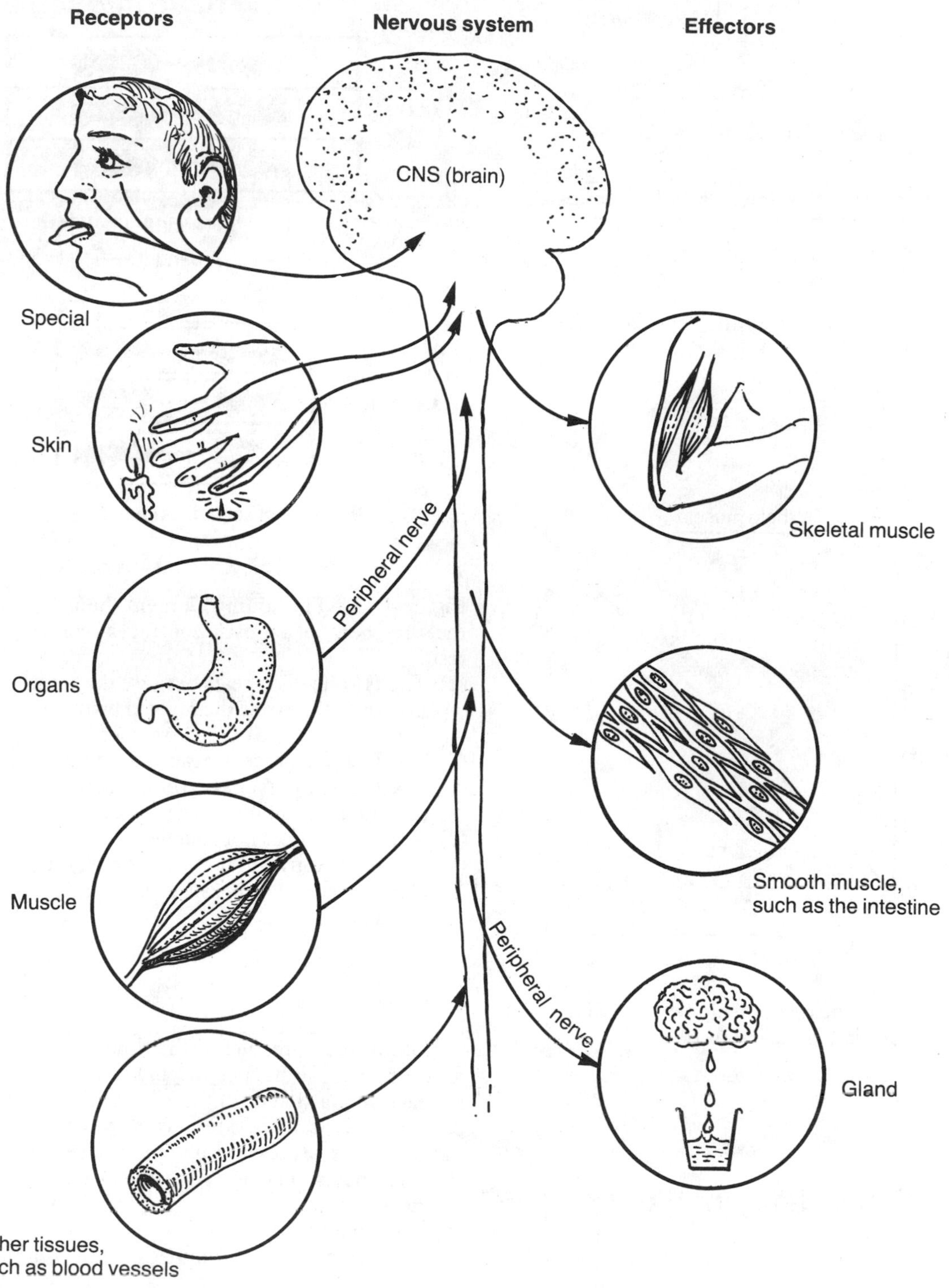

Figure 4.10 The relationship between the central and peripheral nervous systems.

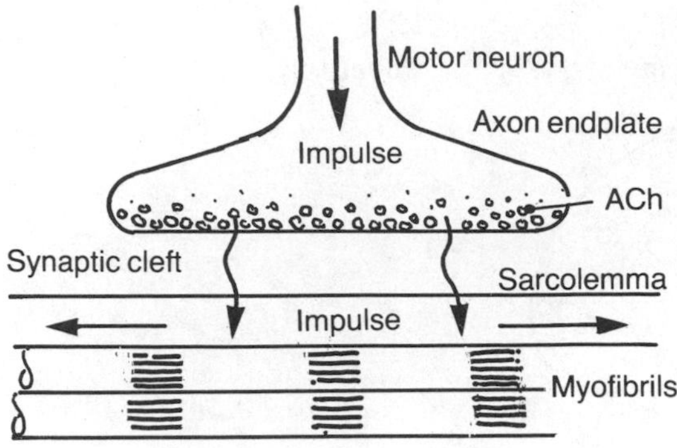

Figure 4.11 Structure of the neuromuscular synapse.

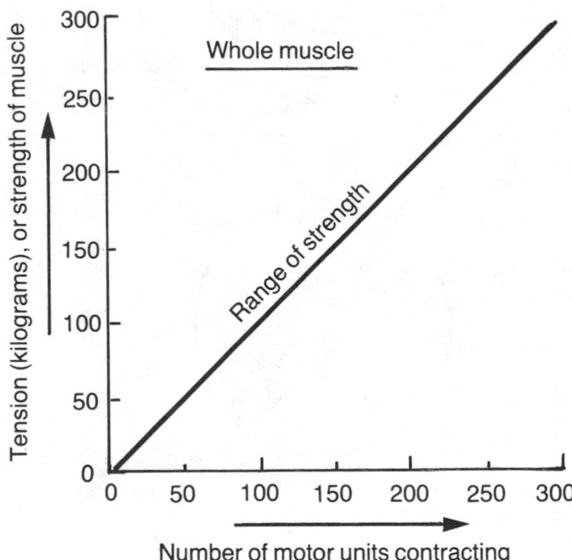

Figure 4.12 The relationship between number of motor units stimulated and muscle tension developed.

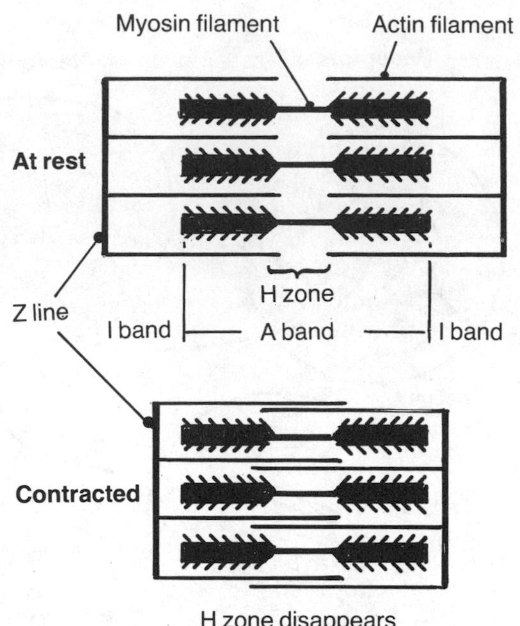

Figure 4.13 **The sliding filament theory.** When the sarcomeres of a muscle contract as compared to rest:

(1) The H zone disappears because the actin filaments slide over the myosin filaments toward the centre of the sarcomere
(2) The I band shortens because the actin filaments attached to the Z lines on either side of the sarcomere are pulled toward the centre
(3) The A band does not change in length
(4) Neither the myosin nor the actin filaments changes in length, because of the sliding mechanism.

The sliding filament theory

Once the impulse reaches the muscle fibres of that motor unit, it stimulates a reaction in each sarcomere between the myosin and the actin. This reaction is called the **sliding filament theory**.

Within the sarcomere, the impulse from the motor neuron stimulates the myosin cross-bridges to reach forward and pull in the actin towards the centre. This can be seen as a rowing type of motion. This process occurs simultaneously in all the sarcomeres. The end process is a shortening of all the sarcomeres, hence myofibrils and fibres of that motor unit (see Figure 4.13).

After this process of stimulation and contraction has finished, the cross-bridges uncouple. Unless stimulated again, the sarcomeres go back to the relaxed position.

Tone

When relaxed, some cross-bridges stay constantly in contact with the actin. This means that the muscle is never totally relaxed; it keeps its **tone**. Tone makes starting a contraction easier, and keeps the body in its correct postural position.

Cramp

Cramp is a muscle spasm caused by rapid, disordered stimulation of fibres within a motor unit. The myosin cross-bridges become locked on to the actin in the contracted position.

Reflexes and the autonomic nervous system

There are two main types of nervous system:

- The voluntary, or **somatic** nervous system, over which we have direct control. We use the somatic nervous system to contract skeletal muscles.
- The involuntary, or **autonomic** nervous system, over which we have no direct control. Reflexes are controlled by the autonomic nervous system.

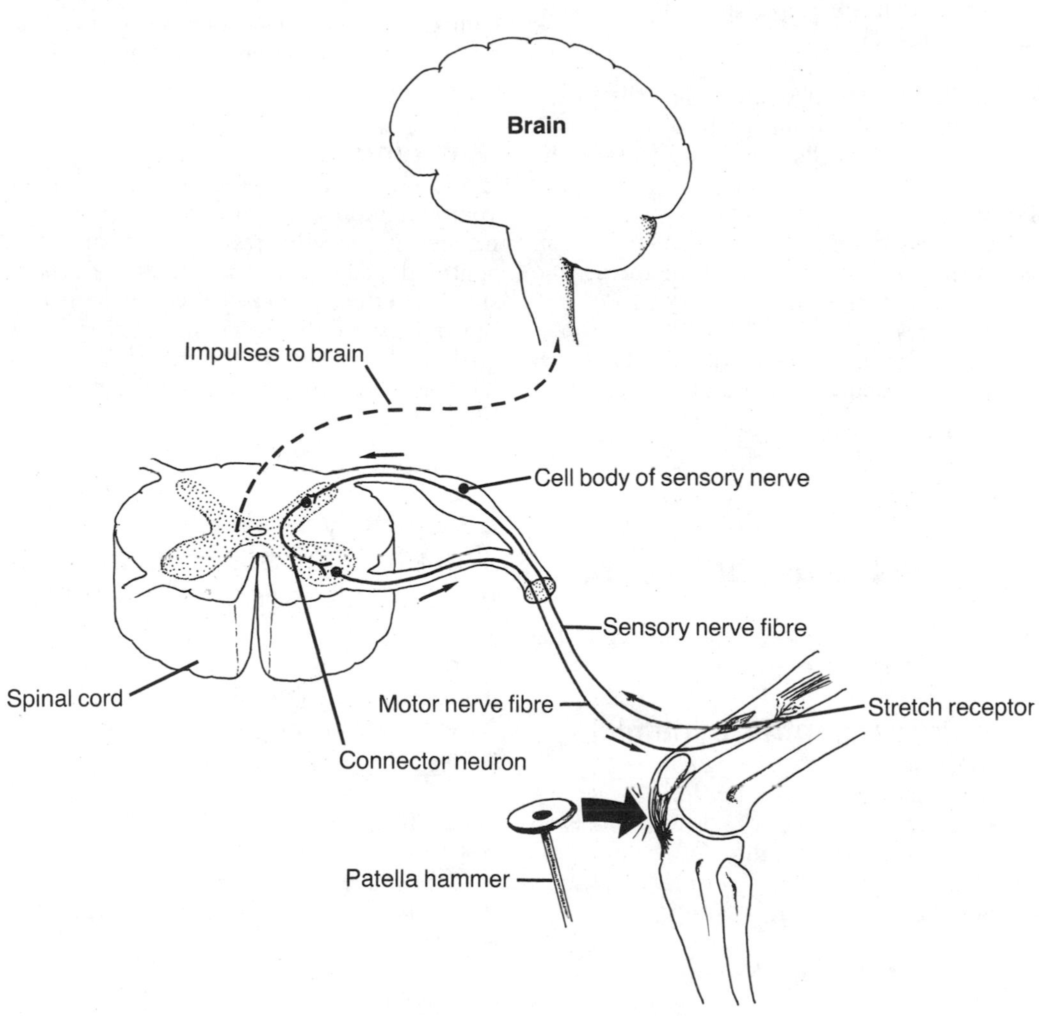

Figure 4.14 The reflex arc (knee-jerk reflex)—the simplest system of communication.

How the reflexes work

The reflex arc bypasses the brain in order to produce a quick response as a means of protection. Figure 4.14 shows how the best-known reflex action, the **knee-jerk reflex**, works:

- The hammer strikes the knee.
- The impulse travels up the sensory neuron.
- The impulse travels through the connector neuron in the spinal cord to the motor neuron.
- The impulse travels down the motor neuron to the quadriceps.
- The quadriceps contract.

Muscle sense organs

The muscle sense organs are units of the autonomic nervous system that are important for movement control. They include:

- **Muscle spindles**

Muscle spindles are small stretchable coils in the muscle that inform the brain of how stretched a muscle is. In turn, this tells how many motor units to fire.

- **Golgi organs**

Golgi organs, which are found in tendons, inform the brain of the force in a muscle. If the force is too large, the muscle is relaxed.

- **Joint receptors**

Joint receptors, found in ligaments and capsules, inform the brain about the angle of the joint.

Types of muscular contraction

Muscle contractions are classified according to the movement that they cause:

(1) Isotonic (concentric, dynamic) contraction

- The muscle shortens under tension
- The muscle shortens with a varying tension whilst lifting a constant load — for example, the bicep curl. (The force produced varies throughout the movement.)

(2) Isometric (static) contraction

The tension develops but the muscle length remains the same. This happens when the resistance is greater than the force generated by the muscle's maximal effort — that is, when the muscle cannot move the resistance. Example: pushing against a wall.

(3) Eccentric contraction

The muscle lengthens while developing tension — for example, when lowering a weight.

(4) Isokinetic contraction

The tension developed by the muscle while shortening is maximal over the full range of the motion. The resistance applied by the machine always equals the amount of force being applied by the muscle. In turn, this allows you to use larger weights by overcoming weak spots. For instance, when using Nautilus equipment, a cam in the equipment is used to vary the load as the muscular force varies at different joint angles.

'Pumping'

In muscle contractions of more than 70 per cent of your maximum strength, blood flow to the working muscle is heavily restricted during the actual contraction. However, after large efforts or during smaller efforts, muscle contraction stimulates blood flow to the working areas, increasing the girth and the volume of the muscles concerned. This is often referred to by athletes as being 'pumped'.

Laboratory work 3: The effect of isometric and isotonic exercise on heart rate

Aim

To compare the effects of isometric exercises with those of isotonic exercises on the heart rates of the subjects.

Materials

- Chair
- Table
- 5-kilogram and 2.5-kilogram weights
- Stop watches.

Subjects

All members of the class divided into groups of four.

Method: Isometric exercise

(1) Record the subject's resting heart rate.
(2) Place the palm surface of the hand in contact with the underside of the table. (Others in the group may need to sit on the table to hold it down.)
(3) The working subject then pushes on the table, but must remain seated, for one minute.
(4) The student taking the heart rate counts the number of pulse beats in the neck over a period of 10 seconds, towards the end of the one-minute exercise. Multiply this figure by six to get the beats per minute.
(5) As the subject relaxes, immediately count the pulse rate again, and for the last 10 seconds of the first, second and third minute of recovery.

Method: Isotonic exercise

(1) Record the resting heart rate.
(2) • The subject works in this exercise at flexing and extending the forearm. Males should use 5-kilogram weights, and females use 2.5-kilogram weights.
• The exercise should be performed as rapidly as possible. Keep recording the time until the subject is exhausted.
(3) Record the heart rate over 10 seconds towards the end of the exercise. Record the recovery heart rate, as in Step (5) of the isometric exercise.
(4) Repeat these experiments on each subject.

Subjects

Heart rate	**1**	**2**	**3**	**4**
Rest				
During exercise				
Immediate post Exercise				
1 min. post ex.				
2 min. post ex.				
3 min. post ex.				

Figure 4.15

Subjects

Heart rate	**1**	**2**	**3**	**4**
Rest				
During exercise				
Immediate post exercise				
1 min. post ex.				
2 min. post ex.				
3 min. post ex.				

Figure 4.16 Isotonic exercise.

Questions

(1) Draw a graph of the heart-rate changes for
• The isometric exercise
• The isotonic exercise.
How is the heart rate affected by the two types of exercise?
(2) Explain any differences in the responses to the two types of activity, as shown in your results.

Laboratory work 4: The reflex arc

Purpose

To cause and observe a knee-jerk reflex, which is an example of a reflex activity of the body.

Materials

Patella hammer (or a ruler).

Procedure

(1) Work in pairs. Take turns to cause and experience the knee-jerk reflex (see Figure 4.14).
(2) Ask your partner to sit with knees crossed, and to relax.

(3) Hit the patella tendon firmly with the edge of the patella hammer (or ruler). The patella tendon is just below the kneecap. Do not hit the kneecap (patella) or the shin bone (tibia).
(4) Repeat this several times until you achieve a consistent response.

Questions

(1) Describe the response that you observe. Ask your partner to describe the response as she or he feels it.
(2) How do you know that your partner's response was a reflex action?
(3) Name the muscles in the leg which produced the movement observed.

Worksheet 4: The muscular system

(1) Describe the structure of a muscle. Make sure that your description includes the following terms:
- Belly
- Tendon
- Fibre
- Myofibril
- Sarcomere
- Myosin
- Actin
- Cross-bridges
- A and I bands.

(2) Why do people who suffer from cerebral palsy have jerky movements?
(3) How does the brain transmit electrical impulses to the muscles?
(4) What is the sliding filament theory?
(5) What is a motor unit?
(6) If someone threw a medicine ball at you at about head height and you caught it, which muscle stops the ball slamming into your face? What sort of contraction is this muscle going through?
(7) What is the one major muscle stressed when doing these exercises? (Use diagrams to illustrate your answers.)
 (a) Vertical jump
 (b) Chest pass
 (c) Chin up
 (d) Toe touch
 (e) Picking up a heavy carton.
(8) Define these terms:
- Origin
- Belly
- Insertion
- Muscle action.

(9) Of which substance are the muscles primarily made?
(10) Describe the three types of muscles to be found in the body.
(11) Give examples of the function of each muscle type.
(12) Explain the roles of the agonist and the antagonist in muscle movement.

5. The meaning of health and fitness

Definitions of health and fitness

Health relates to the total person, while **fitness** relates to the physical properties of a person.

(1) Health

Health has been defined as 'a state of complete physical, mental and social well-being, and not merely the absence of disease and infirmity.'

(2) Physical fitness

(a) Getchell defines physical fitness as 'a capability of the heart, blood vessels, lungs and muscles to function at optimal efficiency'.

(b) Another definition is: 'The capacity to carry out everyday activities (work and play) without excessive fatigue and with enough energy in reserve for emergencies.'

These definitions are very vague. For instance:

(1) What are 'everyday activities'?

(2) What is 'optimal efficiency'?

(3) Do all activities require the same level of fitness?

(4) Does fitness mean only one thing?

Take the following statements:

(1) Jeff is fit. He plays football.

(2) Diane is fit. She runs regularly.

(3) Katrina is fit. She does gymnastics.

(4) Con does weights so he must be fit.

In each case, 'fit' means something completely different. For example:

- Jeff might be fit to play football, but that doesn't mean he can run a long way
- Katrina might be fit to do gymnastics, but that doesn't mean she can lift weights.

'Fitness' and 'fit' mean a number of different things. To discuss the idea of fitness, we must divide it into a number of components.

The components of fitness

(1) Muscular strength

The force that a muscle or group of muscles can exert in a single maximal contraction — for example, when lifting a heavy weight once.

(2) Muscular power

The ability to use strength quickly to produce an explosive effort — for example, the shot put.

(3) Muscular endurance

The ability to work a muscle for long periods at less than maximum effort — for example, strumming a guitar during a two-hour rock concert.

(4) Aerobic power (general endurance)

The capacity to keep performing tasks involving the whole body for extended periods of time, where the energy is produced aerobically (with oxygen). This requires heart/lung (cardio-respiratory) efficiency in delivering oxygen to the working muscles — for example, in long distance running, swimming or cycling.

(5) Anaerobic power (speed)

The ability to put body parts into motion quickly and to sustain high-intensity efforts, where the energy is supplied anaerobically (without oxygen) — for example, during sprints.

(6) Agility

The ability to change the position of the body quickly and precisely — for example, when dodging.

(7) Flexibility, mobility

The ability to stretch a muscle or ligament so that the joint moves freely — for example, when doing the splits.

(8) Skill

Discussed in Part 4: 'Skills acquisition'.

Since fitness consists of all these components, different sports require different types of fitness.

Worksheet 5: Fitness

(1) Fill in the table below. For each activity, tick the two fitness components that you consider to be most important for that activity or sport.

Activity or sport	**Muscle strength**	**Power**	**Local endurance**	**Aerobic endurance**	**Skill**	**Agility**	**Anaerobic speed**	**Flexibility**
Calisthenics								
Tennis								
Weights								
Jogging								
Skating								
Cricket								
Golf								
Football								
Squash								
Cycling								
Netball								
Softball								
Swimming								
Basketball								
Volleyball								
Soccer								
Athletics								

Figure 5.1

(2) Which activities would you perform to develop:
  (a) Aerobic fitness
    (i) ....
    (ii) ....
  (b) Strength and power
    (i) ....
    (ii) ....
  (c) Anaerobic fitness and speed
    (i) ....
    (ii) ....
  (d) Flexibility
    (i) ....
    (ii) ....
  (e) Agility
    (i) ....
    (ii) ....

(3) Discuss the results from the table (Figure 5.1) in class. You should find that the choice of the most important components depends on:
  (a) The standard of competition
  (b) The facets or skills of the game you considered
  (c) Your knowledge of the sport
  (d) Individual bias.

(4) **Question for discussion:** Is there a difference between a sport *requiring* fitness compared to *developing* a certain fitness component?

Points to note

(1) No single activity develops all fitness components. Therefore, to be totally fit, you must excercise in a number of different ways.

(2) Actually playing a game of any sport does not develop all the components of fitness required by that sport. Therefore at training an athlete builds up the specific fitness for his sport; for example, a footballer requires speed, agility, flexibility, strength, skill and aerobic fitness. Some of these are slightly developed during a game whilst others are developed only through specific training.

(3) When you talk about getting fit by doing a sport or activity, look at the demands made on your body by the exercise. Then decide which components of fitness you are really developing. Does this activity suit your needs? For instance, you might do push ups to lose a pot belly, when instead you should be doing sit ups and reducing your kilojoule intake.

6. Muscular strength and endurance

Strength is defined as 'the maximum force exerted by a muscle against a resistance'.

Factors affecting the application of strength

The factors affecting the application of strength are:

- The cross-sectional area of a muscle
- The muscle length
- Muscle fibre types
- Age of the person
- Sex of the person
- Muscle shapes and fibre arrangements
- Speed of contraction.

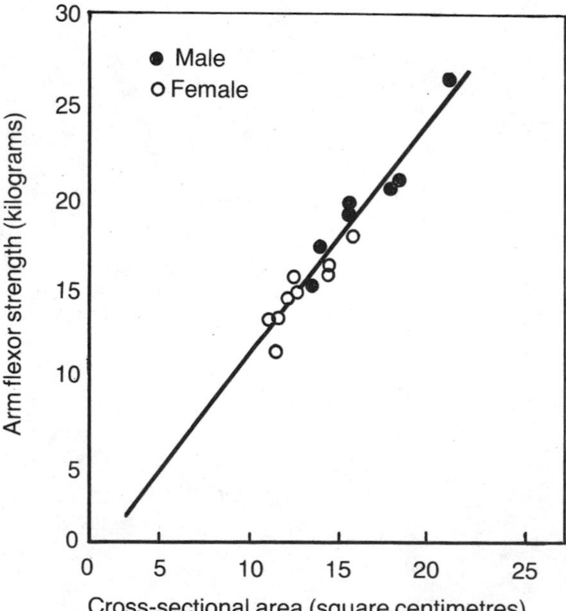

Figure 6.1 Relationship between the strength of the arm flexor muscles and their cross-sectional area. Notice that the relationship is the same for both males and females.

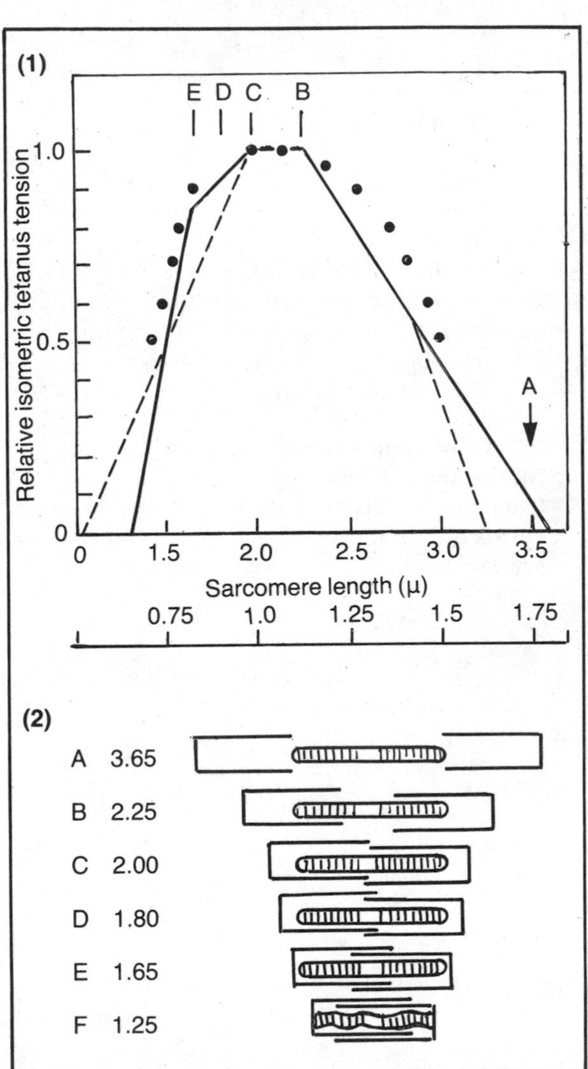

Figure 6.2
(1) Effect of sarcomere length on the tension developed by single muscle fibres (solid line and dots), and the whole muscle (dashed line).
(2) Note the overlap of myosin (thick) and actin (thin) filaments at various sarcomere lengths. Compare with diagram (1).

The cross-sectional area of a muscle

The strength of a muscle is directly related to the cross-sectional area of the muscle — that is, the maximum force that a muscle can exert is approximately 3-4 kilograms per square centimetre of cross-sectional area. Therefore the greater the cross-sectional area, the greater the force that can be applied, and the greater the strength (see Figure 6.1).

The length of a muscle

The amount of tension (force) that a muscle can exert is related to the length of the muscle when it contracts. The optimal length for force application is where there is the optimal combination of:

(a) The greatest number of cross-bridges in contact with the actin (the greatest tension being as the actin touches); that is, maximum myosin and actin overlap (see Figure 6.2).

and

(b) The best joint angle for maximum mechanical advantage (see Figure 6.3). As the lever system of a given joint moves, the force is being applied at a different angle, and this will affect the load that can be moved by the muscle. **Note: the heaviest load that can be moved through the full range of motion of a joint can be no heavier than the heaviest load that can be lifted at the angle at which the muscle is weakest.**

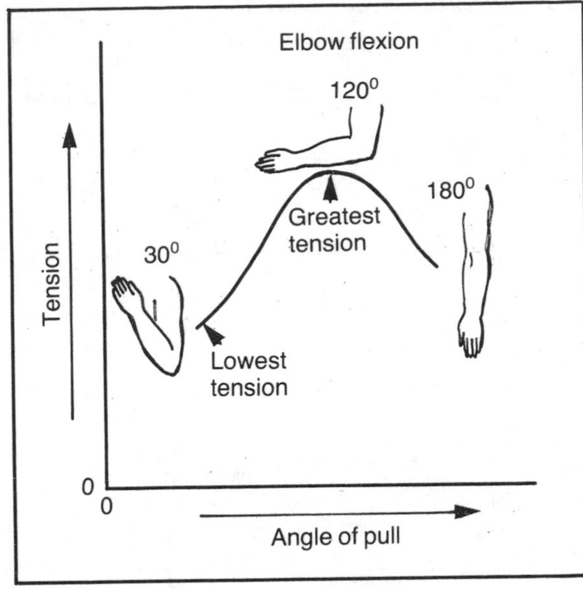

Figure 6.3 The tension developed during elbow flexion when lifting a constant load varies according to the joint angle. The greatest tension (strength) of the biceps is obtained at a joint angle of about 120° and the least tension at 30°.

Muscle fibre types

Skeletal muscles consist of two main fibre types:

(1) Slow-twitch fibres

Slow-twitch fibres are red. They contract slowly, but can contract repeatedly for prolonged periods. These are endurance fibres, suited to aerobic work, such as postural muscles (see Figure 6.6). Slow-twitch fibres are smaller than fast-twitch fibres, and develop less force (see Figure 6.5).

(2) Fast-twitch fibres

Fast-twitch fibres are white. They contract rapidly, but are easily exhausted. These are speed/strength fibres, suited to anaerobic work. Fast-twitch fibres are larger than slow-twitch fibres, and exert greater forces.

Different fibres for different functions

All skeletal muscles contain varying proportions of these fibres, and there are variations in the proportions within different muscles of the one person. For instance, an individual may be a fast throw, because she has a high proportion of white fibres in her arm, yet be a slow runner, because of a large proportion of red fibres in her legs. Your genetic inheritance of these fibres determines your speed or endurance potential (see Figure 6.4).

Age of the person

Strength tends to peak at around 20-30 years,

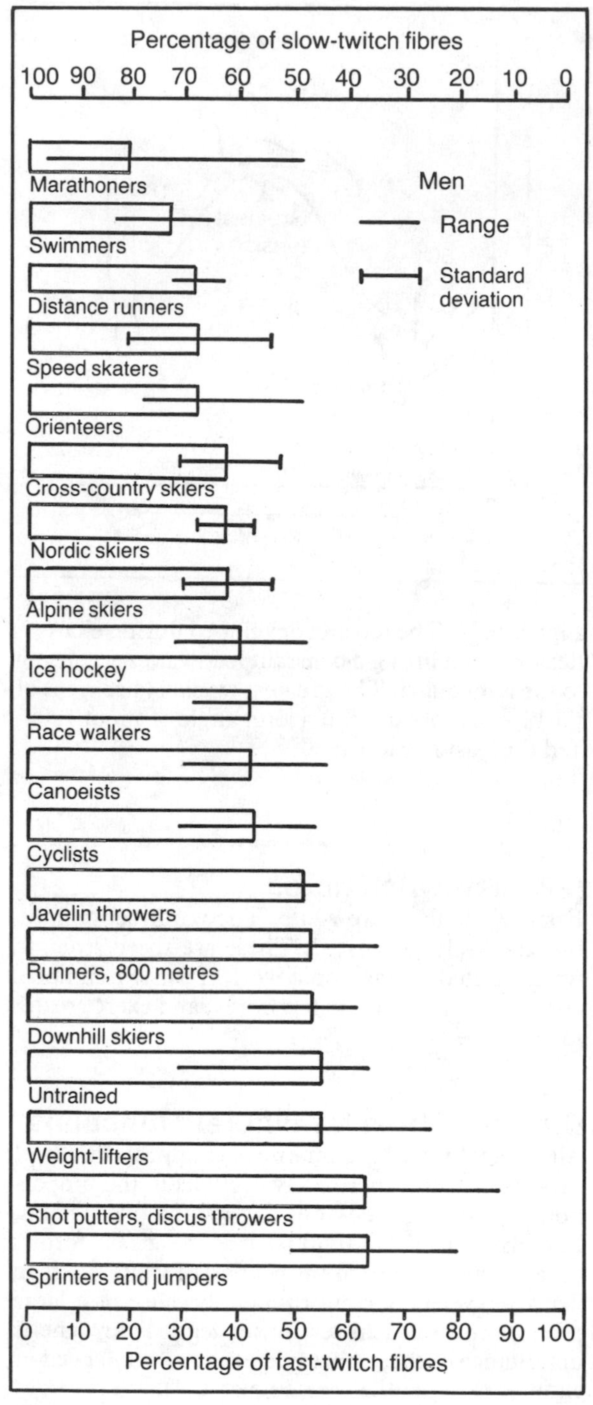

Fig. 6.4 The relationship between fibre type and various motor activities.

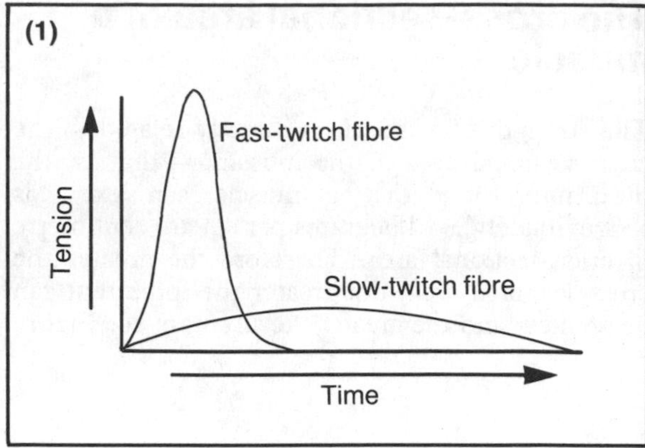

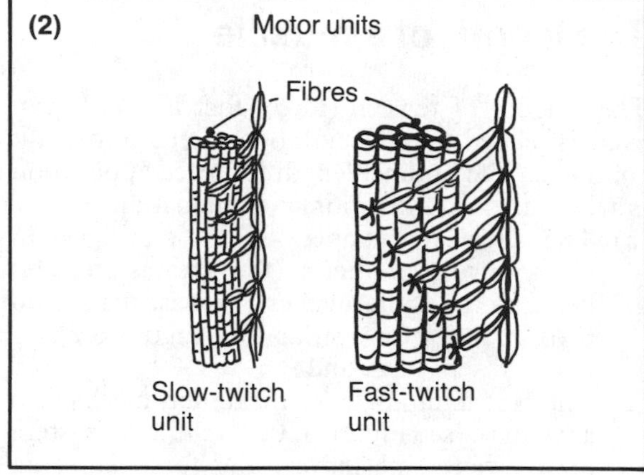

Figure 6.5 The time required for fast-twitch fibres to generate maximal tension is about one-third that required by slow-twitch fibres (1). One of the reasons for this is that the motorneuron controlling the fast-twitch unit is larger than the motorneuron on the slow-twitch unit (2) and, thus, the nerve impulse operates more quickly.

and declines by 40 per cent over the next 40 years. The muscles weaken during ageing because of decreased muscle size. This is caused by loss of protein — the body synthesizes less protein as you grow older.

Sex of the person

In terms of absolute strength, females have an average of two-thirds the strength of males. This variation in strength is not caused by structural

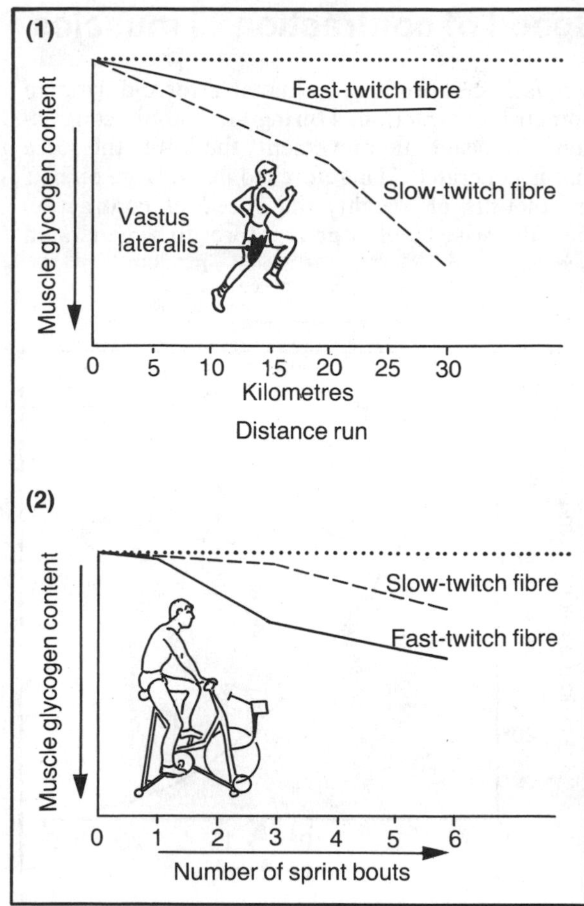

Figure 6.6 Muscle glycogen usage in fast-twitch and slow-twitch fibres during a **30-kilometre race** (1) and during repeated **sprint bouts** (2). Glycogen depletion in the slow-twitch fibres was greatest during the 30-kilometre race; glycogen depletion in the fast-twitch fibres was greatest during the sprint bouts. From this pattern we can see that slow-twitch fibres are preferred for use during prolonged work and fast-twitch fibres during sprint work.

Biochemical characteristic	**Fibre type** Red	White
Aerobic		
• Myoglobin* content	High	Low
• Fat content	High	Low
• Mitochondrial content	High	Low
• Oxidative enzyme levels	High	Low
• Capillary density	High	Low
Anaerobic		
• Glycogen content	Low	High
• PC content	Low	High
• Glycolytic enzyme levels	Low	High
• Speed of contraction	Slow	Fast
• Fatigue factor	Low	High

* Myoglobin is an oxygen-binding pigment similar to haemoglobin. This is what gives the red fibre its colour.

Figure 6.7 Biochemical and functional characteristics of red and white muscle fibres.

differences. Females have the same strength as men relative to cross-sectional area of muscle, but males, with a greater muscle mass, have a larger cross-sectional area.

The trainability of muscle is the same for both sexes, but women tend to make more rapid gains than men, because of their lower initial strength levels. These gains are not accompanied by similar increases in lean body weight, as happens in males. Female hypertrophy (muscle growth) is far less than for males, as they have lower testosterone levels.

Muscle shapes or fibre arrangements

Muscles may be categorized according to fibre arrangement or shape:

(1) Fusiform

The fibres run the length of the muscle belly. An

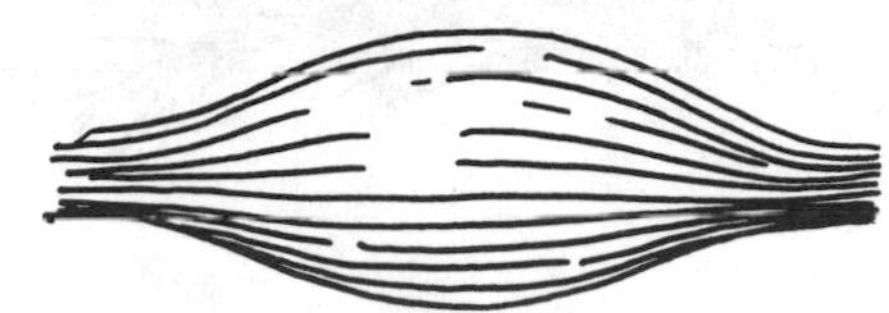

Figure 6.8 Fusiform muscle shape.

example is the biceps, which is designed for mobility, and is highly contractile.

(2) Pennate

(a) **Unipennate**
The fibres are on one side of a central tendon — for example, the semimembranosous of the hamstrings.

Figure 6.9 Unipennate muscle shape.

(b) **Bipennate**
The fibres run off either side of a central tendon, like a plume or quill — for example, the rectus femorus of the quadriceps.

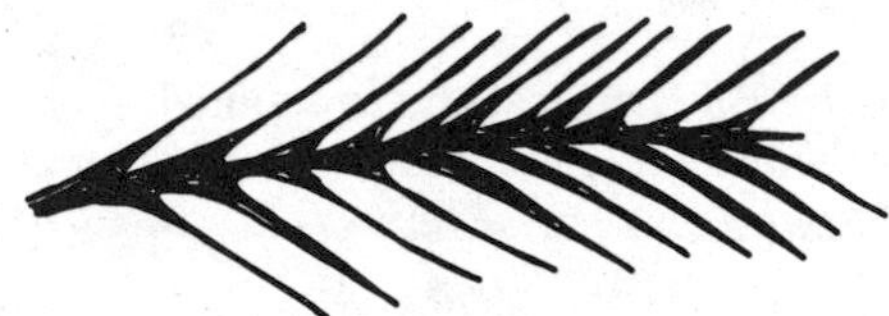

Figure 6.10 Bipennate muscle shape.

(c) **Multipennate**
Small tendons within the muscle converge on to the tendon of insertion. These give limited movement, but are designed for strength and power. An example is the deltoid.

Figure 6.11 Multipennate muscle shape.

Speed of contraction of muscles

A muscle can produce its maximal force during an isometric contraction. During an isotonic contraction, the faster the movement, the lower the force that is generated. Therefore, to move large objects or amounts of weight, the speed of contraction must decrease to allow greater force to be generated (see Figure 6.12).

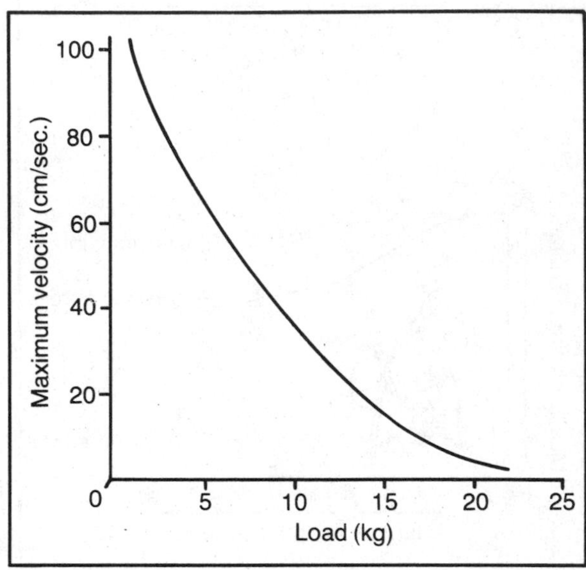

Figure 6.12 Hypothetical relationship between contraction velocity and load.

Local muscular endurance

Local muscular endurance is defined as 'the ability to persist in any given muscular task in which local fatigue rather than general exhaustion becomes the limiting factor'. Examples include the maximum number of sit ups you can do, or the maximum length of time that you can hold a static contraction.

Factors affecting local endurance

(1) **Fibre type**
Red slow-twitch fibres are responsible for endur-

ance performance. For instance, marathon runners usually have 80-85 per cent red fibres in their legs.

(2) **Blood supply to the muscle**

The greater the blood supply to the muscle, the greater the amount of oxygen being transported to the muscle, allowing aerobic energy production.

(3) **Ability to produce aerobic energy**

Muscles with high enzyme and mitachondria concentrations are capable of greater aerobic energy production and so fatigue more slowly.

Muscle fatigue

We cannot say that someone has 'muscle fatigue' as if it is a general condition of the whole body. Muscle fatigue is specific to the task or activity being performed. Some possible causes of muscle fatigue are:

(1) Large numbers of fast-twitch fibres in the muscles being used. Fast-twitch fibres are more easily fatigued than slow-twitch fibres.
(2) Failure of the motor neuron to continue transmitting impulses to the muscle fibres. This usually happens at the end of tasks needing muscular endurance.
(3) Accumulation of lactic acid in the muscle.
(4) Depletion of glycogen stores in the muscle.
(5) Lack of oxygen in the muscle, or inadequate blood flow.
(6) Central nervous system inhibition of fatiguing muscles.

Laboratory work 5: Strength and cross-sectional area of muscle

Procedure

(1) Measure the girth of the upper part of your dominant arm, halfway between your elbow and your shoulder. Record the measurement for yourself and five others.
(2) Lift dumbbells, beginning with 10 kilograms for males, and 5 kilograms for females. Keep increasing the weight until you reach the maximum that you can bicep curl once with your dominant arm.

Note: Stand with your back to a doorway or wall so that you cannot use your back to raise the weight.

Question

Is there a relationship between upper arm size and strength (force exerted)? Discuss.

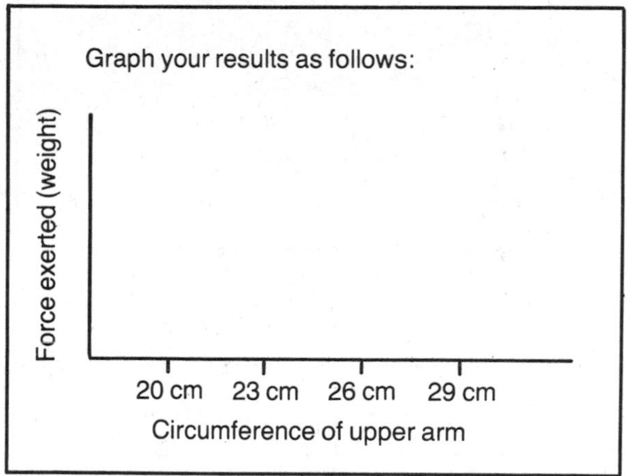

Figure 6.14

Results table

Subject	Self	1	2	3	4	5
Girth						
Max. weight						

Figure 6.13

Laboratory work 6: Strength and the relationship between joint angle and muscle length

Procedure

(1) Using a push-pull dynanometer fixed at one end, measure the force exerted at each of the following joint angles:

Results

Angle	*Force in kilograms (maximum strength)*
180	
160	
125	
90	
45	

(2) Complete the following graph:

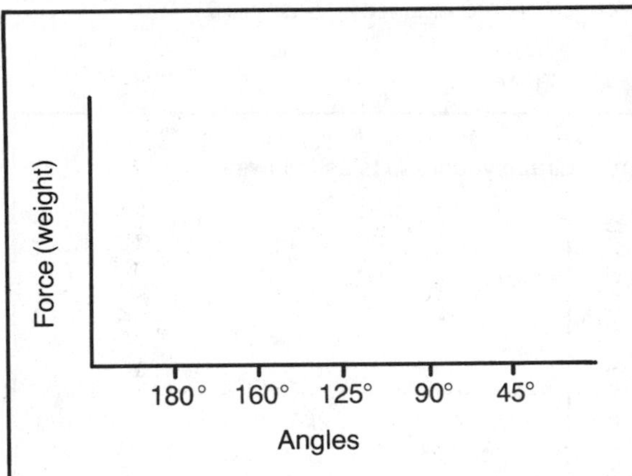

Discuss the results, giving an explanation of the curve shown on the graph.

Laboratory work 7: Muscular endurance

Equipment

- Sphygmomanometer
- 2.5-kilogram weight or small shot put
- Table and chair
- Score sheet.

Method

(1) Sit the subject at the table and extend the non-preferred arm across the table with the hand supinated.
(2) Place the weight in the subject's extended hand.
(3) Instruct the subject to perform wrist flexion-extension as rapidly as possible, ensuring that the elbow remains in contact with the top of the table. The subject continues this exercise until the pain of fatigue makes it impossible.
(4) Count and record on the score sheet the number of flexions performed.
(5) Repeat with all group members.
(6) Begin with the first subject. Place a sphygmomanometer cuff around the upper arm on the non-preferred side. Feel the radial pulse. Inflate the cuff quickly until the pulse can no longer be felt.
(7) Repeat the previous exercise, (3) above, and record the number of flexions performed.
(8) Deflate and remove the sphygmomanometer cuff.
(9) Repeat with all group members.

Results

(1) Does elimination of blood flow to the muscle affect muscular contractions? If so, describe the nature of the effect.
(2) The heart is a muscular organ. What sort of pain would you expect a person undergoing a coronary occlusion (heart attack) to suffer?
(3) Is the pain in the arm related to the amount of work and/or reduction of blood flow? What could be the mechanism producing it?
(4) Does being accustomed to athletic training and competition appear to influence resistance to pain and fatigue? Compare the members in your group.

Worksheet 6: Muscular strength and endurance

(1) 'Males will always be superior in strength events to females.' Discuss this statement.
(2) Why are isokinetic strength machines able to produce greater gains in muscular strength?
(3) Why do elite marathon runners have high percentages of red muscle fibres in their legs?
(4) Explain the difference between *strength* and *endurance*, giving a sporting example of each.

7. Flexibility, agility and speed

Factors limiting flexibility of joints

Flexibility is defined as the capacity of a joint to move through its full range of movement. The factors limiting fexilibity of joints are:

(1) The type of joint

Joints are structured for either strength or mobility. Joints designed for flexibility are, therefore, structurally weak.

For instance, the shoulder joint is structured so that the humerus sits in a shallow cavity. The surrounding muscles provide stability, not the shape of the joint itself.

Another example is the hip joint. Because it must support the body weight, it has a deep socket that is more stable than the shoulder joint, yet allows less movement.

(2) Resting length of muscles

A particular joint becomes less flexible if the muscles, tendons and connective tissue controlling the joint develop short resting lengths. This happens if the muscles are:

- Kept in shortened positions for long periods — for example, the tightening of the hamstrings that occurs after working in a sedentary occupation.
- Strengthened through a short range of motion.

(3) Resting length of the ligaments and joint capsule

Both the ligaments and the joint capsule surrounding a particular joint may be stretched to increase that joint's flexibility.

(4) Body build

Rolls of fat on the body or over-bulky muscles will limit the flexibility of a joint. For example, body builders cannot touch their right shoulder with their right hand because of the size of their biceps muscle.

(5) Muscle temperature

The joints become more flexible if both the internal joint and the attached muscles are warmed. This is why you need a warming-up session before training.

(6) Sex

The joints of females tend to be more flexible than males, because of hormonal differences.

(7) Age

The flexibility of joints tends to decrease from early childhood onwards.

(8) Skin resistance

Because skin is not completely elastic, it can reduce the flexibility of some joints in the extreme movement range.

(9) Bone

In different joints, bones provide different types of resistance. In all joints, however, bone is the only hard tissue that has an effect on the range of motion that the joint can achieve.

Structure	**Resistance to flexibility Percentage of total**
(1) Joint capsule	47
(2) Muscle	41
(3) Tendon	10
(4) Skin	2

Figure 7.1 Soft tissue factors limiting flexibility

Types of flexibility

There are two types of flexibility:

(1) Dynamic (active) flexibility

This is the ability to use the joint and the muscle through the full range of movement, with speed, and without resistance to movement. An example is kicking a football without hamstring and hip joint resistance.

(2) Static (passive) flexibility

This is the ability to use the joint through a great range of movement, such as when doing the splits.

Static flexibility is the magniturde of the range of movement, while dynamic flexibility is the forces that oppose movement throughout a range. Dynamic flexibility is difficult to measure, and therefore is given little attention.

Problems linked with lack of flexibility

Tight, short muscles:

(1) Are far more likely to tear and strain during sports activities than are flexible muscles. For instance, footballers often pull hamstrings when kicking.

(2) Can produce bad body posture. For instance, tight pectorals can cause a cramped chest and round shoulders.

(3) Can produce health problems. For instance, tight hip flexors can pull on the lumbar vertebrae, producing lower back pain.

(4) Can prevent competitive players from fulfilling their potential. For instance:
- A hurdler with limited hip flexibility might clear 10 centimetres above the hurdle, which takes too long.
- A swimmer with poor shoulder flexibility has a reduced distance over which to develop force.

Specific flexibility

Flexibility is:
- Specific to each joint
- Specific to each sporting event. For instance, shot putters have a greater wrist flexibility than wrestlers.

Developing flexibility

(1) PNF = Proprioceptive Neuromuscular Facilitation

In this method:
- Take a muscle to its maximum range, then contract the muscle against an immovable resistance (isometric contraction).
- Passively increase the range.
- Make another isometric contraction and a passive range increase until you reach your limit.

This is the most effective method of increasing flexibility. To develop some muscle groups, you might require a partner's assistance during the isometric contractions.

(2) Ballistic (dynamic/active) stretching

This method involves putting a muscle in stretched position, then bouncing or jerking against the muscle in an attempt to produce greater muscle length. This method can cause muscle injury because the 'bobbing' movements activate the myotatic stretch reflex, and the following contraction under stretch has the potential for injury and pain. It is the ballistic stretching in some aerobic floor classes that causes the acute delayed-onset muscle pain in the following days.

(3) Static (passive) stretching

This method involves taking a muscle to its greatest range and holding this position for 30-45 seconds. This method is better than ballistic stretching because:
- It requires less energy
- It is less likely to damage connective and muscle tissue
- It provides both prevention of and relief from muscle pain and soreness.

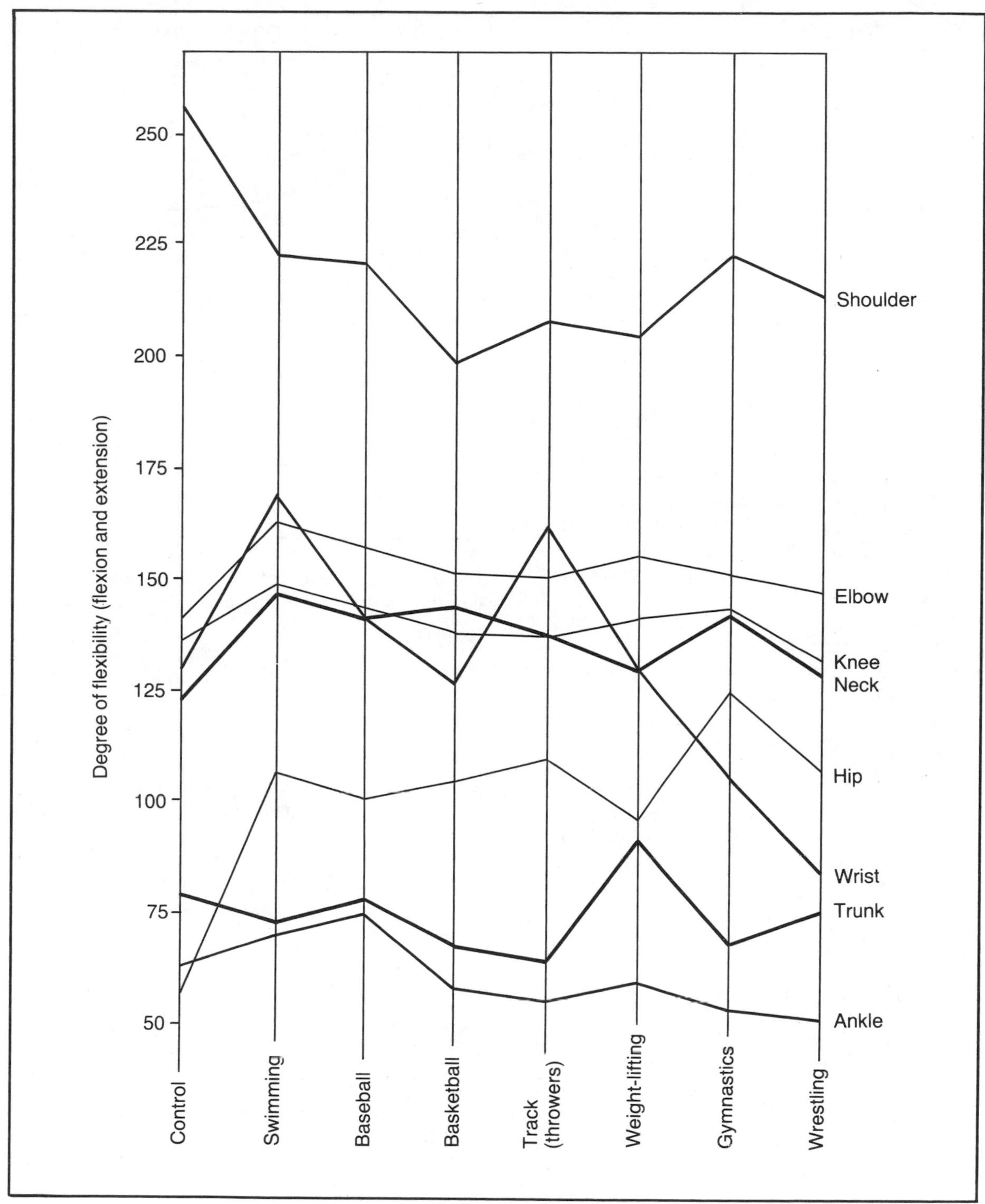

Figure 7.2 Flexion and extension flexibility measures of seven different athletic groups.

The warm up

The warm up is a technique designed:

- To prepare the body for competition or conditioning exercise
- To reduce the possibility of muscle injury or soreness.

The warm up should include exercises that prepare the muscles to be used and activate the energy system required. The warm up should be related specifically to the activity that follows. For instance, sit ups or push ups are not useful as a warm up for running 800 metres. Instead, jogging or run throughs are the best preparation.

Effects of the warm up

Warming up produces beneficial physiological changes:

- There is an increase in the blood flow through the muscle as the small blood vessels dilate, and therefore an increase in the local temperature of the muscle and the oxygen supply.
- It mobilizes the oxidative energy sources so that it is easier to switch to aerobic energy production. This is achieved by increases in the heart and respiratory rates.
- There is reduced viscosity in the muscles, so they can contract and relax more quickly (see Figure 7.3).
- There is increased speed and force of contraction of the muscles.
- The increased temperature increases the enzyme activity within the muscle fibres while improving the extensibility of the fibres and tendons.
- Warming up alerts the nervous system, therefore preparing you physiologically and psychologically for the strain to come.

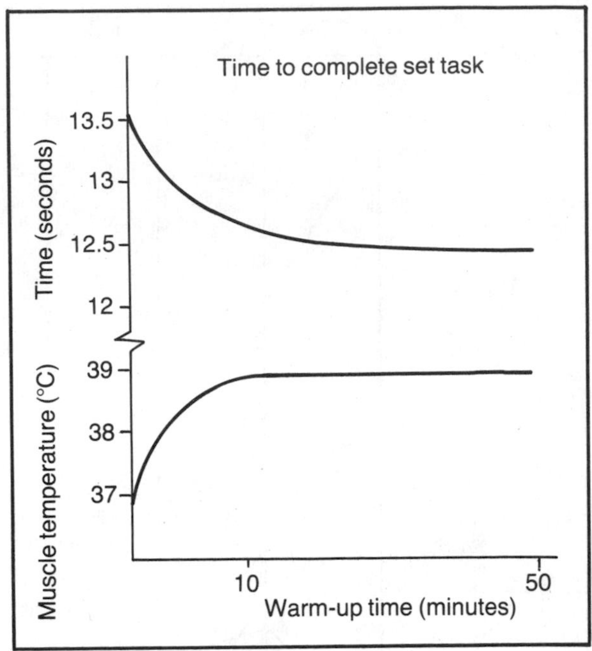

Figure 7.3 Muscle temperature and time to complete a task as a function of warm-up time.

All warm ups:

- Should include flexibility exercises to prevent muscle injury during the strain of a game or work out.
- Should be carried out until you are sweating, which shows increased body and muscle temperature. Warm ups should take much longer on cold days.

The need to warm up

The muscles torn most frequently if you neglect to warm up are the antagonists (such as the hamstrings) to the strong contracting muscles (such as the quadriceps). Cold antagonistic muscles relax slowly and incompletely when the agonists contract, therefore retarding free movement and accurate co-ordination.

At the same time, the force of the contraction of the agonists and the momentum of the moving part exert a great strain on the unyielding antagonists. Without a warm up, this may lead to the tearing of the muscle fibres or the tendons.

Agility

Agility is defined as 'the ability to handle the body quickly and precisely and to change direction accurately while moving quickly'. Agility relies on both flexibility and speed.

Agility is vital in such sports as:

- Football: weaving, dodging
- Basketball: Weaving while dribbling
- Netball: catching and passing on the run
- Tennis: net play.

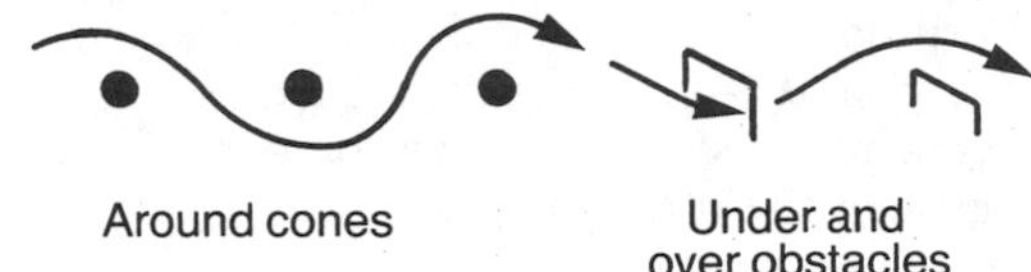

Figure 7.4 An agility run.

Agility can be developed through calisthenics or practices that are related to the sport being played; for example, diving practice for volleyball, tag games and agility runs.

Speed

Speed is defined as 'the ability to put the body or parts into motion quickly'. It is measured as the time taken to complete a specific task, such as a 50-metre sprint. This task completion time (total speed) has two parts:

- **Reaction time (RT)**

The time taken to initiate a response to a specific stimulus. Usually this is about .2 second.

- **Movement time (MT)**

The time taken from the start of movement until it finishes.

Response time

Response time is the addition of the reaction time and the movement time. Response time is what we use to measure speed.

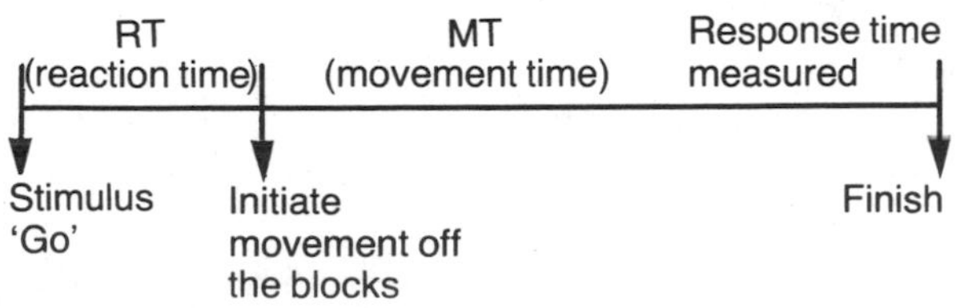

Figure 7.5 Speed of a 100-metre race.

The importance of the reaction time

The total speed of an athlete is the sum of the reaction time and the movement time. It has been calculated that, in a 100-metre sprint, reaction time accounts for 1 per cent of the total time of a race.

At the top levels of competition, this can mean that a runner with a good reaction time can clear the blocks while his competitors are still in contact with theirs.

Reaction time seems to be most important in team games and sprinting, and much less important in sports such as gymnastics, golf and field events.

Factors affecting speed

To develop speed, you need to develop both your reaction and movement times. The factors affecting speed are:

- **Genetic**

The greater the number of white fibres in the muscle, the faster a person will be; the greater the number of red fibres, the slower the person.

- **Distance**

As the distance increases, speed decreases.

- **Duration**

As the duration of the exercise increases, speed decreases.

- **Strength and power**

Initial speed improvements seem to be the result of better neural transmission of impulses to the muscles concerned. However, you can make later improvements by developing your strength and power.

- **Specific function of muscles and joints**

Speed, like flexibility and strength, is specific to each muscle group and joint. For instance, a person who can throw quickly need not be able to run quickly.

Limitations on speed

Limitations on speed include:

- The mechanical structure of joints — that is, the type of lever and the length of the lever arms.
- Lack of mobility in joints (see section on flexibility of joints).
- Load to be moved. As resistance increases, speed decreases.
- Anaerobic threshold; that is, the accumulation of lactic acid.

Laboratory work 8: Flexibility

Aim
To measure the flexibility of various joints.

Apparatus
Board protractor and compass.

Procedure
(1) Write in your notebook the following short table:
Range of motion at:
- Shoulder ....
- Hips ....
- Knee ....

(2) Using the protractor, measure the normal range of motion in joints listed (shoulder, hips, knee), and list your measurements in the table.
(3) Compare the results of all class members. How do you account for the differences?

Laboratory work 9: Range of motion

Aim
To assess the value of the increased range of motion.

Apparatus
- Medicine ball
- Measuring tape.

Procedure
(1) Throw a medicine ball as far as possible:
 (**a**) Seated, hands just above your head (hand movement only)
 (**b**) Seated, maximum arm movement, no wrist movement.
 (**c**) As above, plus full wrist movement.
 (**d**) Standing, trunk extended, soccer-style throw.

(2) Copy the following table into your notebook, and note on it the distances thrown in:
Position (**a**) ....
Position (**b**) ....
Position (**c**) ....
Position (**d**) ....

(3) What reasons can you give for the differences between the different positions?

Laboratory work 10: The effect of warm-up exercises

Aim
To assess the effect of warm-up exercises on the joint range of motion.

Apparatus
Metre stick.

Procedure
(1) Perform the sit-and-reach (trunk flexion) test without warm up. (See box for details of the exercise.)
(2) Perform a five-minute jog, followed by hip region flexibility calisthenics.
(3) Repeat the trunk flexion test.
(4) Write down your results for:
- Trunk flexion test (no warm up)
- Trunk flexion test (after warm up).

(5) Discuss your results, explaining any difference that occurred.

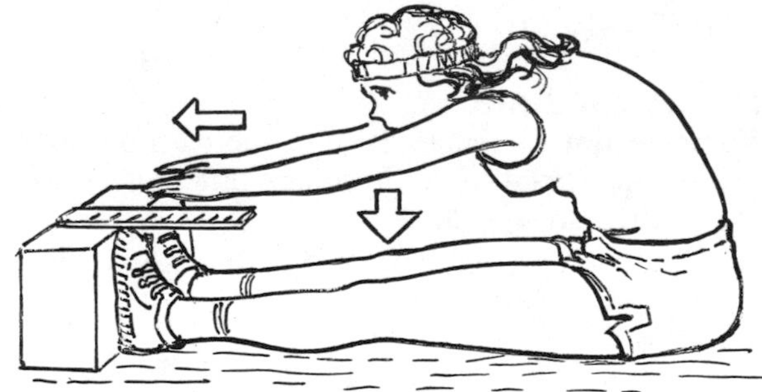

Figure 7.6 Trunk flexion.

Trunk flexion test

Purpose
To measure the amount of trunk flexion and the ability to stretch the back muscles and back thigh muscles (hamstrings).

Explanation

- Sit with your legs fully extended and the bottom of your feet flat against a board projecting from the wall.
- Extend (stretch) your arms and hands forward as far as possible and hold for a count of three.
- With a ruler, measure (in millimetres) the distance before or beyond the edge of the board that you reach. Distances before the edge (not able to reach your toes) are expressed as negative scores; those beyond the edge are expressed as positive scores.

Improper procedures

- Not holding the flexed position for a count of three.
- Bending at the knees.

Laboratory work 11: Speed

Aim

To measure speed.

Apparatus

- Stop watch
- Measuring tape.

Procedure

(1) Sprint 40 metres from a standing start. Starter uses the commands, '1, 2, 3, Go!'

(2) After recovering, repeat the sprint. However, the starter randomly calls 'Go!'

(3) Write down your results:
- 40 metres sprint (with warning) ....
- 40 metres sprint (without warning) ....

(4) Discuss your results.

Laboratory work 12: Reaction time

Aim

To measure reaction time.

Apparatus

Metre rulers.

Procedure

For most people, the dominant hand is usually the one he or she writes or throws with. Most commonly this is the right hand.

(1) Have your partner sit with the dominant hand resting on a desk. Your partner's arm should extend beyond the desk from a point halfway between the wrist and the elbow (see Figure 7.7).

(2) Hold the metre stick at the upper end (100 centimetres) with one steady hand. Let it dangle between your partner's slightly separated thumb and forefinger (see Figure 7.7). Your partner should not be touching the stick at this time.

(3) Line up the 20-centimetre mark on the stick so that it is level with the top of your partner's thumb.

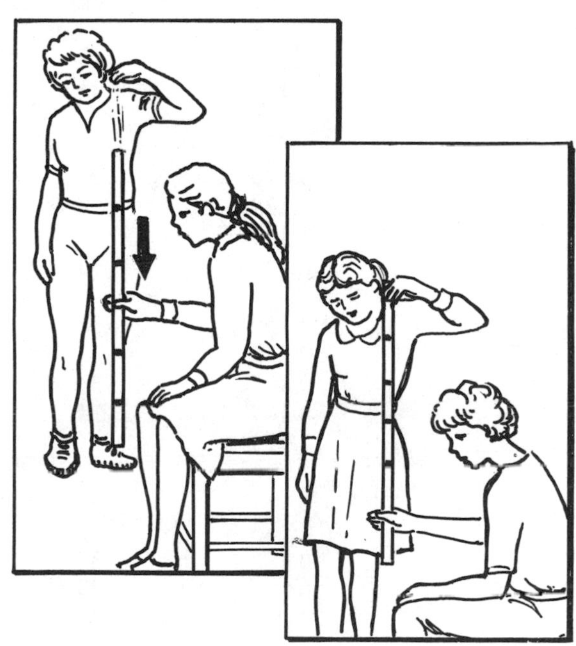

Figure 7.7 Switch places with your partner in order to measure your own reaction time. Again, do five trials and average them.

(4) Instruct your partner to concentrate on the 30-centimetre tape mark. As soon as the stick begins falling, your partner must try to snap the thumb and forefinger closed on that (30-centimetre) mark.
(5) Release the ruler without warning. Your partner will 'freeze', with the thumb and forefinger grasping the ruler.
(6) Count the exact centimetre number from the 20-centimetre mark to the upper edge of your partner's thumb.
(7) Repeat five times; then average the measurements made.
(8) Using the table below, calculate your approximate visual reaction time.

Laboratory work 13: Agility

Aim
To measure agility.

Apparatus
- Stop watch
- Four chairs
- Wet towel.

Procedure
(1) Start in a front lying position behind the starting line, with your arms flexed and hands placed just outside your shoulder.

Distance of fall (cm)	Time of fall (sec.)	Distance of fall (cm)	Time of fall (sec.)	Distance of fall (cm)	Time of fall (sec.)
1	0.045	21	0.207	41	0.289
2	0.064	22	0.212	42	0.293
3	0.078	23	0.217	43	0.296
4	0.090	24	0.221	44	0.300
5	0.101	25	0.226	45	0.303
6	0.110	26	0.230	46	0.306
7	0.120	27	0.235	47	0.310
8	0.128	28	0.239	48	0.313
9	0.136	29	0.243	49	0.316
10	0.143	30	0.247	50	0.319
11	0.150	31	0.252	51	0.322
12	0.157	32	0.256	52	0.326
13	0.163	33	0.259	53	0.329
14	0.169	34	0.263	54	0.332
15	0.175	35	0.267	55	0.335
16	0.181	36	0.271	56	0.338
17	0.186	37	0.275	57	0.341
18	0.192	38	0.279	58	0.344
19	0.197	39	0.282	59	0.346
20	0.202	40	0.286	60	0.349

Figure 7.8

(2) On the command 'Go!', the stop watch starts. Jump to your feet and run as fast as you can to the end line, a distance of 10 metres (see Figure 7.9).
(3) Stop as one foot touches or crosses the end line; then sprint back to the starting line.
(4) Weave in and out around the four chairs spaced 3.3 metres apart, to the end line.
(5) Turn and weave back through the chairs to the starting line.
(6) Sprint to the end line, touch or cross it with your foot, and turn and sprint past the finish line.
(7) Record the time necessary to complete the run to the nearest tenth of a second.

A wet towel may be provided so you can wipe off your feet before the run. This allows better traction.

Do not:

- Touch the lines at each end
- Touch or accidentally touch any of the chairs
- Leave the prescribed course.

Worksheet 7: Flexibility, agility and speed

(1) A student cannot touch his or her toes. What factors could cause such a lack of flexibility? How might you improve this situation?
(2) How can warming up prevent injuries during exercise?
(3) How can flexibility have an influence on sporting performance? In your discussion, give two examples of poor flexibility decreasing performance, and two examples of good flexibility improving perfomance.
(4) Describe two PNF exercises.
(5) What is an agility circuit? Give an example.

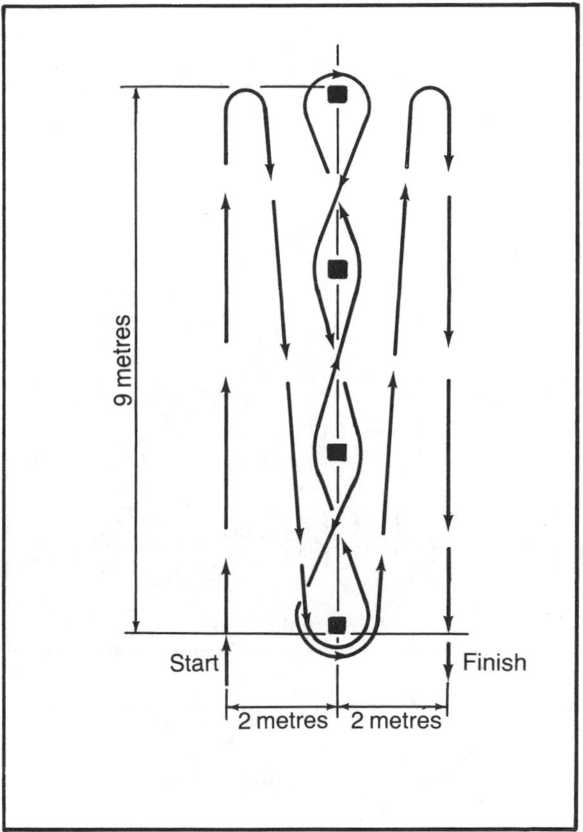

Figure 7.9 Diagram for agility run.

8. Energy systems

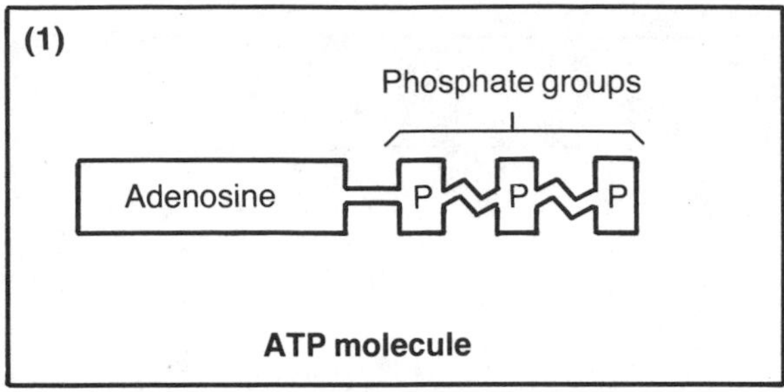

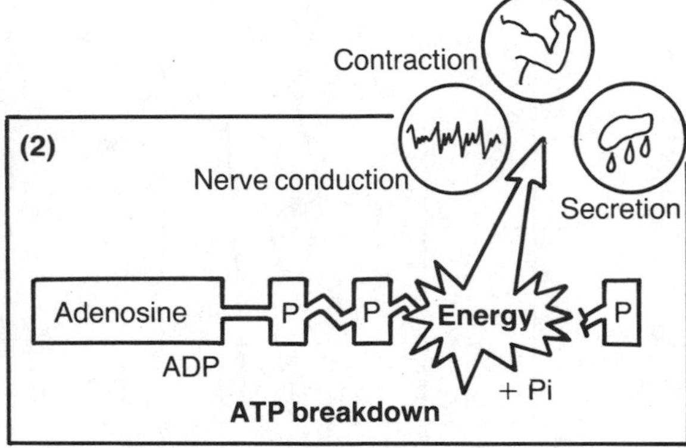

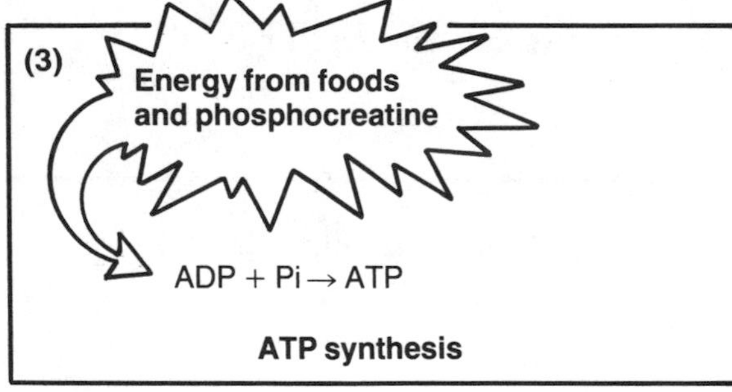

Figure 8.1
(1) ATP consists of a large molecule called adenosine and three simpler components called phosphate groups.
(2) The energy released from the breakdown of ATP is used to perform biological work. The building blocks for ATP synthesis are the by-products of its breakdown, adenosine diphosphate (ADP) and inorganic phosphate (Pi).
(3) The energy for ATP resynthesis comes from the breakdown of foods and phosphocreatine.

The importance of ATP

Energy for muscle contraction comes from the breakdown of a chemical compound named **adenosine triphosphate (ATP)** (see Figure 8.1).

The breakdown of ATP releases energy which stimulates the rowing motion of the myosin cross-bridges. This ATP breakdown is triggered by the arrival of the electrical impulse at the sarcomere from the motor neuron.

Sources of ATP

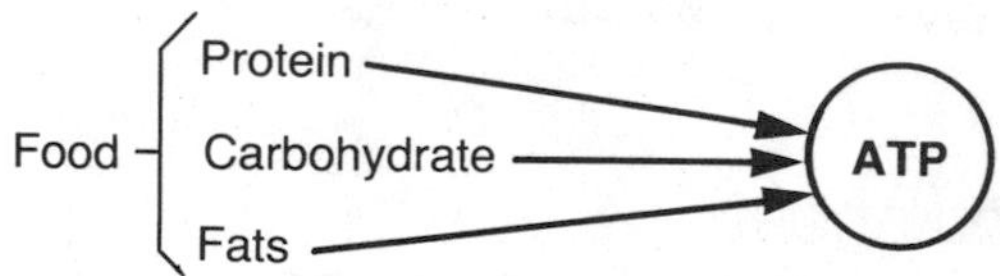

Figure 8.2 Sources of ATP.

Protein

Protein is used to produce ATP only under conditions of prolonged starvation; for instance, in people in prison camps, or perhaps in people competing in ultra-marathon running events.

Carbohydrates

Carbohydrates are broken down to glucose and stored as glycogen in the muscles and the liver. Chemical reactions involving glucose produce ATP. If you take in excess carbohydrate, it is converted to adipose and stored.

Fats

Fats are broken down to fatty acids and triglycerides. Fatty acids are stored as adipose (fat) tissue, or they circulate in the blood. Triglycerides are stored in the muscles. These substances can produce ATP through chemical reactions.

Chemical systems that produce ATP

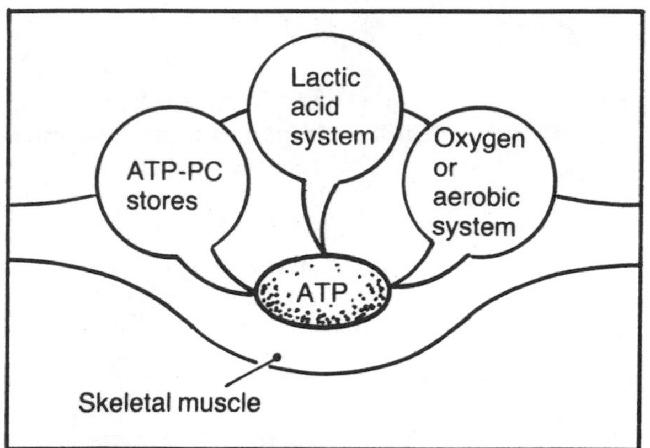

Figure 8.3 ATP is supplied to the muscle in three ways: by the stored phosphagens (ATP and PC); by the lactic acid system (anaerobic glycolysis); and by the oxygen (aerobic) system.

(1) ATP production during resting conditions

(See Figures 8.5 and 8.6.) When the body is at rest, ATP is produced aerobically. The chemical reactions producing this aerobic ATP occur in bean-shaped mitachondria (see Figure 8.4), which are found in the muscle fibres. ATP is produced in the mitachondria and later transported to the myosin cross-bridges.

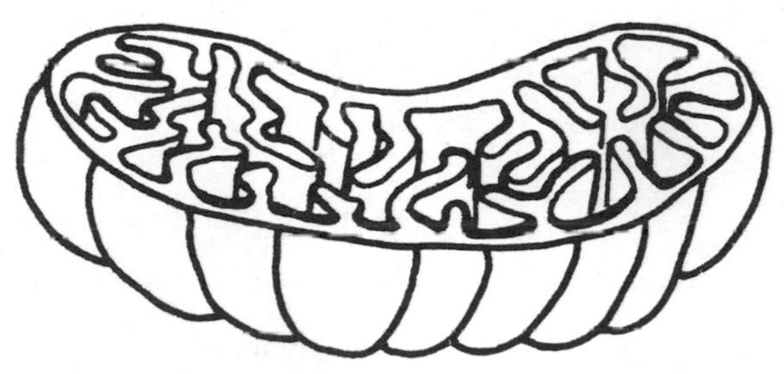

Figure 8.4 A mitachondrion.

$\frac{1}{3}$ Glucose {from muscles and liver} + Breathed in O_2

or

$\frac{2}{3}$ Muscle triglycerides Fatty acids {From adipose tissue and the blood supply}

→ Breathed out ↓ CO_2 + Sweat H_2O + heat

gives energy allowing

ADP + P → ATP (39) {Releases energy for contraction, transport, etc.}

Figure 8.5 Aerobic energy production (cellular respiration).

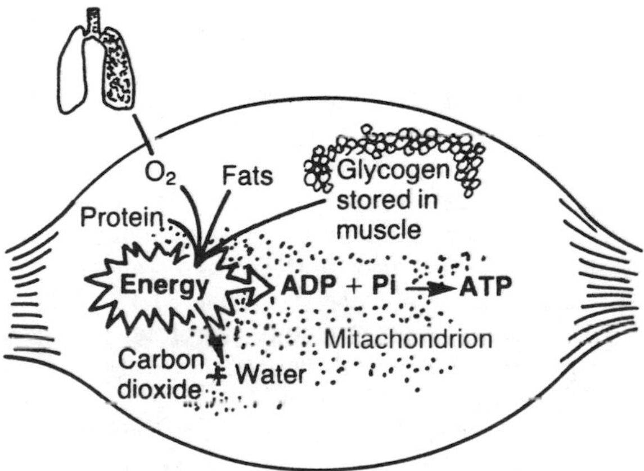

Figure 8.6 **The oxygen, or aerobic, system**. The aerobic breakdown of carbohydrates, fats and even proteins provides energy for ATP resynthesis. Since abundant ATP can be manufactured without yielding fatiguing by-products, the aerobic system is most suited for endurance activities.

(2) ATP production during exercise

During exercise, the energy system being used to produce ATP depends on how long you have been exercising, and at what intensity.

(a) The ATP-CP system

ATP stored at the myosin cross-bridges is broken down to release energy for contraction. The ADP and the phosphate are then converted back to ATP by the creatine phosphate (CP).

$$\text{ATP} \underset{\text{CP}}{\rightleftarrows} \text{ADP} + \text{P} + \text{energy}$$

However, the CP is exhausted after about 10 seconds. This system provides energy for tasks of only about 0-10 seconds duration.

The CP and the stored ATP are restored after about two minutes' rest.

(b) The lactic acid system

This reaction occurs in the muscle fibres. Stored glycogen is converted to glucose, then glucose is converted by enzymes into lactic acid, giving ATP.

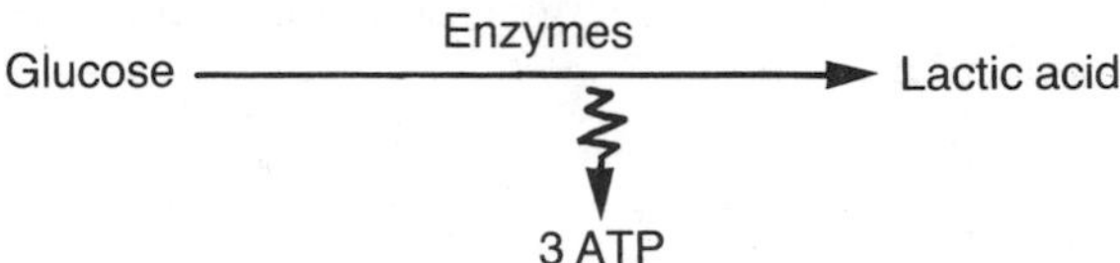

Figure 8.7 Anaerobic glycolysis.

This is called **anaerobic glycolysis** (see Figure 8.8). The lactic acid is slowly removed and broken down into carbon dioxide (CO_2) and water (H_2O), or reconverted to glucose at the liver. Lactic acid is toxic in large amounts, and therefore produces fatigue; for instance, stiff or sore calves after a run.

This system provides energy for a high-intensity task of 30-seconds-to-2 minutes duration, and also gives energy early in submaximal exercise.

As exercise intensity increases and duration decreases, the main fuel becomes carbodydrate (glucose) (see Figure 8.9).

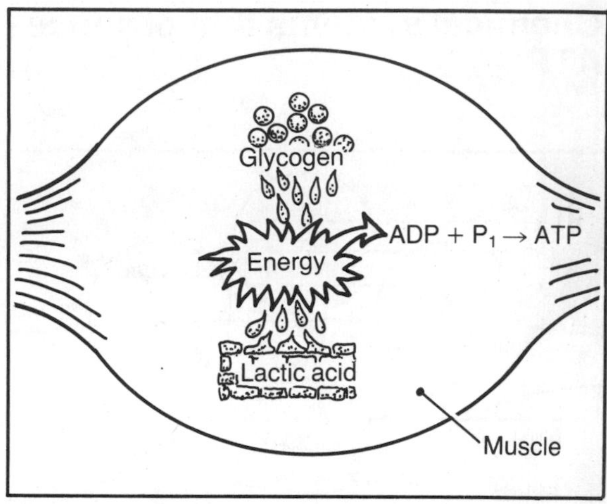

Figure 8.8 **The lactic acid system** (anaerobic glycolysis). Carbohydrate (glycogen) is broken down anaerobically (without oxygen) to lactic acid. The latter causes muscular fatigue. The energy released during this breakdown is used to resynthesize ATP. Exercises performed at maximum rates for between one and three minutes depend heavily upon the lactic acid system for ATP energy.

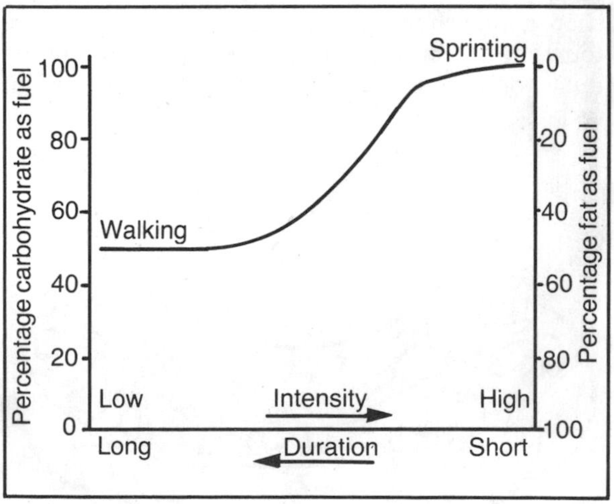

Figure 8.9 As exercise intensity increases and duration decreases, the predominant food fuel shifts toward carbohydrate.

(c) The aerobic system

This system uses, firstly, glucose from either muscle tissue or from the liver; and secondly, triglycerides (from the muscle) and fatty acids

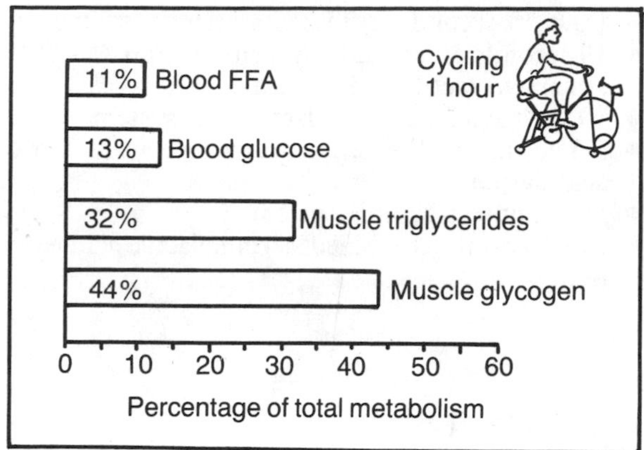

Figure 8.10 During one hour of cycling, the muscular stores of triglycerides and glycogen supply 76 per cent of the fuel, whereas the blood-borne fuels (free fatty acids and glucose) account for the remaining 24 per cent.

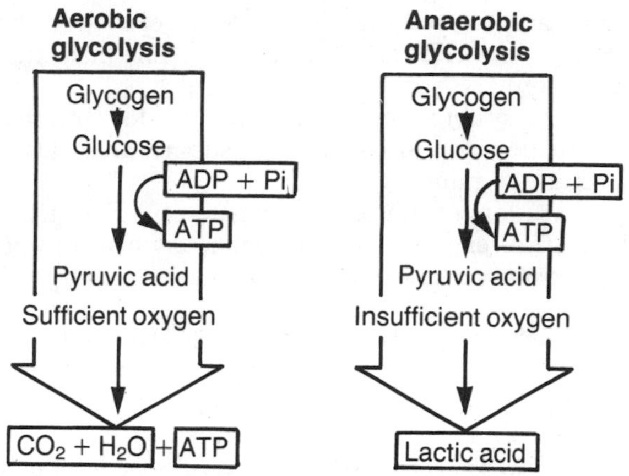

Figure 8.11 **Aerobic and anaerobic glycolysis.** The breakdown of glycogen to pyruvic acid with ATP resythesis does not require oxygen. With oxygen present (aerobic glycolysis) pyruvic acid is further broken down to CO_2 and H_2O with more ATP resynthesized. Without oxygen (anaerobic glycolysis), pyruvic acid is converted to lactic acid, with no further ATP resynthesized.

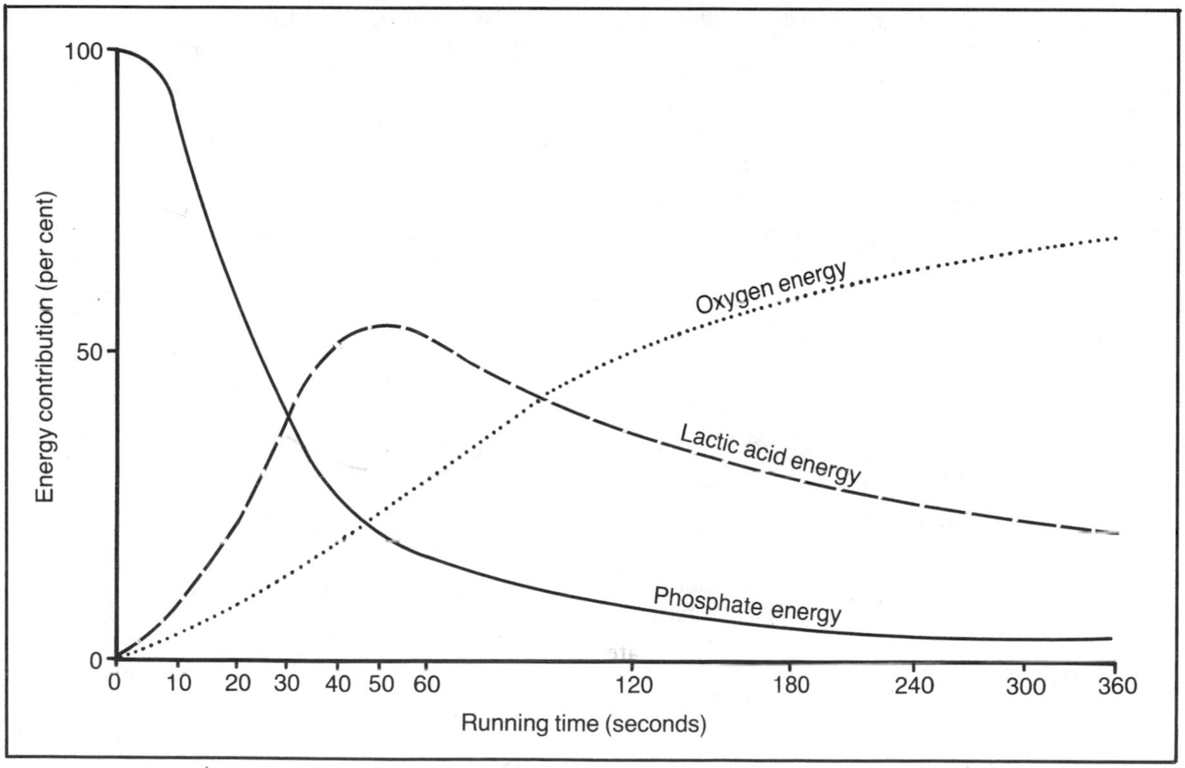

Figure 8.12 Relationship between running time and contribution of different energy systems.

(from adipose and the blood stream) carried to the working muscles (see Figure 8.10). The main fuel is glucose.

This system provides energy for muscle contraction for low-intensity (submaximal) tasks lasting five minutes or more.

Depletion of muscle glycogen can give acute feelings of exhaustion; for instance, when 'hitting the wall' during a marathon run.

Glucose or fatty acids + triglycerides $+ O_2 \rightarrow CO_2 + H_2O +$ heat
↘ 39 ATP

Aerobic energy production produces far more ATP than does the lactic acid system, but does not produce toxic waste.

Energy sources for particular sports

(See Figure 8.14.) The energy sources needed for each sport are specific to the sport being played, its duration and its intensity. Take an example: the 5000-metre race. The energy sources used for such a race are:

- First 10 seconds: ATP/PC system
- 10 seconds-30 seconds: transition from ATP/PC system to lactic acid system
- 30 seconds-2 minutes: lactic acid system
- 2-5 minutes: Transition from aerobic to lactic acid system
- 5+ minutes: aerobic system
- Final sprint: combined aerobic/lactic acid system.

Worksheet 8: The energy systems

(1) Discuss the energy sources you use, from the time you sit down to put on your running shoes until the time you lie back relaxing after finishing a 10-kilometre fun run.

(2) What is the major energy source for:
   (a) A 25-metre sprint?
   (b) The vertical jump?
   (c) Ten push ups?
   (d) Flexibility exercises?
   (e) A gymnastics routine?
   (f) A triathlon?

ATP-PC (phosphagen) system	**Lactic acid system**	**Oxygen system**
Anaerobic	Anaerobic	Aerobic
Very rapid	Rapid	Slow
Chemical fuel: PC	Food fuel: glycogen	Food fuels: glycogen, fats, and protein
Very limited ATP production	Limited ATP production	Unlimited ATP production
Muscular stores limited	By-product, lactic acid, causes muscular fatigue	No fatiguing by-products
Used with sprint or any high-power, short-duration activity	Used with activities of 1 to 3 min. duration	Used with endurance or long-duration activities

Figure 8.13 General characteristics of the energy systems.

Sports or sport activity	% emphasis according to energy systems		
	ATP-PC and LA	LA-O_2	O_2
(1) Baseball	80	20	—
(2) Basketball	85	15	—
(3) Fencing	90	10	—
(4) Field hockey	60	20	20
(5) Football	90	10	—
(6) Golf	95	5	—
(7) Gymnastics	90	10	—
(8) Ice hockey			
(a) Forwards, defence	80	20	—
(b) Goalie	95	5	—
(9) Lacrosse			
(a) Goalie, defence, attack men	80	20	—
(b) Midfielders, man-down	60	20	20
(10) Rowing	20	30	50
(11) Skiing			
(a) Slalom, jumping, downhill	80	20	—
(b) Cross-country	—	5	95
(c) Pleasure skiing	34	33	33
(12) Soccer			
(a) Goalie, wings, strikers	80	20	—
(b) Halfbacks, or link men	60	20	20
(13) Swimming and diving			
(a) 50 yd. diving	98	2	—
(b) 100 yd.	80	15	5
(c) 200 yd.	30	65	5
(d) 100, 500 yd.	20	40	40
(e) 1500, 1650 yd.	10	20	70
(14) Tennis	70	20	10
(15) Track and field			
(a) 100, 220 yd.	98	2	—
(b) Field events	90	10	—
(c) 440 yd.	80	15	5
(d) 880 yd.	30	65	5
(e) 1 mile	20	55	25
(f) 2 miles	20	40	40
(g) 3 miles	10	20	70
(h) 6 miles (cross-country)	5	15	80
(i) Marathon	—	5	95
(16) Volleyball	90	10	—
(17) Wrestling	90	10	—

Figure 8.14 Various sports and their predominant energy system.

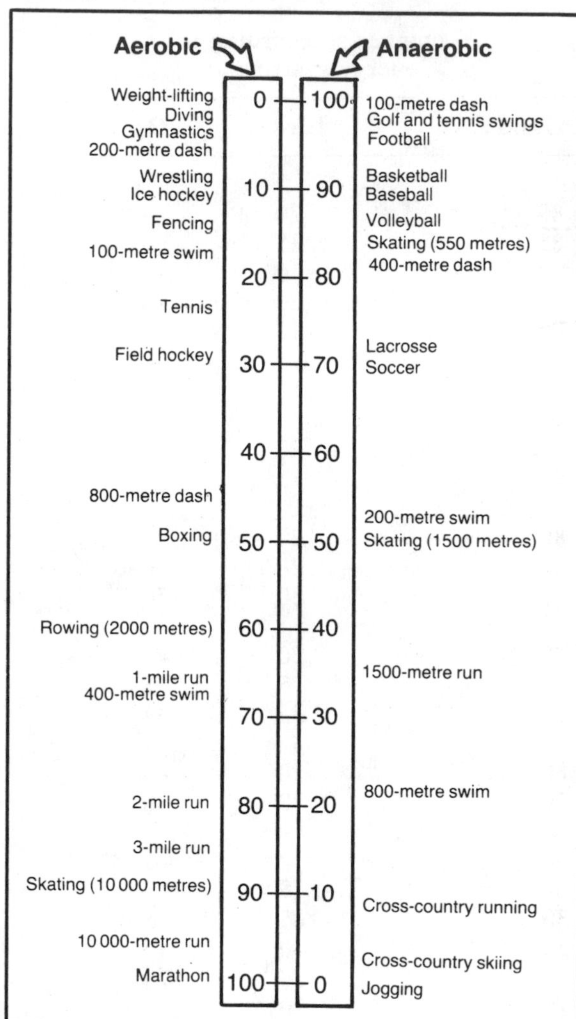

Figure 8.15 The energy continuum and various sports activities. Although both aerobic and anaerobic energy systems contribute some ATP during the performance of various sports, one system usually contributes more, as indicated by the aerobic and anaerobic percentages.

Figure 8.17 (Right) Laboratory evidence for the energy continuum concept.
(1) VO_2 max values for 19 different groups of athletes are shown. Note how the values are high in those who participate in endurance events and low in those who participate in anaerobic events.
(2) Maximal blood lactic acid levels following exhaustive exercise are shown for 11 different groups of athletes. Note that those involved in aerobic events have low values and those involved in anaerobic events have high values.
(3) Values for a stair-climbing test (involving the phosphagen system) are shown; the same trend down in B can be seen.

Figure 8.16 (Below) The approximate percentage of contribution of aerobic and anaerobic energy sources in selected track events.

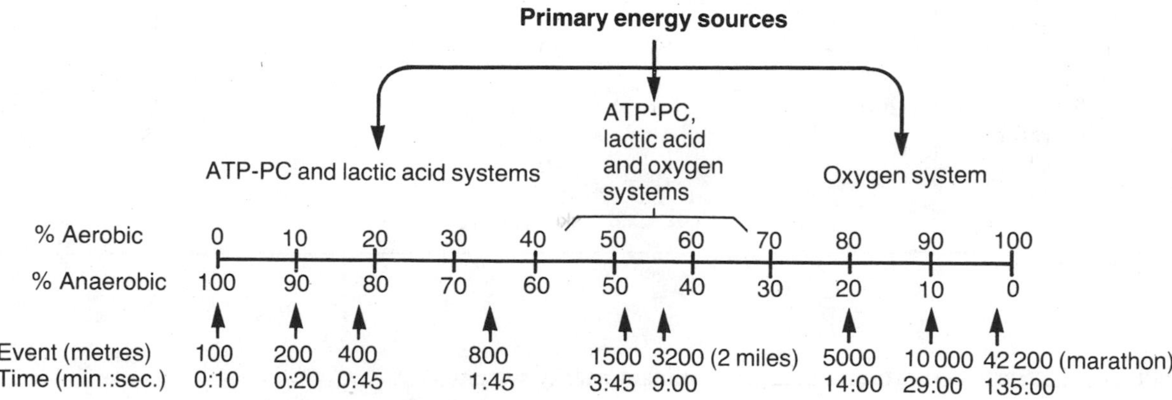

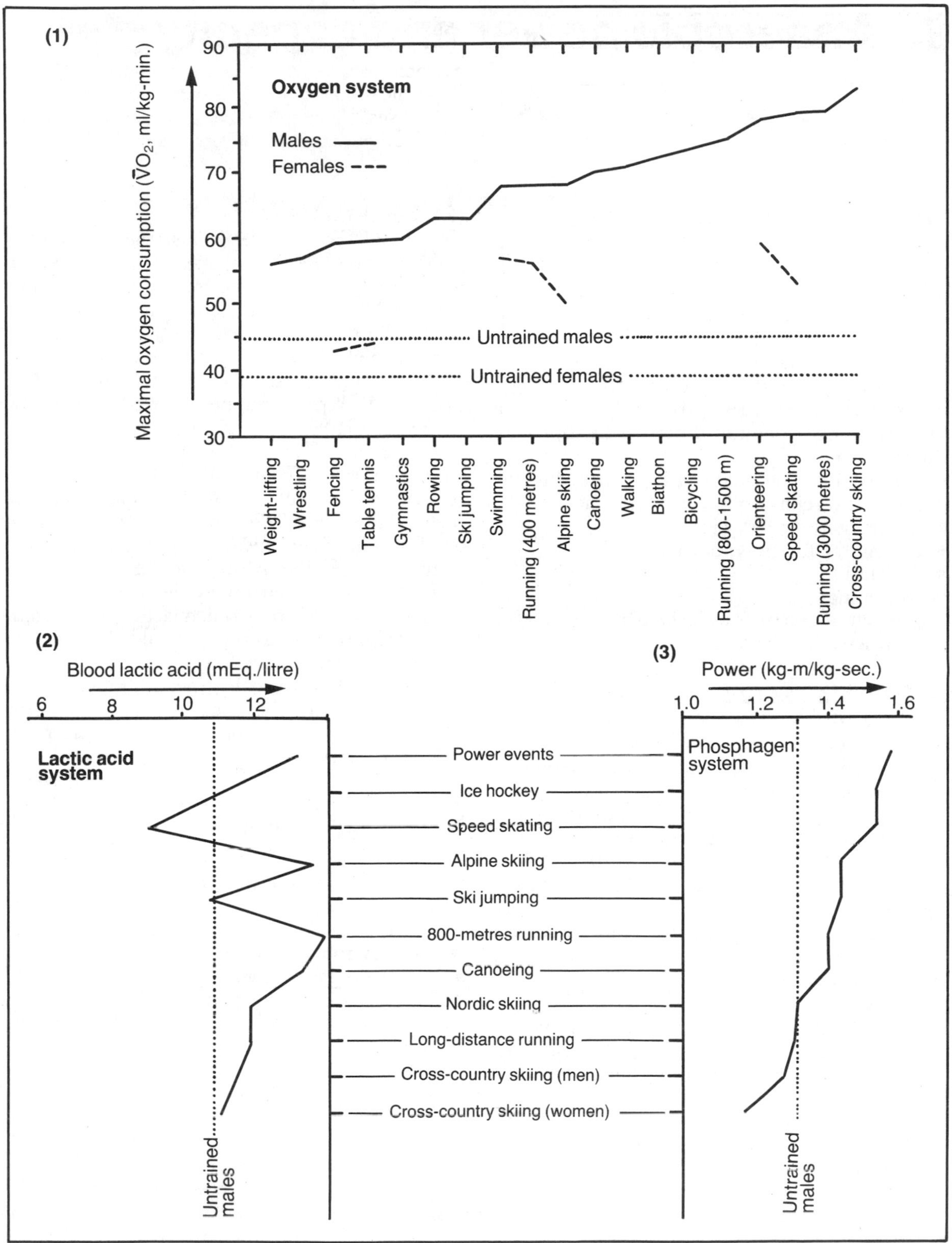
(1)
Oxygen system
Males
Females
Maximal oxygen consumption ($\bar{V}O_2$, ml/kg-min.)
90
80
70
60
50
40
30
Untrained males
Untrained females
Weight-lifting
Wrestling
Fencing
Table tennis
Gymnastics
Rowing
Ski jumping
Swimming
Running (400 metres)
Alpine skiing
Canoeing
Walking
Biathon
Bicycling
Running (800-1500 m)
Orienteering
Speed skating
Running (3000 metres)
Cross-country skiing
(2)
Blood lactic acid (mEq./litre)
6
8
10
12
Lactic acid system
Untrained males
(3)
Power (kg-m/kg-sec.)
1.0
1.2
1.4
1.6
Phosphagen system
Untrained males
Power events
Ice hockey
Speed skating
Alpine skiing
Ski jumping
800-metres running
Canoeing
Nordic skiing
Long-distance running
Cross-country skiing (men)
Cross-country skiing (women)

9. Anaerobic power and capacity

What is anaerobic power?

Anaerobic power may be defined as 'the ability to produce energy by either the **ATP-PC (adenosine triphosphate-creatine phosphate) system** or the **lactic acid system**, and so sustain high-intensity effort whilst tolerating a build up of lactic acid'.

Anaerobic power is needed for short-term, high-intensity speed activities, particularly exercises of less than 2 or 3 minutes duration. Examples include:

- Sprints: 100, 200, 400 and 800 metres running
- Throws: javelin, discus, hammer, shot
- Jumps: long, triple, high
- Hitting: golf, tennis, baseball
- Weight-lifting
- Gymnastics.

Two practical examples of anaerobic energy use are given below:

(1) 800 metres run

The time taken for the 800 metres run is about 2 minutes. As the race begins, there is a rapid acceleration in ATP demand so that the muscles can contract frequently. It would take about 3 minutes of exercise for oxygen consumption to accelerate enough to produce this ATP aerobically.

Therefore at the start of the race the ATP-PC system provides the ATP during the first 10 seconds. This is followed by the anaerobic glycolysis of the lactic acid system, which provides energy for most of the run, although the aerobic system does make some contribution.

Remember that:

(a) Muscle glycogen stores are the only fuel for anaerobic glycolysis. The level of these stores determines how long it will take to tire a muscle.

(b) While the lactic acid system is the main system in use, lactic acid accumulates in the muscles and blood. High lactic acid levels inhibit muscular contraction, and cause fatigue. The ability to tolerate high levels of lactic acid is a prerequisite for success in most athletic events.

(2) 5000-metre race

As the 5000-metre race begins, the demand for ATP increases. Because it takes about 3 minutes to increase oxygen consumption, the two anaerobic systems (ATP-CP and lactic acid) provide the required ATP.

After about three minutes, the oxygen consumption has increased so that the ATP required to maintain this pace can be supplied aerobically. This situation continues until the final laps.

As the pace increases during the final laps, a runner reaches a point where, despite increased oxygen consumption, he or she cannot meet the high ATP demand through aerobic means alone. At this point the runner's body begins using the lactic acid system to produce the extra ATP.

This is called the **anaerobic threshold** — that is, the intensity of effort at which lactic acid accumulates. Usually this at about 85 per cent of the maximum heart rate.

Note that lactic acid is generally broken down and removed within an hour after an event. This removal is more rapid if light exercise is performed during recovery.

Muscular power

Muscular power is often defined as 'the ability to develop and apply force (strength) quickly'. The muscular power that you can produce depends on:

- The anaerobic energy supply
- The muscular strength
- The speed of contraction.

Power is calculated as the time rate of performing work:

$$\text{Power} = \frac{\text{Work}}{\text{Time}} \text{ measured in watts}$$

Remember that white (fast-twitch) fibres are responsible for muscular power development. For instance, elite weight-lifters average 83 per cent fast-twitch fibres in their legs.

Laboratory work 14: The Margaria stair-running test

Procedure

(1) Stand six metres from the foot of the stairs.
(2) Run as quickly as possible up the flight of stairs, taking two steps at a time.
(3) Your partner should time you between the fourth and the twelfth steps. Do three trials; record your best time.
(4) Calculate your anaerobic power, using the formula

$$P = \frac{W \times d}{t}$$

Where:

- W is your weight (in kilograms)
- d is the vertical height of the stairs between the fourth and the twelfth step (in metres)
- t is the time taken (seconds).

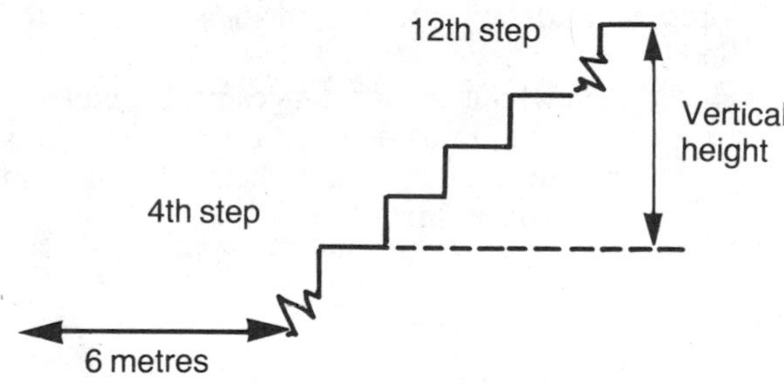

Figure 9.1

Leg Power (kg.m/sec) Male	Female	Performance rating
Below 90	Below 60	Poor
90–119	60–89	Below average
120–149	90–119	Average
150–179	120–149	Above average
180 or above	150 or above	Superior

Figure 9.2 Leg-power standards for young men and women.

Laboratory work 15: The Repco peak power test

Apparatus

- Repco cycle ergometer
- Bicycle.

Procedure

(1) Set up the bicycle correctly for your requirements.
(2) Sprint to your maximum speed in two to three seconds, and continue to 10 seconds.
(3) Record the maximum workload reached during the test, in kilograms per minute or in watts (1 watt = 5.12 kg/minute).
(4) Allow two trials and record the best score.

Worksheet 9: Anaerobic power

(1) Why can anaerobic exercise be maintained for only a short time?
(2) Which of the following are anaerobic activities? (Give reasons for your choices.):
  - Basketball
  - Tennis
  - Sprinting
  - 1000-metres swim
  - Weight-lifting
  - Jogging.
(3) Which fuel is used in the production of anaerobic ATP?
(4) What do you think causes you to suffer fatigue when you perform a maximum push up test?

10. The circulatory system

The main parts of the circulatory system are:

- The blood
- The blood vessels
- The two closed circuits (pulmonary and systemic)
- The heart.

The blood

Composition of the blood

The blood is composed of two main sections:

(1) **Solid section** (45 per cent of blood volume):
- Red blood cells (RBCs)
- White blood cells (WBCs)
- Platelets.

(2) **Liquid section** (55 per cent of blood volume):
- Plasma.

Components of blood

The main components of the blood are:

(1) **Red blood cells (erythrocytes)**

Red blood cells:

- Are biconcave discs.
- Give the red colour to the blood, because of their high concentration.
- Are produced in bone marrow, particularly that of the pelvis, sternum and the skull.
- Have a life cycle of about 120 days; about 2 million are destroyed and replaced every second.
- Contain haemoglobin (Hb), which transports oxygen from the lungs to the cells.
- Contain iron. (We require 1-3 milligrams of iron per day in our diet; iron is absorbed from the intestine according to demand).
- Are demanded more by the body during periods such as pregnancy, menstruation and diarrhoea.

(2) **White blood cells (leucocytes)**

White blood cells:

- Are produced in the bone marrow and lymph tissue
- Move to areas of infection or disease and attempt to engulf the invading bodies; puss is the accumulation of dead white blood cells.

(3) **Platelets**

Platelets are responsible for clotting the blood. They are formed in the bone marrow, and they stick to foreign particles or objects, such as the edges of a cut.

(4) **Plasma**

Plasma is a yellowy solution containing:

- Water, which is absorbed from digestion
- Nutrients (such as glucose, amino acids and lipids), which are absorbed from the small intestine and taken to the various parts of the body
- Hormones, which are substances produced from various glands, transported to the target organs
- Waste products, such as urea being taken from the liver to the kidneys
- Fibrinogen protein, which assists in clotting.

Functions of the blood

(1) Transport

The blood transports nutrients from the digestive system and lungs to the tissues. It also transports waste products to the lungs and urinary system.

(2) Regulation of the metabolism of the body (homeostasis)

Homeostasis includes the transport of hormones and enzymes. These functions include:

(a) **Regulation of the body's fluid content**, through the passing of fluid from blood to tissues.

(b) **Regulation of the body's temperature**. Blood absorbs body heat and carries it to the skin and lungs, where it is dissipated. The body conserves heat by narrowing the blood vessels.

(1) Structure of an artery
The wall consists of three layers

(2) A capillary (not drawn to scale)
Wall consists of one layer of cells

(3) Structure of a vein
The two outer layers are thinner than those in an artery wall

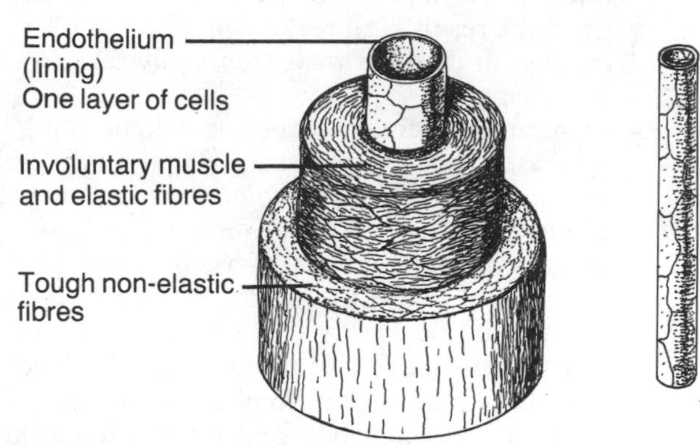

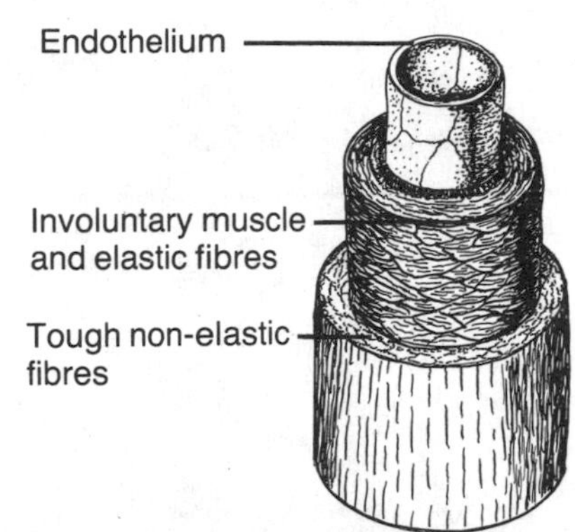

Figure 10.1 **Arteries, capillaries and veins**. Arteries have thick walls and carry blood at high pressure away from the heart. Arteries divide to form extremely narrow vessels called capillaries. Capillary walls are so thin that liquid passes through them from the bloodstream, carrying dissolved food and oxygen to surrounding cells. Capillaries join to form veins. Veins carry blood at low pressure back to the heart, and they contain valves which ensure that blood flows in only that direction.

(c) **Protection of the body**. Blood clotting protects the body from blood loss. The blood also acts to fight off foreign bodies.

The blood vessels (vascular system)

The **vascular system** carries the blood from the heart, distributes it through the body, and returns it to the heart.

The blood vessels that take the blood away from the heart are the **arteries**. These divide into smaller arteries (**arterioles**), which in turn divide into microscopic vessels (**capillaries**).

Capillary walls are extremely thin, and allow nutrients to pass through to the body tissue while waste products are passed back into the blood.

The capillaries rejoin to form small veins (**venules**), and then larger **veins** which carry the blood back to the heart.

Arteries

Arteries (see Figure 10.1):

- Carry blood at high pressure away from the heart
- Have three layers:
  (1) Endothelium lining
  (2) Involuntary muscle, and elastic fibres that control diameter
  (3) Tough fibrous tissue.

The blood is pushed through the arteries by surges of pressure caused by the heart beat. The elastic arterial walls expand with each surge. This can be felt in arteries near the surface of the skin as a pulse.

This pressure lessens as the blood gets further from the heart, and is about one-tenth of its original value by the time that the blood transfers from the capillaries to the veins. As the pressure decreases, so does the speed of the blood flow.

Capillaries

Capillaries (see Figure 10.3):

- Are fed by arterioles (small arteries)
- Are microscopically thin (a layer only one cell wide)
- Are semipermeable — that is, they allow oxygen, carbon dioxide, waste, hormones and nutrients to pass through their walls.
- Are found in clusters called capillary networks which feed joints, muscles, tissues and organs.

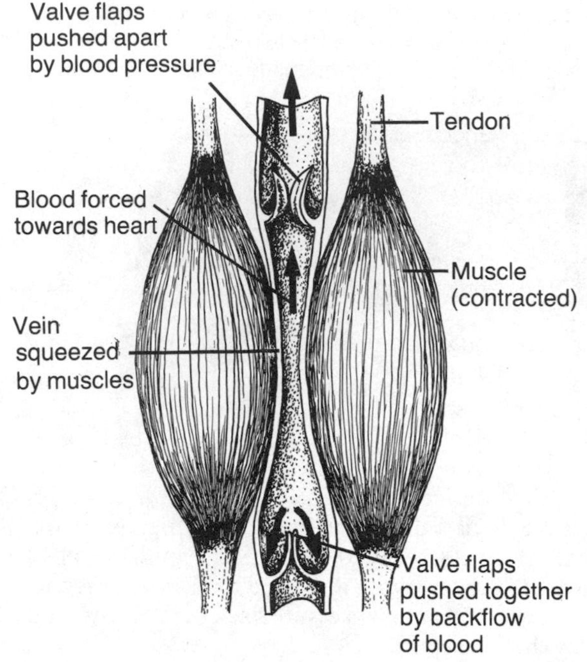

Figure 10.2 Many large veins are situated between muscles. When the muscles are contracted the veins are squeezed, forcing blood in the direction that the valves allow—towards the heart.

Veins

Veins (see Figure 10.1) have thinner walls than arteries. Because the pressure of the heartbeat is too low in the veins to push the blood back to the heart, it is assisted in several ways:

- The muscles surrounding the veins expand and contract, pressing on the veins and causing a pumping effect. This muscle action is particularly important in maintaining venous return during exercise, and is referred to as the '**skeletal pump**' (see Figure 10.2).
- The surges of pressure in the adjacent arteries cause them to push against the veins, creating a regular pumping effect.
- The blood in the veins can only move towards the heart; it cannot fall back to where it came from. This is because at regular intervals there are semilunar **pocket valves** situated in large veins. These allow the free flow of blood towards the heart, but they close to prevent blood flowing away from the heart (see Figure 10.2). Long periods of standing still can result in blood accumulating in the large veins of the legs because of the effect of gravity. This causes a ballooning of the veins, and is called **venous pooling**. If this is repeated over long periods of time, the result is a breakdown of the valves and changes in the vein walls commonly called varicose veins.
- **Inspiration** increases thoracic volume, and so decreases thoracic pressure. The veins in this region expand, causing blood to be 'sucked' through them.
- **Gravity** assists the flow of venous blood from body parts above the heart. However, it also hinders the flow from parts below the heart.
- The pumping action of the heart causes blood to flow in to replace the blood pumped out. This creates a sucking action in the veins close to the heart.
- There is an attraction between the molecules in any fluid moving in a particular direction, and

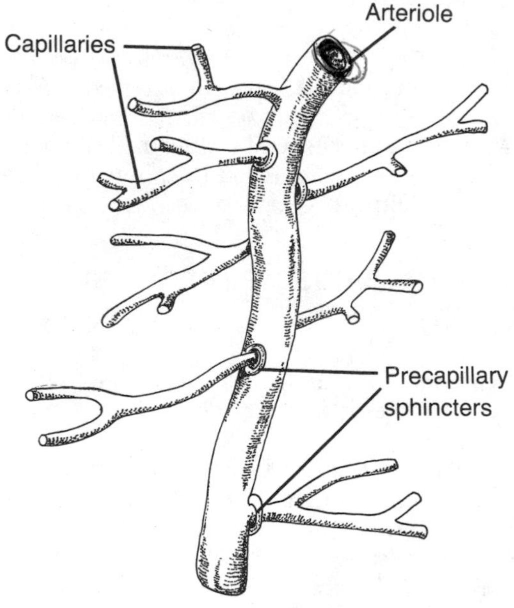

Figure 10.3 **Control of blood flow through capillaries.** The amount of blood entering capillaries is controlled by the diameter of the arterioles and by tiny rings of muscle called precapillary sphincters where some capillaries branch off from arterioles. These sphincters can slow down or stop flow of blood into a capillary network, thus diverting blood to other parts of the body.

this attraction helps maintain the constant flow. This is called **hydrostatic pressure**. This is important in blood, particularly as the fluid column moves back, against gravity, to the heart.

The two closed circuits

(see Figure 10.4)

(1) The pulmonary circuit

(See Figure 10.4.) The pulmonary artery carries oxygen-poor (**deoxygenated**) blood from the heart's **right ventricle** to the lungs, where it is **reoxygenated** and unloads carbon dioxide. The pulmonary vein then carries the oxygenated blood back to the heart's **left atrium**.

(2) The systemic circuit

(See Figure 10.4.) The **aorta** carries oxygenated blood from the heart (the **left ventricle**) to the body tissues via the capillary networks. The venous system then brings the oxygen-poor blood back from the body to the heart's **right atrium** via the **vena cava**.

Major areas of systemic circulation

(1) Coronary circulation

The coronary arteries branch off the aorta and feed the cardiac muscle. During **diastole** (relaxation of the heart), blood flows from the aorta through the coronary circulation. The coronary arteries branch repeatedly as they encircle the heart so that the entire **myocardium** (heart muscle) is supplied with a rich vascular network.

The coronary veins run beside the arteries, and eventually drain into a large vein, the **coronary sinus**. This deposits the coronary venous blood directly into the right atrium.

(2) Portal circulation

Blood from the stomach and intestines returns to the heart through the liver so that:

- Nutrients, such as glucose, can be stored
- The blood can be cleansed; for instance, so that phagocytic cells can remove toxic materials such as alcohol from the bloodstream.

(3) Muscle circulation

There is an enormous increase in muscle circulation during exercise in an effort to provide oxygen for ATP production. This is achieved by vasodilation (increasing the diameter) of blood vessels and shunting of the blood away from unwanted areas. This is called redistribution.

(4) Skin circulation

Skin circulation varies as part of the **homeostatic mechanism** (maintaining a constant internal temperature). For instance, the blood vessels dilate in hot weather, allowing heat to be lost, and are constricted in cold weather, enabling heat to be retained.

The heart

Structure of the heart

The heart is a muscle (the cardiac muscle) that contains four hollow chambers:

- The top two, thin-walled chambers are called **atria**
- The bottom two, thick-walled chambers are called **ventricles** (see Figure 10.5).

How the heart works

- When the cardiac muscle contracts, it squeezes blood out of the heart into the arteries (systole).
- When the cardiac muscle relaxes, it fills with blood from the veins (diastole). The cardiac cycle is:
  (a) Atrial systole while ventricles have diastole
  (b) Ventricle systole while atria have diastole.
- Valves make sure that the blood moves only in the correct direction; that is, from the atria to the ventricles to the arteries (see Figure 10.6).

The heart beat

The heart beat is one contraction plus one relaxation of the heart. It consists of two sounds:

(a) A low-pressure sound, which is the closing of the atrioventricular valves

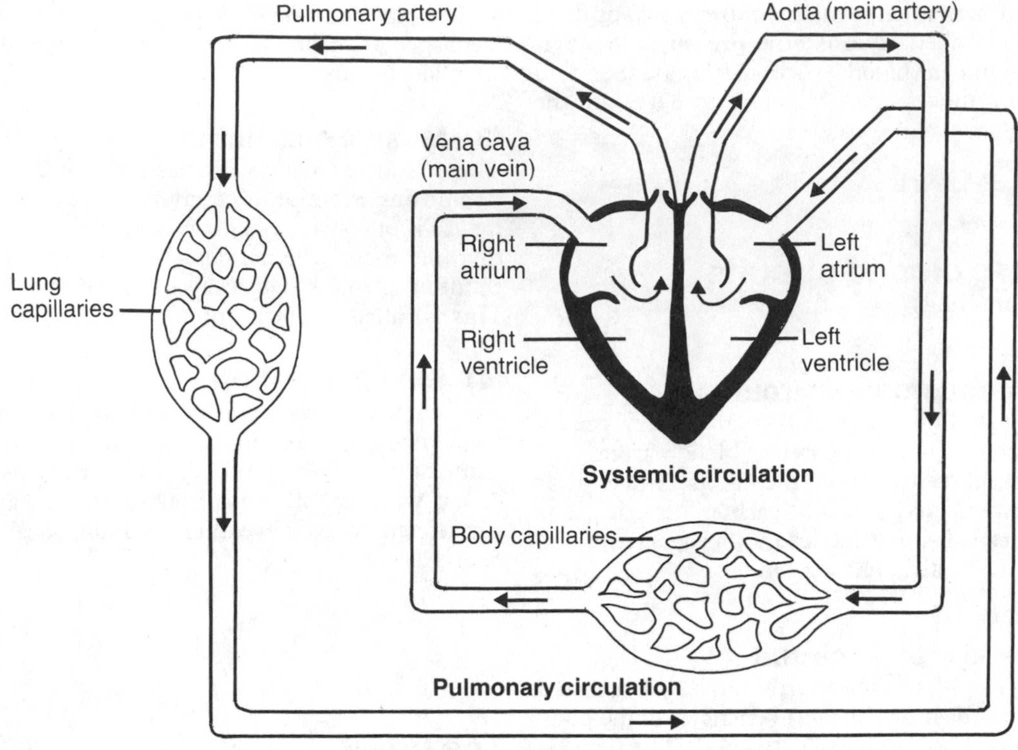

Figure 10.4 **Diagram of the double circulatory system** of humans and other mammals. The pulmonary circulation carries blood from the heart to the lungs and back again. The systemic circulation carries blood from the heart to all parts of the body except the lungs and back again.

(b) High-pressure sound, which is the closing of the aortic and pulmonary valves.

You can hear these sounds by listening to a friend's chest through a stethoscope.

The heart rate

The heart rate is the number of heart beats per minute. It can increase because of such factors as:

- Fear
- Excitement
- Exercise
- Ingestion of food
- Smoking
- Drugs
- Temperature changes
- Age
- Body position.

Heart rate control

The heart rate is controlled by the autonomic (involuntary) nervous sytem. The autonomic nervous system consists of:

- **The sympathetic system**, which stimulates the heart to beat faster
- **The parasympathetic system**, which returns the heart rate to its normal resting level.

Both systems work through the heart pacemaker, the **sino-atrial node**. Electrical impulses from the sympathetic and the paraysympathetic systems pass through the sino-atrial node and stimulate the contraction of both atria together. The impulse passes on to the **AV (atrioventricular) node**, which distributes the impulse to both ventricles, which contract together about .1 of a second after the atria. The rate at which the sino-atrial node sends out impulses determines the heart rate.

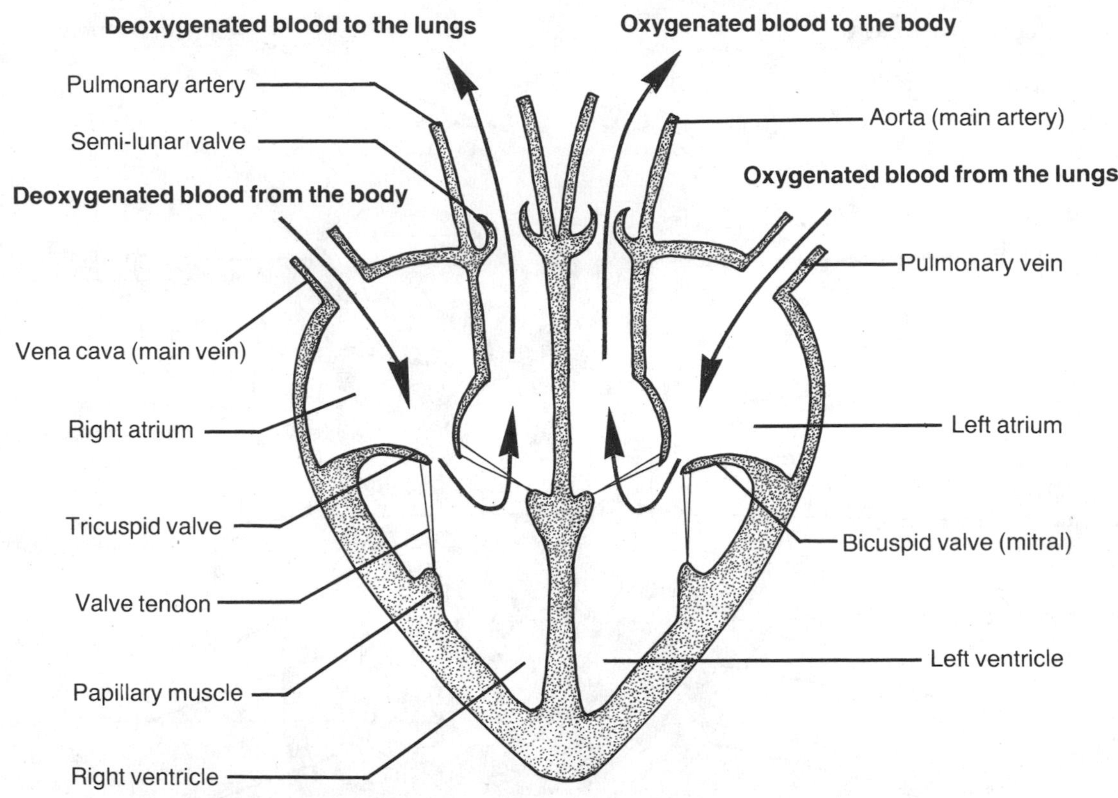

Figure 10.5 **Diagram of the heart** showing the direction of the blood flowing through it. The heart is a bag whose walls are made of cardiac muscle. When this muscle contracts, blood is squeezed out of the heart and around the body. When the muscle relaxes, the heart fills with blood just returned from the body. The heart has four compartments called chambers. Valves ensure that blood can only flow from the upper chambers—called atria—into the lower chambers—called ventricles. Valves at the exits from the heart ensure that blood cannot re-enter the heart by that route once it has left.

Cardiac output (Q)

Cardiac output is the amount of blood pumped out by the heart in one minute. Figures usually refer to the cardiac output of the left ventricle, because blood from this chamber feeds the muscles of the body.

Cardiac output (Q) (left ventricle) (output in litres per minute) = Stroke volume (SV) (Volume of blood ejected into the aorta per beat measured in litres) × Beats per minute

Stroke volume (SV) = End diastolic volume (Volume of blood in ventricle when finished filling) − End systolic volume (Volume of blood remaining in ventricle after contraction)

(See Figure 10.7.)

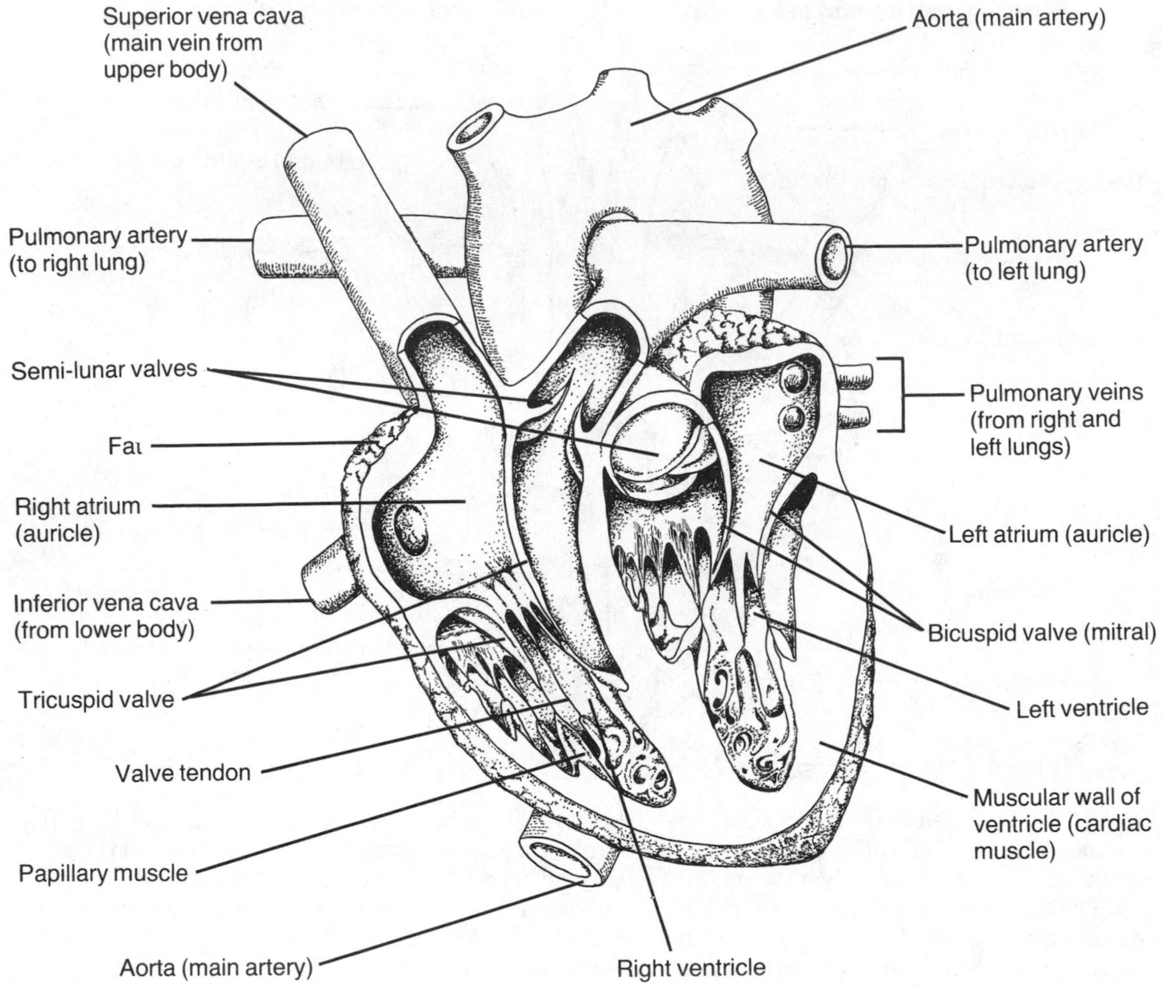

Superior vena cava (main vein from upper body)
Aorta (main artery)
Pulmonary artery (to right lung)
Pulmonary artery (to left lung)
Semi-lunar valves
Pulmonary veins (from right and left lungs)
Fat
Right atrium (auricle)
Left atrium (auricle)
Inferior vena cava (from lower body)
Bicuspid valve (mitral)
Tricuspid valve
Left ventricle
Valve tendon
Muscular wall of ventricle (cardiac muscle)
Papillary muscle
Aorta (main artery)
Right ventricle

Figure 10.6

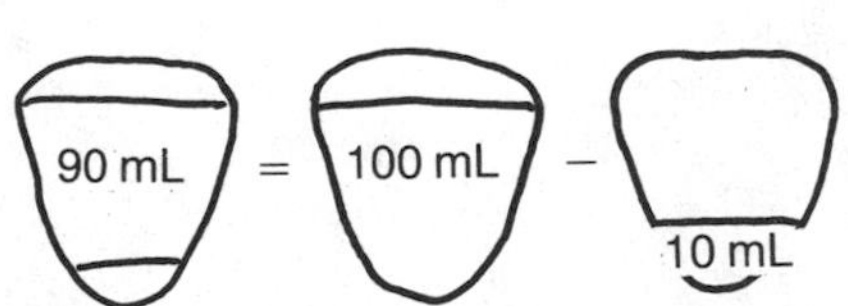

Figure 10.7 Representation of left ventricle.

The arteriovenous oxygen difference ($a-\bar{v}O_2$ diff.)

The arteriovenous oxygen difference represents how much oxygen is extracted or consumed by the tissues from the blood. For instance, in Figure 10.7, the $a-\bar{v}O_2$ diff. (oxygen used up) = 6 mL/100 mL.

Blood pressure

Blood pressure is measured on a sphygmomanometer. The readings are taken on the brachial artery, just above the elbow. There are two readings:

(1) Systolic pressure

The pressure of the blood being forced into the arteries during left ventricle contraction.

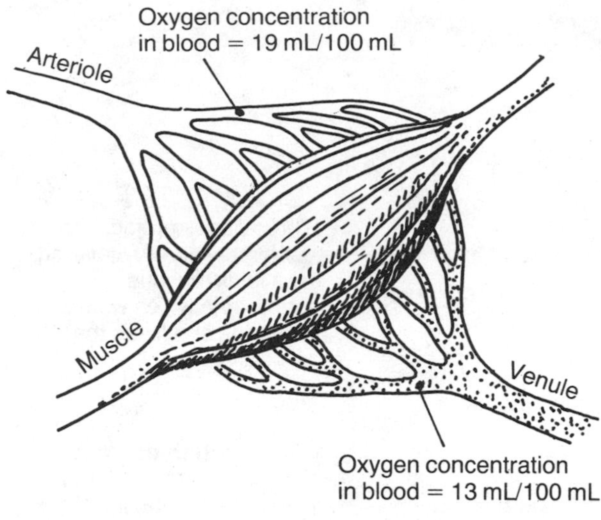

Figure 10.8 The arteriovenous oxygen difference.

(2) **Diastolic pressure**
The pressure of the blood in the arteries during left ventricle diastole.

Blood pressure is expressed as $\frac{\text{systole}}{\text{diastole}}$, for instance, $\frac{120}{80}$.

Blood pressure varies, depending on:

- Sex
- Age
- Exercise
- Condition of the cardiovascular system.

High blood pressure is called **hypertension**. This is closely associated with a loss of arterial wall elasticity; that is, hardening of the arteries.

Note: The right ventricle pumps at a lower pressure because it only has to pump blood the short distance to the lungs.

Pulse

A pulse can be felt over any artery lying near the skin surface. It is caused by the beating heart pushing out blood, which expands and contracts the artery wall. The ejection of blood into the aorta creates a pressure wave that, continuing along the arteries, is what you feel as your pulse.

There are several pulse points:

- **The radial pulse**, at the base of the thumb
- **The carotid pulse**, on either side of the neck, next to the trachea
- **The temporal pulse**, over the temple
- **The femoral pulse**, in the groin.

Note: Always take a pulse with your finger, since the thumb contains its own palpable pulse.

11. The respiratory system

The respiratory system is the bodily system that delivers oxygen, contained in the air we breathe, to the blood, and returns the body's waste products to the atmosphere.

Oxygen is needed if the body is to produce energy for its various functions, such as active transport and muscle contraction. Oxygen is the vital ingredient in aerobic cellular energy production.

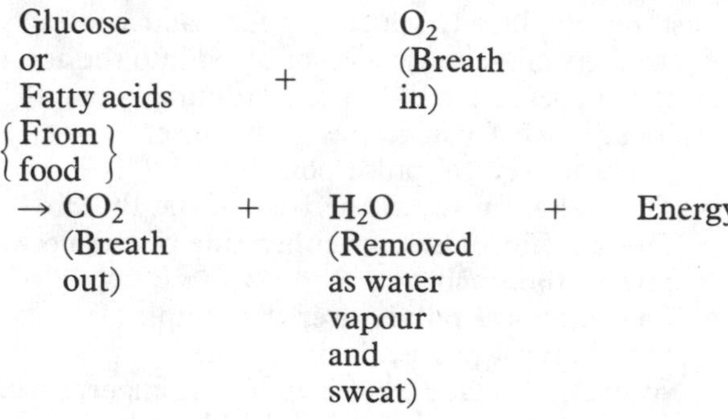

Figure 11.1 Aerobic energy production.

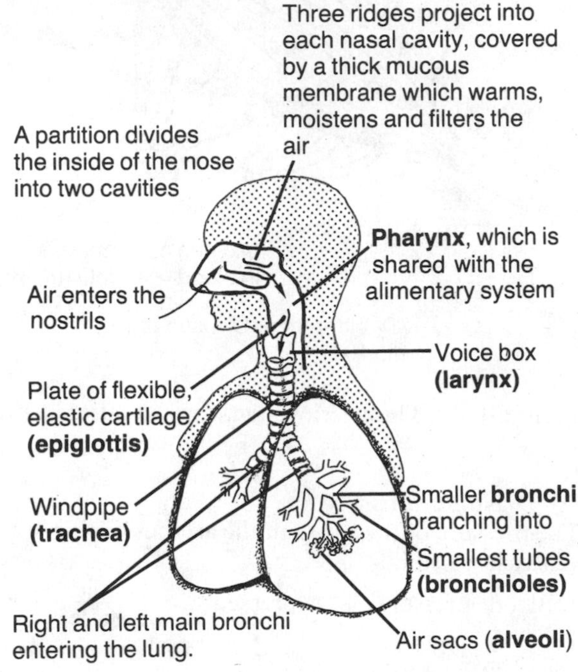

Figure 11.2 Structure of the respiratory system.

The structure of the respiratory system

Air containing oxygen travels from the atmosphere into the nose, where it is warmed and humidified. It moves down the pharynx past the larynx (voice box) and into the trachea (wind pipe). The trachea is a large tube reinforced by cartilage rings and cleansed by ciliated cells and mucous. At the base of the trachea are two major branches: the left bronchus and the right bronchus. Air moves through each bronchus into the brachial tree of each lung. (See Figure 11.2.)

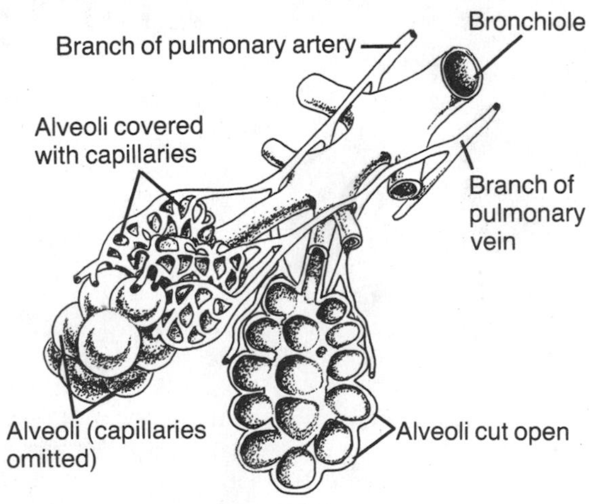

Figure 11.3 Magnified section of lung tissue.

Anatomy of the lungs

The two lungs are housed in the thorax, which is separated from the abdomen by the large muscle

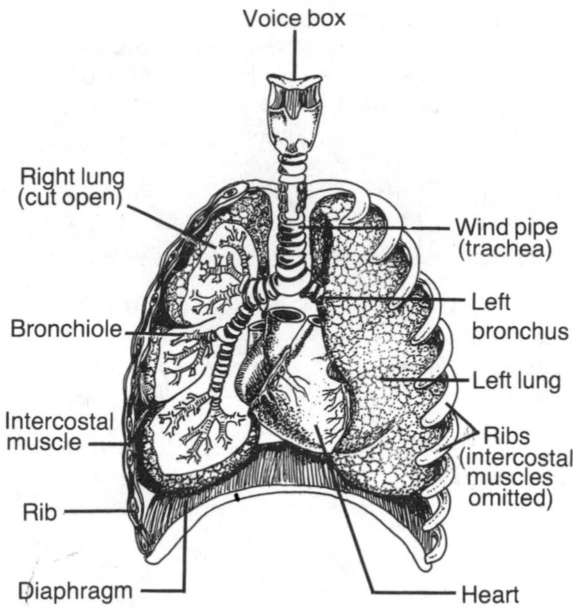

Figure 11.4 The lungs: right-hand side cut open.

sheet called the diaphragm, and protected by the rib cage. The lungs are separated from each other by the heart, blood vessels and the oesophagus.

The right lung consists of three sections called **lobes**, and is slightly larger than the left lung, which has two lobes.

Each lung is surrounded by **pleura**. This is a double layer of membrane that lines the inside of the ribs and envelops the lung completely. It contains some lubricating fluid.

Bronchi and alveoli

The lungs are served by bronchial tubes, which become progressively thinner as they go further into the lung. This is necessary because, in order for the gases to exchange through the walls of the tubes, these walls must become extremely thin.

Each lung is served by a **bronchus**, which subdivides into secondary **bronchi**, one of which serves each lobe. The bronchi finally branch into respiratory **bronchioles**, and the branches of these are called alveolar ducts. Attached to the walls of these ducts are thin-walled **alveolar sacs** containing **alveoli**. They resemble a bunch of grapes clustered around a stem. The exchange of gases takes place within the alveoli.

Oxygen in the blood

The alveoli are covered in capillaries. Deoxygenated blood reaches these capillaries via the pulmonary artery. On the surface of the alveoli, blood discharges carbon dioxide and takes on oxygen. It returns to the left atrium of the heart via the pulmonary veins. (See Figure 11.3.)

In this way the air containing oxygen travels through the brachial tree to the alveoli, where it diffuses into the blood and is carried to the left side of the heart. From the left side of the heart the oxygen-saturated blood travels through the aorta, branching into arteries, then arterioles. Eventually the arterioles reach the capillary networks which surround the muscles and organs. Here oxygen is carried from the red blood cells into the mitachondria by the compound myoglobin.

Gaseous exchange

Gases diffuse along concentration gradients, also called pressure gradients. In other words, gases spread from high contentration areas to low-concentration areas.

The blood in the capillaries arriving at the alveoli is low in oxygen and high in carbon dioxide. Air in the alveoli is high in oxygen and low in carbon dioxide. Therefore oxygen diffuses into the blood (attaching itself to the haemoglobin), and carbon dioxide diffuses into the alveoli, where it is breathed out.

The reverse process occurs at the capillaries that surround the muscle fibres. Here the muscle fibres are low in oxygen, which has been used to produce ATP, but high in carbon dioxide, which is a waste product of ATP production. The capillaries, however, are high in oxygen, and low in carbon dioxide. Therefore oxygen diffuses into the muscle fibres while carbon dioxide moves into the capillaries. (See Figure 11.5.)

Did you know?

- The interior of the lungs is the most extensive body surface in contact with the environment. For instance, an adult has a lung surface area the equivalent of the area of a tennis court.
- When you are at rest, a total of 6 litres of blood passes through your lungs every minute. This figure increases enormously during exercise.

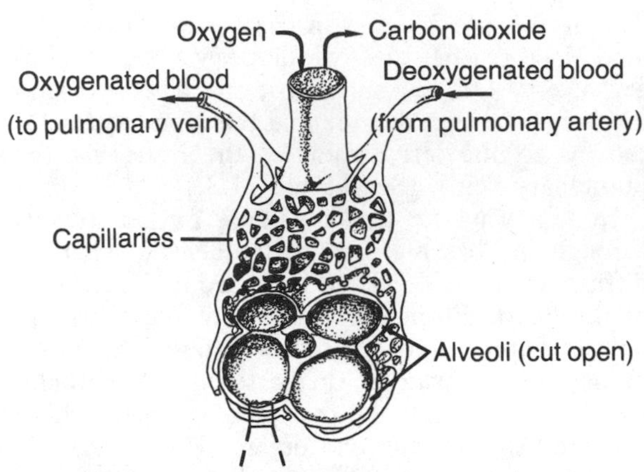

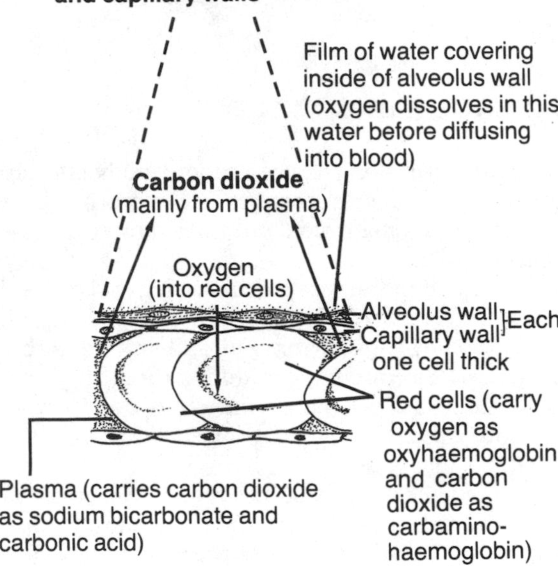

Figure 11.5 **Gaseous exchange** is the absorption of oxygen from the air 'in exchange' for carbon dioxide which is released from the body. This exchange takes place in the alveoli of the lungs. Oxygen breathed into the lungs diffuses through a film of moisture lining the alveoli, and then passes through the alveoli and capillary walls into the red cells. Here it turns into oxyhaemoglobin. Carbon dioxide is carried by blood, mainly as sodium bicarbonate. An enzyme in red cells breaks this down, releasing carbon dioxide gas. This diffuses into the alveoli and is breathed out of the lungs.

	Un-breathed air	**Breathed air from a sleeping man**	**Breathed air from a running man**
Nitrogen	78%	78%	78%
Inert gases	1%	1%	1%
Oxygen	21%	17%	12%
Carbon dioxide	Trace	4%	9%
Water vapour	Variable	Saturated	Saturated

Figure 11.6 Differences between breathed and unbreathed air.

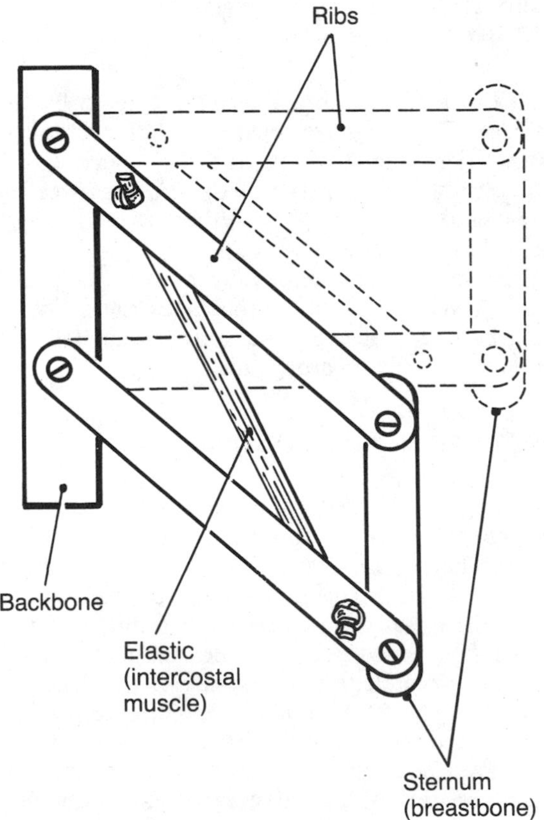

Figure 11.7 Model showing how intercostal muscles move the rib cage.

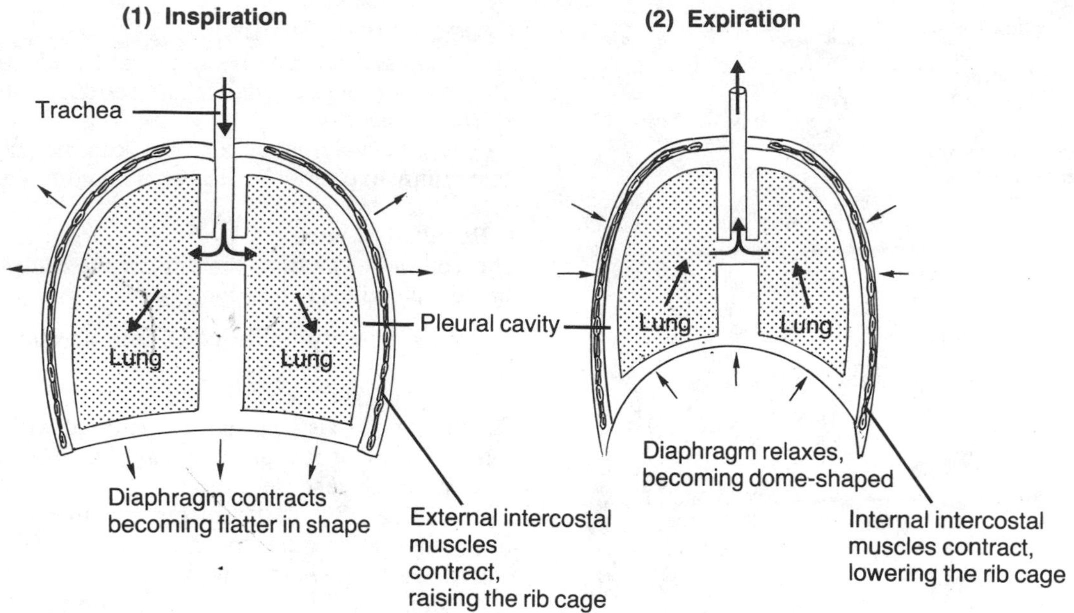

Figure 11.8 Diagram of breathing movements: (1) inspiration and (2) expiration.

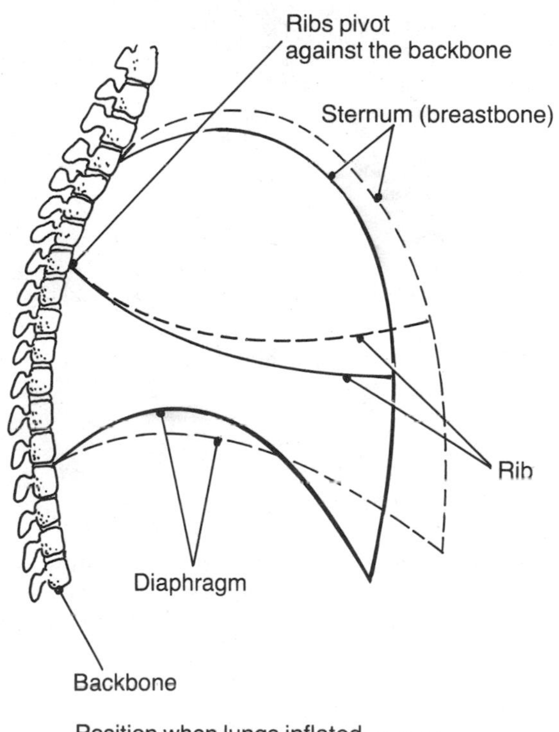

Figure 11.9 Side view of the rib cage showing movement during breathing.

The breathing mechanism

Quiet breathing

During quiet breathing, air moves in and out of your lungs because of the contraction and relaxation of the external intercostal muscles and the diaphragm. (See Figures 11.7 and 11.9.)

(1) Inspiration

During inspiration, the diaphragm contracts and descends, while the external intercostal muscles raise the ribs and push out the sternum, enlarging the thoracic cavity. This process reduces pressure in the lungs, and air rushes in from the atmosphere.

(2) Expiration

During expiration, the diaphragm and the external intercostal muscles relax, allowing the thoracic cavity to return to its normal size. This increases pressure in the lungs, and forces out the air.

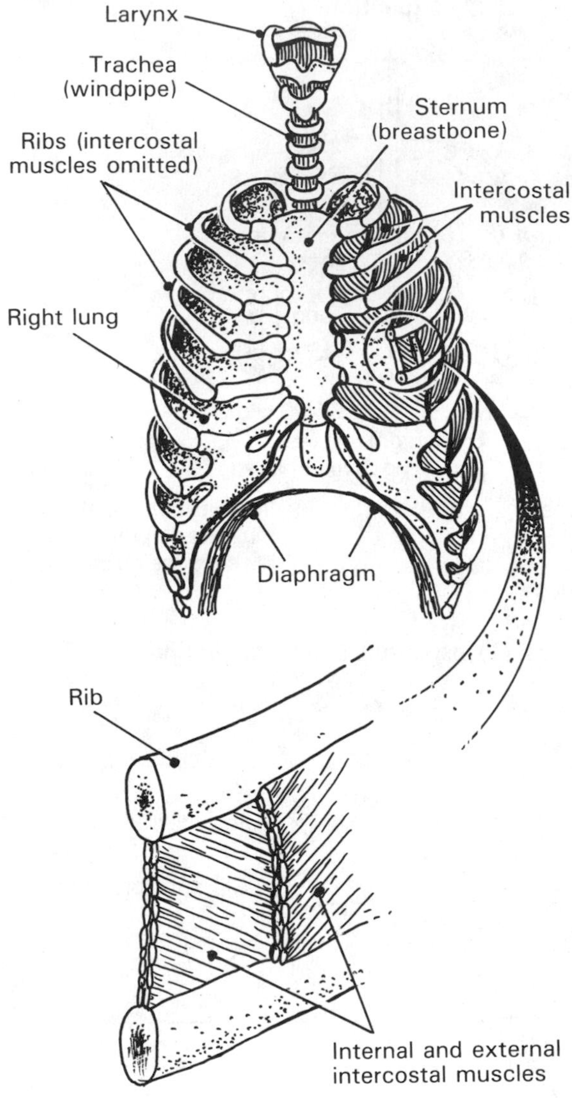

Figure 11.10 Rib cage, showing the position of intercostal muscles.

Lung volumes

Did you know?

- The lung volume of the average male resting is 3 litres
- Normal inspiration increases this volume by half a litre
- Forced maximum inspiration raises the volume to 6 litres
- Forced maximum expiration lowers the volume to 1 litre.

Types of lung volume

The total lung capacity is calculated by adding the vital capacity of the lungs to the residual volume:

- **Vital capacity**

The largest volume of air that can be expired (maximum expiration) after a maximum inspiration.

- **Residual volume**

The volume of air that remains in the lungs after forced maximum expiration.

The vital capacity figure takes into account such factors as:

- **Tidal volume**

The amount of air inspired and expired with each normal breath at rest or during any stated activity.

- **Inspiratory reserve volume**

The volume able to be inspired, during forced inspiration, after quiet inspiration.

- **Expiratory reserve volume**

The volume able to be expired, during forced expiration, after quiet expiration.

Therefore:
Total lung capacity = vital capacity + residual volume
= tidal volume + inspiratory reserve volume + expiratory reserve volume + residual volume.

Note:

- Lung volume figures are not particularly important in determining athletic performance. What is more important is the efficiency of the exchange of oxygen and carbon dioxide between the lungs and the blood, and between the blood and the muscle fibres.
- Smoking interferes with lung volumes. The irritation from tobacco smoke causes mucous secretion which narrows the air passages. One cigarette can reduce the vital capacity of the lungs by 10 to 15 per cent.

Ventilation

Ventilation is the amount of air breathed in one minute. It can be defined by this equation:

Ventilation	=	Tidal volume (amount per breath)	× Number of breaths per minute (Respiratory rate)
Normal	=	.5 litre	× 12 breaths/minute
	=	6 litres per minute	

Lung volume or capacity	Definition	Changes during exercise
Tidal volume (TV)	Volume inspired or expired per breath	Increase
Inspiratory reserve volume (IRV)	Maximal volume inspired from end-inspiration	Decrease
Expiratory reserve volume (ERV)	Maximal volume expired from end-expiration	Slight decrease
Residual volume (RV)	Volume remaining at end of maximal expiration	Slight increase
Total lung capacity (TLC)	Volume in lung at end of maximal inspiration	Slight decrease
Vital capacity (VC)	Maximal volume forcefully expired after maximal inspiration	Slight decrease
Inspiratory capacity (IC)	Maximal volume inspired from resting expiratory level	Increase
Functional residual capacity (FRC)	Volume in lungs at resting expiratory level	Slight increase

Figure 11.11 Definitions of lung volumes and capacities and their changes during exercise as compared with rest.

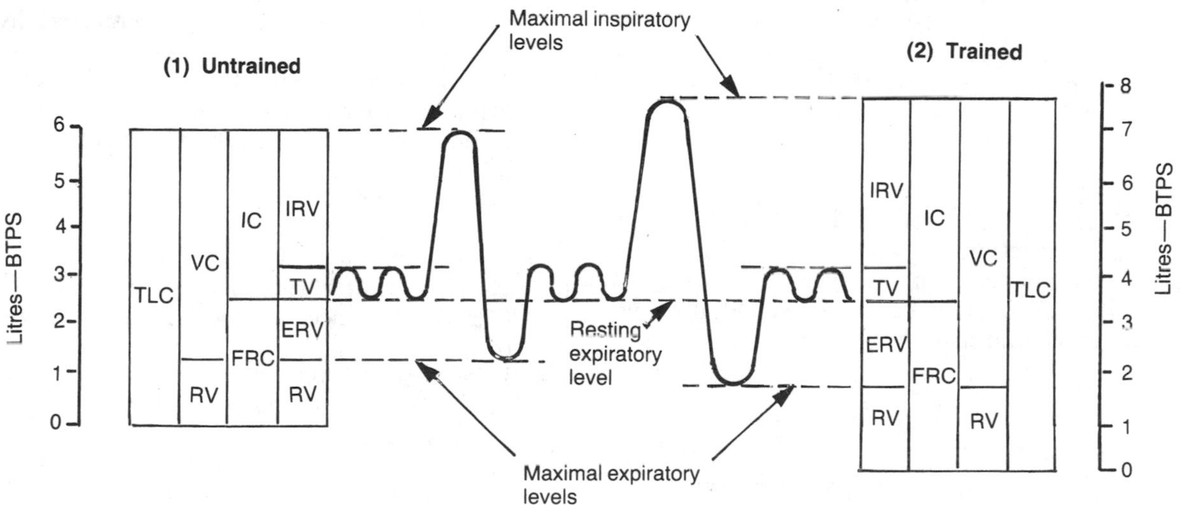

Figure 11.12 Schematic and spirographic tracings of lung volumes and capacities. Various lung volumes at rest (except TV) are generally smaller in (1) untrained, than in (2) trained subjects.

Laboratory work 16: Dissection of a mammalian heart

This experiment is a good introduction to work on the cardiovascular system.

Equipment

- Sheep's heart
- Dissecting trays
- Dissecting instruments.

Method

(1) Examine the heart carefully before cutting.
(2) Work out the location of the right side of the heart. Do this by examining the thickness of the ventricles.
(3) Cut into the right atrium, making the opening wide enough so that you can look down upon the artioventricular orifice. Pour water through the orifice into the ventricle. Watch the valve close as the ventricle fills.
(4) Squeeze the right ventricle over the sink, emptying it. Note the position of the pulmonary artery.
(5) Cut the right ventricle wall. Examine the valves. Note the number of flaps or cusps, and chords.
(6) Run your finger along the septum of the right ventricle until it enters a blood vessel.
(7) Open this vessel with scissors. Examine the valve. Note the direction in which it permits blood to flow.
(8) Examine the left side of the heart in a similar manner.

Results

(1) Draw a diagram of the heart, and label the main structures.
(2) Make a table, listing the types of valves found, the number of cusps and flaps, and any other relevant information.

Worksheet 10: The cardio-respiratory system

(1) What does the term 'cardiovascular' mean?
(2) What is the main difference between arteries and veins?
(3) Name the two circulatory systems of the body, and briefly describe the function of each.
(4) Which is the largest artery in the body?
(5) Why is it so important that the blood enters the coronary and carotid arteries almost immediately after leaving the heart?
(6) Deoxygenated blood enters the heart from the systemic system through two ....?
(7) Name the artery through which blood is pumped from the heart to the lungs.
(8) Describe briefly the structure and function of the capillaries.
(9) A combination of which two factors forces blood through the arteries and away from the heart?
(10) The body compensates for the lack of pressure in the veins in a number of ways. Briefly describe each of these ways.
(11) How do arteries regulate the distribution of blood to where it is most required?
(12) Describe the position of the heart.
(13) Describe the function of the heart.
(14) Describe the basic structure of the heart.
(15) What is the function of the pump on the right-hand side of the heart?
(16) What is the function of the pump on the left-hand side of the heart?
(17) Define these terms:
  (a) Heartbeat
  (b) Heart rate
  (c) Pulse.
(18) At which two arteries is the pulse rate usually measured?
(19) Describe the two chief functions of blood.
(20) Name the four chief constituents of blood.
(21) Define and describe the symptoms of:
  (a) Anaemia
  (b) Haemophilia
  (c) Leukemia
  (d) Thrombosis.
(22) Which type of blood cells takes up oxygen?
(23) Which substance in the blood takes up oxygen?
(24) Define the following terms:
  (a) Tidal air
  (b) Inspiratory reserve
  (c) Expiratory reserve
  (d) Residual volume
  (e) Vital capacity
  (f) Total lung capacity
  (g) Metabolism
  (h) Respiration

(**i**) Breathing
(**j**) Inspiration
(**k**) Expiration
(**l**) Ventilation
(**m**) Pulmonary respiration.

(**25**) Which muscle contracts to regulate inspiration?

(**26**) What causes air to be drawn into the lungs?

(**27**) Describe in detail the pathway taken by the air in travelling from the nostrils to the lungs.

(**28**) How is air in the nostrils and throat warmed, moistened and cleaned?

(**29**) Give the proper names for the following:
(**a**) Voice box
(**b**) Throat
(**c**) Wind pipe
(**d**) Food passage.

(**30**) In what way are the bronchial tubes kept from collapsing in order to ensure a clear passage of air through the lungs?

(**31**) How does the heart muscle receive nutrients?

(**32**) What are cardiac output, stroke volume and heart rate?

(**33**) What is myoglobin?

(**34**) What is the function of haemoglobin?

(**35**) What is the effect of exercise on heart rate, respiration rate, cardiac output and stroke volume?

12. Exercise and the aerobic system

There are two kinds of response to exercise:

- Immediate, short-term responses that last for only the duration of the exercise itself and the recovery period
- Chronic responses, which are long-term adaptations to exercise bouts. We call the summation of these chronic adaptations the **training effect**.

Acute cardiovascular responses to exercise

(See Figure 12.5)

(1) Effects on cardiac output (Q)

At rest, cardiac output is 4 to 6 litres per minute; that is:

70 beats per minutes x 80 mL per beat
= 5.6 litres per minute.

Cardiac output increases linearly with increases in the intensity of exercise up to exhaustion.

(2) Effects on stroke volume

Stroke volume increases, because more blood is returning to heart (venous return), for exercise levels up to 40–60 per cent of a person's maximum capacity. Therefore maximal stroke volume occurs during submaximal work.

(3) Increases in heart rate

The heart rate increases as exercise intensity increases, up to maximum heart rate values. This is called **tachycardia**. It should be noted that your maximum heart rate is approximately 220 minus your age.

(4) Effects on systolic blood pressure

Systolic blood pressure increases linearly with increasing exercise intensity, because of increased cardiac output. For example, at rest systolic blood pressure is 120 mm Hg whilst during exercise it may reach 180 mm Hg.

(5) Effects on blood flow

Blood flow to the working muscles and skin increases because of:

- Increased cardiac output (Q)
- Greater distribution of blood away from non-working areas to active muscles.

Therefore:

- 80–85 per cent Q goes to the working muscles, because of the relaxation of precapillary sphincters
- Blood flow to the kidneys and the abdomen decreases, because of the contraction of the precapillary sphincters
- Blood flow to the lungs increases as the right ventricle increases its activity during exercise.

(6) Effects on the arteriovenous oxygen difference ($a-\bar{v}O_2$ diff.)

When the body is at rest, the arterial oxygen concentration is 19 mL per 100 mL, while the venous oxygen concentration is 13 mL per 100 mL. Therefore 6 mL per 100 mL of oxygen is being used by the working muscles. That is:

$$a-\bar{v}O_2 \text{ diff.} = 6$$

During strenuous exercise, the venous oxygen concentration can drop to 2 mL per 100 mL; that is:

$$a-\bar{v}O_2 \text{ diff.} = 17 \text{ mL/100 mL}$$

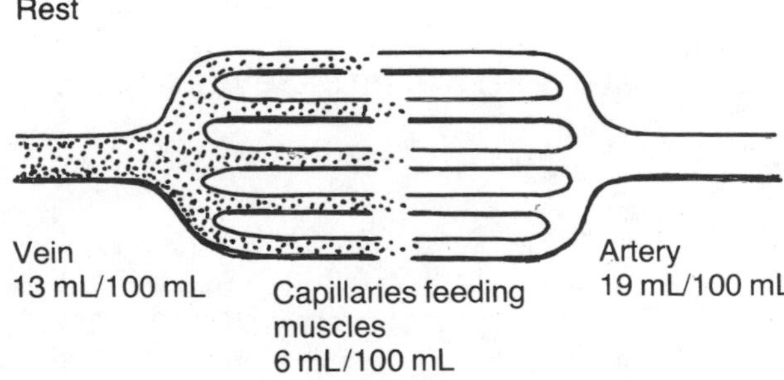

Figure 12.1 The arteriovenous oxygen difference.

Therefore during strenuous exercise there is a threefold increase in the arteriovenous oxygen difference, from 6 mL/100 mL to 17 mL/100 mL.

(7) Effects on blood plasma volume

The blood plasma volume usually decreases during strenuous exercise, especially in hot weather, because of increased sweating. In turn this leads to the loss from the body of water and electrolytes.

(8) Effects on blood acidity

Blood acidity increases, because of increased amounts of lactic acid circulating in the blood.

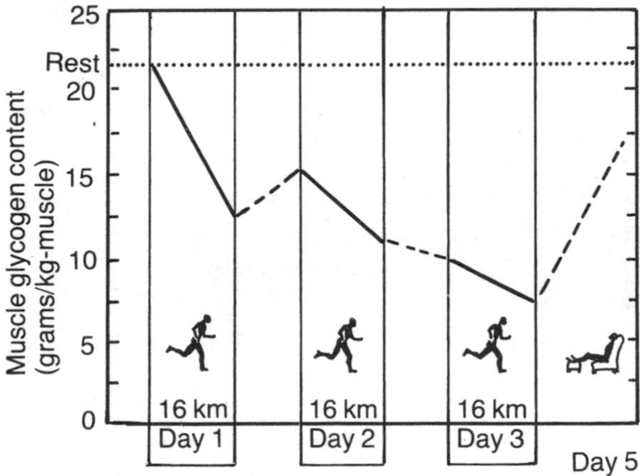

Figure 12.2 Repeated days of intensive endurance training reduce the glycogen stores in the working musculature.

(9) Effects on the muscle glycogen content

There is a decrease in muscle glycogen content during strenuous exercise, as glycogen is being used as a primary energy source. (See Figure 12.2.)

(10) Effects on coronary blood flow

Coronary blood flow increases about fivefold during strenuous exercise, in order to supply oxygen to meet the increased demands of the cardiac muscle.

Acute respiratory adaptations to exercise

(1) Effects on ventilation

Ventilation increases from 6 litres per minute at rest to more than 100 litres per minute during exercise. This is achieved by increases in:

- Respiration rate: from 15 to 40–50 breaths per minute
- Tidal volume: from 10 per cent of vital capacity to more than 50 per cent of vital capacity.

(2) Effects on lung diffusion

During strenuous exercise there is a threefold increase in oxygen diffusion from the alveoli to the blood.

(3) Effects on oxygen uptake or volume of oxygen consumed (VO_2)

Oxygen uptake (VO_2) is the amount of oxygen taken up and used by the body. It reflects the total amount of work being done by the body.

During strenuous exercise there can be a twenty-fold increase in VO_2, which increases linearly with increases in the intensity of exercise. As a person approaches exhaustion, his or her VO_2 will reach a maximum above which it will not increase further. This figure is his or her **VO_2 maximum**; that is, the largest amount of oxygen that a person can utilize within a given time (for example, 50 litres per minute).

Aerobic power (general endurance)

Aerobic power, aerobic fitness and aerobic capacity are all terms that refer to the same thing — the ability of the body to utilize oxygen to perform work or to exercise. Aerobic fitness depends on the efficiency and development of the cardiovascular and respiratory systems, and therefore is sometimes called **cardio-respiratory fitness**.

Heart rate and oxygen consumption during exercise and recovery are good indicators of a person's aerobic efficiency; that is, your cardio-respiratory fitness or capacity.

The aerobic system does not provide energy until after about two minutes of exercise, yet provides all of our energy after five minutes of submaximal exercise.

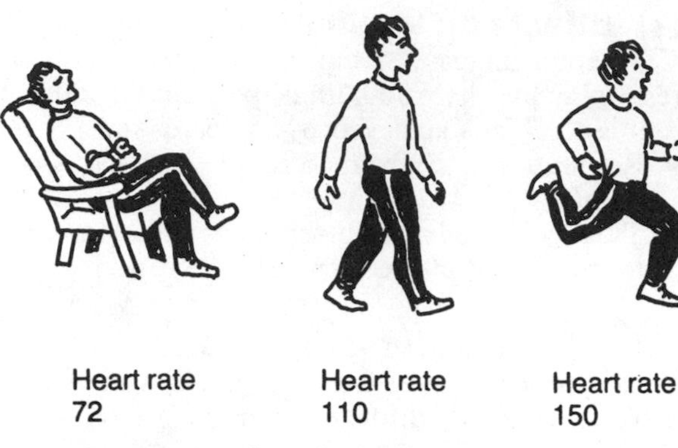

Figure 12.3 The heart rate increases in direct proportion to the work load.

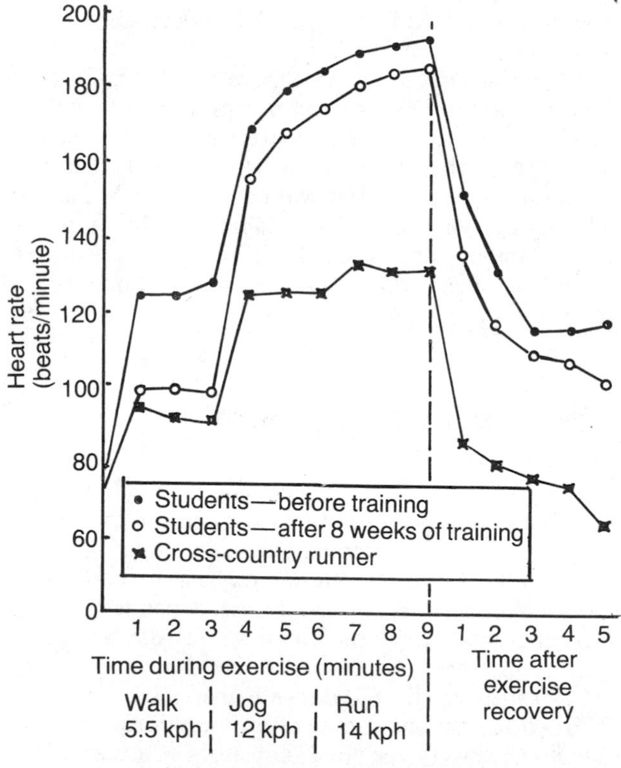

Figure 12.4 Heart-rate response during exercise and recovery.

(1) Heart rate response during exercise and recovery

(See Figure 12.4.) The heart rate increases in proportion to the exercise intensity or workload. However, the better your aerobic conditioning:

- The slower the increase in your heart rate
- The lower and faster you steady state (if doing submaximal exercise)
- The faster you recover after exercise.

While doing submaximal exercise, you might reach a plateau that signifies a constant, no-change condition. This is called **steady state**.

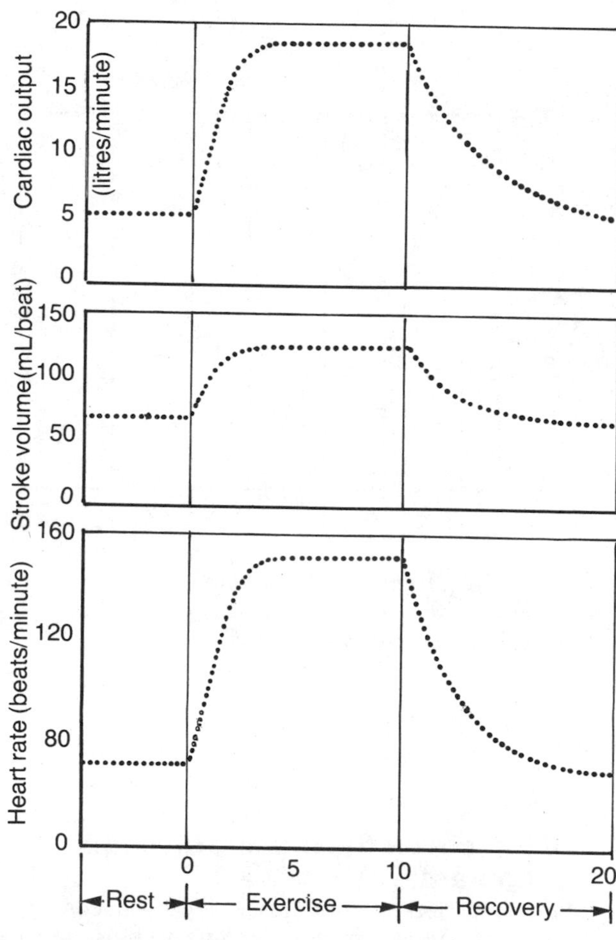

Figure 12.5 Pattern of change in cardiac output (top), stroke volume (middle) and heart rate (bottom) during short-term (5 to 10 minutes) submaximal exercise. There is a sharp rise at the onset of exercise, followed by a steady state, then a sharp decline as exercise stops.

(2) Oxygen uptake or consumption (VO_2) during exercise and recovery

Oxygen consumption increases linearly with exercise up to maximum values; that is, the more exercise you do, the more oxygen you consume, until you reach a maximum. If you are doing submaximal exercise (below your limit), you can perform in an **aerobic steady state**.

If you reach a steady state in oxygen uptake during submaximal exercise, it shows that all the ATP needed to maintain that pace is being supplied aerobically.

During maximal aerobic exercise (which usually lasts for five to ten minutes), you reach **maximum oxygen consumption values**. This is called the **VO_2 maximum**. It is the maximum amount of oxygen able to be taken in, transported to and consumed by the working muscles to produce energy.

This figure can be shown as:

$$VO_2 = Q \text{ (cardiac output)} \times a-\bar{v}O_2 \text{ diff.}$$

Maximum oxygen uptake (VO_2 maximum) is used as the most accurate measure of a person's aerobic power or fitness. A higher VO_2 maximum reflects an increased ability of:

- The heart to pump blood
- The lungs to ventilate large volumes of air
- The muscles to take up oxygen and remove carbon dioxide.

Therefore we find a range of VO_2 maxima, expressed in millilitres per kilogram-minute, as shown on Figure 12.7. Each figure shows the cardio-respiratory endurance fitness of each group. Your VO_2 maximum — that is, your aerobic capacity — declines with age. However, this decline is greater in inactive or overweight people, and can be delayed by aerobic exercising (see Figure 12.8).

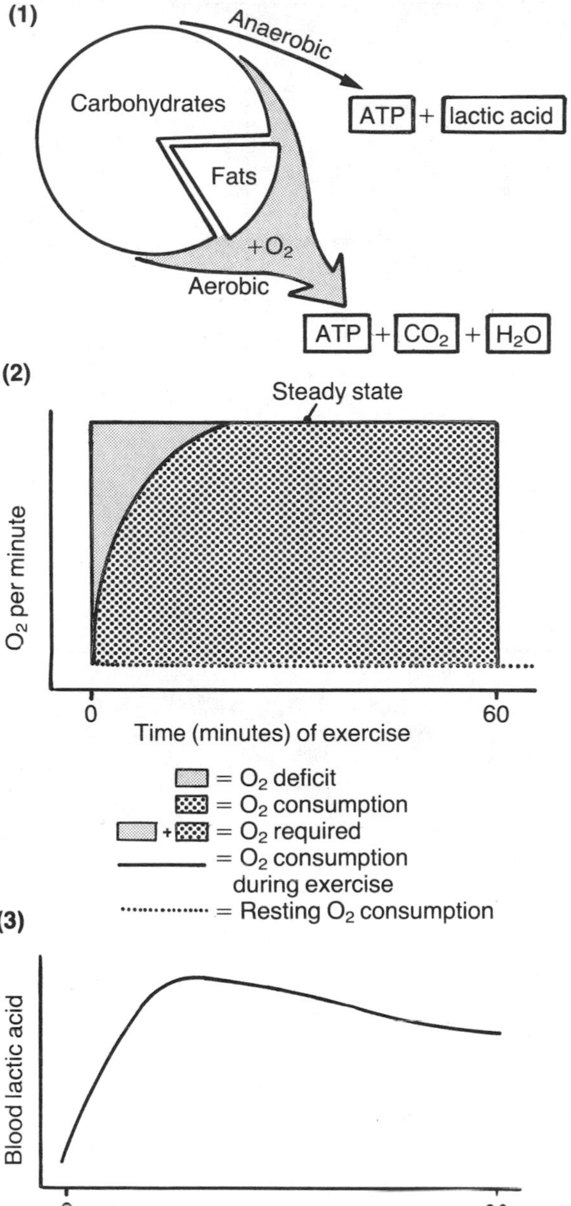

Figure 12.6
(1) During prolonged submaximal exercises, the major source of ATP is through the aerobic system.
(2) Anaerobic glycolysis and the phosphagen system also contribute ATP, but only at the beginning of submaximal exercise (O_2 deficit), before oxygen consumption reaches a constant level (steady state).
(3) Once a steady-state oxygen consumption is reached, the small amount of lactic acid accumulated during the O_2 deficit period remains relatively constant until the end of exercise.

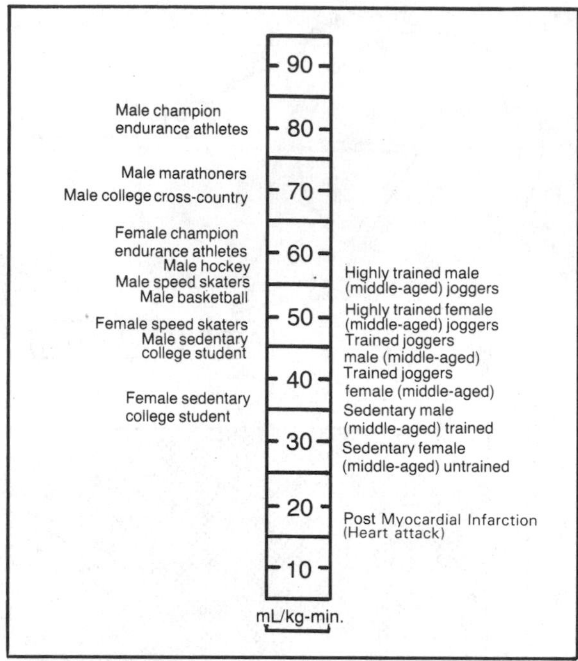

Figure 12.7 Maximal oxygen uptake values for selected activity groups.

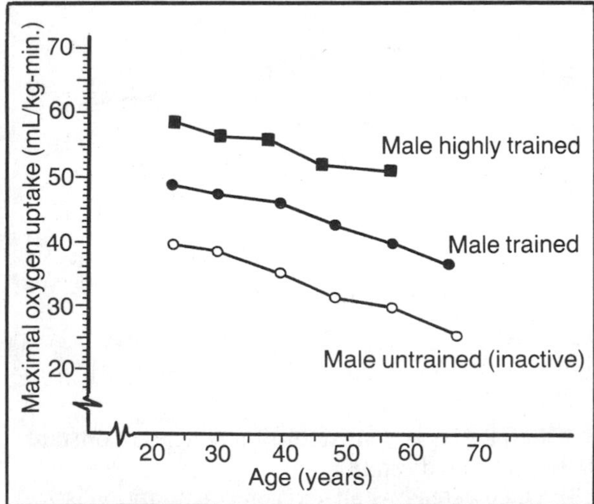

Figure 12.8 Relation of maximal oxygen uptake with age for highly trained and trained joggers, and inactive untrained men.

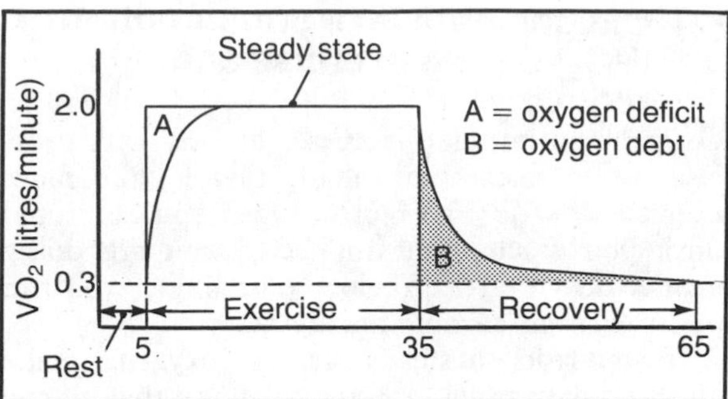

Figure 12.9 Time course of oxygen consumption during rest, submaximal exercise and recovery. VO_2 (volume of oxygen used per unit of time) can be measured any time during steady state. Subtracting resting VO_2 from this amount permits us to report the net cost of the exercise in litres per minute.

Oxygen debt

(See Figure 12.9)

Use of the anaerobic systems

During prolonged exercise (five minutes or more), changes in pace or speed may push you above your anaerobic threshold; that is, above the state at which all the ATP required can be supplied aerobically. At this stage, the lactic acid system makes up the leeway, and lactic acid accumulates in the muscles and blood. In situations like this, the body uses the anaerobic system to provide energy, in the same way as it does at the start of exercise or during high-intensity, short exercise. Thus we develop what is called an **oxygen debt.**

The oxygen debt occurs when the exercise performed is totally or partially anaerobic. When this happens, creatine phosphate (CP) stores are depleted, and lactic acid builds up in the muscle. Oxygen is required to break down the lactic acid and replenish the CP stores. Therefore the heart rate and the respiratory rate remain elevated for a period of time in order to pay back the oxygen deficit during recovery. This payback is called the oxygen debt.

The two concepts may be defined this way:

- The oxygen deficit is the amount of extra oxygen required if the task were to be completed perfectly aerobically

- The oxygen debt is the amount of oxygen consumed during recovery above the amount that ordinarily would have been consumed at rest in the same time.

Types of oxygen debt

Oxygen debt consists of two parts (see Figures 12.9 and 12.12):

(1) Alactacid debt

Alactacid debt occurs when oxygen is consumed in early recovery and used to replenish ATP/CP stores. This takes about 30 seconds to provide 50 per cent replenishment, and three minutes to provide 100 per cent recovery (see Figures 12.10 and 12.11).

This is the oxygen debt for which there is no increase in the lactic acid levels in the muscles or the blood stream. It is the first 2.5 litres of the oxygen debt.

(2) Lactacid debt

This occurs when the oxygen uptake during recovery is used to break down lactic acid; that is, the oxygen debt for which lactic acid levels are increased proportionally.

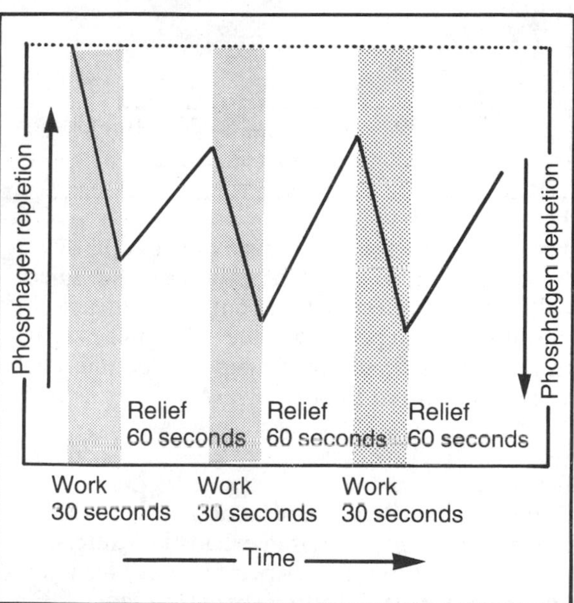

Figure 12.10 The pattern of phosphagen depletion and repletion during intermittent exercise. The work (cycling) intervals were 30 seconds long and the relief (rest) intervals were 60 seconds long.

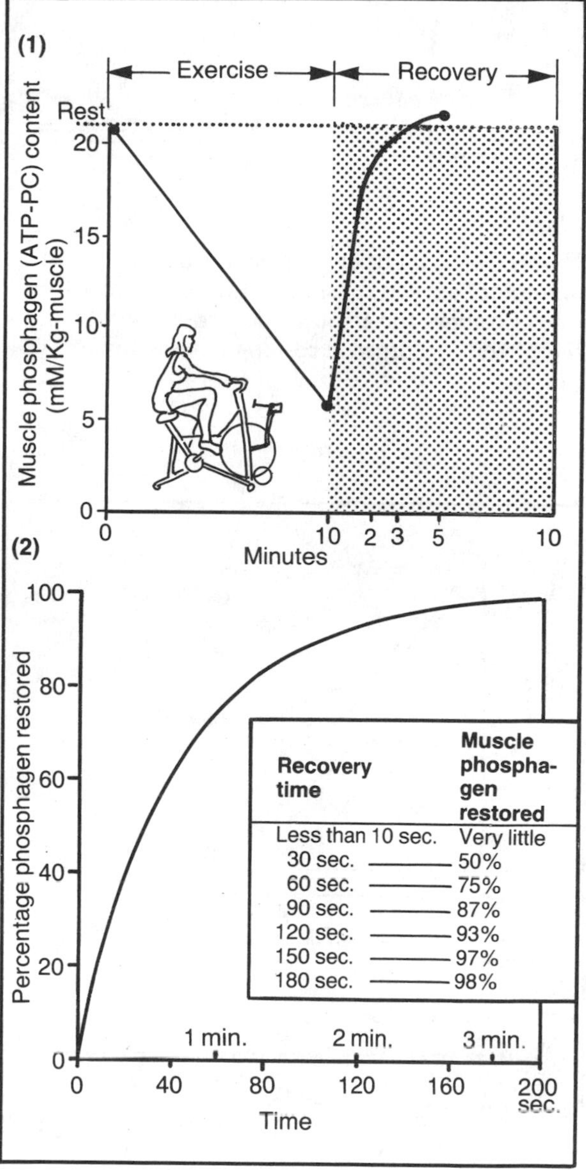

Recovery time	Muscle phosphagen restored
Less than 10 sec.	Very little
30 sec.	50%
60 sec.	75%
90 sec.	87%
120 sec.	93%
150 sec.	97%
180 sec.	98%

Figure 12.11 Replenishment of the phosphagen stores is rapid:

(1) Most of the ATP and PC used during exercise is restored to the muscles within two to three minutes.

(2) The half-time for phosphagen replenishment ranges between 20 and 30 seconds.

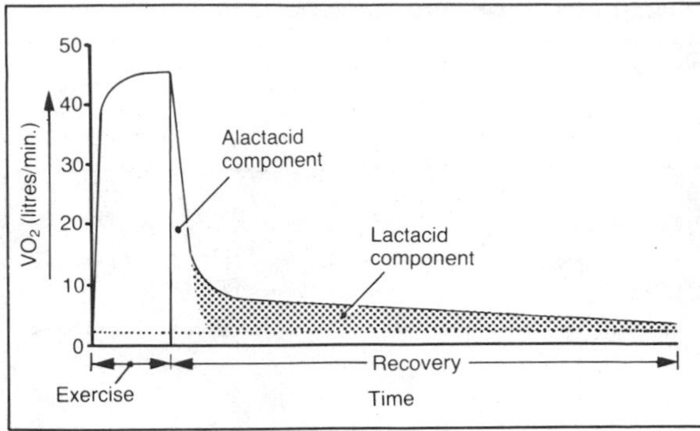

Figure 12.12 The oxygen debt is defined as the amount of oxygen consumed during recovery from exercise above the amount that ordinarily would have been consumed at rest in the same time period.

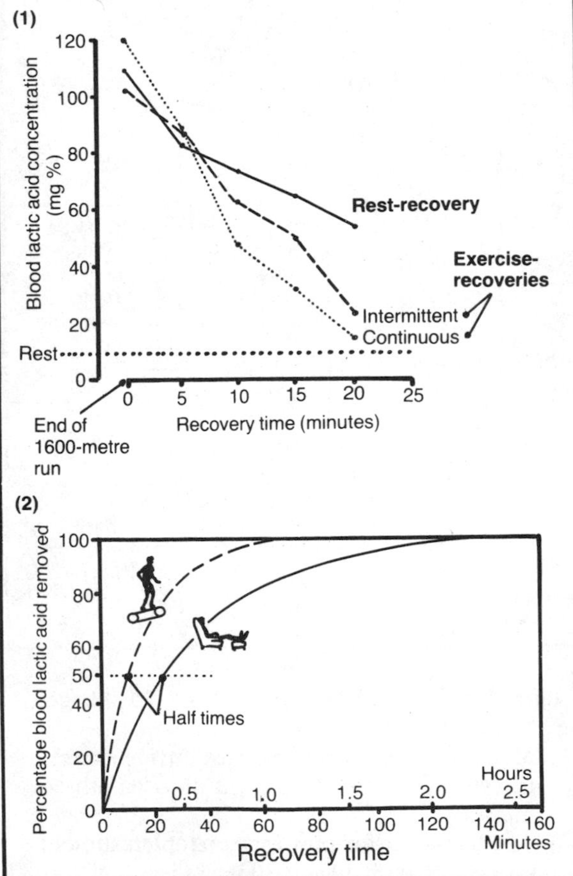

Rates of recovery

Lactic acid takes about an hour to be removed completely (see Figures 12.13 and 12.14). Therefore, if during exercise only 2 litres of oxygen debt accumulates, this amounts to only an alactacid debt, so lactic acid levels remain low. Alactacid debt is repaid thirty imes faster than lactacid debt, so recovery will be fast.

However if, after a hard run, you accumulate 5 litres of oxygen debt, only the first 2.5 litres (alactacid debt) will be repaid quickly, while the other 2.5 litres (lactacid debt) will take a long time to be repaid (see Figure 12.15).

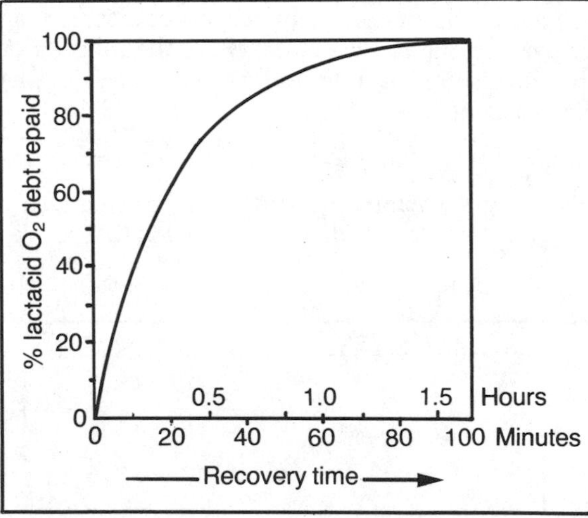

Figure 12.14 The rate of repayment of the lactacid debt following exhaustive exercise. The half-time for repayment is about 15 minutes, meaning that 50 per cent of the debt will be repaid in 15 minutes. 75 per cent is repaid in 30 minutes and 95 per cent in 1 hour.

Figure 12.13 Removal of lactic acid from the blood during recovery from exhaustive exercise is more rapid if the recovery period is used for light exercise rather than resting. In **(1)** the actual decrease in blood lactic acid during rest-recovery and exercise-recoveries is shown. In **(2)**, the rate of lactic acid removal is shown. The time it takes for one-half of the total accumulated lactic acid to be removed during rest-recovery is twice as long as that during exercise-recovery.

Recovery process	Recommended recovery time	
	Minimum	Maximum
Restoration of muscle phosphagen (ATP and PC)	2 min.	3 min.
Repayment of the alactacid O_2 debt	3 min.	5 min.
Restoration of O_2-myoglobin	1 min.	2 min.
Restoration of muscle glycogen	10 hr.	46 hr. (after prolonged exercise)
	5hr.	24 hr. (after intermittent exercise)
Removal of lactic acid from muscle and blood	30 min. 1 hr.	1 hr. (exercise-recovery) 2 hr. (rest-recovery)
Repayment of the lactacid O_2 debt	30 min.	1 hr.

Figure 12.15 Recommended recovery times after exhaustive exercise.

Summary

- The oxygen debt is defined as the amount of oxygen consumed during recovery above what would ordinarily have been consumed at rest in the same time period.

The debt has two components:

- The alactacid debt that supplies the energy for phosphagen replenishment.
- The lactacid debt that supplies energy for the removal of lactic acid from muscle and blood.

Critical threshold and aerobic exercise intensity

Karvonen's principle

In 1957, Karvonen, a Finnish researcher, found that, in order to make appreciable gains in aerobic fitness — that is, develop chronic adaptations (training effects) — the heart rate during exercise must be raised above the resting heart rate by about 60 per cent of the difference between the resting and the maximum heart rate. This is called the **critical threshold**, above which exercise has a training effect on the heart.

According to Karvonen:

- **Maximum heart rate** = 220 − age.

Figure 12.16 Guidelines for developing aerobic fitness.

- **Critical threshold**
  = resting heart rate + 60%
  (maximum − resting heart rate)
  Therefore, for a 20-year-old with a resting heart rate of 72 beats per minute:
  Critical threshold rate = 72 + 60% (128)
  = 72 + 76
  = 148.
- **Duration:** The subject must maintain the critical threshold heart rate for 20 minutes continuously.
- **Frequency:** The subject must train at least three times a week, and preferably four times a week.

Gretchell, in his publication *Physical Fitness*, gives more stringent requirements for developing aerobic fitness (see Figure 12.16).

Pyke's guidlines

Perhaps the best guidelines for developing aerobic capacity are given by Frank Pyke in his book *Towards Better Coaching*:

The maximal oxygen uptake (VO_2 max.) of an athlete is a factor closely associated with potential for endurance events. Elite endurance athletes have values for VO_2 max. superior to all other types of sports performers.

A factor as important as VO_2 max. itself is the percentage of the maximum value that an athlete can use during a sustained effort. As an athlete works at a level close to his maximum, lactic acid begins to accumulate. The intensity of effort at which lactic acid does accumulate is termed the *anaerobic threshold*. The *anaerobic threshold* of untrained subjects and non-endurance athletes is substantially lower than that of endurance performers. Some marathon runners (e.g. Derek Clayton and Frank Shorter) have been successful despite quite moderate values for VO_2 max. They have the ability to use an exceptionally high percentage of this maximum throughout the run, without accumulating lactic acid . . .

The zone for inducing a beneficial cardiovascular effect in continuous training is between 55 and 75 per cent of VO_2 max. or between 70 and 85 per cent of maximum heart rate (140–170 bpm if maximum heart rate is 200 bpm). This zone lies between the threshold for obtaining a cardiovascular training effect and the anaerobic threshold which, if exceeded, results in the accumulation of lactic acid. This is demonstrated in Figure 12.17. The 'talk test' is a useful guide to the intensity of training. When exercising below the anaerobic threshold it is usually possible to converse freely during a continuous training session.

It is useful for the coach to have some idea of the athlete's maximum heart rate. In a group of young adult athletes it is not unusual to have maximum heart rates ranging from 185 to 215 beats per minute. A training heart rate of 170 beats per minute therefore represents a much greater intensity of effort for a person with a maximum of 185 than it does for one with a maximum of 215.

Continuous training forms the foundation for training which involves a greater intensity or speed of effort. Of course the marathoner completes most training using a longer continuous format. It is essential that these long distance athletes, whether they be runners, swimmers or cyclists, train for extended periods to accustom them to the requirements of such tasks.

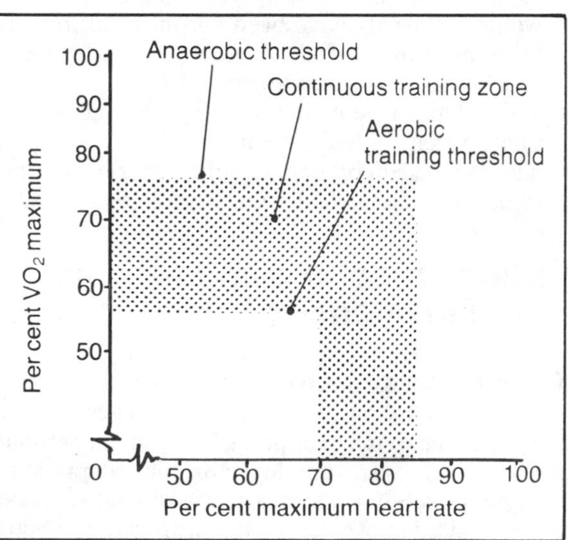

Figure 12.17 The recommended zone of work intensity for continuous training; between the threshold to obtain a training effect and the threshold of anaerobic metabolism.

Summary

- The higher the VO_2 maximum and the higher the anaerobic threshold, the better the performance, because of delayed fatigue.
- Anaerobic threshold increases with training. For instance, in some sedentary individuals, anaerobic threshold may be as low as 50 per cent of VO_2 maximum, but in endurance-trained athletes it could be as high as 85 per cent of VO_2 maximum.

Laboratory work 17: Exercise and the aerobic system

Equipment

- Ergometer (cycle)
- Heart rate monitor
- Stop watch
- Digital sphygmomanometer (blood pressure monitor)
- Stethoscope
- Dry spirometer.

Procedures

(1) The subject will pedal the ergometer for six minutes at the following workloads:
- Males: 600
- Females: 450.

Record the following:

Times	Subject 1		Subject 2	
	PR	**RR**	**PR**	**RR**
Pre-exercise				
Exercise: 1 min. 2 min. 3 min. 4 min. 5 min. 6 min.				
Recovery: 1 min. 2 min. 3 min. 4 min. 5 min.				

(a) Graph the heart rate/pulse rate and respiratory rate responses for each subject; for example:

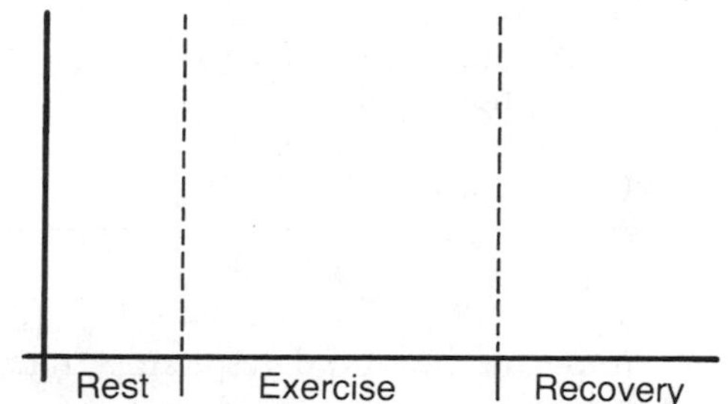

(b) Why do the heart and respiratory rates change during exercise?

(c) Discuss steady state in relation to each subject.

(2) Each subject will pedal the ergometer for as long as possible at a workload 1200–1400. Record the following:

	Subject 1		Subject 2	
Times	**Pulse Rate**	**Resp. Rate**	**P.R.**	**R.R.**
Pre-exercise				
Exercise: 1 min. 2 min. 3 min.				
Recovery: 1 min. 2 min. 3 min. 4 min. 5 min.				

(a) Graph the heart and respiratory rates for each subject.
(b) Why does neither subject achieve steady state?
(c) What factors caused fatigue and the need to stop?
(d) What has happening during the recovery period? Why did recovery take longer than in Procedure (1)?

(3) Record your pulse rate when you get up in the morning. Record it again while sitting in class during the day. Record the two counts:
AM pulse rate . . . .
Class pulse rate . . . .
Explain any difference.

(4) Record your blood pressure using a digital sphygmomanometer (blood pressure monitor):
- Resting . . . .
- After three minutes of rapid bench stepping . . . .

What is the effect of exercise on blood pressure?

(5) Record your pulse rate after each of the following activities:
- Resting . . . .
- Walking 100 metres . . . .
- Jogging 100 metres . . . .
- Sprinting 100 metres . . . .
- Hop skipping 1 minute . . . .
- Jump skipping 1 minute . . . .

What is the relationship between heart rate and excercise intensity?

(6) Record your heart rate using a stethoscope:
- Standing . . . .
- Sitting . . . .
- Lying . . . .
- During inspiration . . . .
- During expiration . . . .

Do (a) body position; and (b) breathing have any effect on heart rate? If so, why?

(7) How many sounds make up each heart beat? What causes them?

(8) Locate and record your pulse rate at the following points:
- Carotid . . . .
- Radial . . . .
- Femoral . . . .
- Temporal . . . .

Laboratory work 18: Lung capacity

Aim
To estimate lung capacity.

Equipment
Dry spirometer.

Procedure
(1) Hold your nose with your fingers throughout the experiment.
(2) Take a deep breath and exhale.
(3) Take another deep breath until you can't possibly take in any more air.
(4) Close your lips tightly and blow into the spirometer. Expel all possible air. When no more air can be expelled while sitting upright, bend forward as far as possible to force the air out of your lower lungs.
(5) Record the reading. This is your vital capacity.
(6) Estimate the residual volume of your lungs:
- Males: RV = 0.24 × VC
- Females: RV = 0.28 × VC.

(7) Estimate your total lung capacity (= RV + VC):
Vital capacity = ...
Residual volume = ...
Total lung capacity = ...

Questions
(1) What lung volumes make up your vital capacity?
(2) What effect does smoking have on vital capacity?

Testing aerobic fitness

Treadmill tests
Treadmill tests that give a VO_2 maximum reading provide the most accurate way of testing aerobic fitness. These tests analyse the oxygen intake and the oxygen expired. From this figure we can calculate oxygen usage.

Subjects run to exhaustion on the treadmill. The machine can take a direct measurement of oxygen uptake from an analysis of expired air. This is done until the VO_2 max. is reached (see Figure 12.18).

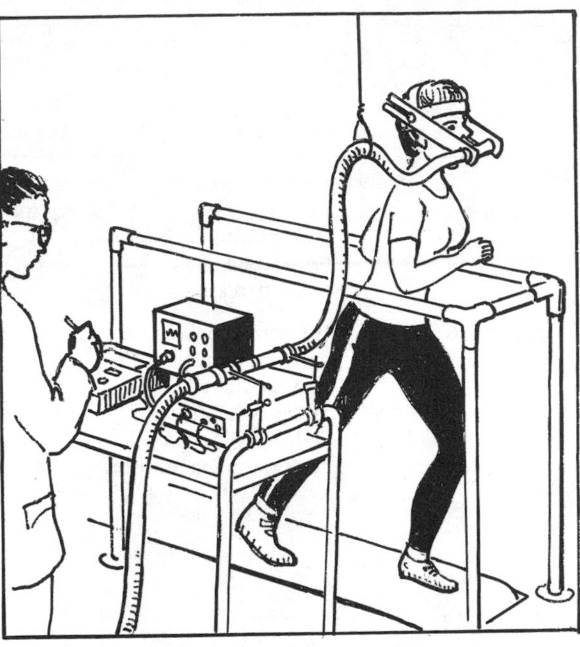

Figure 12.18 Measuring aerobic capacity during a treadmill stress test.

Other tests
Outside the laboratory, three types of field tests are useful for determining aerobic fitness by giving a predicted VO_2 max. value:
- Cooper run tests
- Cycle ergometer tests
- Step tests.

Figure 12.19 gives a list of the advantages and disadvantages of these tests.

Laboratory work 19: Estimation of aerobic capacity (VO_2 max.) by means of the cycle ergometer test

Introduction
An ergometer is any machine for measuring work. The bicycle ergometer is the most widely used type. The work is generated either by overcoming air resistance through vanes on the wheel (as on a Repco) or by overcoming friction force generated by a belt around a fly wheel (as on the Monark). In

Test	Time Required	Procedure	Advantages	Disadvantages	Estimated validity with VO_2 max test
12–15 min. run	12–15 mins.	Distance covered; formulae for determining VO_2 max for trained and untrained athletes.	Simplicity; no equipment.	Needs learning for pacing. Favours runners/walkers. High stress level.	85–90%
Astrand	6 mins.	Constant workload on cycle ergometer. VO_2 max estimated from tables of heart rate (HR). HR taken between 5/6th minute.	Time: simplicity; reasonably accurate; appropriate for ECG monitoring.	Variability in max HR in individuals. Favours cyclists. Underestimates for those with a high maximum HR. As max HR decreases with age, the test over-estimates fitness with advancing age. Correction factors must be used.	80–90%
PWC170	9 mins.	3 workloads on cycle ergometer at 3 min. intervals. By graphing HR responses to these workloads, work which can be completed at HR of 170 can be estimated.	Clear steps on protocol; gradual increase in work intensity; reasonably accurate; appropriate for ECG monitoring.	Time involved in graphing results. Difficulty in gauging 170 bpm level accurately. Favours cyclists.	80–90%
Harvard Step Test	3–5 mins. + 2–4 mins. measuring	Step at rate of 30 steps/ min. on 45.5cm step. HR recorded at 1½, 2½, and 3½ mins. after stopping.	Minimal equipment; easy to conduct; can be self-administering.	High stress level Inappropriate for children. Influenced by variations in max HR.	60–80%
Queen's College Step Test	2 mins. + 15 secs. measuring	Step at rate of 24 steps/ min. (men), 22 steps/ min. (women) on 42.5cm step. HR recorded for 15 secs., 5 secs. after stopping.	Minimal equipment; easy to conduct; little time required; can be self-administering.	Influenced by variations in max HR.	60–80%

Figure 12.19 The advantages and disadvantages of commonly used sub-max tests.

the former type, the load can only be raised by increasing the pedalling rate. In the latter type, the load can be changed by increasing either the pedalling rate or the frictional force (the tightness of the belt).

- Initially a low workload is set, and the subject pedals for several minutes until a stable heart rate is obtained for that load.
- The load is then increased by an amount determined by the initial response, and the subject keeps pedalling until again reaching a stable heart rate. (This usually happens after 3–5 minutes if the loads have been well chosen.)
- Ideally, a third load is then chosen to obtain a third steady heart rate; that is, it varies no more than a few beats from minute to minute.

- If you obtain three loads, you can check the relationship between load and heart rate. The heart rates should fall in the range of 120 to 170 beats per minute. Outside this range there may be a non-linear relationship between the three loads, and the test may no longer be useful. Figure 12.20 gives a flow chart so that you can determine appropriate loads suitable for healthy young adults.

An ECG (electrocardiogram) is the most satisfactory way of obtaining the working heart rate, but it is also possible to gain the same results manually with some practice and care. The carotid pulse is the preferred site, especially as it stands out on the skin during exercise. The counter should stand behind and to the side of the subject with his hand over the subject's shoulder. Time 30 beats for greatest accuracy.

Method

(1) The subject should not have eaten a substantial meal or exercised strenuously for at least two hours before the test.

(2) Weigh the subject lightly clad, and record the weight in kilograms.

(3) Adjust the bicycle saddle height. For maximal efficiency the knee should be almost fully extended when the pedal is at the bottom of its circle of travel.

(4) Take a resting heart rate when the subject is sitting on the saddle. This might be higher than expected if the subject is anxious.

(5) The suggested starting load for males is 300 kg/min. and for females 150 kg/min. With the Repco ergometer this is gained simply by pedalling at the rate necessary to bring the needle on the dial to that value. With the Monark bike these loads can be achieved by various combinations of pedalling rate and belt tension, but normally the pedalling rate is set at 50 cycles per minute (achieved by following a metronome at 100 beats per minute) and the belt tension varied as required. Since 50 cpm at 1 kg tension equals 300 kg, it is easy to calculate the tension required to produce a desired workload.

(6) Commence the first load and the stop watch, and take the heart rate at minute intervals. It is also the tester's responsibility to watch that both the rate and the tension are correct. (The subject may lose concentration and the tension tends to 'creep'). To begin with, it is often best to have two testers for each subject:
- To watch the time and take the pulse
- To watch the load and alter it as required.

(7) When the heart rate has stabilized to within a few beats per minute (usually after 2–3 minutes at lower workloads), increase the load as suggested by the flow chart (on the basis of the heart rate response to the initial load). (See Figure 12.20.)

(8) Repeat for a third load. The heart rate may take longer (4–6 minutes) to stabilize at higher workloads. If the heart rate is over 170 and continues to creep up without stabilizing, you are moving outside the submaximal aerobic zone, and this level should not be used.

(9) Once the heart rate has stabilized at the third workload, remove the tension from the Monark bike or slow the pedalling on the Repco bike for a couple of minutes of warm-down. Record the heart rate at minute intervals for five minutes of recovery.

(10) On a Repco calculator wheel, calculate the VO_2 maximum using the final steady state heart rate, the subject's age and weight, and the final workload.

Laboratory work 20: Estimation of aerobic capacity (VO_2 max.) using the Cooper's twelve-minute-run aerobic test

Introduction

Oxygen consumption expressed in millilitres of oxygen per kilogram of body weight is perhaps the best measure of endurance fitness available today. Kenneth Cooper, MD, has developed a field test that can reasonably predict the ability of the body to utilize oxygen. The running test is based on laboratory treadmill data obtained from groups of varying fitness levels. The data show a linear relationship between the distance run and the amount of oxygen consumed.

Procedure

(1) Describe some precautions needed before the subject goes through the test. (They could include the proper warm up, running mechanics, breathing, intensity of the run and recovery strategy.)

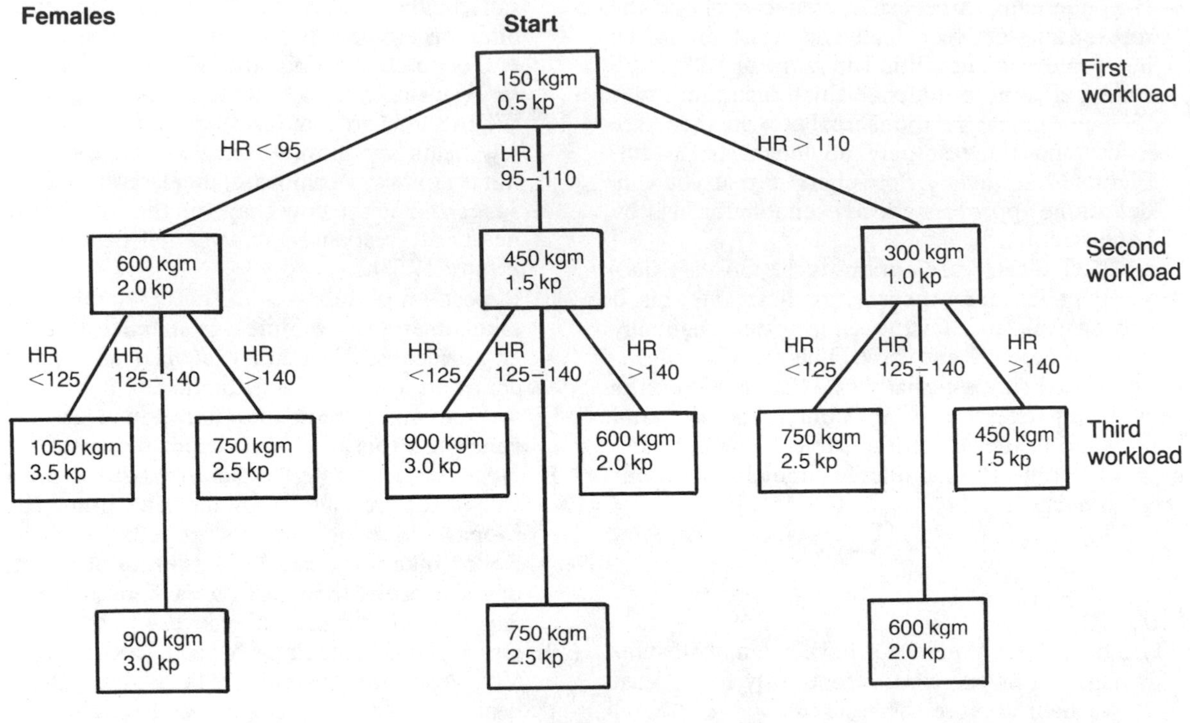

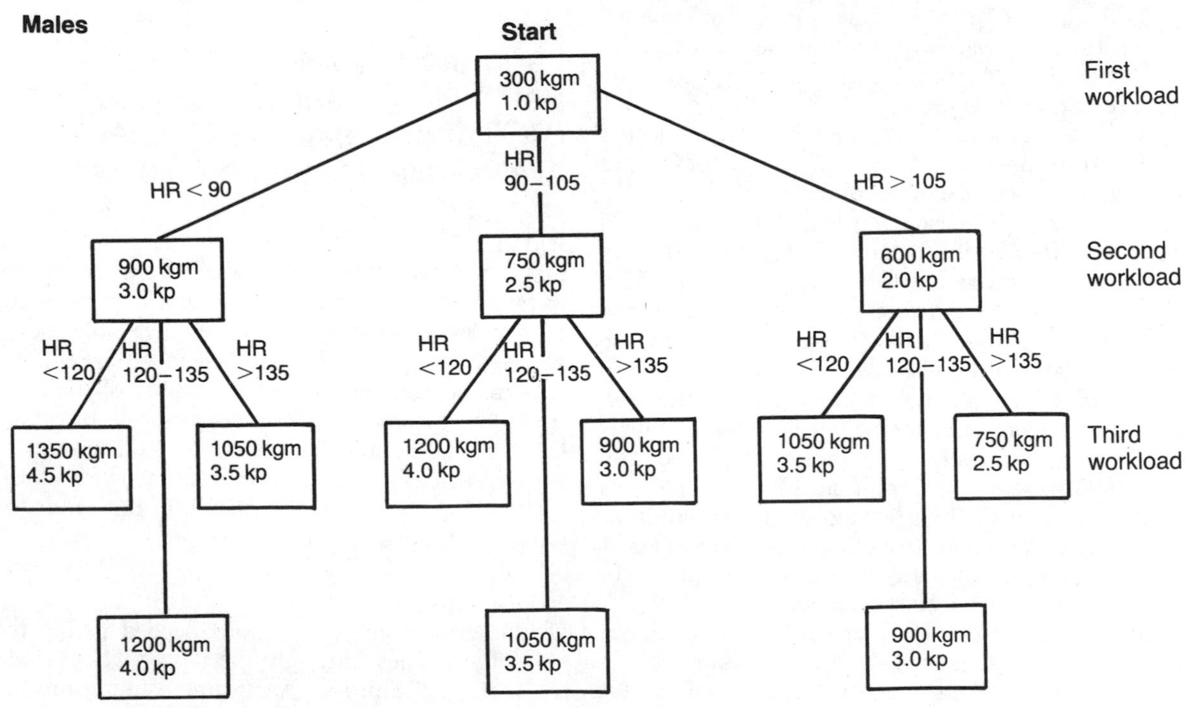

Figure 12.20 Heart rate flow chart.

Fitness category	**Age**			
	Under 30	**30–39**	**40–49**	**50+**
(1) Very Poor	< 1.60	< 1.50	< 1.40	< 1.30
(2) Poor	1.60–1.99	1.50–1.79	1.40–1.69	1.30–1.59
(3) Fair	2.00–2.39	1.80–2.19	1.70–2.09	1.60–1.99
(4) Good	2.40–2.79	2.20–2.59	2.10–2.49	2.00–2.39
(5) Excellent	2.80+	2.60+	2.50+	2.40+

< means less than.

Figure 12.21 Twelve-minute test for men; distance in kilometres covered in twelve minutes.

Fitness category	**Age**			
	Under 30	**30–39**	**40–49**	**50+**
(1) Very Poor	< 1.50	< 1.40	< 1.20	< 1.00
(2) Poor	1.50–1.79	1.40–1.69	1.20–1.49	1.00–1.39
(3) Fair	1.80–2.19	1.70–1.99	1.50–1.79	1.40–1.69
(4) Good	2.20–2.59	2.00–2.49	1.80–2.29	1.70–2.19
(5) Excellent	2.60+	2.50+	2.30+	2.20+

< means less than.

Figure 12.22 Twelve-minute test for women: distance in kilometres covered in twelve minutes.

Fitness category	**Oxygen consumption (ml/kg/min)**			
	Under 30	**30–39**	**40–49**	**50+**
Very poor	< 25.0	< 25.0	< 25.0	
Poor	25.0–33.7	25.0–30.1	25.0–26.4	< 25.0
Fair	33.8–42.5	30.2–39.1	26.5–35.4	25.0–33.7
Good	42.6–51.5	39.2–48.0	35.5–45.0	33.8–43.0
Excellent	51.6+	48.1+	45.1+	43.1+

< means less than.

Figure 12.23 Fitness categories based upon oxygen consumption (mL/kg/min.).

(2) Establish a measured course. This can be on a track or road or in a gymnasium. Develop a chart for converting laps into distance.
(3) Record the distance run in 12 minutes.
(4) Refer to Figures 12.21 and 12.22 to determine the proper fitness category.
(5) Figure 12.23 gives the predicted range of oxygen consumption.

Laboratory work 21: Estimation of aerobic capacity (VO_2 max.) by means of the Harvard step test

Equipment

- Stepping benches or chairs (51 centimetres high)
- Stop watches
- Score sheets.

Method

(1) The subject exercises on the 51-centimetre bench at a rate of 30 steps per minute for five minutes, or until there is a 20-second period during which the rate cannot be maintained.
(2) The subject sits, and his or her radial or carotid pulse is counted from:
   (a) 1–1.5 minutes post exercise
   (b) 2–2.5 minutes post exercise
   (c) 3–3.5 minutes post exercise.

Results

Calculate the physical efficiency index:

(1) **Long form**

Index =

$$\frac{\text{(Duration of exercise in seconds)}}{2\ \text{(sum of pulse counts in recovery)}} \times 100$$

Norms:

- Below 55 = Poor
- 55–64 = Low average
- 65–79 = Average
- 80–89 = Good
- 90+ = Excellent.

(2) **Short form**

Use only the results obtained in 2 (**a**) above; that is, 1–1.5 minutes post exercise.

$$\textbf{Index} = \frac{\text{(Duration of exercise in seconds) x 100}}{5.5\ \text{(pulse count).}}$$

Norms:

- Below 50 = Poor
- 50–80 = Average
- 80+ = Good.

Worksheet 11: Exercise and the aerobic system

(1) Why does a sprinter pant at the end of a 200-metre race?
(2) What factors contribute to increasing the oxygen supply to working muscles during exercise?
(3) What is happening during a steady state exercising condition?
(4) What are the different physiological outcomes of:
   (a) Maximal
   (b) Submaximal
   exercise during the exercising period and recovery?
(5) Explain the term 'VO_2 maximum' and its method of determination.
(6) Why does lactacid debt occur?
(7) Explain the difference between oxygen debt and oxygen deficit.
(8) How should you train to improve aerobic fitness?

13. Cardiovascular disease and exercise

The nature and scope of cardiovascular disease

Cardiovascular disease makes up 50 per cent (60 000) of all deaths each year in Australia, making it the most serious medical problem in this country. It is an epidemic — the estimate is that at any one time 400 000 Australians are suffering from this disease (see Figure 13.1).

The statistics in Figure 13.2 show that Australia is a world leader in deaths from cardiovascular disease.

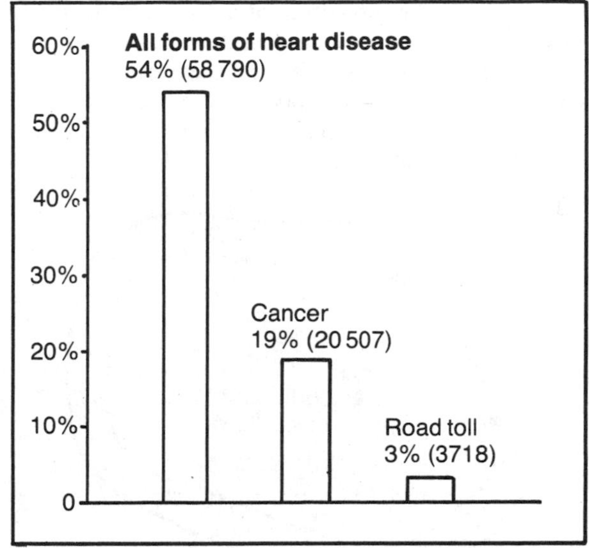

Figure 13.1 The impact of heart disease: some major causes of death, 1975. (Source: Australian Bureau of Statistics.)

Types of cardiovascular disease

Cardiovascular (CV) diseases can be divided into two groups:

(1) **Heart diseases**, such as:
- Coronary heart disease (CHD), making up 50 per cent of all CV deaths
- Angina pectoris
- Myocardial infarction (coronary thrombosis).

(2) **Peripheral vascular diseases**, such as:
- Atherosclerosis
- Arteriosclerosis
- Stroke, making up 20 per cent of all CV deaths
- Hypertension (high blood pressure).

Atherosclerosis

Atherosclerosis is a build-up of fatty deposits, such as cholesterol, on the inner walls of our arteries. These deposits reduce the amount of blood that can flow through the arteries. The built-up deposits are called **plaque** (see Figures 13.3, 13.4 and 13.5).

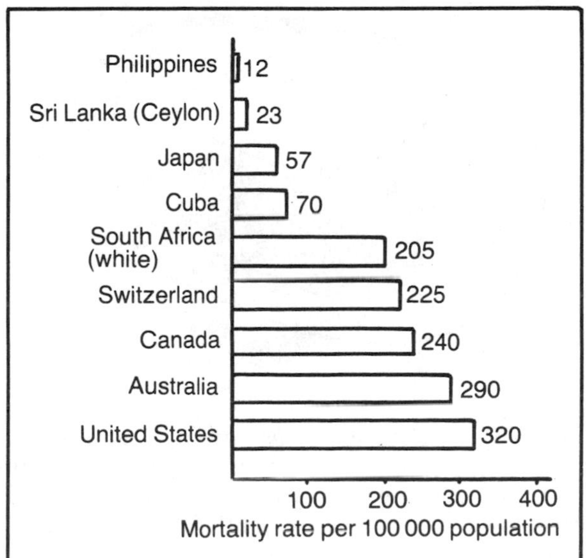

Figure 13.2 Mortality rates from atherosclerosis and degenerative heart disease from certain selected countries. (Based on United Nations data.)

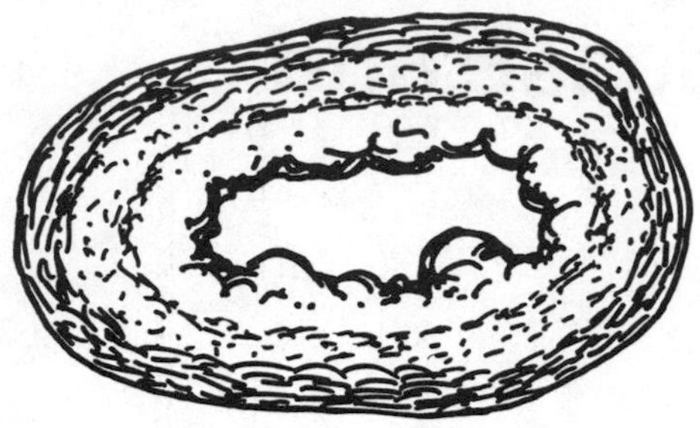

Figure 13.3 **Cross-section of a diseased artery**, showing the build-up of atherosclerosis, or deposits of fatty and fibrous materials, on the inside lining which limits the flow of blood. Over time, the artery becomes narrower, harder and less elastic, a condition which used to be known as 'hardening of the arteries'.

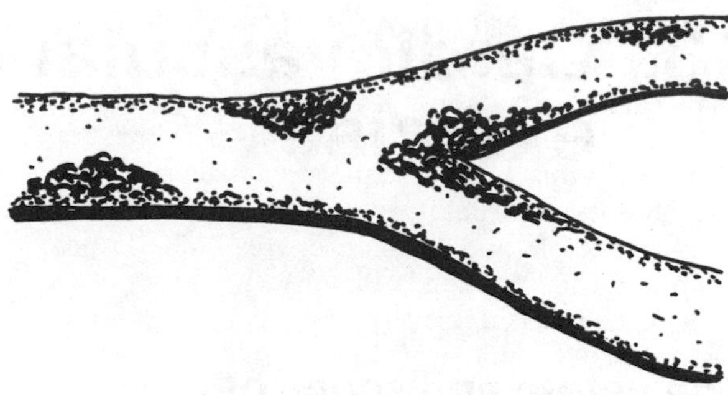

Figure 13.4 Atherosclerosis does not build up evenly throughout the arteries, but tends to collect in patches, depending on the blood flow pattern.

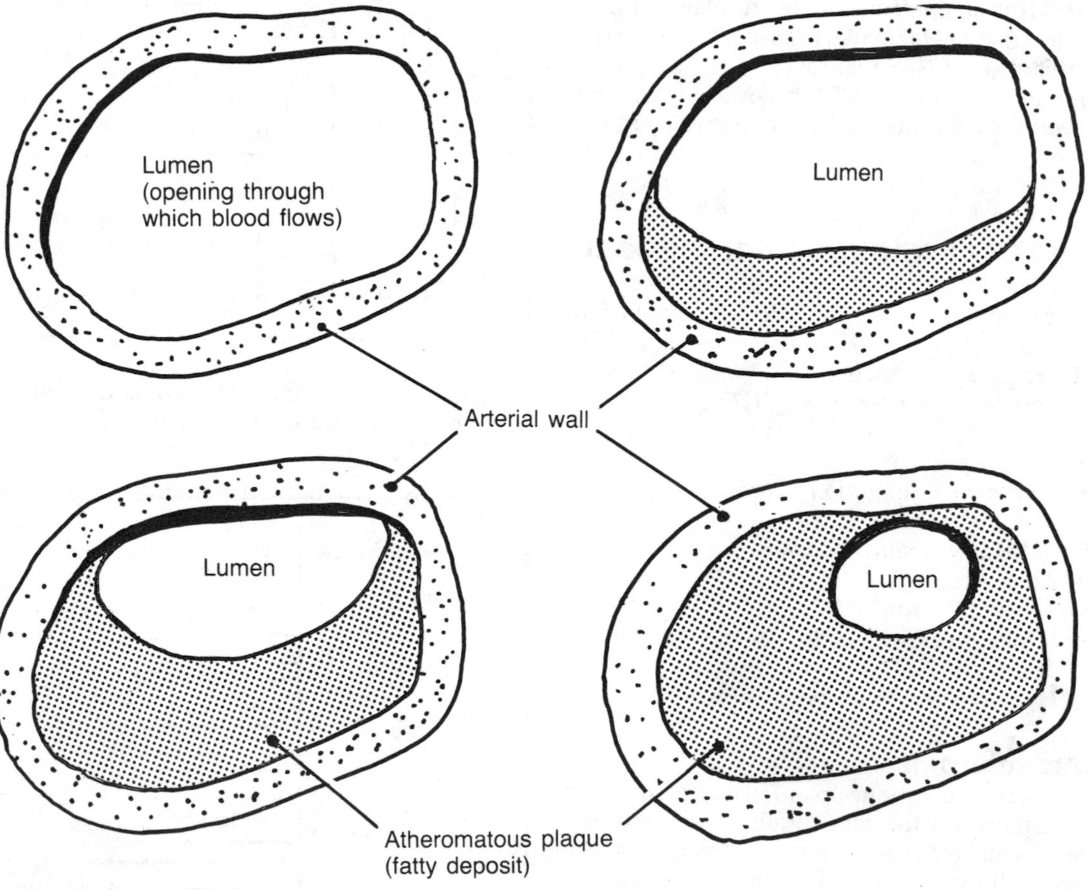

Lumen
(opening through
which blood flows)
Lumen
Arterial wall
Lumen
Lumen
Atheromatous plaque
(fatty deposit)

Figure 13.5 **Progressive narrowing of a normal coronary artery**. During this degeneration process, fatty deposits accumulate on the arterial wall. The wall becomes roughened and loses its elasticity, and the size of the opening becomes smaller. If the opening becomes too narrow, blood flows so slowly that it coagulates, thus delivering insufficient blood and oxygen to the heart itself. This blockage can cause a heart attack.

Coronary heart disease (coronary artery disease)

Coronary heart disease is the formation of atherosclerosis within the coronary arteries that supply the heart muscle. This atherosclerosis may eventually block a coronary artery, or a piece of plaque may break off and become caught in a coronary artery. Either problem will starve the heart muscle of oxygen, causing severe chest pain — that is, a 'heart attack'. The heart attack may take the form of a coronary occlusion, coronary thrombosis or myocardial infarction. The amount of damage depends on which artery was blocked, and whether other arteries can form new branches to take over feeding the starved area (as shown in Figures 13.6 and 13.7).

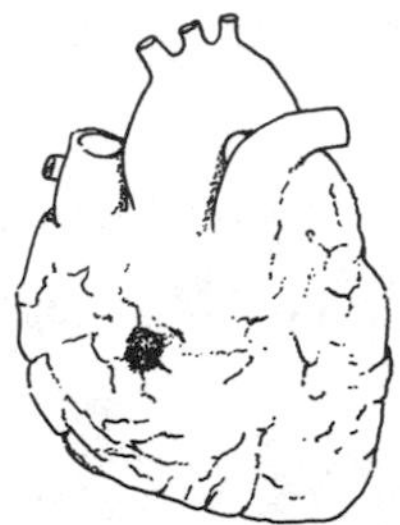

Figure 13.6 In a heart attack, a clot of blood obstructs a branch of a coronary artery and an area of heart muscle beyond the obstruction, starved of blood, becomes very inflamed.

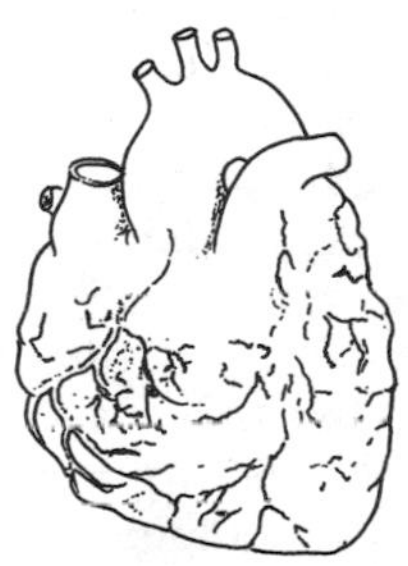

Figure 13.7 Healing begins soon after the heart attack, and the area of muscle affected is reduced as other nearby arteries grow new branches to supply the damaged tissue. Within six to eight weeks, a firm scar has formed over the dead muscle tissue, similar to the scars on injured skin.

Angina pectoris

Angina pectoris can occur when atherosclerosis narrows the coronary artery so much that the blood flow through it might not be enough to supply the heart when it is called on to work hard — during exercise, excitement or tension. When this happens, the heart muscle is temporarily starved of blood. The patient feels severe chest pain, which subsides after rest.

Arteriosclerosis

Arteriosclerosis is usually known as hardening of the arteries. This happens when the artery walls lose their elasticity. It is usually associated with atherosclerosis and hypertension. A major cause is high salt intake in the diet.

Stroke

Stroke occurs when the blood supply to the brain is cut off. This can be caused by:

- Atherosclerosis completely blocking a brain artery
- A blood clot blocking an atherosclerotic artery (cerebral thrombosis)
- Blood bursting through an artery (cerebral haemorrhage).

Damage depends on the area of the brain affected and the length of time it is starved of blood.

Hypertension (high blood pressure)

Hypertension affects 1.5 million people in Australia. It is closely associated with arteriosclerosis and atherosclerotic build-up, and is the major cause of stroke and coronary heart disease. This condition can be reduced by stopping smoking, reducing excess weight, cutting down salt intake in the diet and by exercising.

Lifetime problems

Cardiovascular disease begins at birth and continues throughout life. Cardiovascular degeneration has been found in autopsies conducted on eight-year-old boys and in 77 per cent of Korean War veterans. The incidence of cardiovascular disease has increased greatly in the last 50 years, mainly because of our modern sedentary lifestyle, but also because of increases in longevity.

The risk factors in the development of coronary heart disease (CHD)

Coronary heart disease (CHD) is a multi-causal disease, with much factor interaction. These causes include:

(1) **Factors that cannot be changed:**
- Family history
- Race
- Age
- Sex.

These are **hereditary, genetic causes**, and as such are unalterable.

(2) **Factors that can be altered by lifestyle modifications:**
- Physical inactivity
- Overweight
- Smoking
- High blood pressure
- High blood fat and cholesterol levels
- High stress levels
- Diabetes.

These are called **environmental risk factors.**

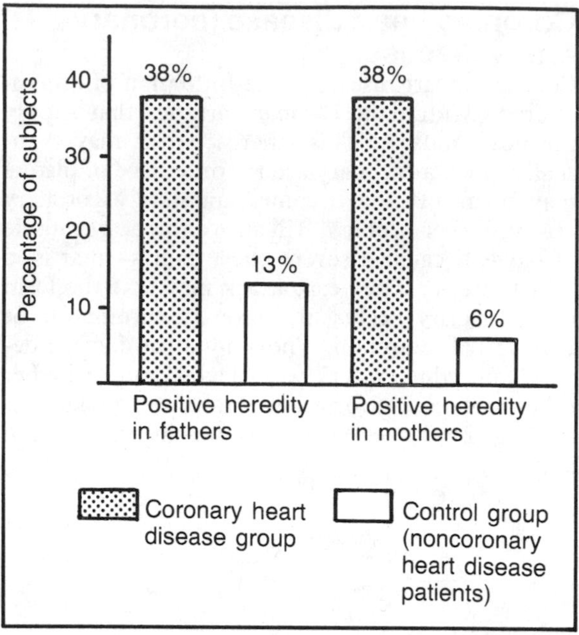

Figure 13.8 Family history as related to incidence of heart disease.

Hereditary and genetic factors

(1) Family history
The evidence indicates that a history of heart disease in the immediate family increases the possibility of contracting the disease (see Figure 13.8).

(2) Sex
Research shows that the incidence of heart disease is lower in pre-menopausal women than in men of much the same age.

(3) Age
The incidence of heart attacks and deaths from heart disease increases with age. For instance, in the age group 15 to 24, only 11 per cent of deaths are caused by cardiovascular disease, compared with 60 per cent for the group aged 65 years and over.

(4) Race
Certain races appear to be more prone to cardiovascular disease. For instance, black Americans have a greater incidence of heart attacks, hypertension and stroke than white Americans.

Factors that can be altered by lifestyle changes (environmental causes)

(1) High blood fat and cholesterol levels
(See Figures 13.9 and 13.10.) The higher your intake of saturated fats, the higher your blood fat and cholesterol level will be, and the greater your chances of suffering from coronary heart disease. It appears that the excess fat and cholesterol are deposited on the artery walls, causing atherosclerosis. By reducing your saturated fat intake and doing regular aerobic exercise, you reduce your blood fat and low density lipoprotein (LDL) cholesterol levels, and so improve your chances of avoiding coronary heart disease.

There are two types of cholesterol:
- Low density lipoprotein (LDL)
- High density lipoprotein (HDL).

High levels of LDL are associated with atherosclerosis, whilst high levels of HDL appear to prevent cardiovascular disease.

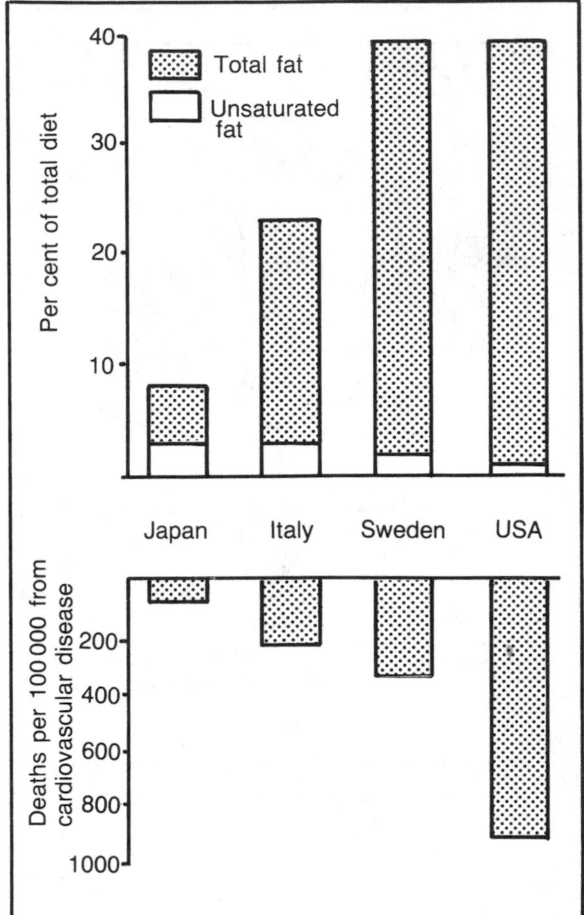

Figure 13.9 Comparison between the amount and type of fat in the diet of four countries and the death rates dues to cardiovasular heart disease.

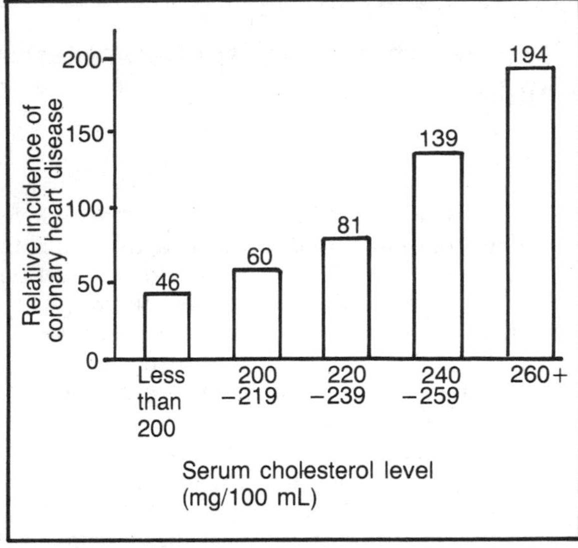

Figure 13.10 Risk of developing coronary heart disease according to cholesterol levels.

Aerobic exercise increases the usage of blood fats as muscular fuel, and at the same time increases HDL levels.

(2) Obesity and overweight

(See Figure 13.11.) Excess body fat — obesity — is closely associated with coronary heart disease because it places an added burden on the heart. The heart has an added work load in supplying blood to the extra tissue. Obesity causes high blood pressure (hypertension), and is accompanied by high blood fat and cholesterol levels.

It has been found that people who are 10 or more kilograms overweight are three times as likely to have coronary heart disease as people who the correct weight for their age. Aerobic exercise burns calories, and can therefore help to control weight and reduce overweight conditions.

Social attitudes must take some of the blame for obesity in the community, since we are all encouraged to overeat during special occasions, such as at Christmas, Easter and birthday celebrations. Society's reward systems reinforce overeating.

The seven ages of the Australian male.

(With apologies to W. Shakespeare)

At first the youngster,
Nourished and cared for with his mother's love,
Active from dawn to dusk in thoughtless health.
And then the youth — a surfie with his surf-board,
Or, say, a football hero, stern in training,
Eating lean steaks, eschewing wild excess,
Still vigorous and strong. And then the lover,
Wedded at last, who thinks his heart is only
The seat of his affections. Soon he merges
Into the husband, loafing round at night,
Watching his action on a TV screen.
And then the family man — his little woman
Delights in setting lavish meals before him.
And so he plays his part. The sixth age comes
When, far from lean, this sandalled, swelling goon,
Driving his car, forgetting use of legs,
Eats heartily, not well, until his waist
Is double what it should be. Last scene of all
May end this strange eventful history,
When, still not old, but far too fat, he snores,
Sans sense, sans health, sans looks, sans everything.

Figure 13.11 **The seven ages of the Australian male**

• Aged 17

• Aged 27

• Aged 57

• Aged 67

(3) High blood pressure

High blood pressure accelerates the process of atherosclerosis and hardening of the arteries. Treatments for the condition include:

- If you are overweight, reduce weight
- Stop smoking
- Use aerobic exercise to normalize blood pressure levels. This normalizing effect of aerobic exercise is produced by decreased resting and exercising heart rates and a decrease in vascular resistance.

(4) Smoking

(See Figure 13.12.) Smokers are 3 to 5 times more likely to suffer heart attack than non-smokers, and in the 40–50 years age group, smokers are 9 times more likely to suffer death from coronary heart disease than non-smokers.

Smoking constricts the blood vessels, raising the blood pressure, and causes an increase of 10–20 beats per minute above the normal heart rate. Smokers have fewer red blood corpuscles available to carry oxygen, so oxygen delivery to the body's tissues is reduced.

People who excercise regularly tend:

- Not to take up smoking
- To smoke at reduced levels, because of an indirect effect on lifestyle modification.

The effects of smoking

The benefits of giving up

The National Heart Foundation sees the major benefits of giving up smoking in terms of far less risk of heart disease and other serious illnesses, but if you are unimpressed with these negative or preventive arguments, here are some of the positive benefits:

- If you are a 20-a-day smoker, you save $12 a week.
- Despite what the TV commercials say, a non-smoker is more attractive to the opposite sex than the smoker. Who likes a smoker's breath at close range? Try blowing a cloud of smoke into your partner's eyes one night.
- You'll feel better when you give cigarettes up. Your morning cough will go, your wind will improve and you'll lose the sour taste from your mouth.
- Food and drink will taste better.

What are the effects of smoking on health?

The links between cigarettes and disease has shown up time and again in different studies and research projects conducted over the past 20 years in Britain, the United States and other nations. They all show the same facts about Western man:

A man smoking a pack of cigarettes a day can expect to live five years less than the non-smoker. For the 40-a-day man, life expectancy is eight years less.

Death from heart attack is three times as common in cigarette smokers as in non-smokers. And for those smoking more than one pack per day the risk is about five times as high. But once a smoker gives away the habit his risk of heart attack falls fairly quickly to that of the non-smoker.

Death from coronary heart disease generally is much more common among smokers. The heavier the smoker, the higher the risk. Among men aged 40-50, deaths from coronary heart disease are nine times more common in smokers than in non-smokers.

Smokers have 10 times the risk of lung cancer and are much more likely to have cancer of the larynx, oesophagus and bladder.

Smokers are six times more likely to die from the crippling respiratory diseases emphysema and chronic bronchitis.

The sum total of all this in Australia is that 40,000 people die each year from diseases strongly associated with smoking — one death every 12 minutes.

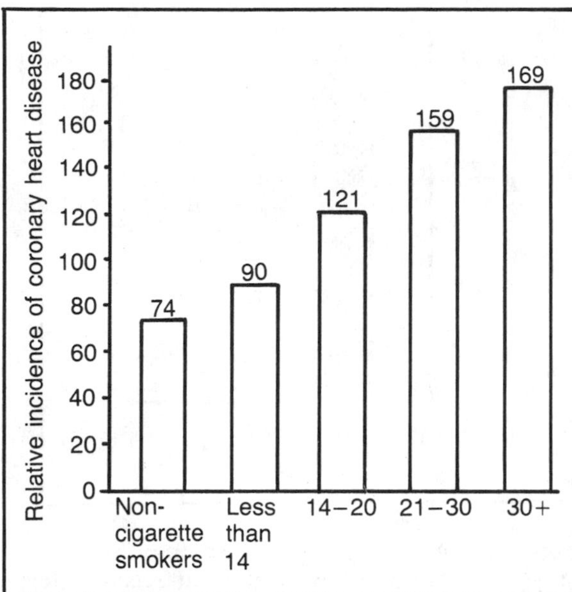

Figure 13.12 Relationship between number of cigarettes smoked and incidence of coronary heart disease. Note that the incidence of coronary heart disease increased as the number of cigarettes smoked increased.

How does smoking affect the body?

The mixture of nicotine, carbon monoxide, tarry droplets and other hot gases which you inhale when you light up a cigarette has a marked effect on the breathing system, the heart, the blood vessels and the nervous system.

Nicotine constricts the blood vessels, particularly the coronary arteries, raises blood pressure, increases the heart rate, causes irregularities in heart rhythm and increases the heart's demand for oxygen. Recent research has also shown that nicotine tends to speed up the clogging of the arteries which leads to coronary heart disease and eventually heart attack.

While nicotine is causing the heart's demand for oxygen to rise, the **carbon monoxide** in cigarette smoke cuts the supply of oxygen to the tissues. Heart muscle, which has a great demand for oxygen, is already partially starved of it if the coronary arteries are diseased. Thus the heart is even more seriously handicapped by carbon monoxide inhalation.

The **tarry materials** in tobacco smoke are of two kinds. Some of them actually start cancer, others speed up development of the disease.

Irritant substances in the smoke clog up the self-cleaning mechanism in the windpipe and its branches. If the action of this mechanism is stopped, dust, smoke particles, tars, smog and bacteria can easily enter the lungs and establish a foothold for disease.

Some wrong assumptions about smoking

Cigarettes don't hurt women.

Wrong. Statistics for men are more often used because they have been smoking longer and are thus more easily studied. But the risks are high in both sexes.

There's no risk if you don't inhale.

Not true. Less inhalation will cut down the risk but not reduce it entirely. And often, smokers don't realise that they are inhaling.

Filters make cigarettes safe.

No. While filters do tend to reduce nicotine and tar inhaled, they never eliminate them completely.

Time for action

Making the break with cigarettes is difficult, particularly if you have been smoking for a long time. But scientists believe it is not so much an addiction as an acquired habit. If you want moral support it's a good idea to ask your doctor for help — he will be best able to advise you on any measures to make the road easier. Those who want physical assistance should contact organisations such as their state Anti-Cancer Council.

A final word to those who won't or can't give cigarettes away. If you must smoke, bear in mind that the last inch of the cigarette causes the most damage.

— National Heart Foundation

(5) High stress levels

Stress is defined as the physical or emotional factor that causes bodily or mental tension. Stress levels can be increased by work commitments or tension, tension in one's lifestyle (such as always rushing about) or problems at home. High stress levels lead to high blood pressure, overeating, increased smoking, high blood cholesterol levels, personality changes and a high chance of contracting coronary heart disease, because of the way the risk factors interact (see Figures 13.15 and 13.16).

People may be classified into one of two stress risk categories:

- **Type A people**, who show high stress levels, and are therefore most at risk. Type A people have high rates on ambition, competitiveness, aggressiveness, drive and time urgency.
- **Type B people** show low stress levels, because they can relax more easily and seldom let outside factors influence their emotional state.

Therefore Type A people are more at risk of developing cardiovascular disease (see Figure 13.13).

Occupational stress is possibly the most common source of stress leading to coronary heart disease (see Figure 13.15).

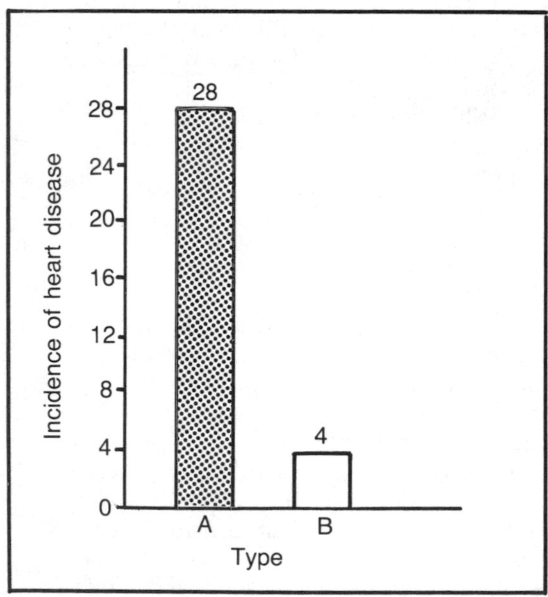

Figure 13.13 Comparison of Group A (high stress) and Group B (low stress) with regard to incidence of coronary heart disease (age range 30 to 59 years).

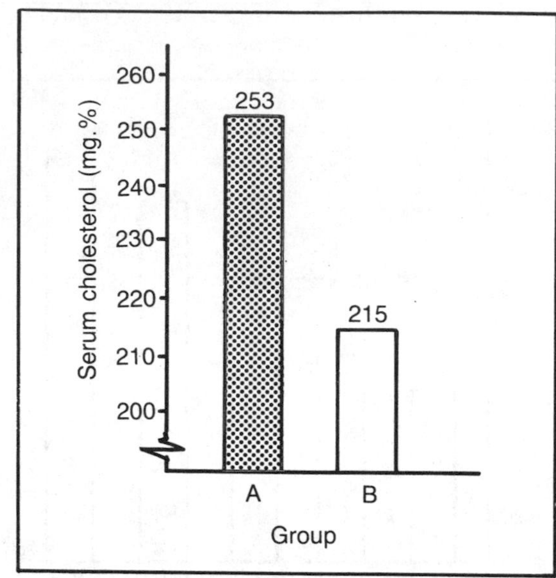

Figure 13.14 Comparison of Group A (high stress) and Group B (low stress) with regard to level of serum cholesterol (age range 30 to 59 years).

Aerobic exercise therapy

Aerobic exercise seems to be important in managing stress. Research shows that fifteen minutes of aerobic exercise immediately reduce stress levels for at least an hour after ceasing the exercise. Aerobic exercise over an extended period of time produces permanent reductions in stress levels.

Many factory managers now provide an industrial gymnastics programme, including breaks every two hours for exercising, and opportunities for exercising at lunch time and after hours. Unstressed workers, it is believed, are likely to be more productive than workers who have no opportunity to exercise during work hours.

(6) Physical inactivity

(See Figure 13.17.) For many years, studies have shown that physical (aerobic) activity is an essential factor in reducing one's chances of suffering from coronary heart disease (CHD):

- **Morris's studies**

Morris performed two significant studies comparing the incidence of coronary heart disease in active compared with inactive occupations.

He found that London bus drivers (inactive)

were twice as likely to develop CHD as bus conductors (active). Walking up and down steps on a double decker bus an average of 8.24 times every hour is a form of interval training (see Chapter 18).

Morris also found that telephone operators (inactive) were twice as likely to suffer from CHD as postmen (active).

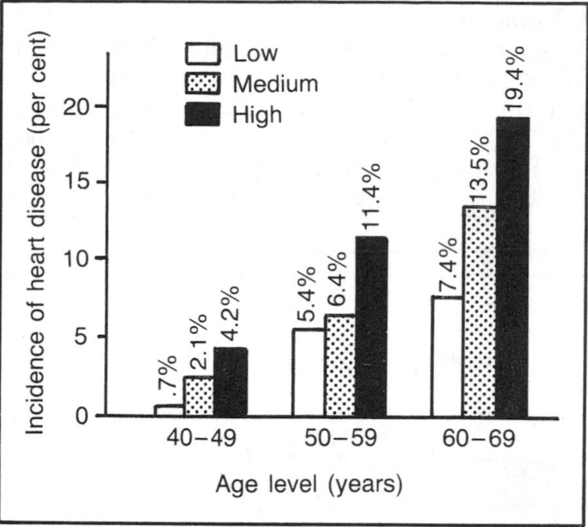

Figure 13.16 Incidence of coronary heart disease according to stress level (low, medium and high) and age.

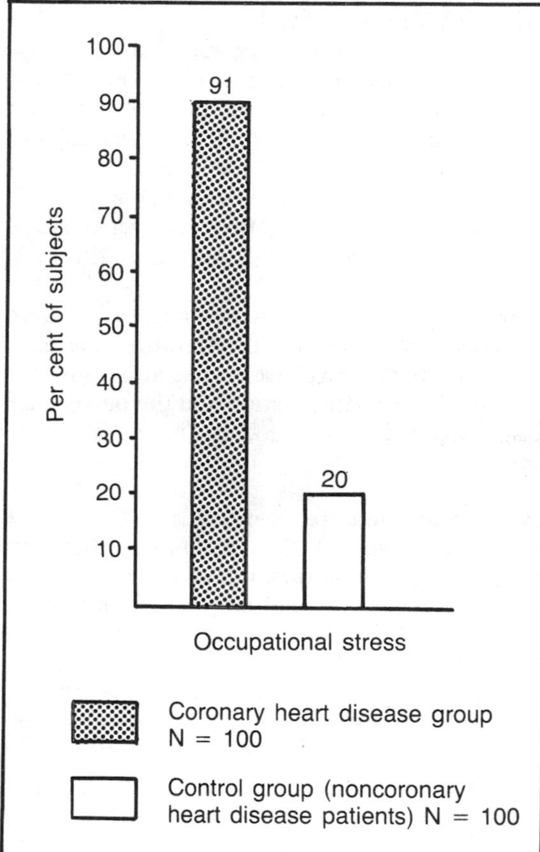

Figure 13.15 Comparison of a coronary heart disease group and a noncoronary heart disease control group with regard to the incidence of occupational stress (age range 25 to 40 years).

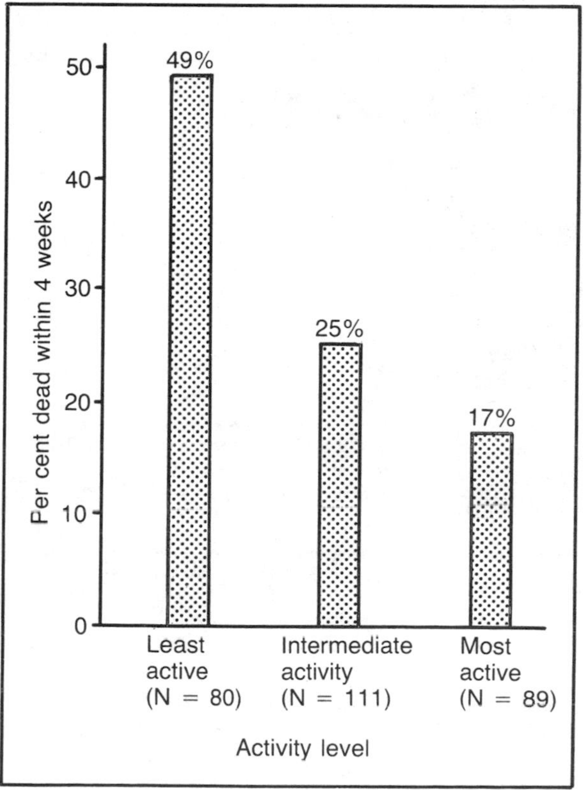

Figure 13.17 Relationship between death associated with coronary heart disease and level of activity. Note the higher incidence in the death rate among the least active group.

• **Bruner's study**

Bruner studied workers in Israeli kibbutzes (communal settlements). Settlers in the kibbutzes had uniform living conditions and diet, irrespective of work or profession. Over a fifteen-year period, 10 514 men and women aged from 41 to 65 were studied. Although all other lifestyle factors were equal, angina pectoris and fatal myocardial infarction occurred 2.5 to 4 times more frequently among sedentary workers than among non-sedentary workers. Also the mortality rate of those who had suffered heart attacks and survived was three times as great for the sedentary workers.

The results of these studies are summarized in Figure 13.18.

Sedentary / Active (relatively)	Age / Ratio
Executives, judges, lawyers, physicians / Farmers, miners, labourers	45+ / 5.7
Professional business, clerks / Active workers	35–64 / 1.3
Bus drivers / Bus conductors	35–64 / 1.8
Postal clerks and telegraphers / Postmen	35–64 / 1.3
Nonfarmers / Farmers	35–74 / 1.5
Railroad clerks / Railroad maintenance workers	40–49 / 2.3
Professional men / Unskilled workers	All / 3.7

0 50 100 150 200 250

Deaths or disease per 100 000

Figure 13.18 Coronary heart disease and CHD deaths related to occupation—sedentary versus active. 'Age' refers to the age range of subjects; 'ratio' is the ratio of sedentary to active.

• **The Irish Brothers Study**

The 'Irish Brothers Study' showed that Irish migrants to the USA had a much greater risk of suffering from CHD than their brothers who had remained in Ireland. The diet of the Americans was *lower* in cholesterol, and their smoking and drinking habits were similar. The only variable factor was physical activity: the brothers who remained in Ireland were *physically more active* than the migrants.

As working time has decreased and leisure time has increased over the last half-century, the incidence of coronary heart disease has also increased (see Figure 13.19). Automation and the passive use of leisure has led to our modern, sedentary, unfit society.

• **Exercise and leisure study**

In a recent survey of the relationship between exercise and leisure, it was found that:

(a) 50 per cent of men and 66 per cent of women

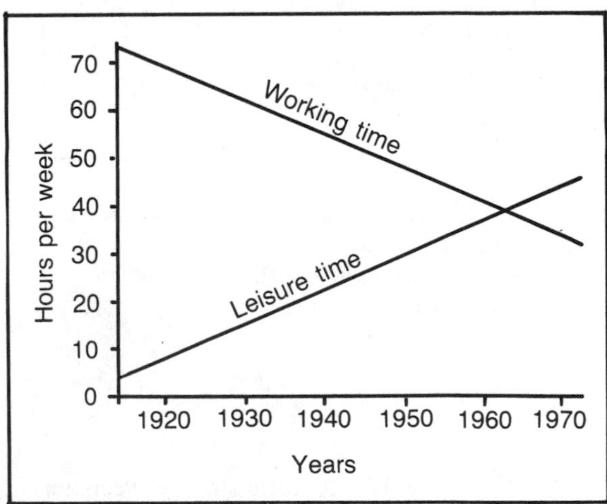

Figure 13.19 Decrease in work time and increase in leisure, 1920 to 1970.

Figure 13.20 Our modern lifestyle fosters unfitness.

Summary: The role of aerobic exercise in reducing the risk of developing coronary heart disease

To avoid coronary heart disease, part of our increased leisure time must be used for aerobic leisure activity. In particular, they should be activities that require critical threshold heart rate intensities to be maintained for twenty-minute periods three times per week.

Regular aerobic exercise helps to reduce the risk of developing CHD by:

(a) Improving cardiovascular capacities and efficiency, thus normalizing blood pressure
(b) Dissipating stress
(c) Burning calories, thus preventing or reducing overweight
(d) Promoting healthy lifestyle modifications, such as giving up smoking
(e) Utilizing blood fats as energy, thus reducing the circulating level of blood fats, and increasing the proportion of high density lipoprotein (HDL) cholesterol.

said that they rarely or never engaged in active exercise. The proportion of women participating was significantly lower than that of men in the younger age groups.

(b) Only 16 per cent of men and 9 per cent of women engaged in regular vigorous exercise at least three times a week.
(c) Only about 1 in 4 people reported walking regularly for relaxation or exercising three times a week or more.
(d) Most people did not use their daily trips to and from work as a means of taking moderate exercise. Only 7 per cent of men and 3 per cent of women walked more than 2 kilometres on the way to or from work. Very few people used bicycles to travel to and from work, and only 1.5 per cent of men and 0.4 per cent of women rode a bike three times a week or more.

The role of exercise in cardiac rehabilitation

To rehabilitate cardiac patients, therapists now use submaximal aerobic programmes. These include such activities as walking, jogging or cycling that begin with very low intensities and gradually increase in workload. Exercise of this nature assists the collateral circulation to the damaged area, enhancing recovery.

The heart workload for cardiac patients is measured by: cardiac workload = systolic blood pressure x the heart rate.

Activities unsuitable for cardiac patients are:

- High intensity anaerobic work
- Isometric or heavy resistance exercise
- Any activites involving holding the breath.

By increasing	By decreasing
• Coronary collateral vascularization Myocardial efficiency Efficiency of peripheral blood distribution and return Fibinolytic capability Red blood-cell mass and blood volume Tolerance to stress Prudent living habits Physical work capacity Stroke volume • Diastolic period of the heart beat Maximal cardiac output Maximal oxygen uptake Arterial-venous oxygen difference • Restitution of heart rate post exercise • Myocardial hypertrophy Pulmonary blood-flow distribution Vital capacity Maximal breathing capacity	Serum lipid levels, triglycerides, and cholesterol Glucose intolerance • Arterial blood pressure Neurohormonal influences • 'Strain' associated with psychic 'stress' resulting in less depression, better sleeping habits, and improved self-image • Heart rate Lactate levels of following all levels of work

Figure 13.21 The apparent benefits of a trained heart.

AMERICANS DYING SITTING ON THEIR BEHINDS: STUDY

NEW YORK. — Medical researchers at Harvard and Stanford universities who have studied the habits and health of 17,000 middle-aged and older men have reported the first scientific evidence that even modest exercise helps prolong life.

The researchers concluded that sedentary lifestyles, even among former university athletes, lead to heart and lung diseases that shorten lives.

They urged in the strongest possible terms that Americans undertake some form of regular exercise, even brisk walks four times a week, to help ward off cardiovascular and pulmonary disease.

'We have found a direct relationship between the level of physical activity and the length of life in the college men we have studied,' said Dr Ralph Paffenbarger, the visiting professor of epidemiology at the Harvard School of Public Health, who is the principal author of the report.

Dr Paffenbarger said two previous reports dealing with the health of these college men had linked the lack of physical fitness to high blood pressure and cardiovascular disease. But he added that he believed the current report was the first epidemiological study linking physical fitness to longer life. It has long been assumed that people who stay fit through exercise generally live longer than those who do not, but until now no scientific proof has been offered.

'This is the first good evidence that people who are active and fit have a longer life span than those who are not,' Dr Paffenbarger added.

A parallel research report from doctors in Dallas also concluded, after studying the lives and habits of 6000 men and women, that the physically fit were less likely to develop hypertension . . .

The two studies were published in the current

issue of the journal of the American Medical Association.

The issue contains 25 articles and editorials dealing with a variety of athletic problems and observations. Among the accounts were these reports from the following universities:

- The University of Oregon department of medicine found that weight training over a four month period, even by once-sedentary men and women, could lead to substantial reductions in fatty substances in the blood, such as cholesterol.
- The University of Maryland exercise science laboratory found that weight lifters who take large doses of male sex hormones to increase performance may also increase cholesterol . . .

Dr Bruce Dan, the editor of the special sports issue of the journal, said he considered the studies from Harvard, Stanford and Dallas extremely important.

'The real discovery of this research is not that people who exercise have strong cardiovascular systems, rather it is that sedentary people have more cardiovascular disease,' Dr Dan said. 'Sedentary people have shrivelled hearts and most of us who do not exercise have an atrophied body.'

He said physicians had been aware of these connections for years but had had a difficult time convincining the public.

'We can now prove that large numbers of Americans are dying from sitting on their behinds.'

— Richard Lyons, *New York Times*, reported in the *The Age*, Melbourne

THE ECONOMICS OF FITNESS

What price health?

That's a question often asked by Governments and industry. In the absence of an answer, the excuse for failing to support preventive (as opposed to treatment) programs has typically been that they cost too much. And the returns are unknown.

In 1982 the Recreation Ministers' Council of Australia (consisting of Ministers of Recreation from each of the 7 state and 2 territory governments) commissioned a study to examine the economic benefits of exercise.

The study was carried out by Dr Allan Roberts, Senior Lecturer in Human Movement at the Ballarat College of Advanced Education in Victoria. Among his finds:

- that only between 10% and 20% of Australian adults are active often enough and hard enough to help in the prevention of heart disease
- that if this proportion was increased to 50%, the economic savings to the community (based on reductions in heart disease) would be around $274 m per annum, rising to $400 m per annum by the year 2000
- that these savings would accrue to Governments ($93 m), business organisations ($74 m) and individuals and their families ($107 m).

Dr Roberts' findings are based on research carried out since the early 1950s and now amounting to over one million person-years of observation. They show convincingly that a sedentary person has roughly twice the risk of suffering from heart disease as a person who's regularly active.

But being active or athletic only when you're young doesn't guarantee protection. In fact, American studies show that the former college athlete who fails to remain active has perhaps a greater risk of heart disease than a person who has always been inactive. The reasons are unclear, but it's possibly because of other risk factors (aggression, high achievement orientation) that are characteristic of this type of person.

The amount of exercise necessary to provide protection against heart disease is regarded as between 21–32 kj (5–7.5 calories) per min. or 8400 kj (2000 calories) per week. This rate per minute is about the equivalent of a brisk walk.

To get protection against heart disease, and at the same time reduce body fat, an activity level of around 1260 kj (300 calories) per session is needed. This is the equivalent of approximately 60 minutes of walking, 30 minutes of freestyle swimming, or 20 minutes of jogging.

According to Dr Roberts, the research carried out to date shows that the negative consequences of exercise are minimal. Despite popular press publicity about sudden death during exercise, ▶

research shows that this accounts for only around 4% of all heart disease deaths. And in these cases the cause is rarely the exercise, but an inherent weakness magnified by effort.

In summary, Dr Roberts says: '. . . the benefits of encouraging an increased proportion of the adult population of Australia to participate in regular physical activity are substantial. These benefits cannot be ignored as they relate to the efficient management of the economy, and to the quality of life of Australians.'

For reference: Roberts, A. (1982): 'The economic benefits of participation in regular physical activity' (Report to the Recreation Ministers' Council of Australia; Ballarat College of Advanced Education.)

Laboratory work 22: Risko: How to assess cardiovascular disease risk

Risko

The purpose of this game is to give you an estimate of your chances of suffering heart attack. The game is played by making squares which—from left to right—represent an increase in your **risk factors**. These are medical conditions and habits associated with an increased danger of heart attack. Not all risk factors are measurable enough to be included in this game.

Rules

Study each risk factor and its row. Find the box applicable to you and circle the large number in it. For example, if you are 16, circle the number in the box labelled 10 to 20. After checking out all the rows, add the circled numbers. This total—your score—is an estimate of your risk.

If you score:

- 6–11: risk well below average
- 12–17: risk below average
- 18–24: risk generally average
- 25–31: risk moderate
- 32–40: risk at a dangerous level
- 41–62: danger urgent; see your doctor now.

Heredity

Count parents, grandparents, brothers and sisters who have had heart attack and/or stroke.

Tobacco smoking

If you inhale deeply and smoke a cigarette way down, add one to your classification. Do **not** subtract because you think you do not inhale or smoke only a half-inch on a cigarette.

Exercise

Lower your score one point if you exercise regularly and frequently.

Cholesterol or saturated fat intake level

A cholesterol blood level is best. If you can't get one from your doctor, then estimate honestly the percentage of solid fats you eat. These are usually of animal origin–lard, cream, butter, and beef and lamb fat. If you eat much of this, your cholesterol level probably will be high. The US average, 40 per cent, is too high for good health.

Blood pressure

If you have no recent reading but have passed an insurance or industrial examination, chances are you are 140 or less.

Sex

This line takes into account the fact that men have from 6 to 10 times more heart attacks than women of child-bearing age.

Age	1 10 to 20	2 21 to 30	3 31 to 40	4 41 to 50	6 51 to 60	8 61 to 70 and over
Heredity	1 No known history of heart disease	2 1 relative with cardiovascular disease over 60	3 2 relatives with cardiovascular disease over 60	4 1 relative with cardiovascular disease under 60	6 2 relatives with cardiovascular disease under 60	7 3 relatives with cardiovascular disease under 60
Weight	0 More than 3 kg below standard weight	1 −3 to +3 kg standard weight	2 4-10 kg overweight	3 5−16 kg overweight	5 17−25 kg overweight	7 26−35 kg overweight
Tobacco smoking	0 Non-user	1 Cigar and/or pipe	2 10 cigarettes or less a day	4 20 cigarettes a day	6 30 cigarettes a day	10 40 cigarettes a day or more
Exercise	1 Intensive occupational and recreational exertion	2 Moderate occupational and recreational exertion	3 Sedentary work and intense recreational exertion	5 Sedentary occupational and moderate recreational exertion	6 Sedentary work and light recreational exertion	8 Complete lack of all exercise
Cholesterol or fat % in diet	1 Cholesterol below 180 mg.% Diet contains no animal or solid fats	2 Cholesterol 181−205 mg.% Diet contains 10% animal or solid fats	3 Cholesterol 206−235 mg.% Diet contains 20% animal or solid fats	4 Cholesterol 236−255 mg.% Diet contains 30% animal or solid fats	5 Cholesterol 256−280 mg.% Diet contains 40% animal or solid fats	7 Cholesterol 281−300 mg.% Diet contains 50% animal or solid fats
Blood pressure	1 100 upper reading	2 120 upper reading	3 140 upper reading	4 160 upper reading	6 180 upper reading	8 200 or over upper reading
Sex	1 Female under 40	2 Female 40−60	3 Female over 50	5 Male	6 Stocky male	7 Bald stocky male

Laboratory work 23: How to estimate myocardial oxygen consumption (MVO_2)

Aim

To estimate myocardial oxygen consumption (MVO_2), both at rest and during exercise.

MVO_2 = systolic BP × heart rate.

Apparatus

- Stethoscope
- Sphygmomanometer.

Procedure

(1) Measure the systolic blood pressure and the heart rate of the subject at rest.
(2) Estimate his or her myocardial oxygen consumption at rest.
(3) Repeat this procedure straight after the following activities:
(4) **Isotonic exercises:**
  (a) One-minute running on the spot
  (b) One minute of push ups.
(5) **Isometric exercises:**
  (a) Pull with maximum effort on the upright of the chin-up bar for 60 seconds
  (b) Hold a static push up for as long as possible (60 seconds maximum).

Results

Write down the result for MVO_2:
(1) At rest ....
(2) After running on the spot ....
(3) After push ups ....
(4) After pull on bar ....
(5) After static push up ....

Was there any difference in the results after isotonic and isometric exercises?

Worksheet 12: Cardiovascular disease

(1) What are some of the factors leading to high blood pressure?
(2) How does physical training help to bring blood pressure back to normal?
(3) Turn to the results you wrote down when playing Risko:
  (a) List your risk category
  (b) Which factor had the highest score?
  (c) What can be done about your two highest risk factors?
(4) What factors might lead to a decrease in MVO_2 during exercise?
(5) Would training influence any of these factors?
(6) Which person is most likely to have a problem: **A**, **B**, **C** or **D**? (The results were obtained after doing the same workload.)

Subject	Blood pressure	Heart rate	MVO_2
A	180	135	
B	225	129	
C	170	150	
D	200	165	

(7) What type of exercise would best help a cardiac patient?
(8) Explain why the heart rate and blood pressure are so high during isometric activities.
(9) Explain this statement: 'CHD is a multicausal disease with appreciable factor interaction.'
(10) Suggest reasons why males less than 45 years old are more susceptible to CHD than females of the same age.
(11) What percentage of Australian men and women engage in regular aerobic activity?

14. Diet and nutrition

Nutrition is the study of the food we eat and how the body uses it.

Nutrients are those essential elements in food that we need for life and growth. They include proteins, carbohydrates, fats, minerals, vitamins and water.

Main nutrients of the body

(1) Protein

Protein is the basic structural substance of the cell, forming bone, skin, muscle, hormones, enzymes, haemoglobin and platelets. When eaten, proteins are broken down into amino acids, which link into chains to form new structures vital for life.

Major sources of protein are such animal products as meat, fish, poultry, eggs and milk. For vegetarians, major sources of protein are peas, beans and nuts.

Protein should form 15 per cent of the daily diet.

(2) Carbohydrates

There are two types of carbohydrates: **starches** and **sugars**. Carbohydrates provide the primary energy for:

- Forming new compounds
- Transmitting impulses (through the nerves)
- Exercise.

Major sources of starch are potatoes, beans, peas, grains (especially wheat and oats), flour, noodles, bread and cakes.

Major sources of sugars are fruits, juices, honey, jam, confectionery and table sugar. (Note that table sugar is not pure glucose, and that sugar gained from other sources is more beneficial to the body).

The role of sugars and starches is to provide glucose (the major energy source in metabolism). Fifty-five per cent of the food we eat should be carbohydrates, and 40 per cent of this should be carbohydrates other than table sugar, confectionery or other products made out of refined sugar.

(3) Fats

Fats are broken down by the body into fatty acids. Fats act as insulators, protect vital organs and are a secondary energy source for muscular activity. Fats should form 30 per cent or less of what we eat.

There are two types of fat:

(a) **Saturated fats**

Saturated fats are known to raise cholesterol levels. They should form only 10 per cent of our fat intake. Major sources are meat, milk, cheese and butter — that is, dairy products.

(b) **Unsaturated fats** (also called **polyunsaturated fats**)

They should make up at least 20 per cent of our fat intake. Sources include peanut oil, safflower oil, corn, soybeans and margarine.

Cholesterol is a fat-like substance found in animal products, especially in egg yolk, liver, shrimp and lobster. Cholesterol is necessary for the body, but the body already produces it. Excess cholesterol tends to settle on the walls of blood vessels and impair circulation.

(4) Minerals

Minerals give strength and rigidity to certain body parts, and assist in many vital body functions. For instance:

- **Calcium:** formation of bones and teeth
- **Phosphorus:** production of ATP
- **Iron:** necessary to form haemoglobin
- **Potassium and sodium:** necessary for impulse transmission in the nerves.

It is possible to eat too much of some minerals. For instance, sodium is contained in salt and many other products. If you absorb too much sodium, especially through salt, you run the risk of developing high blood pressure.

(5) Vitamins

Vitamins are needed for the proper functioning of muscles and nerves, the growth of body tissue, and for the release of energy from foods.

Vitamins are required only in small amounts, and most of them are not stored in the body. If you take excessive vitamins, they will be excreted in the urine. All required vitamins are contained in a balanced diet.

(6) Water

Water is second in importance only to oxygen as a nutrient of the body. It is the medium for transporting nutrients, removing waste and regulating body temperature. Water is ingested both from drinking and the food you eat.

Energy intake and expenditure

Calories and kilojoules

The **calorie** is a term that can be used either as a unit to measure heat, or to measure energy production in the body. The word calorie that is used in ordinary speech about food is **actually 1000 calories** (heat measurement).

The metric term for measuring energy production in the body is the **kilojoule**. 1 calorie (1 kilocalorie) = 4.2 kilojoules.

The calorie is the term still used most commonly in conversation. It can be used to express the potential energy of food or the amount of energy used by the body in performing various activities (see Figures 14.1 and 14.2).

Basal metabolic rate (BMR)

The basal metabolic rate (BMR) is the minimum rate of energy required to maintain the life processes of the body at complete rest.

To calculate BMR:

- **Males**

1 kilogram of body weight burns about 1 calorie per hour. For example, a male weighing 77 kilograms burns 77 calories per hour, or 1848 calories per day.

- **Females**

1 kilogram of body weight burns about .9 of a calorie per hour. For example, a female weighing 55 kilograms:

= 55 × .9 × 24 hours
= 1200 calories per day.

The basal metabolic rate is the main way in which we burn fuel. It accounts for the largest single daily caloric expenditure (50–70 per cent).

BMR is influenced by:

- Body size
- Body composition.

For instance:

- Tall, thin people with large body surface areas have greater heat loss than short, muscular people. Therefore the BMR of tall people will be greater than that for short people.
- Muscle tissue uses more energy than fatty tissue, so fat people have a lower BMR than thin people. Also, women's bodies have a higher fat content than men's bodies, so their BMR is usually lower than men's.
- BMR decreases with age.
- Some diseases, such as fever, increase the BMR.
- Cold weather increases BMR and hot weather lowers it.

Calculating daily caloric expenditure

In order to calculate **daily caloric expenditure**, add to your BMR the calorie or kilojoule costs of the various activities that make up your day. The **energy expenditure** of each activity can be calculated by measuring the amount of oxygen used to perform the activity.

There is a direct relationship between energy expenditure and oxygen consumption, because oxygen is burnt in the body to produce energy. It takes about 1 litre of oxygen to burn 5 calories of food. Therefore it is possible to perform an activity for a given time and to measure the amount of oxygen that you use. This figure can be converted to the number of calories used in performing the task.

Energy expenditure for different tasks will vary according to a person's skill level, body weight and other factors. However it is possible to work out a fairly accurate figure for a person's energy expenditure by consulting tables prepared from actual measurements.

Calculating energy expenditure for a particular activity

(See Figure 14.2.) To determine the energy expenditure for a particular activity, you must consider:

- The rate of work
- The time spent performing the activity

Food description	Serving size	Approximate calories
Fruits and juices		
Banana	1 medium	100
Grapefruit	$\frac{1}{2}$ medium	50
Grapefruit juice (sweetened)	113 mm	65
Orange	1 medium	50
Orange juice	113 mm	55
Rhubarb (cooked with sugar)	$\frac{1}{2}$ cup	193
Watermelon	10 × 20 cm wedge	115
Miscellaneous		
Tomato sauce	1 tbsp	15
Coleslaw (with mayonnaise)	$\frac{1}{2}$ cup	255
Mustard	1 tbsp	4
Macaroni and cheese	1 cup	560
Margarine (regular)	1 tbsp	100
Marshmallow	1 average size	25
Pickles, dill	1 medium	10
Pickles, sweet	1 medium	20
Pizza, with sauce & cheese	$\frac{1}{4}$ of 30 cm pie	575
Popcorn, with oil & salt	1 cup	40
Potato chips	10 medium	115
Pretzels, thin twist	1 twist	25
Relish	1 tbsp	20
Spaghetti with meat sauce	1 cup	390
Soybean oil	1 tbsp	125
Tapioca	$\frac{1}{2}$ cup	280
Tomato and lettuce salad (no dressing)	$\frac{1}{2}$ cup	60
Tuna and celery salad (with mayonnaise)	$\frac{1}{2}$ cup	255
Fast food stores		
Colonel Sanders' Chicken	'3 piece special'	660
MacDonald's	Quarter pounder	414
	Quarter pounder with cheese	521
	Big Mac	557

Figure 14.1 Sample calorie chart.

- The person's body weight.

Example: A woman weighs 54 kilograms. She jogs at a pace of 10 minutes per mile. She uses .1471 calories per minute per kilogram. If she jogs for 30 minutes, the total calories used

= .1471 × 30 mins. × 54 kg

= 237 calories.

Since one milk shake is about equal to 250 calories, it is necessary to control your food intake in order to control your body weight.

Calculating the daily calorie intake

Energy is available only from carbohydrates, fat and protein. Therefore the content of these nutrients in a food determines the calorie or kilojoule

Activity	Cal/min/lb
Archery	.034
Badminton:	
Moderate	.039
Vigorous	.065
Basketball:	
Moderate	.047
Vigorous	.066
Baseball:	
Infield-outfield	.031
Pitching	.039
Bicycling:	
Slow (5 mph)	.025
Moderate (10 mph)	.05
Fast (13 mph)	.072
Bowling	.028
Calisthenics:	
General	.045
5BX	.098
Canoeing	
2.5 mph	.023
4.0 mph	.047
Dancing:	
Slow	.029
Moderate	.045
Fast	.064
Fencing:	
Moderate	.033
Vigorous	.057
Fishing	.016
Football (tag)	.04
Gardening	.024
Gardening-weeding	.039
Golf	.029
Gymnastics:	
Light	.022
Heavy	.056
Handball	.063
Hiking	.042
Hill-climbing	.06

Figure 14.2 Energy cost of selected activities.

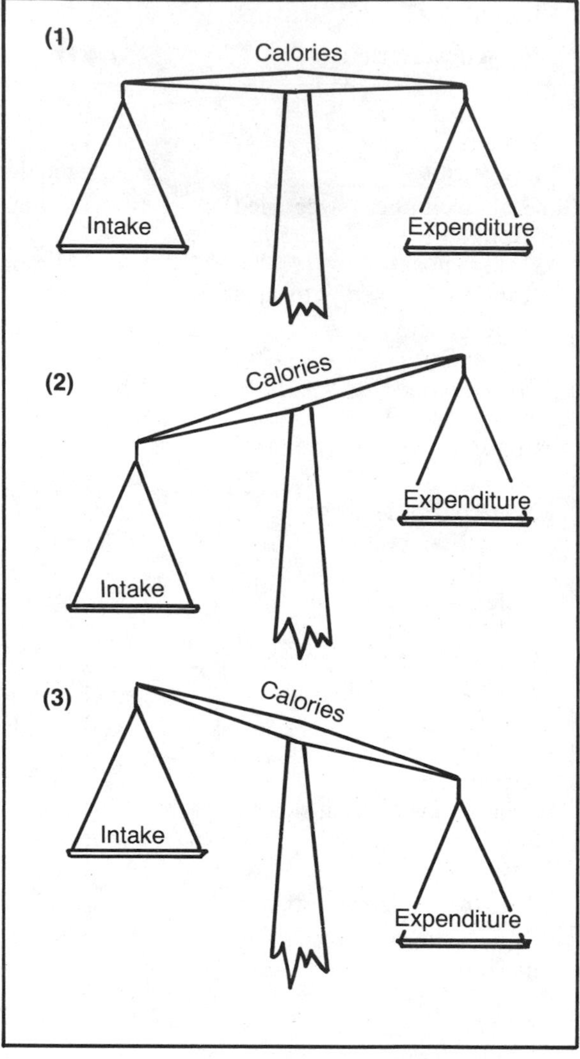

Figure 14.3
(1) Neutral energy balance, in which caloric intake and caloric expenditure are balanced.
(2) Positive energy balance, in which the caloric intake is greater than the caloric expenditure.
(3) Negative energy balance, in which the caloric expenditure is greater than the caloric intake.

value of that food, as shown on calorie equivalence tables. (See Figure 14.1.)

Record your total food intake for each 24-hour period, and use calorie or kilojoule tables to determine the calorie content of all the food and drink you have consumed (see Figures 14.5 and 14.6).

Energy balance

You achieve a neutral energy balance when your caloric intake is equal to the caloric expenditure. When you achieve this, your body weight should remain constant, and should neither increase nor decrease.

A positive energy balance exists when the caloric intake is greater than the caloric expenditure. The excess nutrient is stored as fat and the body weight increases. (See Figure 14.3.)

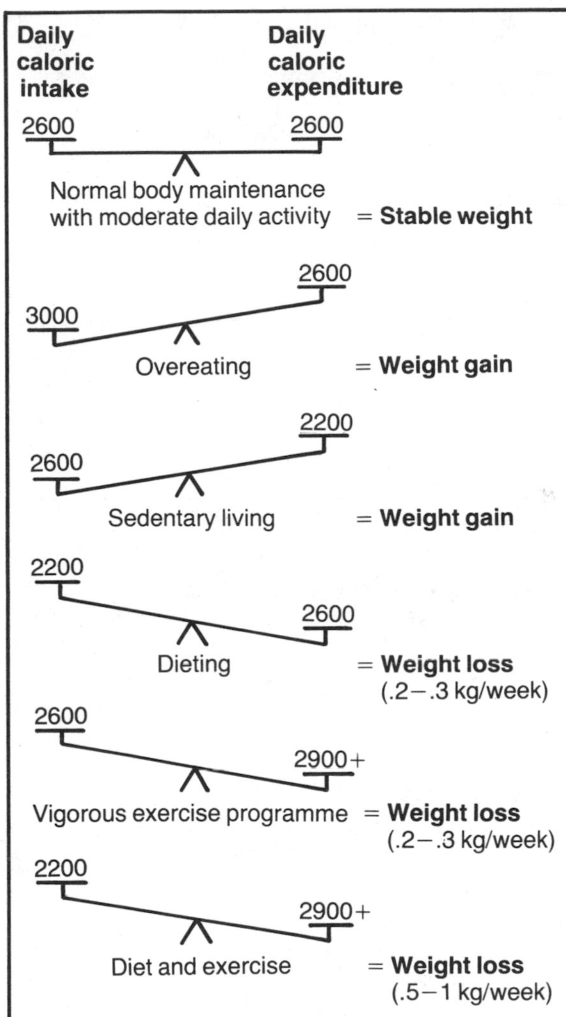

Figure 14.4 Energy balances.

In a **negative energy balance**, the number of calories used exceeds the number of calories consumed. The extra energy is supplied by the burning of fat, and the body fat or weight will be reduced. (See Figure 14.5.)

Note:

- 1 pound of body fat = 4077 calories
- 1 kilogram of body fat = 36 000 kilojoules.

Methods of body fat measurement

Body weight has two components:

(1) **Lean body mass** or **fat-free mass:** This is the mass of the bones, muscles, connective tissue and organs.

(2) **Body fat:** Accumulated adipose tissue.

Measuring body weight on a set of scales gives no information on body composition. Therefore you need to make specific measurements to determine your body fat percentage:

(1) Underwater weighing, or specific gravity method

The subject is weighed in air, then weighed while totally submerged in water. In this way, the specific gravity (body density) can be calculated:

$$\text{Specific gravity} = \frac{\text{Weight in air}}{\text{Weight in air} - \text{weight in water.}}$$

With this information, and knowing the specific gravity figures for muscle, bone and other parts of the body, you can calculate the lean body mass and the body fat.

This method is very accurate, but requires enormous expense and complicated calculations. Therefore it is not a practical method.

(2) Skinfold measurement

With this method, skinfolds are measured at specific body sites with skinfold calipers. These skinfold measures are then used in a nomogram (a graph of three interconnected scales; see Figure 14.19) to give an estimate of the total body fat percentage.

When an individual gains fat, much of this adipose tissue occurs in subcutaneous areas in certain parts of the body. The subcutaneous fat can be pinched; as individuals get fatter, the skinfolds get larger.

Skinfold calipers are designed to measure the thickness of this skin and subcutaneous fat.

The main advantage of the skinfold measurement technique is that it needs only inexpensive equipment, can be performed quickly, and gives a reliable estimate of body fat percentage.

The main disadvantage is that it requires practice in order to be able to use the method accurately.

Calorie/energy intake		
Meal	**Food**	**Calories**
Breakfast	2 toast, peanut, margarine White tea and sugar	530 120
Snack	2 cordials	300
Lunch		
Snack	Water	0
Tea	Steak Potatoes Peas Tomato sauce 2 pieces chocolate Water	880 270 115 45 110 0
Snack	Bananas, ice cream and sugar 1 bottle flovoured mineral water	526 360
	Total	3256

Calorie/energy expenditure	
Activity	**Calories**
Teaching	811
Walking/running during lessons	500
Sitting writing, 2 hrs.	230
Sitting eating	106
BMR	1800
14 km riding	580
1 hr. gym.	547
7 km run	505
Total	5079

Negative energy balance of –1823 calories, therefore less than .5 lb of weight lost.

Figure 14.5 Sample calorie balance record.

(3) Height, weight and age tables

Tables which compare height, weight and age measurements give the desirable weight for a person of a given height. For example, a male of 178 centimetres should weigh 81 kilograms.

Disadvantages of this method include:

(a) The tables give just a weight, but do not distinguish between someone who is 81 kg of lean body weight and someone who is 81 kg, mostly of adipose.

(b) Because muscle weighs more than fat, and these tables do not take body composition into consideration, most well-muscled athletes are classified as overweight.

(c) The desirable weights are simply the weight of an average person in our society of a given height. Since our society is overweight, the average is an overweight average, not a desirable weight.

(d) The tables allow for increases in weight with age which are unjustifiable.

Note: The average body fat percentages are:

- Males: 13-15 per cent
- Females: 18-20 per cent.

Causes of overweight and obesity

(1) Glandular malfunction

This is exceptionally rare, and accounts for only 2 per cent of all overweight cases.

(2) Positive energy balance

This is the consumption of more calories than you expend; excess calories are stored as adipose tissue. The major causes of positive energy balance are:

- Overeating
- Lack of aerobic exercise.

Causes of overeating

There are several contributing causes of overeating:

(1) Family environment

Children tend to imitate their overeating parents.

Day/date: ---------------------------------- Name: ----------------------------------

Calorie/energy intake			**Calorie/energy expenditure**	
Meal	**Food**	**Calories**	**Activity**	**Calories**
Breakfast	2 pieces toast Peanut butter Margarine Tea with sugar and milk	$55 \times 2 = 110$ $184 \times 2 = 368$ $50 \times 2 = 100$ $51 + 41 = 92$	Bike to school (25 mins.)	$= 0.72$ cals/min./lb $= .072 \times 25 \times 161$ $= 290$ cals.
Snack	Glass of water	0	Walking/running during lessons (1 hr.)	$\approx .064$ cals./min./lb $\approx .062 \times 60 \times 161$ $= 600$ cals.
Lunch	4 pieces brown bread 6 slices chicken loaf Margarine Cream cheese 1 Prima	$55 \times 4 = 220$ $50 \times 6 = 300$ 202 106 135	Basal metabolic rate (BMR)	**Male.** 1 cal/kg/hr. $= 1 \times 75 \times 24$ $= 1800$/day
Snack	2 glasses water 2 biscuits	0 $2 \times 70 = 140$	Sitting writing (4 hrs.)	.012 cals./min./lb $.012 \times 240 \times 161$ $= 463$ cals.
Tea	Steak Peas 3 potatoes Carrots Broccholi 4 glasses mineral water and cordial	880 111 $118 \times 3 = 354$ 44 44 57	Teaching/lecturing (6 hrs.) Sitting eating (1 hr.)	.014 cals./min./1b $= .014 \times 360 \times 161$ $= 811$ cals. .011 cals./min./1b $= .011 \times 60 \times 161$ $= 106$ cal.
Snack	Peaches and ice cream 2 toast and peanut butter	$79 + 160 = 239$ 580		
	Total	**4082 cals.**	**Total**	**4075 cals.**

Since 1 pound fat = 4077 cals., a difference of 7 cals. means no effective change in weight.

Figure 14.6 Sample calorie balance record.

Once a poor food intake pattern has been established, it is hard to break the familial trend to overweight.

If babies are overfed between birth and the age of two, the number of their fat cells increases rapidly, making it difficult to control their weight in later life.

(2) Psychological dependence

There are two types of psychological dependence: developmental and reactive:

- **Developmental obesity**

Developmental obesity begins during childhood, when eating becomes a refuge from loneliness, insecurity and social isolation.

• **Reactive obesity**
Reactive obesity begins after childhood, in reaction to an upsetting experience, such as a broken love affair, illness or bereavement. Overeating is used to compensate for the upset.

Figure 14.7 When you eat more than your daily energy needs, the excess energy is stored as body fat.

Figure 14.8 A fat baby is not necessarily a healthy baby.

(3) Body type

(See Figure 14.9.) There are three basic body types:

(a) **Endomorph** (O): Prone to being fat because of an excellent food absorption system
(b) **Mesomorph** (▽): Prone to muscularity
(c) **Ectomorph** (|): Thin because of a poor food assimilation system.

Everyone has some part of each of the three types, but those high in endomorphic characteristics must regulate calorie intake to avoid overweight.

(4) Cultural background

Certain cultures consider overweight a sign of affluence, and therefore foster overeating in their children to impress their peers.

(5) The fast food ('junk food') craze

Various types of food sold over the counter, in shops or restaurants, are known as 'fast foods', 'takeaway foods' or 'junk foods'. They are nutritionally poor because they contain additives and have been heavily processed. A major problem is their high calorie content, and fact that they are extensively advertised without giving any information on their nutritional quality. They are a major contributor to positive energy balances.

(6) Advertising

Advertising in our society encourages people to eat vast quantities of high calorie food for a wide variety of subtly presented reasons. For instance, there are slogans such as 'Real men eat ....' or 'Join the in crowd; eat ....'.

Figure 14.9 **Major body types.**

(1) **Endomorph:** oval-shaped person with concentration of weight in the centre of the body, abdominal sag, flabby limbs and poorly toned muscles.
(2) **Mesomorph:** husky, big-chested person endowed with dense muscles and huge, strong bones. Although the body mass is well poroportioned, this body type had a tendency to accumulate adipose tissue in later adult years, especially if inactive.
(3) **Ectomorph:** extreme thinness, protruding neck, sunken chest, round shoulders, undersized musculature and a fragile skeletal system.

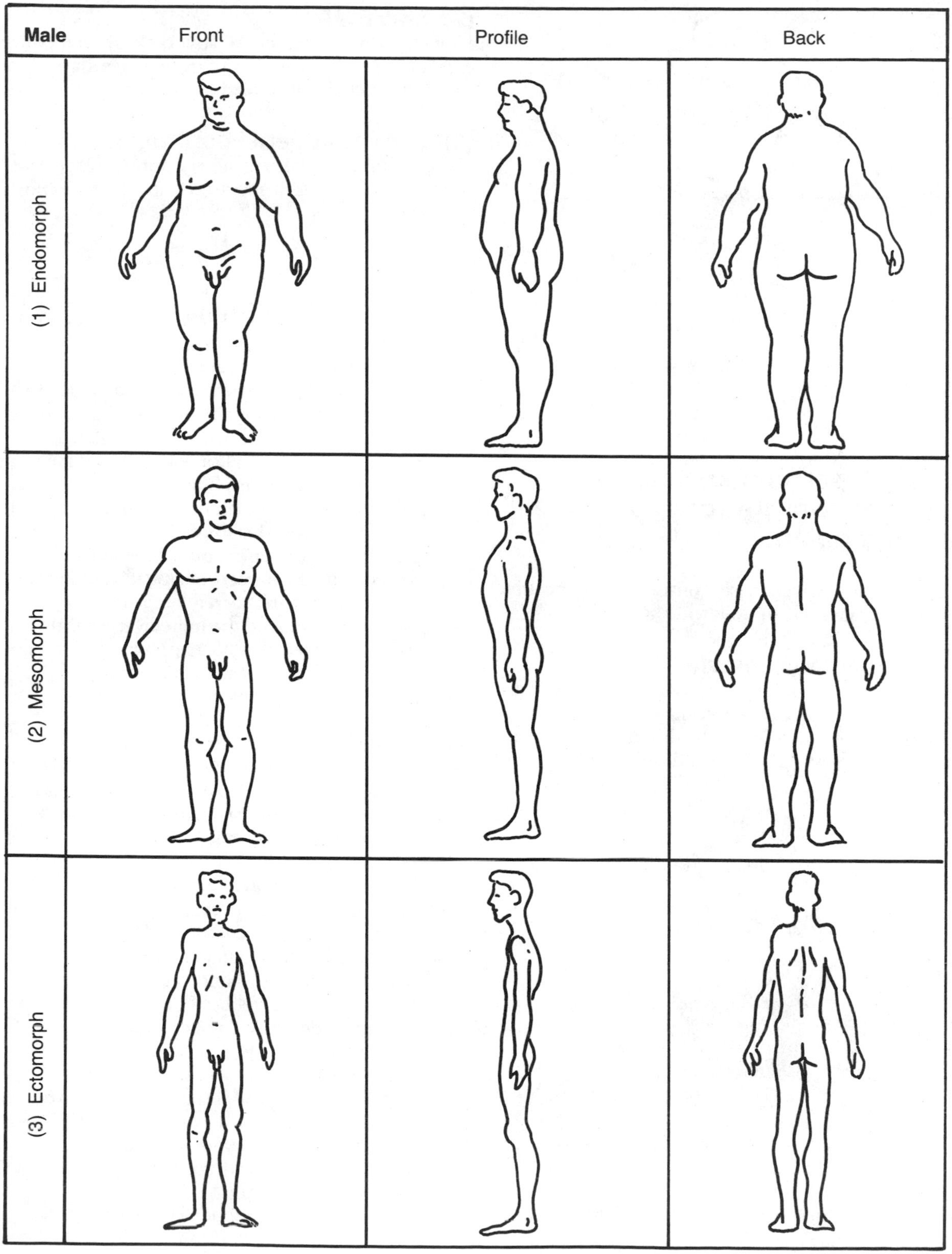

Male	Front	Profile	Back
(1) Endomorph			
(2) Mesomorph			
(3) Ectomorph			

Figure 14.10 Inactivity is the real culprit in 'creeping obesity'.

Lack of aerobic exercise: a major contributor to positive energy balance

Lack of aerobic exercise contributes to positive energy balance in the following ways:

(1) Sedentary lifestyle

If you have a sedentary lifestyle, you are using a small number of calories each day — only a few calories above your BMR. In this case, you would need to eat very little to avoid overweight.

Figure 14.11 For those who do not exercise regularly, the other alternative for weight control is sedentary living and lifelong hunger.

(2) Low BMR

If your BMR remains relatively low, you will expend only a low number of calories per day, and therefore become overweight.

(3) Lack of appetite control

Since aerobic exercise causes improved appetite control, lack of it leads to rampant overeating habits.

DOES OVERWEIGHT MATTER?

Does it really matter if we are rather too round, and the doctor tells us that we weigh too much? The scientists, medical men, and life insurance people think it *does*. Life insurance companies consider overweight people a poor risk and make them pay extra premiums. They say, for instance, that if at 45 a man is 25 lb above the desirable weight then his life expectancy is decreased by 25 per cent. Thus, if the normal life expectancy was 80 years of age, it would now be reduced to 60 years, merely because he weighed too much. And the more overweight you are, the shorter your life expectancy.

Excessive weight puts an added burden on the heart and legs, and means more work for the lungs and digestive system. A heart surrounded by fat finds it difficult to pump; added to this there is more work to be done pumping blood to all the additional blood vessels in the additional fatty tissue. It has been calculated that for 30 lb overweight there are 25 miles of extra blood vessels through which blood must be pumped.

It has long been known that overweight people are more prone to develop diabetes, arthritis and gout, cardiovascular, liver, and gall-bladder disorders than people of normal weight. Overweight is a handicap in cases of pregnancy and surgery; obesity tends to delay puberty and to decrease fertility. And last but certainly not least, the legs have too much weight to carry. Imagine yourself carrying a suitcase of 10, 20, or 30 lb around wherever you go, to say nothing of one of 40 or 50 lb. Think just how it would hinder your every move. How much more readily everything could be done *without* that added weight!

— National Heart Foundation

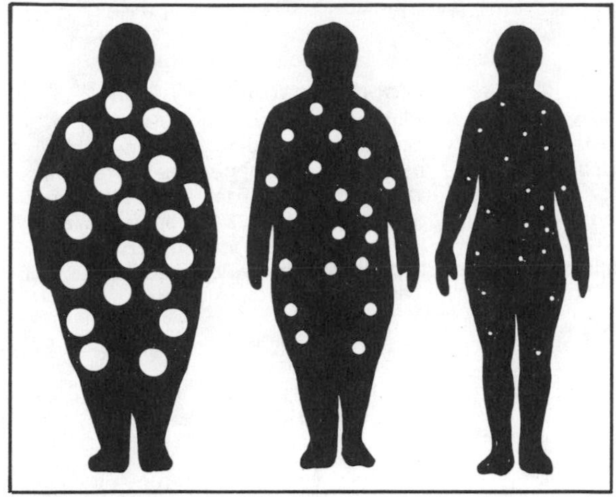

Figure 14.12 The number of fat cells remains the same. As you gain weight, they increase in size.

Methods of controlling overweight

(1) Reduce calorie intake

Reducing calorie intake assists in producing a negative energy balance. The reduction diet must still supply balanced nutritional requirements, but add up to fewer calories per day — for example, an energy balance of −500 calories per day.

For a reducing diet to be effective:

- You need to set **long-term goals** — for instance, 13 kg in a year — and **short-term goals** — for instance, .25–.5 kg per week. These goals must be realistic.
- You should not begin radical changes to your food pattern. For instance, if you are used to three meals a day, you do not change this basic pattern, but simply reduce the number of calories per meal.

(2) Aerobic exercise

Aerobic exercise:

- Increases calorie expenditure on each day that you train.
- Increases the basal metabolic rate (BMR) so that calorie expenditure after exercise also increases.
- Results in voluntary *decreases* in food intake, since the internal mechanisms of appetite regulation and satiety (feelings of fullness) function correctly.

Therefore increased exercise *does not* result in increased appetite and food consumption.

(3) Surgery

Two surgical methods are sometimes used to control overweight:

- **Duodenal bypass**

This is the removal of part of the bowel. This results in a lower rate of food absorption and helps to suppress appetite. This method can lead to malabsorption of nutrients and diarrhoea. A person who has had a duodenal bypass might need vitamin and mineral supplements.

- **Stomach stapling**

A person who has undergone surgery for stomach stapling would feel satiated more quickly than before, and so would eat less.

(4) Drug treatment

- **Thyroid hormones and amphetamines**

Thyroid hormones and amphetamines increase a person's BMR, but they have harmful effects if used regularly.

- **Bulk fillers**

Bulk fillers are tablets to make you feel that you have eaten already. They can be used for only short periods of time — four weeks at the most.

- **Diuretics**

Diuretics are drugs that increase urination and, therefore, fluid loss from the body. This gives some slight loss of weight, but leads to dehydration of the body, and does nothing to break down the body's store of fat.

(5) Behaviour modification

It is possible to decrease obesity by changing behaviours that lead to overeating. For instance, one method of behaviour modification is to avoid people, places or situations which are likely to lead to overeating.

(6) Group therapy

Peer pressure and reward can be used to modify a person's eating habits. An organization such as Weight Watchers uses this method to help people reduce obesity.

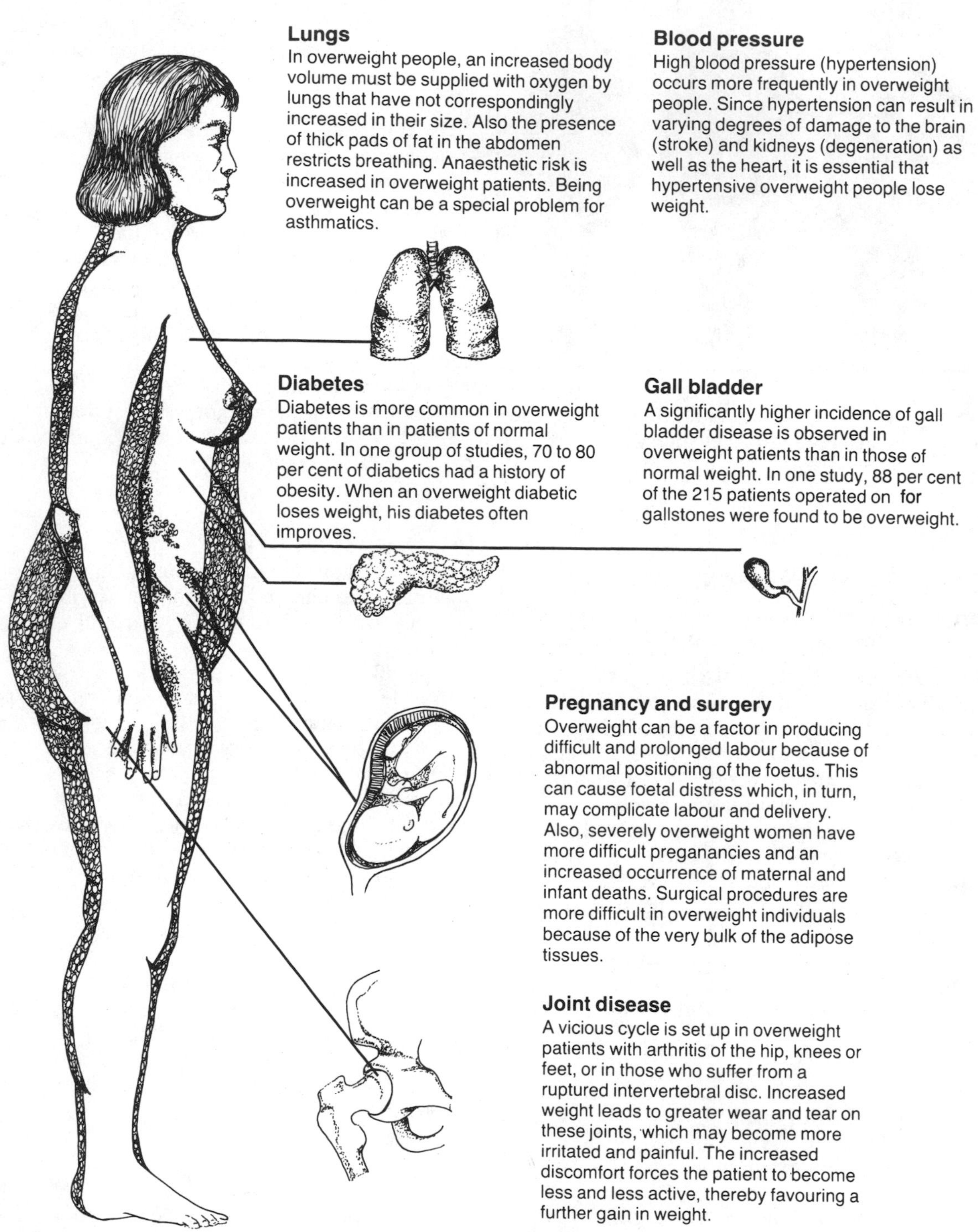

Lungs
In overweight people, an increased body volume must be supplied with oxygen by lungs that have not correspondingly increased in their size. Also the presence of thick pads of fat in the abdomen restricts breathing. Anaesthetic risk is increased in overweight patients. Being overweight can be a special problem for asthmatics.

Blood pressure
High blood pressure (hypertension) occurs more frequently in overweight people. Since hypertension can result in varying degrees of damage to the brain (stroke) and kidneys (degeneration) as well as the heart, it is essential that hypertensive overweight people lose weight.

Diabetes
Diabetes is more common in overweight patients than in patients of normal weight. In one group of studies, 70 to 80 per cent of diabetics had a history of obesity. When an overweight diabetic loses weight, his diabetes often improves.

Gall bladder
A significantly higher incidence of gall bladder disease is observed in overweight patients than in those of normal weight. In one study, 88 per cent of the 215 patients operated on for gallstones were found to be overweight.

Pregnancy and surgery
Overweight can be a factor in producing difficult and prolonged labour because of abnormal positioning of the foetus. This can cause foetal distress which, in turn, may complicate labour and delivery. Also, severely overweight women have more difficult preganancies and an increased occurrence of maternal and infant deaths. Surgical procedures are more difficult in overweight individuals because of the very bulk of the adipose tissues.

Joint disease
A vicious cycle is set up in overweight patients with arthritis of the hip, knees or feet, or in those who suffer from a ruptured intervertebral disc. Increased weight leads to greater wear and tear on these joints, which may become more irritated and painful. The increased discomfort forces the patient to become less and less active, thereby favouring a further gain in weight.

Figure 14.13 **Being overweight can hurt more than just your looks.**

Heart

As one gains weight, the heart must work harder to supply nutrients to all tissues of the body. The greater the body mass, the greater the strain on the heart. There is a higher incidence of heart disease in people who are overweight.

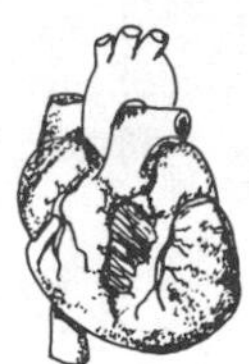

Atherosclerosis

Athesclorosis is the deposit of fatty material in the lining of the arterial wall. It can result in rupture of the blood vessel or in narrowing of these vessels, which may lead to stroke or heart attack. Studies show that there is a marked increase in the occurrence of atherosclerosis in overweight people.

The omentum

Many overweight people assume that their 'pot-bellied' appearance is due not to fat but to a protruding stomach. Actually, their shape is only partially due to the accumulation of fat under the skin; most of the bulge results from fat accumulated within the abdominal cavity—in the omentum.

Hernia

Certain types of hernia, involving displacement of the upper part of the stomach into the chest cavity, are more prevalent in overweight individuals than in those of normal weight.

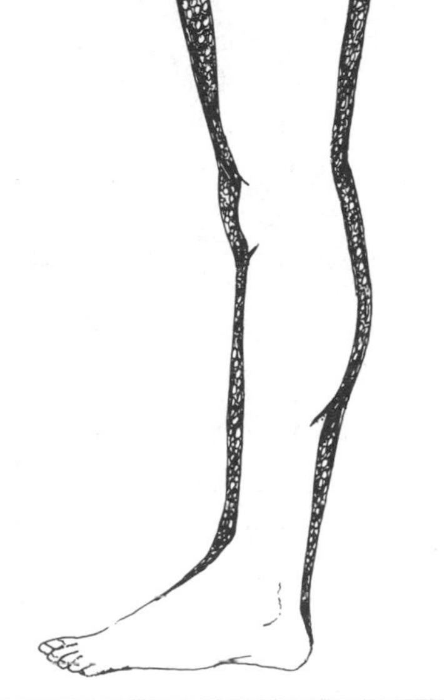

Adipose tissue

Adipose tissue is composed of cells which are highly elastic and contain varying amounts of fatty deposits acquired from the bloodstream. The tissue is situated throughout the body—under the skin in protective pacs covering vital organs, and in association with muscle. Excessive fat deposits are found in virtually all soft tissues and organs in overweight people. The degree of overweight depends upon the number of fat cells present and the amount of fat they contain. In the course of weight reduction, fat cell volume is decreased but the number of fat cells remains constant.

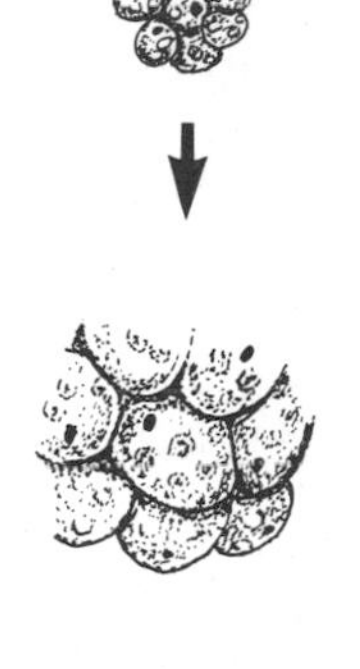

Baby fat

Baby fat is not cute. When excess weight is gained during childhood, the number of fat cells in the body increases. Since the fat cells developed in childhood remain throughout life, it becomes exceedingly difficult to lose weight as an adult.

Common misconceptions about reducing obesity

People who wish to reduce obesity often become enthusiastic about methods that, in the long term, are unhelpful or quite dangerous:

(1) Fad diets

Fad (or currently fashionable) diets come in a wide variety of forms, many of which contradict each other. Some recent fad diets are 'high fat', 'high protein' and 'liquid only' diets. Usually fad diets:

- Enable a person to lose some weight rapidly
- Can be undertaken only for short periods of time
- Are nutritionally unbalanced
- Are ineffective in the long term
- Produce unpleasant side effects, such as nausea and diarrhoea.

(2) Fasting and crash diets

Such diets are essentially types of starvation. The body reacts just as it would if you were starving: it conserves its fat deposits and lowers your BMR so that you can survive. When you go back to normal eating patterns, your BMR remains low and the body adds new deposits of fats to those it conserved. A person who resumes a normal diet after losing weight using a crash diet will often gain more weight than he or she lost in the first place.

The crash diet itself can often cause extreme bodily reactions, including liver and heart malfunctions.

(3) Cellulite

Cellulite is simply stored fat, and appears dimpled because of the swollen adipose cells stretching the adjacent tissue. The word cellulite is a made-up term that has no scientific basis.

(4) Spot reduction

Fat can only be removed from the body when it has a negative energy balance. When that happens, fat is metabolized from throughout the whole body. Therefore do not believe claims that such methods as hot baths, body wraps, cellulite brushes, creams, vibrating belts and specific calisthenics can stimulate fat removal from specific parts of the body.

(5) Sweating

It is both futile and dangerous to try losing weight by exercising in plastic or rubber suits, or by spending a lot of time in saunas, spas or steam baths. The massive increase in sweating can cause dangerous fluid loss and heat stroke. Any weight loss is caused only by fluid depletion, and will be restored as soon as you drink.

Figure 14.14

Laboratory work 24: Estimation of energy balance over three days

Apparatus

Kilojoule tables.

Method

Copy out Figure 14.15 and fill in your results f[illegible] three consecutive days.

Questions

(1) What is your energy balance for the t[illegible]
(2) Is your energy balance positive or [illegible]
(3) If your eating and activity ha[illegible] stant, how much weight wo[illegible] lose or gain every three d[illegible]

Calorie/energy intake			Calorie/energy expenditure	
Meal	**Food**	**Calories**	**Activity**	**Calories**
Breakfast				
Snack				
Lunch				
Snack				
Tea				
Snack				
	Total		**Total**	

Energy balance = --------------

Figure 14.15 Energy balance record sheet.

Laboratory work 25: Skinfold measurement to estimate body fat percentage

Body fat evaluation

Dr A. W. Sloan and his fellow researchers have developed formulas for estimating body density and percent body fat, using two skinfold measurements as predictors:

- For young men, the fat thickness of the subscapula and thigh sites have proven to be a good gauge of overall body fatness.
- For young women, the triceps and suprailiac sites are the best predictors.

Below are the proper methods of measuring skinfolds with calipers, as well as the formulas for calculating body density and fat. Graphs (**nomograms**) have been included to help determine body density and percent fat without doing the calculations.

Procedures

(1) You need someone to measure you.
(2) Measure skinfolds on the right side of the body using a skinfold caliper.

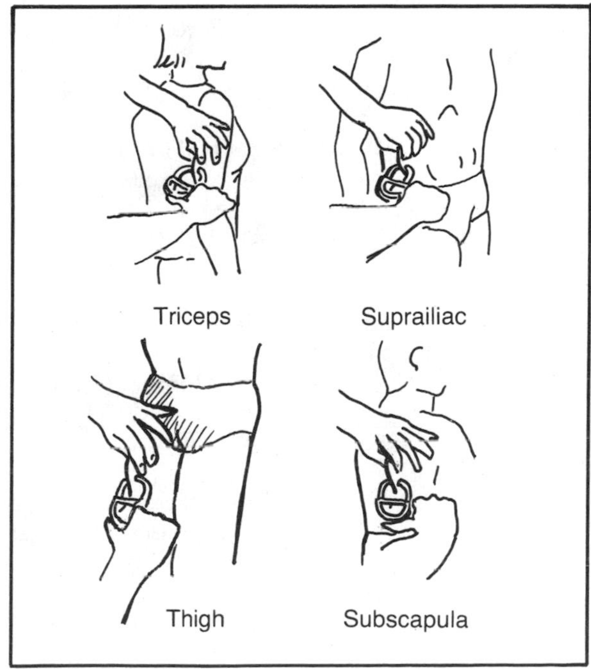

Figure 14.16 Skinfold sites.

(3) Grasp the skinfold between the thumb and forefinger. The skinfold should include two thicknesses of skin and subcutaneous fat, but not muscle.
(4) Apply the calipers about one centimetre below the fingers holding the skinfold, at a depth equal to the thickness of the fold.
(5) Take each fold in the vertical plane while the subject is standing, except for the subscapular, which you should pick up on a slight slant running laterally in the natural fold of the skin.
(6) Repeat the technique of measurement completely for each site before going on to the next site. This includes regrasping the skinfold.

Women

Skinfold assessment (millimetres)

	Trial 1	*Trial 2*	*Trial 3*	*Mean*
(1) Tricep	*13.0*	*16.0*	*15.0*	*15.5*
(2) Suprailiac	*7.5*	*8.0*	*7.5*	*7.5*

Computation for body density (gm/cc)

Body density = 1.0764 − (0.00088 × tricep) − (0.00081 × suprailiac)
= 1.0764 − (0.00088 × *15.5*) − (0.00081 × *7.5*)
= 1.0764 − (*.01364*) − (*.00608*)

Body density = *1.057* gm/cc

Computation for percentage of body fat:

Percentage body fat = (4.570/body density − 4.142)100
= (4.570/ *1.057* − 4.142)100
= *.1816* × 100
Percentage body fat = *18.2* %

Men

Skinfold assessment (millimetres)

	Trial 1	*Trial 2*	*Trial 3*	*Mean*
(1) Subscapula	*11.5*	*11.0*	*11.0*	*11.0*
(2) Thigh	*15.0*	*15.0*	—	*15.0*

Computation for body density (gm/cc)

Body density = 1.1043 − (0.00131 × subscapula) − (0.001327 × thigh)
= 1.1043 − (0.00131 × *11.0*) − (0.001327 × *15.0*)
= 1.1043 − (*.01441*) − (*.01991*)
Body density = *1.070* gm/cc

Computation for percentage of body fat:

Percentage body fat = (4.570/body density − 4.142)100
= (4.570/ *1.070* − 4.142)100
= (*.1290*)100
Percentage body fat = *12.9* %

Figure 14.17 Skinfold assessment.

Whenever you find a difference greater than 0.5 millimetre, make a third reading. The mean of the two closest readings represents the value for the site being measured.

(7) The anatomical landmarks for the skinfold sites are:
- **Subscapula**
  The bottom point of the shoulder blade (scapula).
- **Thigh**
  The front side of the thigh midway between the hip and knee joints.
- **Triceps**
  The back of the upper arm midway between the shoulder and elbow joints.
- **Suprailiac**
  Just above the top of the hip bone (crest of the ilium) at the middle of the side of the body.

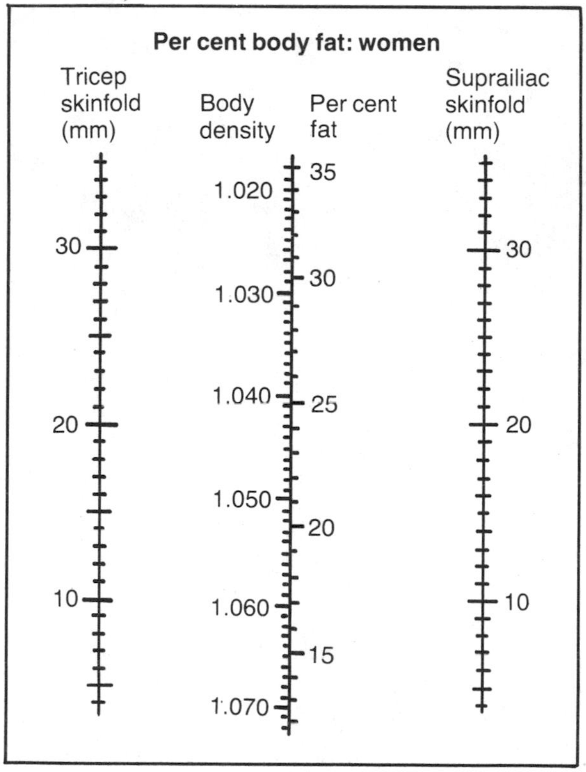

Per cent body fat: women

Tricep skinfold (mm): 10, 20, 30
Body density: 1.020, 1.030, 1.040, 1.050, 1.060, 1.070
Per cent fat: 35, 30, 25, 20, 15
Suprailiac skinfold (mm): 10, 20, 30

Figure 14.18 Nomograms for predicting body fat. Body density and percentage of body fat can be quickly assessed for women and men from the graphs presented below. A straight line joining your skinfold values will intersect the corresponding values for body density and percentage of fat.

Calculations for body fat

The formulas below are for calculating the body density and per cent of body fat in both men and women. These measurements can provide a good estimate of your relative body fat. Two examples, one for women and one for men, are given to help you in making your own calculation.

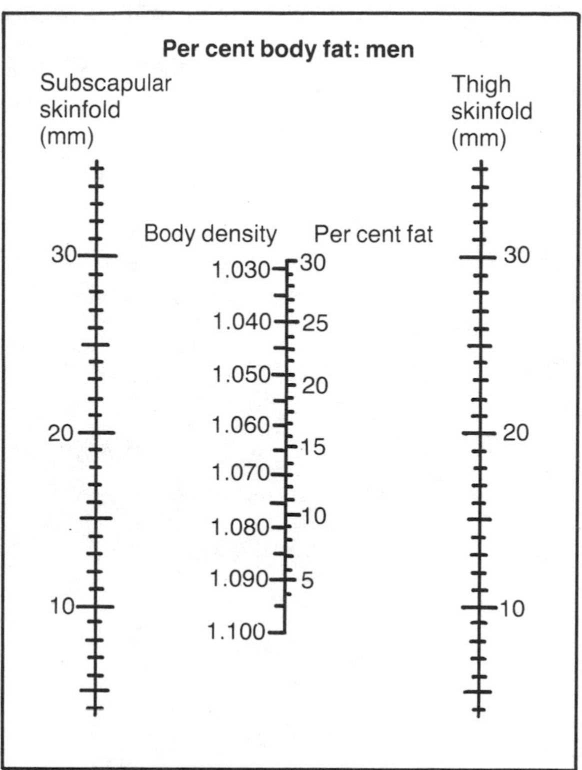

Figure 14.19 Body fat norms: a body-fat classification chart for college-aged men and women. A normal rating refers to the average for the group that was measured. This does not necessarily mean this is the most desired rating.

Worksheet 13: Diet, nutrition and exercise

(1) What are the six main categories of food?
(2) What are the three main functions of food?
(3) What is the function of carbohydrate?
(4) Why is it unwise to eat only carbohydrate if all the energy we require can be obtained from it?

(5) What are the two chief functions of fats?

(6) Why is it more difficult to burn the energy we acquire from 1 kilogram of fat than it is to burn energy acquired from 1 kilogram of carbohydrate?

(7) What is the chief function of protein, and under which circumstances can it be used to provide energy?

(8) What is the definition of essential amino acids?

(9) Name one vitamin and one mineral. What is the chief function of each? What is a major food source of each?

(10) Define the following:
- Protein
- Fat
- Carbohydrate
- Minerals
- Vitamin
- Basal metabolic rate
- Lean body weight
- Obesity
- Calorie
- Kilojoule
- Positive energy balance
- Negative energy balance.

(11) 'Hereditary obesity is caused by environment and not heredity.' Explain this statement.

(12) What is the basic cause of obesity?

(13) Outline a sensible way to overcome obesity.

(14) List and describe three types of diet pills.

15. Posture and body mechanics

Why is good posture important?

The human body operates best when its parts are in the correct alignment, and maintained that way during sitting and standing (**static posture**) and walking and lifting (**dynamic posture**). Good posture allows the internal organs to function at their best. A person with good posture gives the impression to other people of enthusiasm, confidence and initiative (see Figure 15.1).

Centre of gravity

The centre of gravity is a resultant point through which gravity can be said to act. In the body, the centre of gravity passes between the hips and forward of the sacrum.

The body is in a state of balance when its centre of gravity falls within its base of support. We maintain our balance by means of our:

- Eyes (visual cues)
- Middle ear (sense of equilibrium)
- Receptors in our joints and muscles.

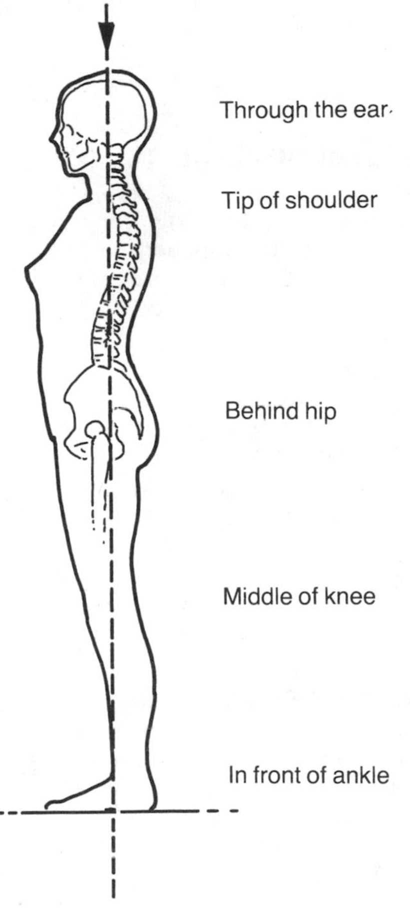

Figure 15.1 Correct vertical alignment: when the body is in good standing posture, the rotatory effect of the force of gravity is kept to a minimum.

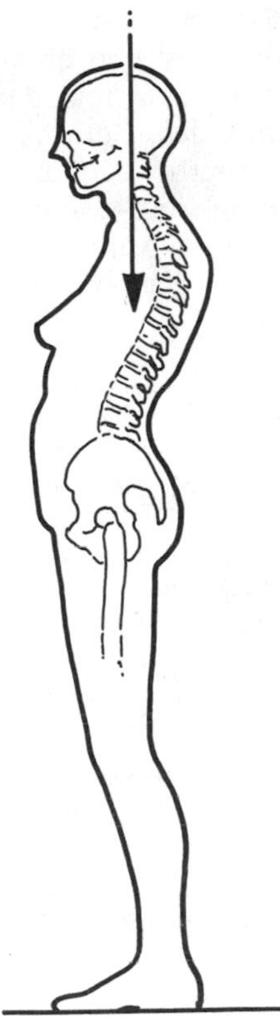

Figure 15.2 When the body is in a poor standing posture, the force of gravity has an exaggerated rotatory effect on the weight-bearing segments.

Upright, the human body is unstable, with a small base of support (feet) and a high centre of gravity. Since the body consists of many bones (levers), bound by muscles and ligaments at many joints, gravity constantly pulls on these joints, dragging them out of line.

If the body is well aligned, the bones take the pressure of resisting gravity, and the muscles maintain the correct alignment.

If the body is badly aligned, muscles and ligaments must bear the strain of resisting gravity's rotary effects. These effects can lead to muscle imbalance and strain. This causes postural deviations, as the spinal curves become increased or flattened (see Figure 15.2).

At this stage, it is worth revising 'The curves of the spine' (Figure 1.2).

Gravity-assisting and gravity-resisting muscles

Posture is controlled by two opposing groups of muscles: the gravity-resisting muscles and the gravity-assisting muscles. Both groups need exercise to develop strength and flexibility.

(1) Gravity resisting (anti-gravity) muscles

The following muscles primarily require strengthening work so that the body can maintain correct posture:

- Precervicals
- Trapezius and rhomboids
- Abdominals
- Gluteals
- Quadriceps
- Tibialis anterior.

(2) Gravity-assisting muscles

The following muscles primarily require stretching work so that the body's posture can stay aligned correctly:

- Postcervicals
- Pectorals and latissimus dorsi
- Erector spinnae
- Ilio psoas
- Hamstrings
- Gastrocnemius and soleus.

Causes of poor posture

In brief, the main causes of poor posture are:

- **Poor standing, sitting and walking posture.**
- **Poor nutrition:** for instance, rickets causes bow legs.
- **Physical defects:** for instance, a person with eyesight or hearing problems might tilt to one side or the other.
- **Lack of exercise:** the muscles atrophy and have a low resistance to gravity.
- **Fatigue or sickness,** which cause decreased muscle tone and strength.
- **Emotional factors:** for instance, shyness or worry can lead a person to hunch shoulders to avoid being looked at.
- **Clothing:** for instance, high-heeled shoes can cause lordosis, and tight shoes can cause claw and hammer toes.
- **Poorly designed furniture:** for instance, C-shaped chairs can cause C-shaped backs.
- **Specific sports:** for instance, breaststroke swimmers can develop round shoulders, and gymnasts can develop lordosis.

Postural deviations

Wolfe's Law says that structure is related to function — change the function and you change the structure. Postural deviations may be either functional or structural. Eventually functional deviations become structural.

- **Functional deviations**

Because functional deviations involve soft tissues, and respond to exercise, they can be corrected.

- **Structural deviations**

Structural deviations involve permanent changes in bone structure, changes that cannot be corrected without surgery or restraint by a cast or brace.

Most postural deviations are caused by incorrect spinal curvature and/or incorrect pelvic tilt. Some of the more common deviations are:

(1) Increased pelvic tilt

Increased pelvic tilt is associated with increased lumbar lordosis, lower back pain and waddle walk.

This condition may be caused by:

- Weak abdominals and gluteals
- Tight quadriceps and erector spinnae.

The main methods of correction are:

- Sit ups to increase abdominal strength
- Squat jumps to increase gluteal strength
- Quadricep stretch (see Figure 15.3)
- Toe touch to stretch erector spinnae

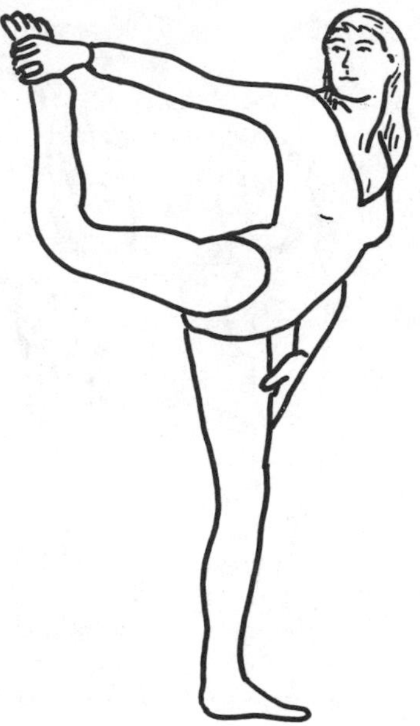

Figure 15.3 Quadricep stretch.

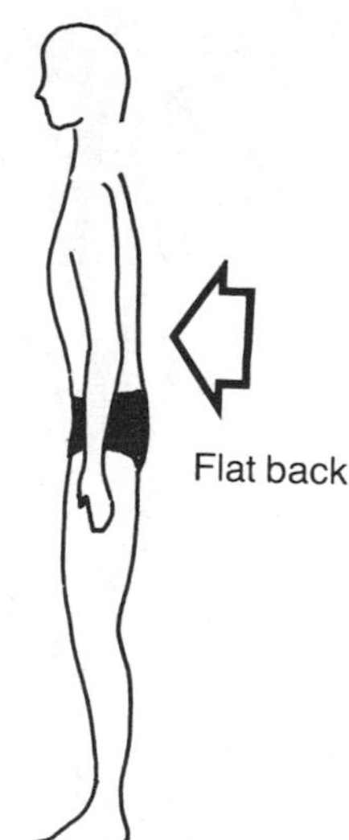

Figure 15.4 Flat back.

(2) Decreased pelvic tilt

Decreased pelvic tilt is associated with flat back, round shoulders and kyphosis.

This condition may be caused by:

- Tight hamstrings
- Weak quadriceps.

The main methods of correction are:

- Touch toes, which stretch the hamstrings
- Squats, which strengthen the quadriceps.

(3) Lordosis (abnormal lumbar lordosis)

Lordosis is an exaggerated hyperextension of the lumbar spine. (See Figure 15.5.)

The main causes of this condition are:

- Tight erector spinnae and ilio psoas
- Weak abdominals — therefore lordosis will usually be accompanied by a sagging stomach (ptosis).

The main methods of correction are:

- Toe touches, which stretch the erector spinnae
- Ilio psoas stretch (see Figure 15.6)
- Bent-knee sit ups, which increase abdominal strength.

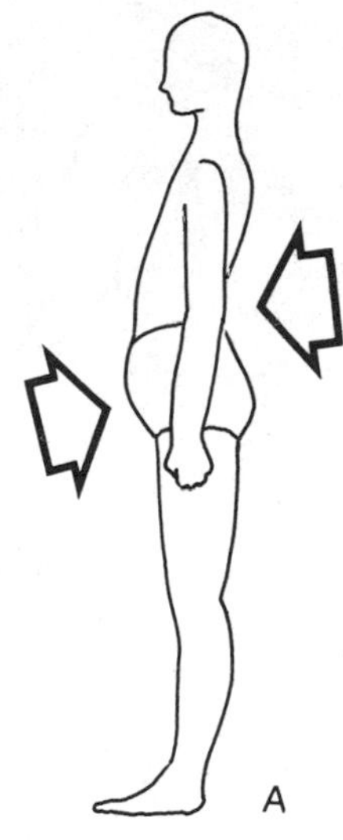

Figure 15.5 Ptosis and lordosis.

Figure 15.6 Ilio psoas stretch.

(4) Kyphosis (abnormal thoracic kyphosis)

Kyphosis is the abnormal hyperflexion of the thoracic spine. It is associated with round shoulders and a hump back. (See Figure 15.8.)

The main causes of this condition are:

- Weak trapezius and rhomboids
- Tight pectorals.

The main methods of correcting this condition are:

- Prone arm raises, which strengthen the trapezius and the rhomboids
- Passive chest lifts, which stretch the pectorals.

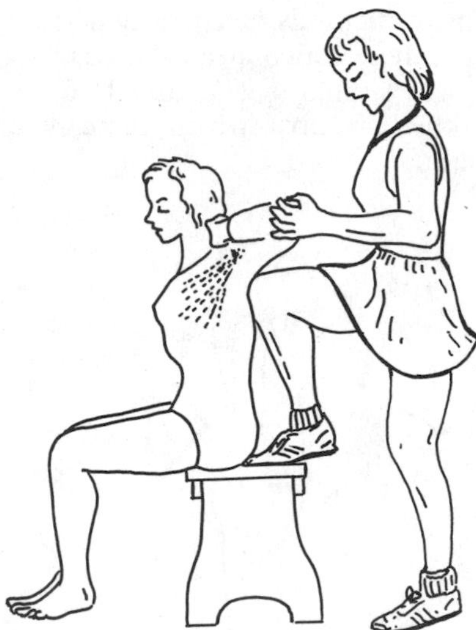

Figure 15.7 Passive chest lifting for stretching the pectoral muscles. (The dotted lines indicate the position of the pectoralis major. Pectoralis minor is beneath it.)

(5) Kypholordosis

Kypholordosis is the combined exaggeration of both spinal regions, usually with one compensating for the other. (See Figure 15.9.)

(6) Round shoulders

Round shoulders are associated with kyphosis and poke chin. (See Figure 15.10.)

The main causes of this condition are:

- Weak trapezius and rhomboids

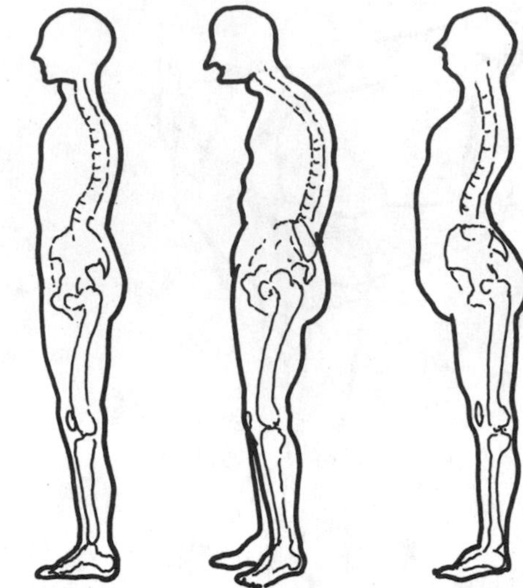

Figure 15.8 Normal posture, kyphosis and lumbar lordosis.

Figure 15.9 Fatigue slump with kypholordosis.

- Tight pectorals and latissimus dorsi.

The main methods of correction are:

- Stretching the pectorals (see Figure 15.7)
- Hanging from the arms to stretch the latissimus dorsi
- Prone arm raises, to strengthen the trapezius and rhomboid.

Figure 15.10 Forward (round) shoulders.

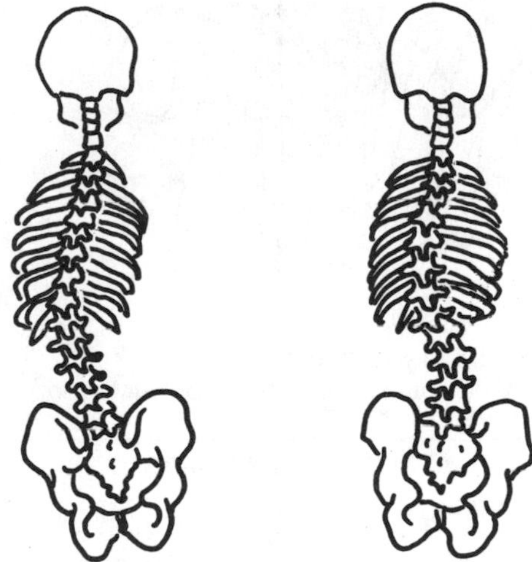

Figure 15.11 C-shaped and S-shaped scoliosis.

(7) Poke chin

Poke chin is a combination of exaggerated cervical lordosis and forward sloping neck. (See Figure 15.10.)

The main causes of this condition are:

- Weak precervicals
- Tight postcervicals.

The main method of correcting this condition is to strengthen the precervicals by tucking a tennis ball under the chin and holding it there.

(8) Scoliosis

Scoliosis is the rotolateral curvature of the spine in either a C shape (functional deviation) or an S shape (generally a structural deviation). (See Figure 15.11.)

The main causes of this condition are:

- Hipshod standing (standing with one leg straight and one leg bent)
- Carrying weight (such as a schoolbag) mainly on one side of the body.

The main method of correction is specialist treatment. However, hanging at full stretch is a good preventative exercise for this condition.

(9) Bowlegs and knock knees

- **Bowlegs (genu varum)**

Bowlegs occur where there is a gap between the knees when the inner malleoli touch. Specialist treatment is the main method of correction.

- **Knock knees (genu valgum)**

Knock knees occur where there is a space between the medial malleoli when the knees are brought together.

Figure 15.12 Bow legs.

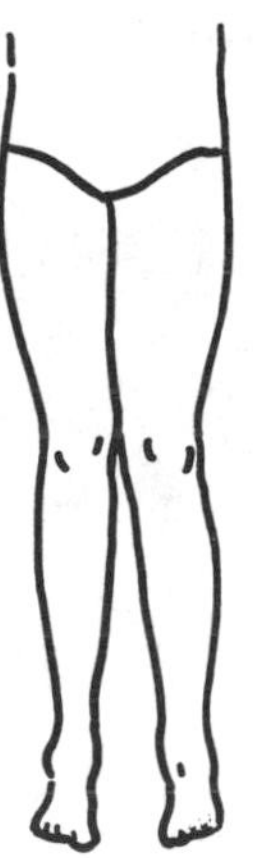

Figure 15.13 Knock knees.

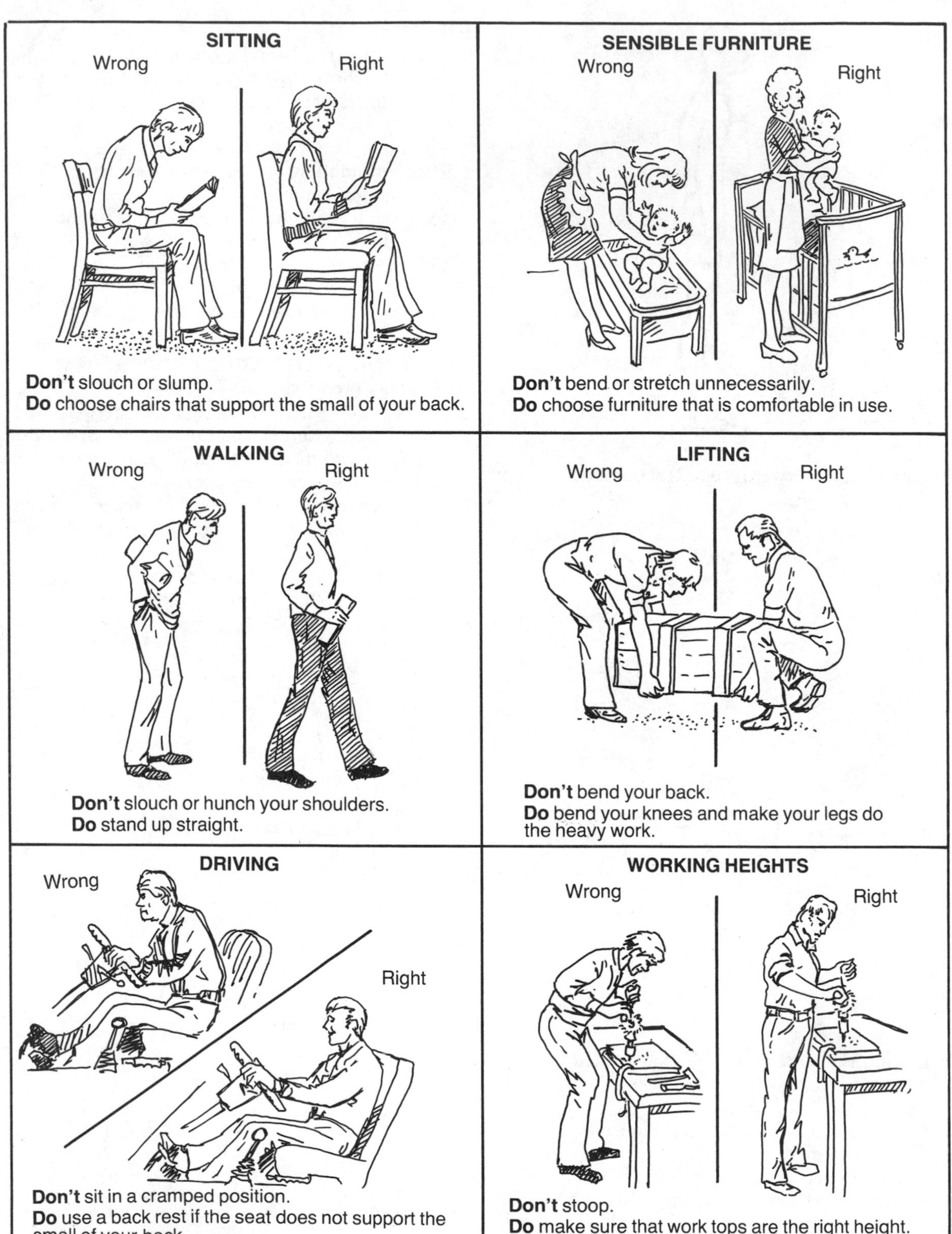

Figure 15.14 Domestic and occupational postural techniques.

Hip flexor stretch

Sit ups: for abdominal strength

Calf stretch

Spine mobilizer

Sitting hamstring stretcher

Gluteal, and post-cervical stretch

Pelvic tilt flattener:
for abdominal strength

Gluteal pinch:
for increased strength

Figure 15.15 General postural exercises.

(10) Flat feet

Flat feet occur when the arches of the feet are pressed flat against the floor when a person is walking.

To determine the height of the foot's arch under weight-bearing conditions, try the finger test of arch height:

(a) The student should stand in his or her normal position, with the body weight equally balanced.

(b) The teacher, with palm up, slides his or her second and third fingers under the arch to determine the height of the arch at the points of the cuneiform bones:
- If the fingers cannot slide under the arch, this is called complete flat foot.
- If the fingers slide as far as the head of the first metatarsal, this is slight flat foot.
- If the fingers slide completely under the arch, this is called high arch (pes cavus).

The main method of correcting flat feet is to pick up towels or hold coins between the toes.

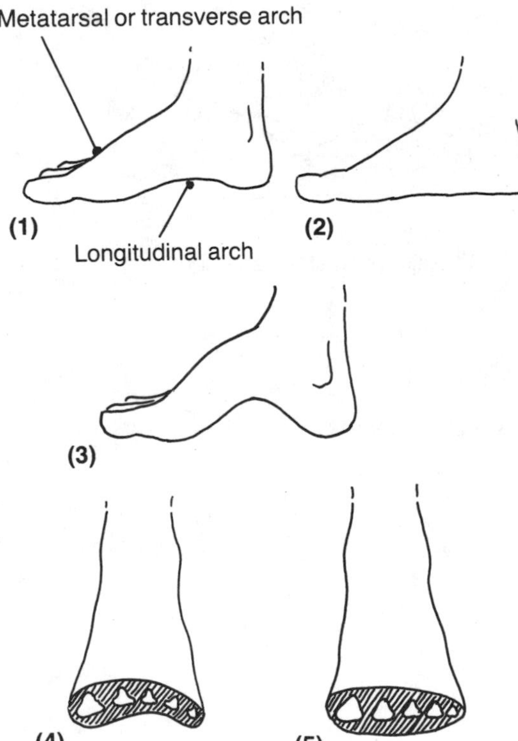

Figure 15.16 Arches of the foot:
(1) The normal foot
(2) Pes planus
(3) Pes cavus
(4) Normal metatarsal arch
(5) Flat metatarsal arch.

Correct posture for various tasks

(1) Lifting and carrying technique

Improper lifting habits can lead to serious back problems. There are several key rules for lifting:

- Never bend forward without bending your knees. Reaching down to pick up a load with your knees straight causes the pelvis to tilt forward amd the lower back to arch.
- Never lift anything above the level of the elbows. When you lift an object higher than the waist, the hips rotate forward to maintain balance, and the back arches. Depending on the load being lifted, a painful strain can result.
- Always keep your back flat and straight.
- Keep your eyes forward when lifting.
- Keep objects as close to your centre of gravity as possible.
- Extend your legs to lift.

(2) Sleeping techniques

(See Figure 15.18.) Incorrect sleeping positions can impose a great deal of strain on the back:

- Sleeping face down will cause the back to strain.
- Sleeping on your back with the legs straight also causes arching.

The correct posture for sleeping is on your side, with your hips and knees bent and your head supported by a pillow.

Another possibility, though not very practical, is lying on your back with your knees flexed.

(3) Sitting techniques

A good basic rule for sitting is always to have your knees higher than your hips. When the knees are lower than the hips, the back tends to overarch. When you drive a car, position the seat so that your knees are above your hips.

Figure 15.17 Correct postural procedure for standing work.

(4) Standing techniques

Standing is very tiring for the back. As fatigue sets in, the hips begin to sag forward. If you are fat in the abdominal region, you will suffer further arching. High-heeled shoes also lead to the over-arching of the lower back. You can solve this postural problem by lifting either foot. Su[illegible] a measure takes the arch out of the back. The [illegible]ic rule is that when you stand in one position [illegible] a long time, you should flex one of your hips by supporting one foot higher than the other. As long as one hip is flexed, the lower back does not tend to strain forward.

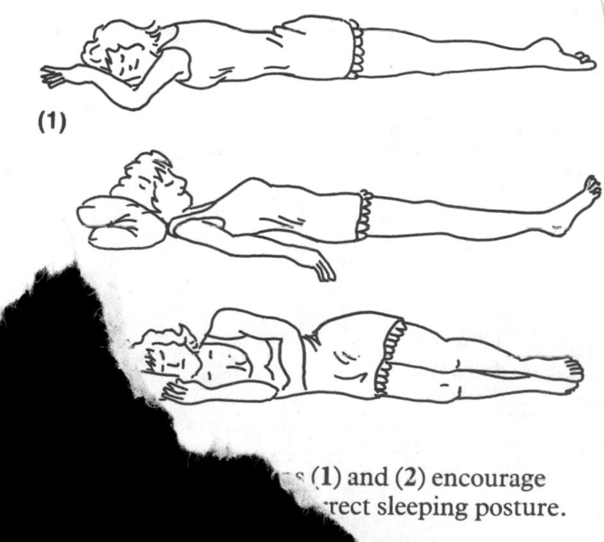

[illegible]s (1) and (2) encourage [illegible]rrect sleeping posture.

Laboratory work 26: New York Posture Rating Test

There are thirteen items in the test. Each test item is scored on a 5–3–1 basis. In the appropriate block, record the score for each item. The score is based on the criteria and drawings located on the form.

The maximum score under this procedure is 65. A single item score of 1 or a composite score of 39 or below would show that the person being tested had posture problems.

Test

(1) Record the name of the student you are testing.

(2) Use a constructed posture grid to evaluate another student (see Figure 15.19).

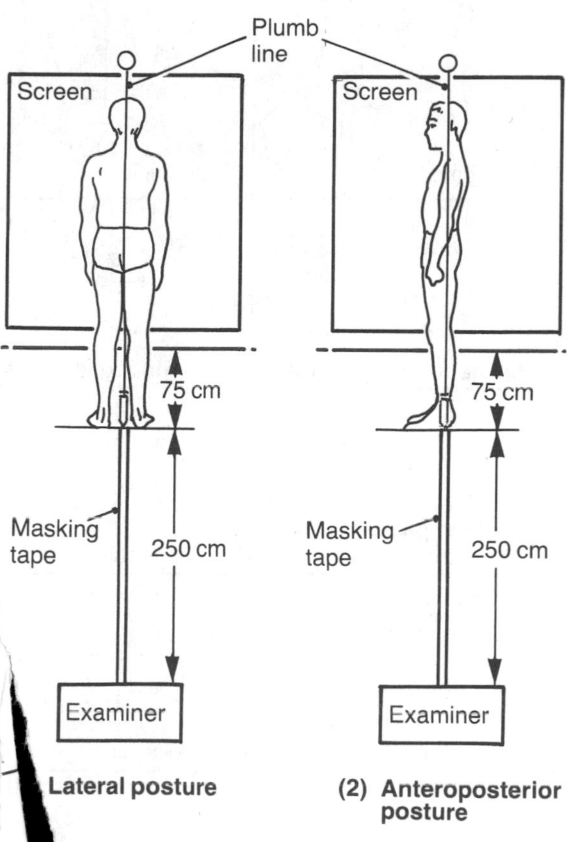

[illegible] 15.19 Posture rating test.

Rater's initials

Date of test

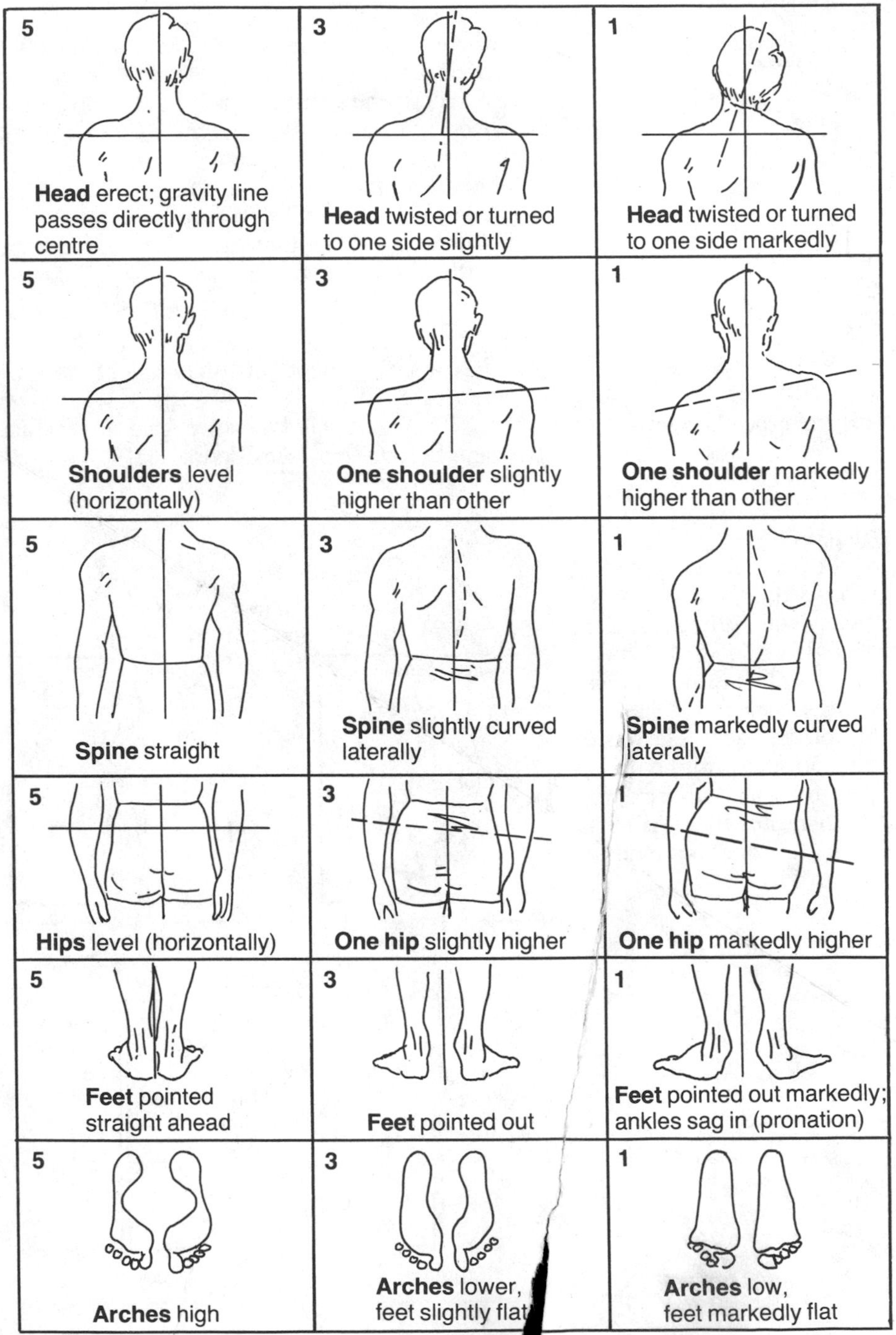

5 **Head** erect; gravity line passes directly through centre	3 **Head** twisted or turned to one side slightly	1 **Head** twisted or turned to one side markedly
5 **Shoulders** level (horizontally)	3 **One shoulder** slightly higher than other	1 **One shoulder** markedly higher than other
5 **Spine** straight	3 **Spine** slightly curved laterally	1 **Spine** markedly curved laterally
5 **Hips** level (horizontally)	3 **One hip** slightly higher	1 **One hip** markedly higher
5 **Feet** pointed straight ahead	3 **Feet** pointed out	1 **Feet** pointed out markedly; ankles sag in (pronation)
5 **Arches** high	3 **Arches** lower, feet slightly flat	1 **Arches** low, feet markedly flat

Total page 1

Figure 15.20 **Posture rating chart.**

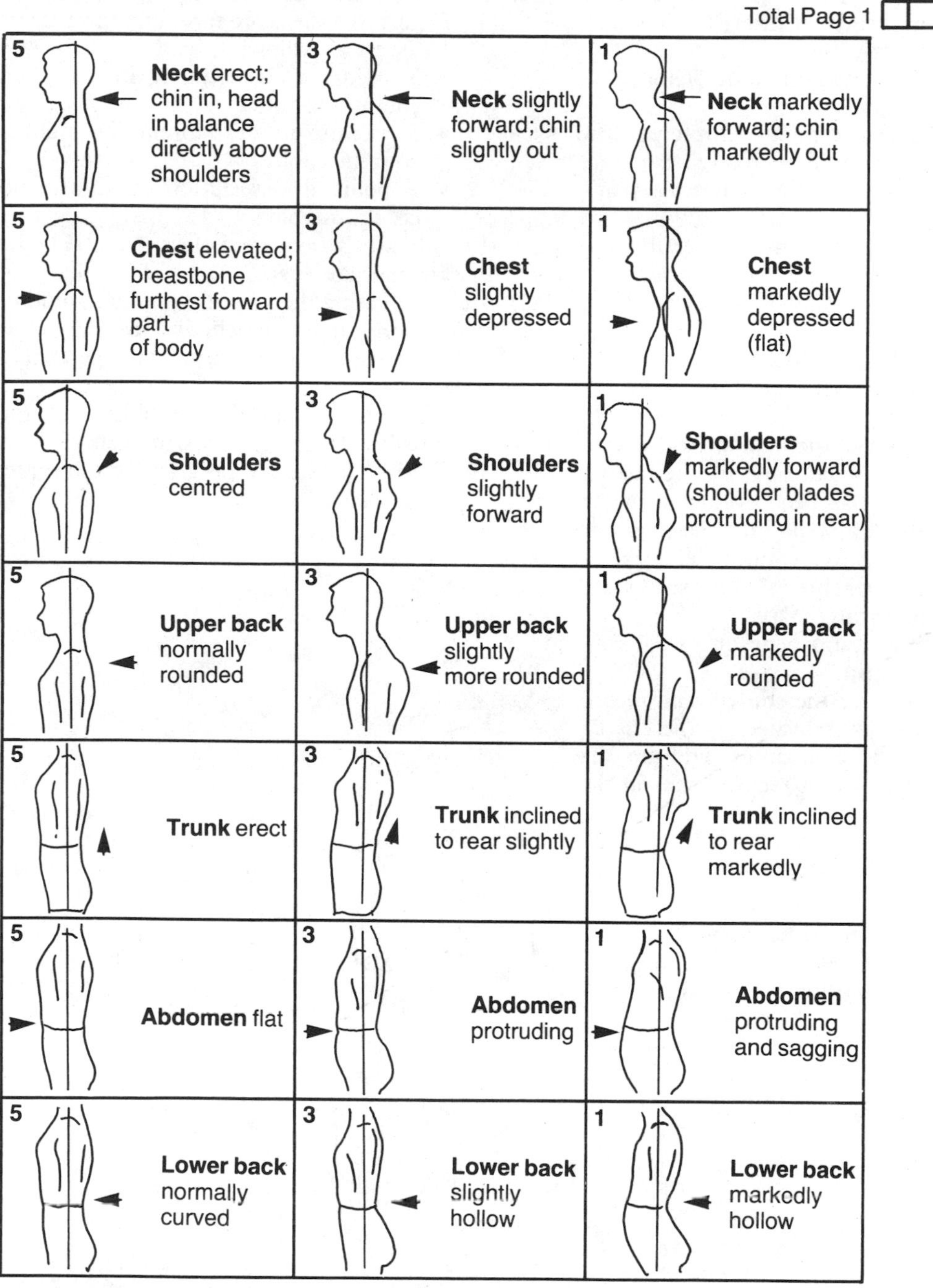

Total Page 1 ☐☐

5	3	1
Neck erect; chin in, head in balance directly above shoulders	**Neck** slightly forward; chin slightly out	**Neck** markedly forward; chin markedly out
Chest elevated; breastbone furthest forward part of body	**Chest** slightly depressed	**Chest** markedly depressed (flat)
Shoulders centred	**Shoulders** slightly forward	**Shoulders** markedly forward (shoulder blades protruding in rear)
Upper back normally rounded	**Upper back** slightly more rounded	**Upper back** markedly rounded
Trunk erect	**Trunk** inclined to rear slightly	**Trunk** inclined to rear markedly
Abdomen flat	**Abdomen** protruding	**Abdomen** protruding and sagging
Lower back normally curved	**Lower back** slightly hollow	**Lower back** markedly hollow

To obtain the total raw score:

(1) Determine the score for each of the 13 items as follows:
- 5 points if description in left-hand column applies
- 3 points if description in middle column applies
- 1 point if description in right-hand column applies

(2) Add all 13 scores, and place total in the appropriate space.

Total raw score ☐☐

(3) Obtain a metal or plastic tray with a foam rubber or other absorbent insert filled with a foot disinfectant solution.
(4) Have the student stand in front of the constructed posture grid.
(5) As evaluator, note five points in reference to the plumb line or midline reference point. The plumb line or midline reference point should:
  (a) Coincide with the midline of the body
  (b) Pass behind the centre of the head
  (c) Pass behind the spinous processes of the vertebrae
  (d) Bisect the gluteal folds
  (e) Be equidistant between the lower extremities.
(6) As evaluator, observe the student and record the proper scores as indicated by the chart.
(7) When the student has been evaluated in the rear view, she or he steps into the metal or plastic tray, then on to a white sheet of paper to check for foot problems. The scores are recorded on the rating chart.
(8) The student then stands side on to the constructed posture grid.
(9) As evaluator, observe the student and record the proper scores as indicated by the chart.
(10) After finishing the evaluation, add up the scores on each item and record them in the proper block.
(11) To obtain the total raw score:
  (a) Determine the score for each of the above 13 items as follows:
    - 5 points if description in left-hand column applies
    - 3 points if description in middle column applies
    - 1 point if description in right-hand column applies
  (b) Add all 13 scores and place the total in the appropriate space.
(12) After evaluating the score for another student, make sure that somebody in the class evaluates your postural score and percentile rank:
  (a) List your postural deviations and the possible cause or causes of each.
  (b) Devise an exercise programme to correct these deviations.

Achievement level	Percentile rank	Posture score
10	99	—
9	98	65
8	93	63
7	84	61
6	69	59
5	50	55–57
4	31	49–53
3	16	45–47
2	7	39–43
1	2	35–37
0	1	0–33

Figure 15.21

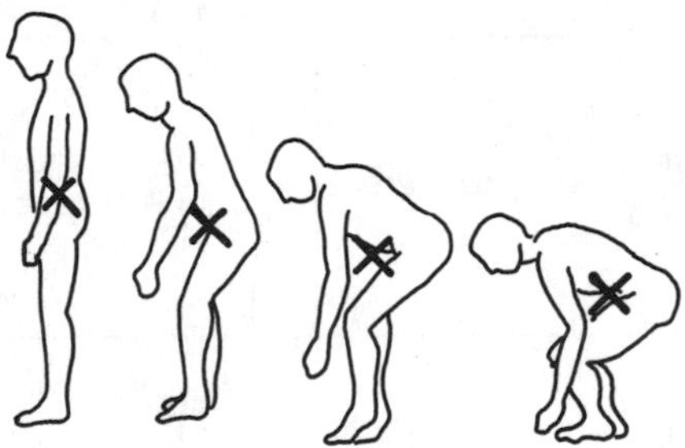

(1) Instinctive way of lifting

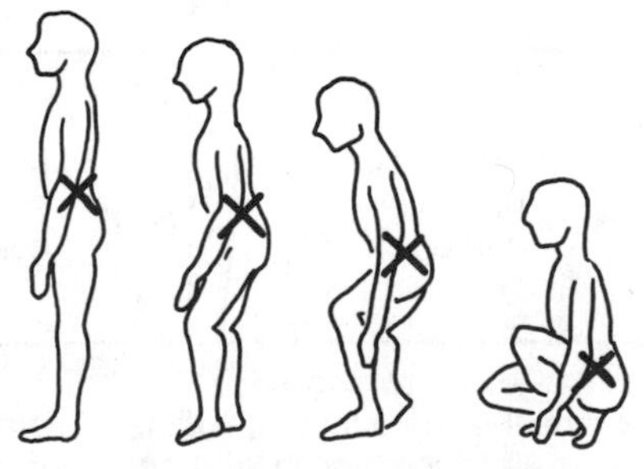

(2) Recommended way of lifting

Figure 15.22 Lifting techniques. The 'x' marks the position of the centre of gravity.

Worksheet 14: Posture

(1) Design a corrective exercise programme for each of the following conditions:
- **(a)** Lordosis
- **(b)** Kyphosis
- **(c)** Flat back
- **(d)** Scoliosis.

Each programme should be about five minutes long and should consist of at least three exercises.

(2) From the information in your background reading, describe how poor posture can affect performance in the athletic event of your choice.

(3) For Figure 15.22, analyse movements **(1)** and **(2)** in terms of:
- Safety factors
- Energy expenditure.

Discuss the findings of your analysis.

(4) Describe some situations common in the home or at school which lead to the development of faulty posture.

Part Two:
Applied aspects of exercise and activity

16. Fitness components and assessment

Fitness components

These components of fitness have been discussed already in Chapter 5. As can be seen from the above diagram, the concept of 'fitness' can mean many different capacities and abilities, and every sport requires a different set of specific abilities. The athlete and the coach need to become familiar with each fitness component, and the variety of tests that can be used to assess one's capacity in each component. Before deciding which components to test and which tests to use, you need to make a rigorous analysis of the sport you are interested in. Also you need to examine such factors as facilities, equipment, time and money.

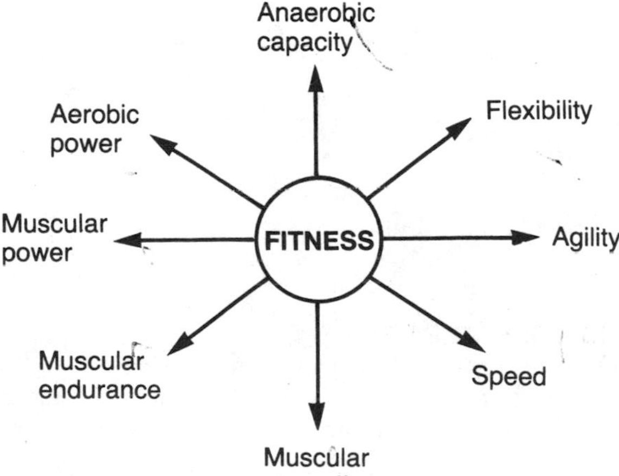

Figure 16.1 Fitness components.

Methods of fitness assessment

(1) Aerobic power

For more detail on tests for aerobic power, see chapter 12, which covers:

- The Astrand-Rhyming Bicycle Ergometer Test
- The Harvard Step Test
- The Cooper Twelve-Minute Run Test.

(2) Muscular endurance

They include:

- Maximum push ups in one minute
- Maximum bench jumps (50 cm for males; 45 cm for females) in one minute
- Maximum sit ups in one minute (see Figure 16.3 and box).

(3) Anaerobic power

(a) **Alactacid:**

- The Margaria-Kalamen Stair Climb Test
- The Vertical jump (see Figure 16.4 and box).

(b) **Lactacid:**

The Wingate Sixty-Second Bicycle Ergometer Test.

(c) **Speed:**

The 40-metre sprint.

(4) Muscular strength

(a) **Isotonic:**
- Pull ups
- Modified pull ups (for both, see Figure 16.7)
- Dips (see Figure 16.9).

(b) **Isometric:**
- Push/pull dynamometer
- Handgrip dynamometer (see Figure 16.14).

(5) Agility

Tests for agility include:
- The Illinois Agility Run (see Chapter 7).
- The Vic. Fit Agility Test
- Modified Zelenka Tests
- Squat thrusts (see Figure 16.8 and box).

(6) Flexibility

- **Sit and reach:** trunk flexion (see Chapter 7 and Figures 7.6 and 16.2).
- **Shoulder hyperextension**
- **Trunk hyperextension** (see Figure 16.5 and box below).

(7) Body composition

(a) Somatotyping
(b) Percentage body fat (see Chapter 14).

(8) Skill

Sports-specific tests, such as the Zelenka Skill Circuit, are needed to test particular skills.

	Women	**Men**
Normal range	101 mm to +250 mm	−152 mm to +202 mm
Average (mean)	+50 mm	+25 mm
Desired range	+50 mm to +152 mm	+25 mm to +127 mm

Figure 16.2

Sit ups (Bent knee)

One minute for women; two minutes for men.

Purpose

To determine the strength and endurance of the abdominal muscles.

Explanation

(1) Assume a supine position with hands interlocked behind your neck. Draw back your feet toward the buttocks until they are flat on the floor (knees bent). The angle of your legs to your thighs should be about 90°.
(2) A partner should kneel on one knee, placing it between your feet while grasping both your ankles.
(3) A full sit up is counted when you have curled your back and raised your trunk until your *lower back* is at least perpendicular to the floor, and then returned to the starting position.
(4) Repeat the procedure as many times as possible within the time limit. The holder counts out loud, emphasizing every fifth sit up. This assists the performer and also lessens the risk of losing count. The score is the number of sit ups completed in the selected time period. Resting is permitted, but only on your back with hands in the proper position.

Figure 16.3 Sit up.

Improper procedure

(1) Not coming all the way up to the vertical position. (Do not let your elbows touch your knees — your elbows should pass your knees.)
(2) Releasing your hands from behid your neck. (Do not count these.)

Vertical jump

Purpose

To test the power of the extensor muscles of the hips, knees and ankles.

Explanation

(1) Face the jumping board and stand slightly in front of it, with your feet flat on the floor and both arms fully extended overhead. Note the point where the extended tips of the middle fingers touch the board.
(2) Turn, so that a side of your body is to the jump board. Without moving your feet (you are not allowed to step into the jump), take a deep squat and jump, touching the board as high as possible with the fingers nearest the board.
(3) After a brief rest, try a second jump.
(4) Record the greatest distance obtained between your standing reach and your jumping reach, to the nearest 10 millimetres.

Figure 16.4 Vertical jump.

Improper procedures

(1) Not getting a true standing reach.
(2) Moving the feet in preparation to jump.

Trunk hyperextension

Purpose

To measure the range of motion (flexibility) of the back.

Explanation

(1) Lie in a prone position (face down) on the floor. Have a partner kneel and straddle your legs, holding your buttocks and legs down.
(2) With your hands grasped behind your back, raise your upper trunk (chest and head) off the floor and hold for a count of three.
(3) Measure the distance from your chin to the floor.

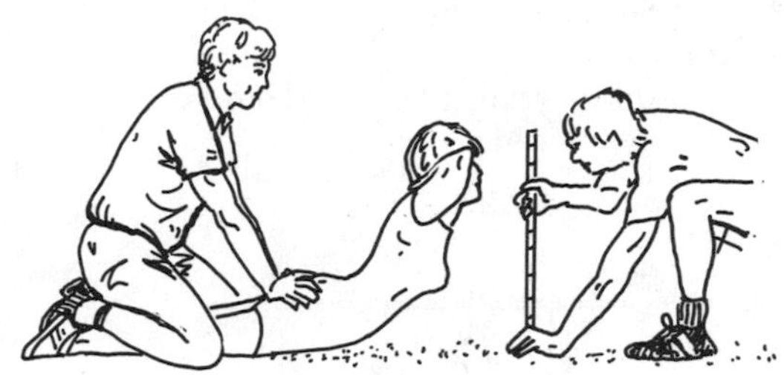

Figure 16.5 Trunk extension.

Improper procedures

(1) Not holding the measuring device in a perpendicular position while measuring.
(2) Raising the hips off the floor.
(3) Not holding the extended position for a count of three.

	Women	**Men**
Normal range	305 mm to 762 mm	101 mm to 686 mm
Average (mean)	533 mm	381 mm
Desired range	381 mm to 635 mm	381 mm to 508 mm

Figure 16.6 Norms for trunk extension.

Pull up

Purpose
To test the strength of the flexors of the arms, shoulder girdle and upper back muscles. (Although no values for women are presented in the tables — see later in this chapter — they can safely perform this exercise.)

Explanation
(1) Jump, grasp the overhead bar (palms facing away) and let your legs hang with arms fully extended.
(2) Pull up until your chin clears the top of the bar.
(3) Lower yourself to a position of *arms fully extended*.
(4) Repeat this procedure until you can no longer continue.
(5) In scoring, record only the complete chins.

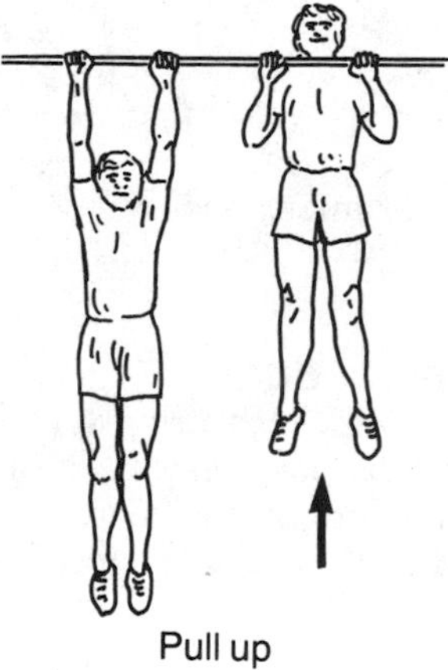

Figure 16.7 Modified pull up.

Improper procedures
(1) Legs swinging or kicking.
(2) Failure to return to a 'dead hang' (elbows straight; this is a *must* for the exercise to be valid).
(3) Failure of the chin to rise above the bar.

Modified pull up

This test can be used for people who are unable to do a complete pull up on an overhead bar. Women are ordinarily tested this way; however, this test can be used for men who are very weak in the upper body or who are very obese.

Purpose
To test the strength and muscular endurance of the flexors of the arms, shoulder girdle and upper back muscles.

Explanation
(1) An adjustable horizontal bar should be set at about the height of the apex of your sternum.
(2) Grasp the bar, palms outward. Slide your feet under the bar until your body and extended

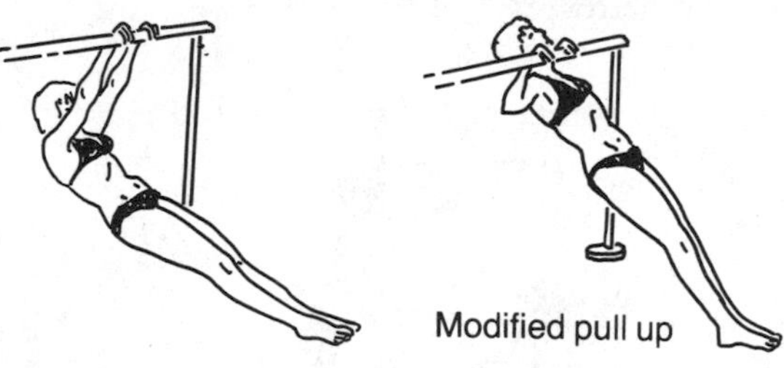

arms form a right angle. Your body should be held in a firm straight position, with your weight on the rear of your feet.
(3) Your partner should kneel on one knee, placing it between your feet while supporting your ankles.
(4) Begin from this extended body and arm position and pull your chest to the bar.
(5) Repeat as many times as possible, keeping your body straight.
(6) In scoring, record only properly performed pull ups.

Improper procedures
(1) Body sags.
(2) Hips rise (hip motion).
(3) Failure to complete pull up.

Squat thrusts

Purpose
To determine your ability to move large muscle groups rapidly and to sustain this total body movement for a specific period of time.

Explanation
(1) Stand erect with feet together and hands at your sides. This is a four count exercise.
(2) Assume a position with hands on the floor in front of your feet, with knees bent.
(3) Thrust your legs back to an extended position (a front support position).
(4) Quickly bring your legs back to the squat position.
(5) Straighten to a standing position. This gives one complete repetition.
(6) Your score is determined by the number of complete and partial repetitions you can perform in 30 seconds. For example, if you complete 15 repetitions and are in the squat position before standing at the end of 30 seconds, you would score 15–3.

Figure 16.8 Squat thrusts.

Improper procedures
(1) Not coming to the squat position before extending out to the front support position.
(2) Not returning to the squat position before standing.
(3) Not standing erect at the end of each repetition.

Dips

Purpose
To test the strength of the extensors of the arms, shoulder girdle and upper back muscles.

Explanation
(1) Start from an arm rest position at the end of parallel bars, with arms fully extended.
(2) From this position, lower your body to a right-angle arm-bend position.
(3) Push (extend arms) to the starting position.
(4) Record only the complete dips when scoring.

Figure 16.9 Dips.

Improper procedure
(1) Swinging or kicking up into a dip.
(2) Partial dips. (You must lower yourself all the way down so that your upper arm is parallel to the horizontal.)

Tables

	Dominant grip (kg.)	One-minute sit ups (no.)	Modified pull ups (no.)
Super	45.0 42.5 40.0	45 41 38	41 37 34
Excellent	39.0 37.5 36.5	37 35 33	32 30 29
Good	35.0 34.0 32.5	31 29 28	27 25 23
Average	31.5 30.0 29.0	26 24 23	22 20 18
Fair	27.5 26.5 25.0	21 19 17	16 15 13
Poor	24.0 22.5 21.5	15 14 12	11 9 8
Very poor	20.0 17.5 15.0	10 6 3	6 3 0

Figure 16.10 Muscular strength and endurance (women).

	Dominant grip (kg.)	Two-minute sit ups (no.)	Pull ups (no.)	Dips (no.)
Super	73.0 69.5 65.5	91 85 79	19 17 15	28 25 23
Excellent	64.0 62.0 60.0	76 73 69	14 13 12	22 20 19
Good	58.5 56.5 55.0	67 65 62	11 10 9	18 17 15
Average	53.0 51.0 48.5	59 56 52	8 7 6	14 13 11
Fair	48.0 45.5 44.0	50 47 44	5 4 3	9 8 7
Poor	42.0 40.0 38.0	41 38 35	2 1 0	6 4 3
Very poor	36.5 33.0 29.0	32 26 21	0 0 0	2 0 0

Figure 16.11 Muscular strength and endurance (men).

	Vertical jump (cm)	Agility run (sec.)	Squat thrusts (no. in 30 sec.)
Super	69.9 67.3 64.8	15.3 15.7 16.1	23 22 21
Excellent	63.5 62.2 61.0	16.3 16.5 16.7	$20\frac{1}{2}$ 20 $19\frac{1}{2}$
Good	59.7 58.4 57.2	16.9 17.1 17.3	19 $18\frac{1}{2}$ 18
Average	55.9 54.6 53.3	17.5 17.7 17.9	$17\frac{1}{2}$ 17 $16\frac{1}{2}$
Fair	52.1 50.8 49.5	18.1 18.3 18.5	16 $15\frac{1}{2}$ 15
Poor	48.3 47.0 45.7	18.7 18.9 19.1	$14\frac{1}{2}$ 14 $13\frac{1}{2}$
Very poor	44.5 41.9 39.4	19.3 19.7 20.1	13 12 11

Figure 16.12 Power and agility (men).

	Vertical jump (cm)	Agility run (sec.)	Squat thrusts (no. in 30 sec.)
Super	51.0 47.0 44.5	15.9 16.8 17.7	19 18 17
Excellent	43.2 42.0 41.0	18.1 18.6 19.0	16½ 16 15½
Good	38.1 36.8 35.6	19.5 19.9 20.4	15 14½ 14
Average	34.3 33.0 31.8	20.8 21.3 21.7	13½ 13 12½
Fair	30.5 29.2 28.0	22.2 22.6 23.1	12 11½ 11
Poor	26.7 25.4 22.9	23.5 24.0 24.4	10½ 10 9½
Very poor	21.6 19.1 16.5	24.9 25.8 26.7	9 8 7

Figure 16.13 Power and agility (women).

Grip strength (dominant hand)

Purpose
To test the strength of muscles of the fingers, hand and forearm.

Explanation
(1) Using a grip dynamometer, adjust it so that it fits your dominant hand comfortably.
(2) Squeeze the dynamometer vigorously. A downward thrust is allowed.
(3) Repeat the test, and record your best score, as read from the dial, in kilograms.

Figure 16.14 Grip strength.

Improper procedure
Do not allow your hand, arm or elbow to touch the body or any object while performing the test.

Worksheet 15: Fitness components and assessment

(1) To test the power of the lactacid system, use a:
  (a) Standing broad jump
  (b) 600-metre running time trial
  (c) A 12-minute run
  (d) None of the above.
(2) The Margania Kalaman step test is a method of testing:
  (a) Aerobic capacity
  (b) Anaerobic capacity: ATP/PC
  (c) Anaerobic capacity: lactic acid
  (d) Agility.
(3) Which of the following tests would be considered useful for the assessment of endurance fitness (aerobic power)?:
  (a) Margaria stair climb test
  (b) A 50-metre dash
  (c) Astrand bicycle ergometer test
  (d) Vertical jump test.
(4) In order to assess a basketball player's speed around the court, which one of the following tests would provide the most relevant information?
  (a) A vertical jump
  (b) A timed 100-metre dash
  (c) The Margaria stair test
  (d) A timed agility run, where the player is required to touch the four corners of the court and then jump to touch the ring.
(5) Which of the following is not correct? Skinfold measures are taken:
  (a) On either side of the body
  (b) Between the thumb and forefinger
  (c) One centimetre below the fingers holding it
  (d) Generally in the vertical plane.
(6) The average male has:
  (a) A higher percentage of body fat than the average female
  (b) The same percentage of body fat as the average female
  (c) A lower percentage of body fat than the average female
  (d) Half as much body fat as the average female.
(7) (a) List the components of fitness.
  (b) For each component, give one sport that has a high requirement for that fitness component.

Laboratory work 27: Fitness testing

(**1**) Choose a fitness test for each of the following fitness components:
  (**a**) Muscular strength
  (**b**) Muscular endurance
  (**c**) Anaerobic capacity
  (**d**) Aerobic capacity
  (**e**) Agility
  (**f**) Flexibility.

(**2**) Perform each test. From your results compile a personal fitness profile.

17. Games analysis methodology

Player	Disposals			
	Under pressure		**Not under pressure**	
	To Snakes	**To Opposition**	**To Snakes**	**To Opposition**
Long	IIIII (5)	III (3)	IIII (4)	I (1)
Spitten	I (1)	IIIIIIII (8)		II (2)
Kobra	IIII (4)	IIIII (5)	IIIIII (6)	III (3)
Whith	IIIIIIIIII (10)	IIII (4)	IIII (4)	I (1)
Beede	IIII (4)	IIII (4)	IIIIII (6)	III (3)
Iyes	II (2)	III (3)	IIII (4)	I (1)
Ande	IIIIII (6)	IIIII (5)	IIIIIIII (8)	III (3)
Falk	II (2)	III (3)	IIIII (5)	II (2)
Tung	IIIIIII (7)	III (3)	IIIIII (6)	II (2)

Figure 17.1 Effectiveness of disposal skills related to game conditions.

(1) **Soccer**

Player	**Disposal skill**				
	Inside foot	**Outside foot**	**Heel**	**Laces**	**Head**

(2) **Football**

Player	**Kicks**	**Handball given**	**Handball received**	**Marks**	**Free kicks**	**Goals**

(3) **Basketball**

Player	**Chest**	**Overhead**	**Bounce**	**Overarm**	**Dribble**	**Layup**	**Jump**

Figure 17.2 Basic game statistics.

The purpose of games analysis is to supply a coach or player with the information that will assist in improving individual or team performance. There are three possible methods of analysis:

- Observation
- Observation and statistical recording
- Videotaping and statistical recording. Videotaping allows the most accurate results, because it allows the viewer to 'freeze' the play and reobserve it.

Skill analysis

Skill analysis is used to determine how often and how effectively a player used a particular skill. For an example, see Figure 17.1.

These statistics show that Spitten had 11 disposals. However, 10 of these went to the opposition, while Whith had 19 disposals and only five went to the opposition. This would show the coach the type of training practice that Spitten needs to improve his performance — that is, disposal drills while under pressure.

To gain this information, the coach or player must list the basic possession and disposal skills important to the particular sport, and then record both individual and team statistics (see Figure 17.2).

Fitness analysis

Fitness analysis has two uses:

- To calculate the work requirement of a sport by analysing the performance of top players
- To calculate the work output of you or your team and compare this information with what is required.

To record fitness information, a coach must list the locomotion and work statistics that are important to the sport, and record the results for the team and for individuals. Information recorded should include:

(1) Activity or movement patterns

Such figures should give the distance covered and intensity of effort. (Statistics from heart-rate telemetry provide the most accurate information.) These statistics give the coach a clear picture of the total energy demands and work output of a player or team and, in particular, show the energy systems that require development during training (see Figures 17.4 and 17.5).

(2) The work-to-rest ratio

The coach must find out the percentages of work and rest demanded during a game. He uses this information when planning training efforts and the recovery between successive efforts — for instance, during interval training sessions.

(3) Additional involvements

This information suggests further fitness components that require development (see Figure 17.3).

For example, the second rover, whose statistics are given in Figure 17.3, sustains 85 body contacts

Player and position	Tackles	Bumps: Hit opponent	Bumps: Hit ground	Jumps	Chases
Centre half back	3	35	11	25	1
Full forward	3	44	17	21	7
Rover	14	52	15	10	8
Wing	3	9	7	16	7
Ruck	5	54	9	48	13
Rover	17	44	24	11	23

Statistics compiled during WANFL final series, 1977.

Figure 17.3 Additional involvements in game skills.

from either tackles or bumps. This suggests that the player will find it difficult to avoid injury and remain an effective rover unless, during training, he includes strength training combined with suitable flexibility work.

Also in Figure 17.3, the ruckman makes 48 jumps per game, and therefore needs to develop his leg and hip power and endurance if he wants to outjump his opponent.

Therefore fitness analysis gives the coach the information needed to establish:

- Fitness goals
- Training methods
- Suitable practice drills.

The accumulation of the information recorded on the activity pattern record sheets gives information such as:

First half

Intensity	10 metres	20 m	30 m	40 m	50 m
Sprint	IIIIIII ⑦	IIIIIIIIII ⑩	IIIII ⑤		III ③
Cruise		III ③	IIIIIIIII III ⑫		IIIIIII ⑦
Jog	IIIII ⑤	I ①	IIIIII ⑥	III ③	IIIIII ⑥
Walk	IIIIIIIII III ⑫	I ①			

Figure 17.4 A sample of a tally sheet for the compilation of data on the field movements of players.

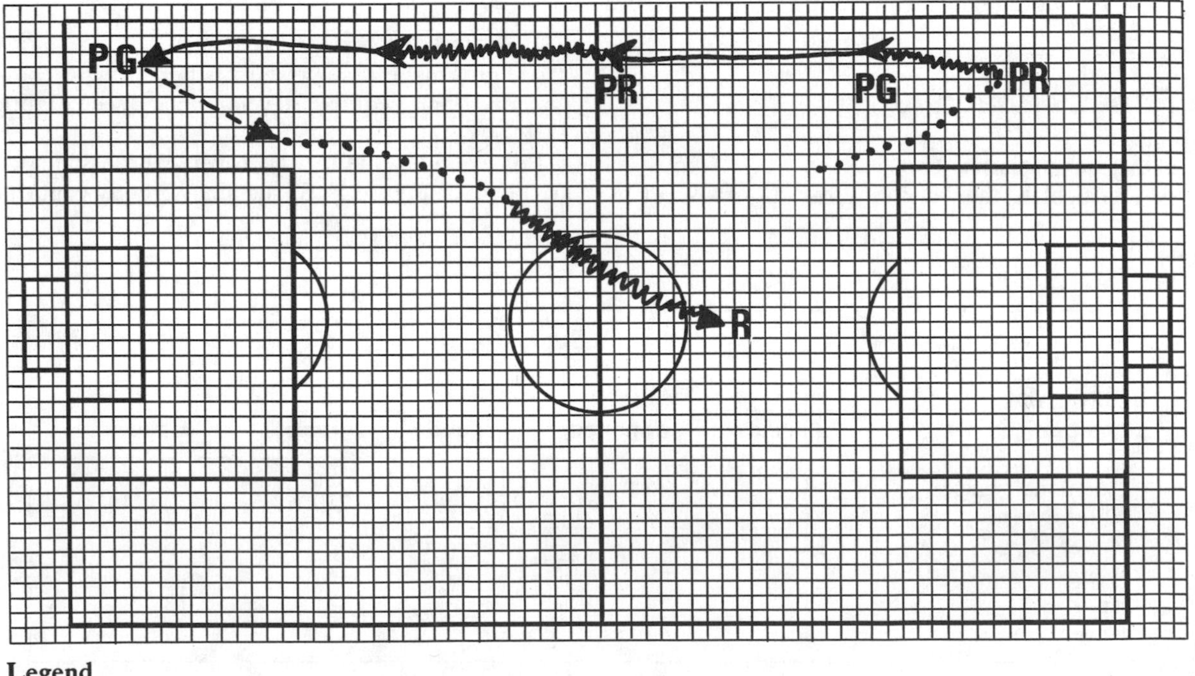

Legend

······ Jog ⁓⁓> Cruise. ⟶ Sprint --------- Walk. R Rest.
PR Pass received PG Pass given

Figure 17.5 Charting player movement patterns and game involvement.

Team analysis

Team analysis is the gathering of information about team tactical play and style (for instance, the effectiveness of different defensive or offensive patterns).

A volleyball coach or player might want to know whether to use short-centre spikes or high-corner spikes, or the position of the back-court setter when the team loses the majority of points. The coach might then change the spike pattern of the team or be able to detect defensive weaknesses when players rotate into particular positions.

Figure 17.6 shows the possession patterns of two teams, with the team controlling the ball losing. The coach should use this information to change his offensive pattern.

Figure 17.7 shows clearly that a team is more likely to maintain possession if it passes with the inside of the foot. Therefore inside foot passing must be an integral part of team play and drilled in training sessions.

Laboratory work 28: Analysis of the requirements of a sport

(1) Choose a sport that is both interesting and familiar to the group. Obtain a video of a competitive game in this sport.
(2) Analyse the skill, fitness and team requirements of this sport by allotting recording tasks to all class members. For example, the following tasks require one or more recorders:
 (a) Disposal skills
 (b) Possession skills
 (c) Movement patterns
 (d) W:R (work-to-rest ratio)
 (e) Additional involvements
 (f) Offensive plays
 (g) Defensive plays.
(3) Pool your results and discuss the implications of the statistics you have compiled.

	Kicks	Marks	Handball	Total possessions	Total points	Scoring shots
Melbourne	205	64	112	381	70	29
Collingwood	200	40	75	315	85	28

Figure 17.6 Number of team possessions.

Disposal methods	Number of disposals	Number of effective disposals	Number of ineffective disposals
Inside of foot	410	380	30
Laces	154	94	60
Outside of foot	65	50	15
Heel	15	8	7
Head	217	162	55

Figure 17.7 Effectiveness of disposal.

Worksheet 16: Games analysis

(1) The main value of games analysis is to:
- (a) Set standards of achievement
- (b) Find out what is involved in the game
- (c) Motivate players to try harder
- (d) Find out which players are not trying their hardest.

(2) Functional training should be designed to develop:
- (a) All aspects of fitness in a general way
- (b) The particular aspects of fitness that closely resemble the demands of the game
- (c) A selection of aspects of fitness in a way that concentrates on the strengths of individual players.

(3) A coach would use an activity pattern analysis to:
- (a) Check a player's skill level
- (b) Check on team performance
- (c) Measure a player's work output
- (d) None of the above.

(4) How could you use a heart-rate monitor, attached to a player, to help you analyse the predominant energy system during a game?

(5) Explain the term 'anaerobic threshold'.

(6) Discuss the methods, values and importance of games analysis.

(7)
- (a) Outline *one* method of analysing the fitness requirements of a team *or* individual game of your choice.
- (b) How might such an analysis aid the development of a training programme?

18. Training: Principles, planning and sessions

Training principles

For any training programme to be effective, the coach or player must follow a number of essential principles:

(1) Specificity

You should train the muscles, energy systems and skills that are specific to the sport for which you are training.

Fitness is specific to the type of exercise being performed. For instance, weight training develops strength, but continuous running develops aerobic capacity.

Specific exercises produce special biological responses. For instance, weight training increases recruitment and fibre size in the muscles being exercised.

Remember that:

- Specific individuals respond differently to the same exercises.
- Specific sports demand specific types of fitness, as assessed during video analysis.

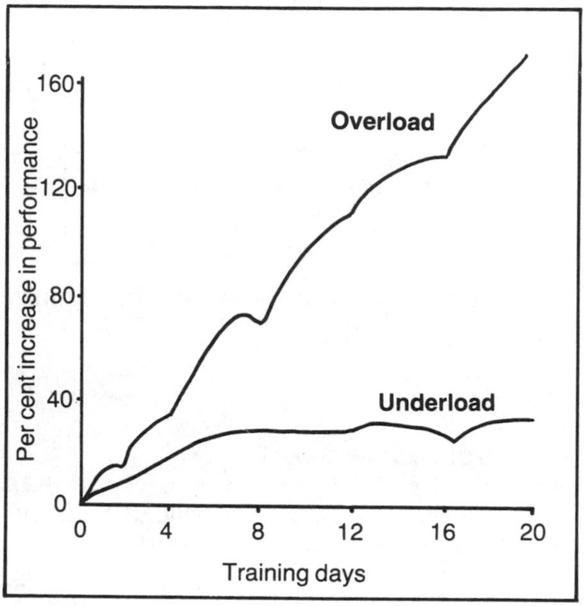

Figure 18.1 **The overload principle**. Gains in strength and endurance are most pronounced when the muscle is exercised in the overload zone; that is, with resistances above those normally encountered by the muscle.

Training aspect	Endurance (aerobic) training	Sprint (anaerobic) training
Frequency	4–5 days/wk.	3 days/wk.
Intensity	Heart rate = 85–90% of maximal heart rate	Heart rate = 180 beats/min. or greater
Sessions/day	One	One
Duration	12–16 wk. or longer	8–10 wk.
Distance/workout	5–8 kilometres	3–4 kilometres

Figure 18.2 Guidelines for estimating frequency, intensity, duration and distance of aerobic and anaerobic training programmes in running.

Event	Training frequency (days/wk)		Distance per workout (kilometres)	
	Run	Swim	Run	Swim
50 m	—	5–6	—	6½–8
100 m	5–6	5–6	6½–8	6½–8
200 m	5–6	6–7	6½–8	8–10
400 m	5–6	6–7	11–13	2–13½
500 yd	—	6–7	—	13–14½
800 m	6	—	13–16	—
1000 yd	—	6–7	—	13½–15
1500 m	7	—	14½–16	—
1650 yd	—	6–7	—	13½–15
1 mile	7	—	14½–16	—
2 miles	7	—	16–18	—
3 miles, 5000 m	7	—	19–21	—
6 miles, 10 000 m	7	—	21	—
Marathon	7	—	21+	—

Figure 18.3 Guidelines for estimating training, frequency and distance in running and swimming programmes.

(2) Progressive overload

The overload principle, as shown in Figure 18.1, governs all fitness and skill training. If the individual wants to improve, the individual must exercise at an intensity greater than his or her existing capacity, and this intensity must move towards his or her performance objective. For instance, when training for running, take note of the distance covered in a particular time, and try to improve each run. If the training load exceeds the load to which the body is accustomed, the body will adapt physiologically so that a higher load is required for further improvement.

(3) Frequency

The training frequency varies according to the chosen activity. However, it is possible to make the following general statements:

- For most **endurance athletes**, the training frequency should be four to five days per week, although runners, swimmers and triathletes may require frequencies of six to seven days. Training for two sessions per day is not necessarily more productive than training for one session per day.
- The training frequency for **non-endurance athletes** should be three days per week, although track and swimming sprinters might require frequencies of five or six days.

(4) Intensity

Training intensity should be determined by the heart rate. For endurance training programmes to be useful, heart rates should reach 70 to 85 per cent of maximum. For sprint training programmes the training heart rate should be 180 beats or more per minute.

Note: With interval training, the most important factor is intensity of training, not frequency or duration. Therefore three intense sessions per week are adequate for interval training.

(5) Duration

Duration refers to the length of a training programme. In order to develop aerobic fitness, you need to undertake training programmes that are not less than 12 weeks long, and may be more than 18 weeks long. However, for anaerobic fitness improvement, you need a training programme only eight to ten weeks long.

(6) Regularity

Training and fitness improvements are the summation of biological adaptations induced by regular

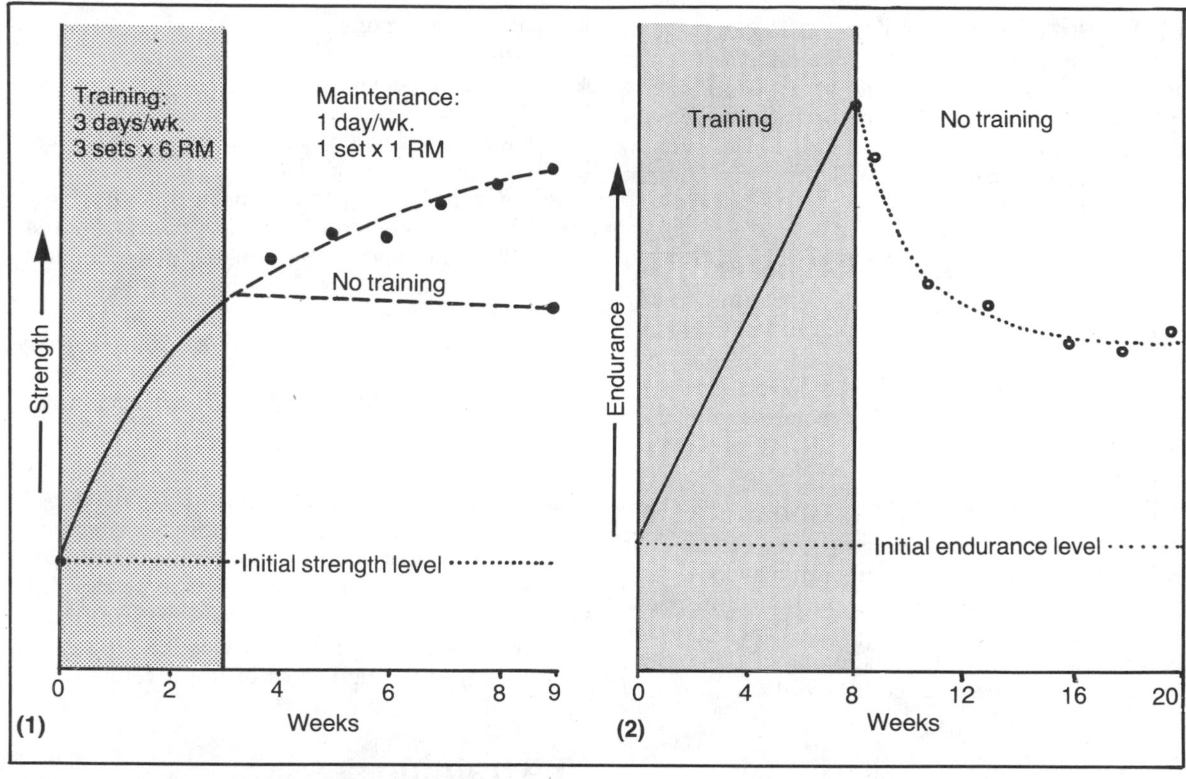

Figure 18.4 **Retention of strength and endurance.**

(1) (**a**) The strength gained during a three-day-per-week, three-week isotonic training programme (three sets of 6 RM) was not lost during a subsequent six-week period of no training (dotted line)

(**b**) Strength was further improved during a subsequent six-week training programme involving only one set at a 1 RM load performed twice a week.

(2) Retention of muscular endurance. The programme was performed three days per week for eight weeks, with each session consisting of an exhausting bout of elbow flexions at a work rate of 40 repetitions per minute against an 11-pound load. Although endurance was lost most rapidly during the first few weeks of the detraining (no training) period, after 12 weeks of no training, 70 per cent of the endurance gained was still retained.

exercise. 'Regular exercise' is that undertaken at optimum training session frequency repeated regularly for the duration of the training programme. Without a regular exercise programme, the desired biological adaptations either do not take place or occur at too slow a rate.

(7) Training effects are reversible

As Figure 18.4 shows, the biological adaptations produced by training will be reversed if training ceases. The longer the build up, the slower the reversal process will be. This is sometimes called the 'detraining effect'.

(8) Generalization before specialization

A competitive athlete in any sport should develop a sound general fitness, including all fitness components, before specializing in the dominant components of a particular sport. An athlete who specializes too quickly runs the risk of injury or never fulfilling his or her genetic potential.

(9) Quality is better than quantity

Working at top speed or maximum effort is far more productive than working for twice as long at half pace. For instance, the footballer who jogs around during circle work at training is learning to function at half pace, and will probably act that way during a game.

(10) Right practice makes perfect

Practice must come as close as possible to the performance required of a player in the game situation. If that does not happen, the player is learning a new game that may not have anything to do with the game he or she is required to play on Saturday.

(11) Progress should be measurable

Players should be able to see improvements in their performance. Such improvements may be tested regularly, or the player can make comparisons between his or her recent performance and the performance given at the beginning of the season. Training diaries are a valuable record and source of motivation.

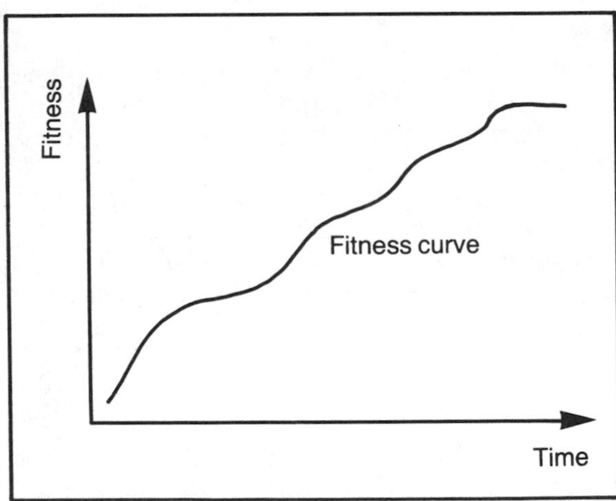

Figure 18.5 **The fitness curve**. Note how it shows the law of diminishing returns: the gains are greatest during early training.

(12) Variety adds spice

Training sessions can be varied by such means as:

- Emphasizing different skills
- Changing fitness work
- Visiting local gyms
- Running on beaches
- Training at pools.

In this way, players are less likely to become psychologically and physically stale or bored, and less likely to stay on a plateau.

Initial gains in fitness are made quickly. However, fitness levels tend to reach a plateau — that is, remain stationary after the build up. Plateau performances may last for varying lengths of time. An athlete may experience a number of plateaux during a season, but they can be shortened by changing training techniques, laying off for short periods of time, and changing his or her psychological attitude.

(13) Group and individual training

Group training is an excellent method of maintaining training motivation. However, within any group, training must be tailored to the needs of the individual. Specific members of the group may need more or less intense work, depending on their existing capacities and rates of improvement.

The training session

Each workout should consist of four sections:

- The warm up
- The conditioning phase
- The skill or team-play phase
- The warm down.

(1) The warm up

Before reading on, revise the section on 'The warm up' in Chapter 7.

Remember that every session should begin with a warm up, which should incorporate the following:

- **A continuous activity**

Jogging is often used as a continuous activity that increases blood flow to the muscles and therefore increases muscle termperature. This activity should be kept up until sweating begins.

- **Light exercises**

Undertake a series of light resistance exercises that will work the muscles to be used in the conditioning bout.

- **Flexibility exercises**

Go through a series of flexibility exercises that increase the range of motion at the joints to be used in the conditioning bout.

(2) The conditioning phase (fitness phase)

Whether this precedes or follows the skill phase depends on the fitness standard desired and the level of competition. For highly fit players, the idea of pressure training is to perform skills while coping with fatigue, so the conditioning phase follows the warm up.

During the conditioning phase, the specific fitness components required for a specific sport are developed using the training methods favoured by the coach. At all times the coach should stick to the principle of overload and other training principles.

(3) Skill or team-play phase

During this section of a training session, players perform activities designed to improve both individual and team skills. Examples include:

- Hockey: corner practice
- Basketball: man-to-man drills
- Volleyball: spiking practice.

(4) Warm down (cool down)

The warm down is the tapering off after completion of the workout. It should be a continuation of the activity at a very reduced intensity. For example, after running, keep walking.

The warm down is needed to prevent venous pooling — that is, pooling of blood in the veins. After strenuous exercise, the heart keeps pumping out blood at a rapid rate. If you end your workout abruptly, the muscles are no longer contracting — helping to propel the blood back to the heart — so blood may pool in the veins and tissue. This can result in insufficient venous return, therefore re-

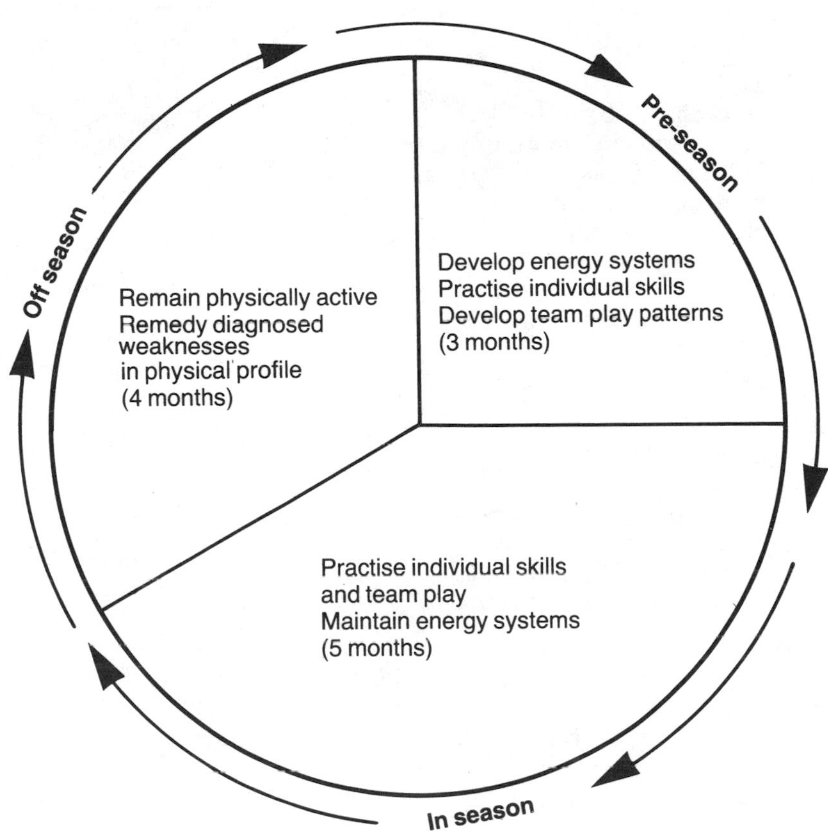

Figure 18.6 Suggested phases of training throughout the year for a team game. The pre-season period may be reduced to six weeks for lower grades.

ducing the flow of blood for other vital organs. Less blood is reoxygenated, and waste (lactic acid) is not being removed from the muscles that have just been working.

Therefore the warm down is essential, and must be long enough for the heart to recover to between 100 and 120 beats per minute.

All warm downs should include either static or PNF-stretching excercises for all muscle groups involved in the conditioning bout and the skill phase.

The training year

The majority of sports are seasonal. The competition usually lasts for a period of about five months, and is preceded by a two- to three-month period of preparation. This leaves an off-season period of four to five months remaining in the year.

Off-season training

Training during this period should be devoted to remaining reasonably active without necessarily staying involved in the chosen sport. Players should monitor their percentage body fat and activity levels so that they begin pre-season training at or close to their 'playing weight'. However, the off-season period should also include specialized weight training and skill development programmes to remedy any diagnosed weaknesses.

Pre-season training

Pre-season training usually lasts for between six weeks and three months. It involves progressive development of the energy systems that are important in the sport, and practice of the basic skills. In team games, the coach must spend time in combining the talents of individuals to produce an effective style of play.

In-season training

The emphasis during the competitive season should be on skill and strategy with maintenance of pre-season fitness. The coach should be aware of the need to supplement skill sessions with more intensive weight, sprint or endurance training where it seems necessary. Injured athletes, in particular, need to be carefully and progressively rehabilitated before being allowed to return to competition.

Figure 18.6 shows the sequence of the three different phases of training.

Training intensity and peaking

The greater the intensity of training through the pre- and in-season sessions, the faster the rate of improvement. However, intense training can also lower the peak performance and maintain this peak for a shorter time.

Alternatively, a less intense training programme with more gradual overloads over a longer period gives a slower improvement but a higher peak performance and a longer maintenance of that peak.

Therefore it may be better to aim for peak performance during the middle of the season (not

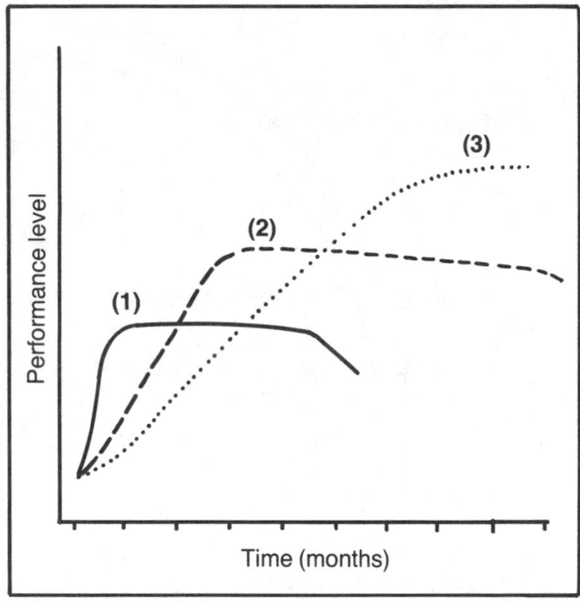

Figure 18.7 A proposed relationship between the rate of improvement and the absolute level of improvement (during one competitive season). Workout schedule (**1**) is very intense, and the corresponding rate of improvement is very rapid as compared to workout schedule (**3**), which is less intense. Workout schedule (**2**) falls between them. The rate of improvement is inversely related to the final level of performance and to the length of time an athlete can maintain maximum performance.

at the start) so that the performer can maintain his or her peak into the finals.

Peaking for individual competitions

Peaking for specific matches or competitions during a season (for instance, a Final or vital match) requires some rest from practice or at least an easing up on the daily stress of practice sessions. This allows the body complete recovery and a build up of peak strength and endurance on the competition day.

This reduction in intensity begins usually one week before the big competition.

Laboratory work 29: Alternative recovery strategies

Randomly divide the class into three groups, with each group performing one of these alloted tasks:

Group 1 task

(1) Perform three 400-metre runs, each at three-quarters of your maximum pace. Rest for three minutes between each run by walking slowly another 400 metres.
(2) Shower and change immediately after your third recovery walk.

Group 2 task

(1) Perform three 400-metre runs, each at three-quarters of your maximum pace. Recover for three minutes between each run by slowly walking or jogging another 400 metres.
(2) After your last recovery walk, perform the following static flexibility exercises:
   (a) Toe touch
   (b) Calf stretch
   (c) Quadricep stretch
   (d) Groin stretch.

Group 3 task

(1) Perform three 400-metre runs, each at three-quarters of your maximum pace. Rest for three minutes between each run by lying down.
(2) After your final 400-metre run, lie down until you feel better; then shower and change.

Results

(1) Each subject, irrespective of group, should keep the following subjective record of how his or her legs felt:
   (a) 1 hour after the runs
   (b) 6 hours after the runs
   (c) 24 hours after the runs
   (d) 48 hours after the runs.
(2) In class, discuss any differences in perceived pain between or within groups.

Worksheet 17: Training principles and planning

Choose the correct response for Questions (1)–(7).

(1) Peaking is related to intensity of training in that:
   (a) The greater the training intensity, the higher the peak
   (b) The greater the training intensity, the longer the peak
   (c) The slower the build up of intensity, the higher the peak
   (d) None of the above.
(2) During pre-season training, the main emphasis is on:
   (a) Remedying weaknesses
   (b) Maintaining skill and fitness
   (c) Developing skill and fitness
   (d) Controlling your weight.
(3) When peaking for a big match or event, you should:
   (a) Increase your training intensity up to match day
   (b) Taper off your training intensity the week preceding the game
   (c) Have a complete layoff in the week before the match
   (d) Continue training as usual.
(4) The major reason for warm down is to:
   (a) Prevent venous pooling
   (b) Remove lactic acid
   (c) Avoid muscle tightening
   (d) All the above.
(5) During warm up, increased body and muscle temperatures promote increases in:
   (a) ATP-PC production
   (b) Blood flow and oxygen availability
   (c) Radiation
   (d) Lactic acid production.

(6) The most efficient method of judging the intensity of a training programme is by noting the:
- **(a)** The amount of tiredness
- **(b)** The exercise respiration rate response
- **(c)** The exercise heart rate response
- **(d)** The duration of the programme.

(7) 'You get what you train for' is a phrase that could be expressed more correctly by the term:
- **(a)** Overload
- **(b)** Specificity
- **(c)** Intensity
- **(d)** Training effect.

(8) Two important principles of training are 'specificity' and 'generalization before specialization'. Explain how these seemingly contradictory principles can both be applied in training.

(9) What is meant by 'overload' when it is used in relation to training?

(10) List three training principles. For each:
- **(a)** Define and discuss it.
- **(b)** Give a practical example of how it is applied in a training programme.

(11) 'Warming up is of no value — it doesn't improve performance.' Discuss.

19. Training methods

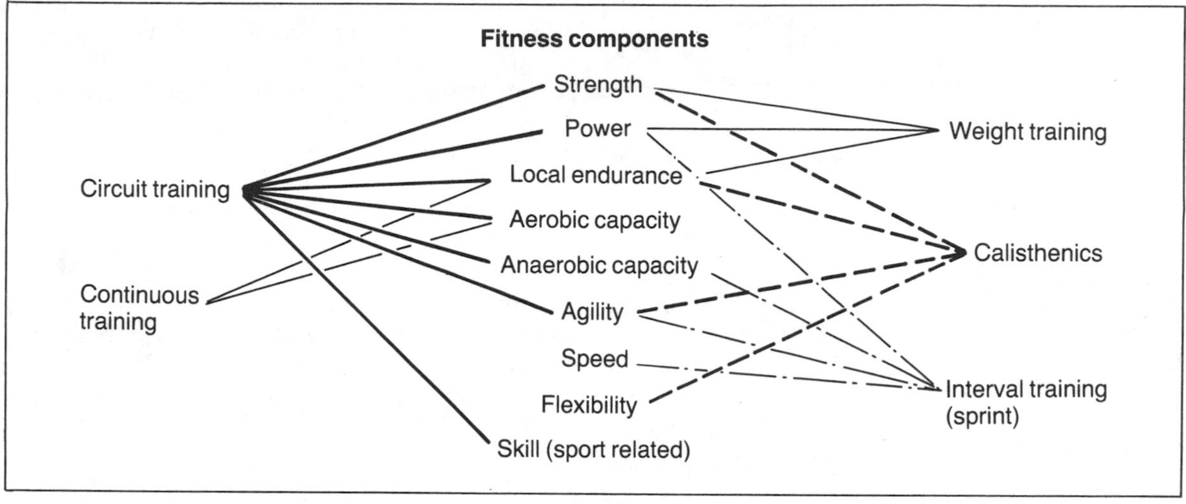

Figure 19.1 **Fitness training methods.** Specific fitness training methods are predisposed to developing specific components of fitness. The coach must choose the methods that best suit his sports requirements.

Continuous training

In Chapter 12, we discussed Karvonen's Principle: that for aerobic training to be successful, the heart rate must remain at a critical threshold for at least 20 minutes continuously during at least three or four sessions per week.

Pyke uses the term 'continuous training zone', which he defines as the zone where the heart rate stays between 70 and 85 per cent of maximum during a session of between 15 and 60 minutes long, for at least four sessions per week.

During such training, your heart rate (workload) must remain below your anaerobic threshold.

Continuous training improves the cardio-respiratory and local muscle function, thus improving aerobic capacity.

The main types of continuous training activity are:

- Running and jogging
- Cycling
- Swimming
- Floor classes.

Fartlek training (speed play)

Fartlek training, or speed play, is continuous training, but with regular bursts of speed, of from five to ten seconds, every two or three minutes during a session. These sessions increase the involvement of the anaerobic energy systems, while heavily using the aerobic system.

Weight training

During weight training, subjects perform a series of resistance exercises designed to develop the fitness component they require in specific sport-related muscles.

When taking part in weight training, begin with light weights and a general programme. However, once you have established a basic foundation, change the programme so that it is more specific to the muscles required in your sport and, if possible, mimic the movement patterns of that sport (for instance, throwing actions or leg drive actions).

Within each session, reduce the effect of fatigue

Exercise	Muscle group
(1) Chin ups	Back
(2) Bench press	Chest
(3) Squats (half)	Legs
(4) Crunches	Abdomen
(5) Seated press	Shoulders
(6) Seated rowing	Back
(7) Flat flyes	Chest
(8) Leg extension	Legs
(9) Sit ups	Abdomen
(10) Bicep curl	Arms

Figure 19.2 Order of exercises to rotate muscle groups in a weight-training programme.

by arranging the exercises so that you do not involve the same muscle groups in succession (see Figure 19.2).

There are three types of weight training:

- Isotonic (traditional)
- Isometric
- Isokinetic.

(1) Isotonic (traditional) weight training

In the terminology of training:

- One repetition (rep) is one performance of an exercise — for instance, one push up or one bicep curl.
- A set is a number of repetitions of an exercise performed consecutively without rest. For instance, 8 bicep curls equals 1 set of 8 reps, or 1 x 8.
- A repetition maximum is the maximum weight you can lift a certain number of times. For instance, 1 RM is the maximum weight you can lift once; 10 RM is the maximum weight you can lift 10 times.

Isotonic weight training occurs when the load or weight remains constant throughout the range of movement. Isotonic weight training is based on performing sets of RMs. Overload is achieved by increasing the weight at regular intervals.

Isotonic weight training can be used to develop three components of fitness:

- **Strength**

Use 6–10 RM weights, performing three sets with two minutes rest between sets — that is, 3 × 10 RM.

- **Power**

Maximum power is developed at about 30 per cent of the maximum speed of contraction and about 30 per cent of the maximum force of contraction. Therefore use 30 per cent of 1 RM weights (about 15 RM), performing three sets of about 10 reps *as fast as possible*, with three or four minutes rest between sets.

- **Endurance**

Use weights of more than 30 RM, and perform 3–5 sets, resting between sets until recovery.

(2) Isometric weight training

During isometric training, hold a maximum contraction for five seconds, recover briefly, and repeat five times.

Isometric training is valuable only in sports like judo or gymnastics, where you might need to hold a

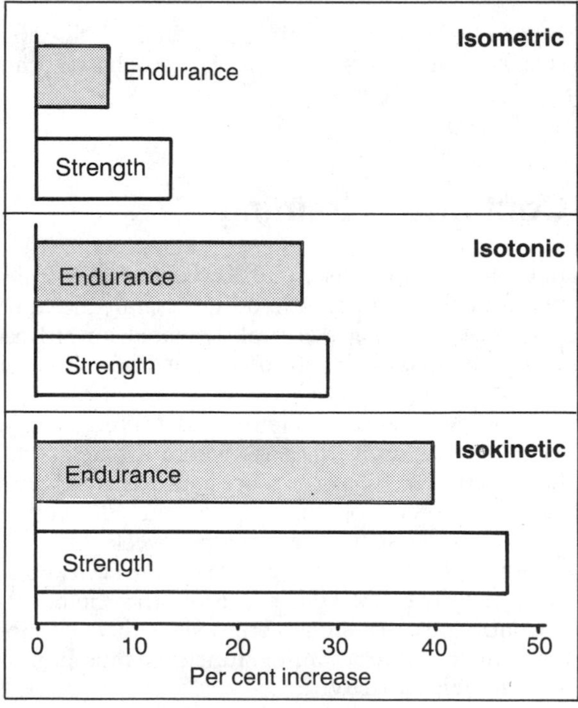

Figure 19.3 Comparison of isokinetic, isotinic and isometric programmes. All programmes were performed four days per week for eight weeks. The isokinetic programme was superior to the other programmes in both strength and endurance gains.

position for several seconds. Since in isometric training strength gains are specific to the joint angle, coaches must select angles that are specific to the sport being trained for.

(3) Isokinetic weight training

Isokinetic training requires expensive equipment, such as Nautilus, Hydragym or Cybex. These machines **permit a person to work at a constant speed against a resistance or weight that changes as the muscular force changes throughout the movement range**. In this way, these 'accommodating resistance' devices ensure that muscles are worked evenly at all stages of the movement.

These machines also permit the duplication of certain sports movements, such as throwing and kicking.

As Figure 19.3 shows, strength gain is faster with isokinetic training than with either isometric or isotonic training.

- Strength: 3 × 6–10 RM
- Power: 3 × 15–20 RM.

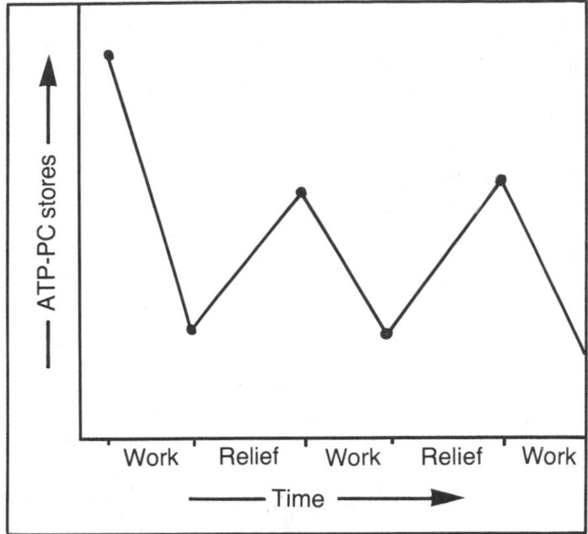

Figure 19.4 During the relief intervals of inermittent work, a portion of the muscular stores of ATP and PC that were depleted during the preceding work inervals will be replenished via the aerobic system.

Interval training

Interval training involves alternating work followed by recovery periods or intervals. Interval training allows high-intensity work to be performed without the fatigue associated with a continuous session of equal intensity (see Figures 19.4 and 19.5). Hence, equal work can be gained from:

- One continuous 400-metre sprint in 60 seconds (**high fatigue**)

or

- Ten repetitions of sprint of 40 metres, each in six seconds, with a 30-second recovery interval (**low fatigue**).

Interval training allows the three energy systems to be developed according to the length of the work interval. The variables that can be manipulated in an interval routine are:

- Duration of the work period or distance
- Intensity of work (speed)
- Number of work or recovery repetitions
- Duration of recovery periods and activity.

Comparing work duration to recovery duration gives the work-to-rest ratio (W:R ratio). The W:R ratio is the key to interval overload and adapting interval training to specific sports.

The heart rate during interval training should reach 180 beats per minute during work, and recover to 120 beats per minute in the rest interval.

A person capable of running 400 metres in 64 seconds may wish to be programmed for 400-metre intervals in a 20-minute training session. If the intensity of work required is 80 per cent of maximum, the speed of each 400-metre run can be calculated by multiplying the best time (64 seconds) by 100/80. In this case it equals 80 seconds.

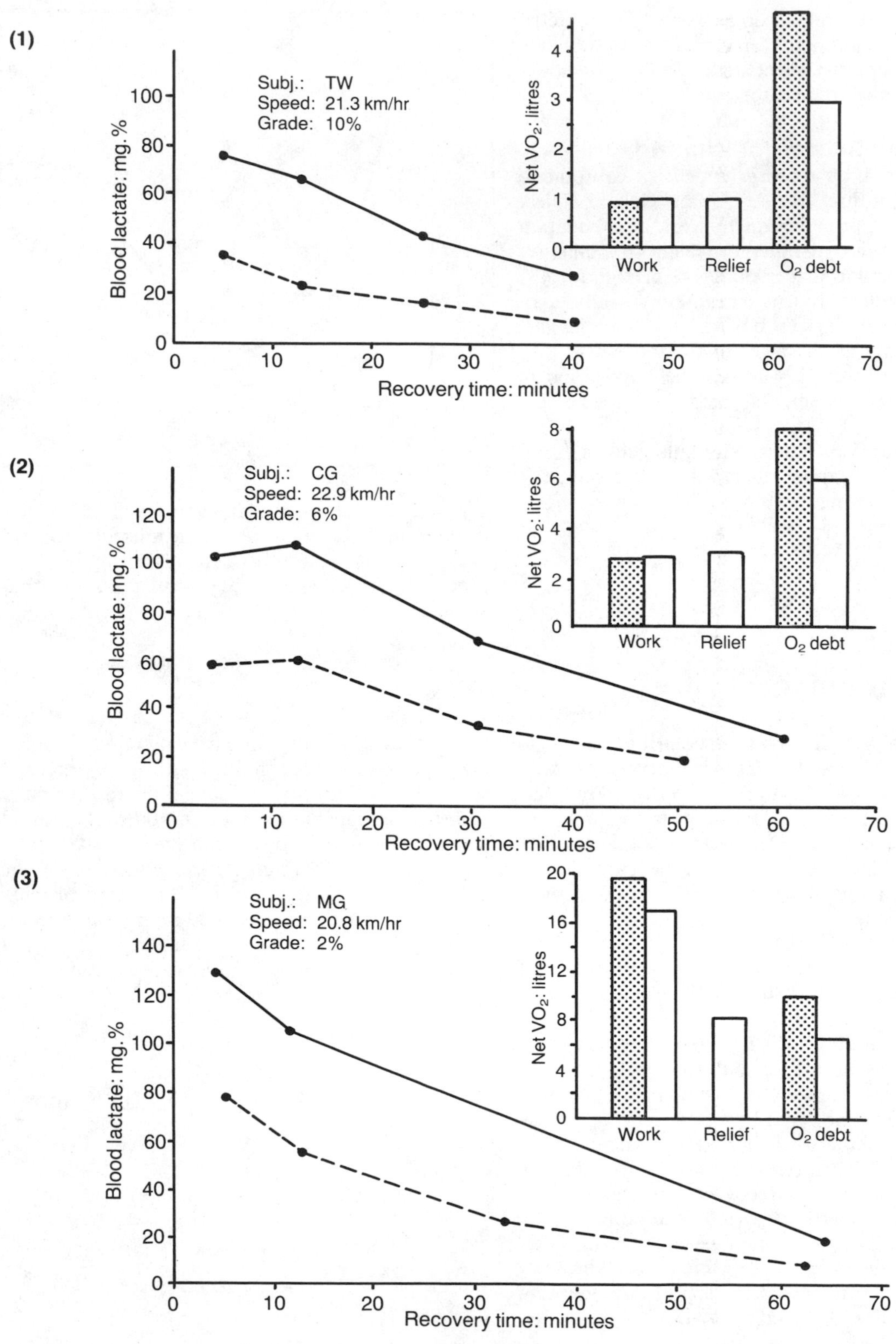
(1)
Subj.: TW
Speed: 21.3 km/hr
Grade: 10%
Blood lactate: mg. %
Recovery time: minutes
Net VO_2: litres
Work
Relief
O_2 debt
(2)
Subj.: CG
Speed: 22.9 km/hr
Grade: 6%
Blood lactate: mg. %
Recovery time: minutes
Net VO_2: litres
Work
Relief
O_2 debt
(3)
Subj.: MG
Speed: 20.8 km/hr
Grade: 2%
Blood lactate: mg. %
Recovery time: minutes
Net VO_2: litres
Work
Relief
O_2 debt

Figure 19.5
(1) Blood lactate during recovery from a continuous run (solid line) and interval runs (dashed line) involving the same amount of work. In the continuous run the subject ran for 30 seconds; in the interval run he ran three intervals of 10 seconds each with 20 seconds of rest-relief between intervals. Net O_2 consumption (VO_2) during work, during the rest-relief intervals, after work (O_2 debt) for the continuous (hatched bar) and interval (open bar) runs are also shown.
(2) Similar measurements during and after a continuous run of 60 seconds' duration and an interval run of five 12–second runs with 20 seconds of rest-relief between intervals.
(3) A continous run of 300 seconds' duration and an interval run of five 60–second runs with 60 seconds of rest-relief between intervals. Symbols the same as in (1).

Best 400 metre run time = 64 seconds	
Duration of work period	80 seconds
Intensity of work	80% maximum
Duration of recovery period	160 seconds
Repetitions of work/recovery sequence	5

Figure 19.6 Interval training.

In order to make this prescription simpler, the programme may be written as follows:

Repetitions		Distance		Time		Despatch time
5	×	400 m	in	80 sec;	every	4 min.

The work period of 80 seconds, the recovery period of 160 seconds and the despatch time every 4 minutes represents a work/recovery ratio of 1:2.

There are basically two types of interval training:

- Long interval training
- Short interval, or sprint training.

(1) Long interval training

(See Figures 19.7 and 19.8.) This training uses both aerobic and anaerobic energy pathways, and is typically used by:

- Athletes involved in sports with efforts of from one to six minutes
- Middle distance athletes
- Team game athletes.

Note: During all recovery periods, the athlete should be encouraged to continue in light activity, as this promotes the faster removal of lactic acid than does inactive recovery.

Longer, slower interval training	
• Duration of work period	15 sec.–3 min.
• Intensity of work	80–85% maximum
• Duration of recovery period	30 sec.–3 min.
• Work/recovery ratio	1:1–1:2
• Repetitions of work/ recovery sequence	5–20

Figure 19.7 Long interval training.

Best 400 metre run time = 60 seconds

Repetitions		Distance		Time		Despatch Time
5	×	400 m	in	75 secs.	every	4 min.
5	×	300 m	in	55 secs.	every	3 min.
5	×	200 m	in	35 secs.	every	2 min.

(2) Short interval, or sprint training

This training relies on the phosphate energy system, and increases its capacity and restorative powers. Therefore an improved alactacid source is necessary for a sustained sprint or the stop-and-go action of many team sports.

Using the interval training format the guidelines for developing a short sprint programme are as follows:

- Duration of work period — 0–15 sec
- Intensity of work — 100% (maximum)
- Duration of recovery period — 1–2 min.
- Work/recovery ratio — 1:5–1:10
- Repetitions of work/recovery sequence — 5–15

Repetitions		Distance		Time		Despatch time
10	×	60 m	in	8 sec.	every	90 sec.

Figure 19.8

The duration of sprint repetitions must be kept very short (from five to ten seconds) so that maximum speeds can be achieved without the occurrence of early fatigue. Long recovery periods are permitted. Tired athletes may practise incorrect mechanics. Pyke gives a selection of activities that produce the desired effect.

- **Reaction drills**

Reaction time is the delay between sensing the need to move and actually moving. If the reaction time is too long, it can represent a significant portion of the time required to move to an appropriate position, avoid an opponent or make a critical interception. It can be improved by practising responses to common stimuli, such as sight or sound. Team games training groups can respond to commands and imitate the arm, leg and total body movements of a leader.

- **Acceleration sprints**

Acceleration sprints are conducted for less than five seconds, with the athletes in a variety of starting positions — lying, sitting, kneeling or standing — depending on the sport.

- **Longer sprints**

Because acceleration work does not allow enough time for maximum sprinting speed to be reached, it is necessary to extend the length of the sprint. This can be done in 20-second efforts, in which maximum speed is held for five seconds, after ten seconds of gradual acceleration.

- **Agility sprints**

The ability to change direction quickly and accurately can be trained by short shuttle runs or obstacle runs around tyres, cones or markers.

- **Technique training**

Correct technique is an important part of speed. This requires a gradual build up to maximal speed after several weeks of learning at submaximal rates. Seniors possessing a long history of working with a poor technique may take longer than juniors to make the appropriate changes.

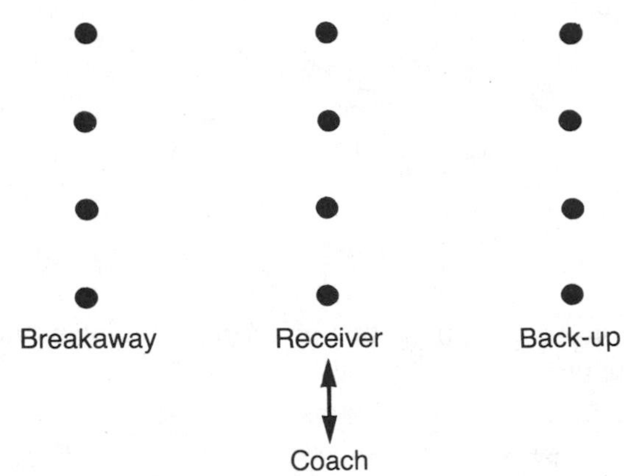

Figure 19.9 A typical alignment of players in an interval skill drill for a team sport.

(3) Interval skill drills

Interval drills, which enable the simultaneous practice of skills and the development of aerobic and anaerobic systems, are an important part of a team game training system. An ideal situation is to present a group of three or four players with a task that takes about 10 seconds to complete. Three other groups then take the next three 10-second periods to do the same exercise. The result is that the groups are operating on a 1:3 work:recovery ratio within the confines of a skill practice. This is shown in Figure 19.9. The work periods should be kept to less than 15 seconds; hence recovery is less than 45 seconds. Such efficient utilization of energy sources allows a high intensity of effort to be continued for 10 to 15 minutes without fatigue interrupting the skill-learning process.

Interval skill drills can also be developed to practise effective patterns of play in team games. The creative coach should pay careful attention to the number of players in each sub-group and to the specific responsibilities of each player. The objectives of play pattern drills should be to:

- Assign players to positions and responsibilities that are similar to those experienced in a game
- Position the players in such a way that the ball can be moved forward in a co-ordinated manner
- Utilize the energy sources that are used mainly in the game.

The skills of a team game can also be practised separately. For example, each of the four sections of the field hockey playing area can be used to practise a different skill, within the interval training format. During a period of five to ten minutes, four players in each quadrant can work on drills that involve, for example, trapping and shooting, trapping and pushing, tackling and intercepting, and dribbling. At the end of the period, the groups change activities until all skills have been completed. The 'grid' system of organization leaves the coach free to identify and remedy skill problems rather than simply administer a practice session. This system is being used in many team sports and, because the players are well organized, it makes the best use of training time and effort.

The same principles of interval skill drills can be applied to the racquet sports. Tennis players can be involved, in turn, in a sequence of shots most likely to be encountered in the game. The coach can feed five balls to different parts of the court so that the player hits a forehand drive, backhand drive, forehand approach shot, volley and smash in that order. The player then retrieves the balls and replaces them in the coach's supply bucket. Six players can be involved in the drill, which provides skill practice and energy utilization that is appropriate for tennis.

The coach may need to supplement interval skill drills with some shorter, faster interval sprint training completed outside the confines of skill practice. This is because the commitment to skill often inhibits the team game player from running at top speed. Hence the energy systems involved are not fully taxed.

Exercise	Circuit Number		
	A	B	C
(1) Shuttle runs	10	15	18
(2) Medicine ball rebound	20	30	40
(3) Sit ups	25	30	40
(4) Skipping	85	100	120
(5) Bench stepping	30	40	50
(6) Burpees	10	15	18
(7) Trunk curls	10	15	20
(8) Rope swings	10	15	20
(9) Bench jumps	10	15	20
(10) Bench arm blasts	10	15	20

Figure 19.10 Sample circuit.

Circuit training

Circuit training consists of a series of exercises (usually 10) arranged in order and designed to develop general body fitness or specific sport-related fitness and skill (see Figure 19.10).

Types of circuit training

There are two main types of circuit training:

(1) Fixed load circuits

Here each player begins on circuit A and tries to complete three laps within a time limit. When this is achieved in successive training sessions, the player attempts circuit B, and so on.

(2) Individual load circuits

Each individual is tested on each exercise for the maximum number of repetitions completed in one minute. These repetition numbers are then halved to indicate the number that must be completed in each lap. Each player performs three laps each session, trying to improve his or her time for the three laps.

Advantages of circuit training

The great advantage of circuit training is that it can be used to develop strength, power, local endurance, agility, anaerobic capacities and aerobic capacities simultaneously (depending on the exercises chosen) in a limited time and limited space.

Overload is achieved in circuit training by:

- Reducing target times

- Increasing exercise resistance (difficulty of the exercise)
- Increasing repetition numbers.

Note: Circuit training must be supplemented by a flexibility programme.

Calisthenics

Calisthenics are basic exercises used to develop strength, power, local endurance, agility or flexibility, depending on the exercise chosen and the training method used.

(1) Resistance calisthenics

Any exercise that requires a muscle to contract against a resistance can develop strength, power or local endurance. For instance:

- Strength: 3 x 10 RM; example: one-arm push ups
- Power: 3 x 15 RM as fast as possible; example: clap push ups
- Endurance: 3-5 x 30+ RM; example: sit ups.

Overload or progression is achieved either by increasing the number of reps or by increasing the resistance to movement — for example, push up progressions.

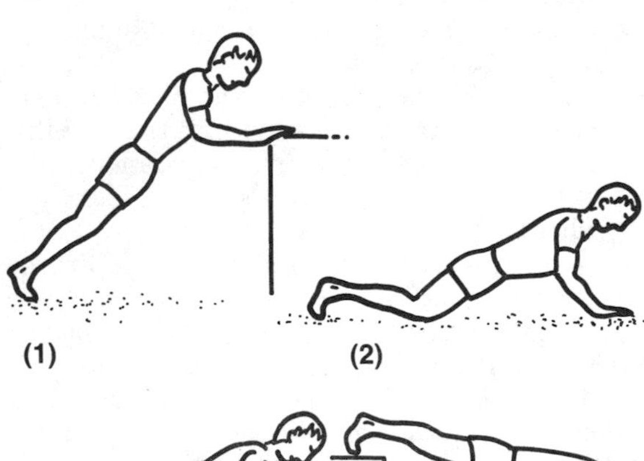

(5) One arm, or as for **(4)**, but clap on push up.

Figure 19.11 Push up progressions.

(2) Development of flexibility

Flexibility calisthenics include any exercise that puts a muscle in a stretched position — for example, the toe touch. There are two satisfactory methods:

(a) Static stretching

The muscle is stretched slowly to its greatest possible range and held there for 30–45 seconds.

(b) PNF

The muscle is taken to its end point, contracted isometrically against a resistance for six seconds, restretched, and contracted again. The cycle can be repeated four or five times.

Precautions

The following precautions must be followed when doing these exercises:

- A 10-minute period of warm up, including total body activity such as jogging and general mobilizing exercises, should precede the stretching work. Muscles will not stretch easily unless they are warm.
- The isometric contraction should never be explosive, but should involve a gradual increase in effort in the first two seconds, which is then sustained for an additional four seconds.
- After the isometric contraction, the partner should not force the person into a new position of improved flexibility. This manoeuvre should be unaided or, at the most, assisted by only light pressure.
- The exercises should be performed with less than maximum effort until both the person and the partner are accustomed to them and confident that no injury will result.

(3) Agility

Any calisthenic that requires the whole body to be moved quickly and precisely can develop agility — for example, the burpee.

Choosing calisthenic exercises

To discover which muscles are affected by certain calisthenics:

- Look at and analyse the movement performed — for instance, is it flexion, extension or abduction?
- Ask which muscle causes such a movement.
- Find out whether the exercise is designed to strengthen this muscle by working it against a

resistance (gravity) or to stretch the opposite muscle.
- Perform the exercise and feel which muscle or muscles are affected.

Laboratory work 30: Experience of the range of training methods

Procedure
On consecutive days, perform the following training sessions to widen your experience in the various training methods:

(1) **Day 1**
A 20-minute submaximal run or cycle.

(2) **Day 2**
3 × 10 RM for each exercise:
(a) Bench press
(b) Leg extension
(c) Overhead pulldown
(d) Crunches
(e) Seated press
(f) Bicep curl.

(3) **Day 3**
A 15-minute submaximal run or cycle interspersed with 10-second sprints every 3 minutes.

(4) **Day 4**
1 × 30 for each exercise:
(a) Sit ups
(b) Push ups
(c) Trunk curls
(d) Depth jumps (tuck jumps)
(e) Burpees.

(5) **Day 5**
A running session performing the following (all performed at three-quarters of your maximum pace):
(a) 1 × 400 metres; 400 metres walk recovery
(b) 2 × 200 metres; 200 metres walk recovery after each
(c) 2 × 100 metres; 100 metres walk recovery after each
(d) 2 × 50 metres; 50 metres walk recovery after each.

(6) **Day 6**
(a) Toe touch: 2 x 30 seconds
(b) Calf stretch: 2 x 30 seconds
(c) Quadricep stretch: 2 x 30 seconds
(d) Groin stretch: 2 x 30 seconds
(e) Pectoral stretch: 2 x 30 seconds.

Results
For each session:
(1) Identify the training method.
(2) Identify the major fitness component being developed.
(3) Describe your feelings of fatigue, both during and after the training session.
(4) Describe any detectable physiological changes during the session.

Worksheet 18: Alternative methods of training

For Questions (1)–(4) decide whether the answer is true or false.

(1) To maximize improvements in strength, try to follow a daily weight-training programme
(2) Aerobic training would be of no value to a badminton player
(3) Fartlek training involves a continuous run that includes spurts of faster running
(4) Improvements in VO_2 max. can be maintained by aerobic training once a week.

Choose the correct response for Questions (5)–(14):

(5) When training to increase muscle endurance, you should:
(a) Use heavy weights with many repetitions
(b) Use light weights with many repetitions
(c) Use heavy weights with few repetitions
(d) Use light weights with few repetitions.

(6) The type of relief interval that is most useful when training the ATP-PC system is:
(a) Work relief — that is, light to mild jogging
(b) Rest relief — that is, walking
(c) Complete rest
(d) None of the above.

(7) Which of the following variables is most important to an interval training programme?
(a) Rate and distance of the work interval
(b) Number of sets and repetitions during each session
(c) Duration of rest or relief intervals
(d) Frequency of training per week
(e) All of the above.

(8) Circuit training:
(a) Is a series of calisthenic exercises

(b) Develops all the fitness components except flexibility
(c) May be individual or fixed load
(d) All of the above.

(9) The best strength gains are made during weight training using:
(a) Isokinetic contractions
(b) Isotonic contractions
(c) Concentric contractions
(d) Isometric contractions.

(10) When training for muscular strength, it has been found that the best results are brought about by:
(a) Overload
(b) Underload
(c) Cross-education
(d) None of the above.

(11) Training that is of low intensity and long duration would be described as:
(a) Continuous
(b) Interval
(c) Repetition
(d) Fartlek.

(12) An athlete performed a vertical jump and scored in the 'excellent' category. Which of the following muscle-fibre combinations would you expect that athlete to have?
(a) High white fibre, low red fibre
(b) High red fibre, low white fibre
(c) Equal proportions of red and white fibres
(d) 100 per cent white fibres.

(13) In a weight-training programme for strength, which of the following is the most effective?
(a) Increasing the number of repetitions of the exercise
(b) Increasing the number of sets of the exercise
(c) Increasing the frequency of training sessions from three to five times per week
(d) Regularly increasing the resistance applied to the muscle.

(14) In interval training, you are more likely to stimulate improvement in:
(a) Fast-twitch fibres
(b) Slow-twitch fibres
(c) Specificity
(d) All muscle fibres.

(15) Identify two fitness components used in a motor activity of your choice, and discuss the following:
(a) A fitness test used to measure them.
(b) Training methods available for improving them.

(16) List four methods of training. For each:
(a) Give the major component of fitness that each method develops.
(b) Give a sample training session.

(17) Why is it important to have 'work relief' intervals when training the lactic acid system, but 'rest relief' intervals when training the ATP-PC system?

20. Chronic physiological training effects

Chronic training effects (or adaptations) are achieved only after a period of training, ranging from weeks to months, and once produced, remain a permanent feature of the body unless training ceases. If you stop training, your body will gradually revert to its past condition.

The training effects that you develop are specific to the training methods that you use, the duration, frequency and intensity of the training methods you use, and your individual capacities.

The training effects cause the desired improvements in performance after a period of training, and justify the hours of hard work.

Cardio-respiratory training effects

The effects of training on the cardio-respiratory system must be broken down into those **evident at rest** and those **evident during exercise**.

(1) Training effects evident at rest

(a) Cardiac hypertrophy

(See Figure 20.1.) Training increases the size of the heart. Endurance athletes develop larger chambers (particularly the left ventricle) and non-endurance athletes increase the thickness of the ventricular wall.

(b) Increased stroke volume

As the heart develops larger chambers, thicker walls and improved extensibility and contractility, it ejects a greater volume of blood with each beat.

(c) Decreased heart rate (bradycardia)

Since the cardiac output required at rest is constant, increases in stroke volume are accompanied by corresponding decreases in the heart rate.

(d) Increased blood volume and haemoglobin

Training stimulates increased plasma and red blood cell volumes, thus improving the effectiveness of oxygen delivery and waste removal.

(e) Blood pressure

Hyptertensive subjects who follow a training pro-

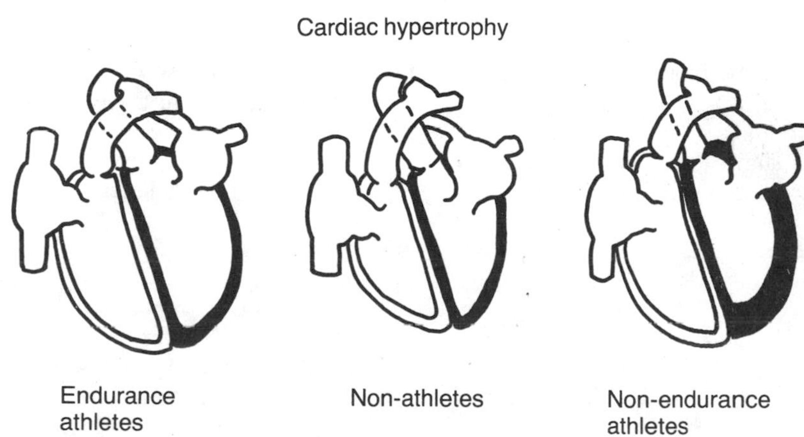

Figure 20.1 **Cardiac hypertrophy**. In endurance athletes (such as distance swimmers and runners), cardiac hypertrophy consists of an increase in the size of the left ventricular cavity. **There is no increase in the thickness of the heart's walls.** In non-endurance athletes (such as wrestlers and shot-putters), cardiac hypertrophy consists of an increase in the ventricular wall's thickness; there is no increase in the size of the cavity.

Variable	Training effects Rest	Submaximal Exercise*	Maximal Exercise
Cardiac hypertrophy	Increased	—	—
Cardiac output	Unchanged or decreased (?)	Unchanged or descreased	Increased
Heart rate	Decreased	Decreased	Decreased or unchanged
Stroke volume	Increased	Increased	Increased
Total haemoglobin and blood volume	Increased	—	—
Blood pressure			
• Hypertensives	Decreased	Decreased	Decreased
• Normals	Unchanged	Unchanged	Unchanged
Lung volumes	Increased	—	—
Pulmonary diffusion capacity	Increased (?)	Increased	Increased
Minute ventilation	Unchanged	Decreased	Increased
Oxygen consumption (VO_2)	Unchanged	Decreased or unchanged	Increased
Oxygen extraction by muscle	Unchanged	Increased	Increased
Muscle glycogen depletion	—	Decreased	Increased
Lactic acid levels (in muscle and blood)	Unchanged	Decreased	Increased
Anaerobic threshold	—	Increased	—
Blood flow to working muscles (per kg muscle tissue)	—	Increased	Unchanged

*Same amount of work before and after training.

Figure 20.2 Summary of the major cardiorespiratory effects of training.

gramme find that their blood pressure reduces towards normal.

(f) Respiratory effects

Training induces slight increases in all lung volumes, and increases a person's pulmonary diffusion capacity.

Respiratory changes

↑ ed* Maximal minute ventilation
↑ ed Tidal volume
↑ ed Breathing frequency
↑ ed Ventilatory efficiency
↑ ed Lung volumes
↑ ed Diffusion capacity

Other changes

Changes in body composition
↓ ed Total body fat
No change or slight increase in lean body weight
↓ ed Total body weight
↓ ed Blood cholesterol and triglyceride levels
↓ ed Exercise and resting blood pressures
↑ ed Heat acclimatization
↑ ed Breaking strength of bone, ligaments, and tendons

* ↑ ed = increased; ↓ ed = decreased.

Figure 20.3 Changes induced by training on respiration and other systems.

(2) Training effects evident during submaximal exercise

(See Figure 20.2.) Because training produces an increased stroke volume in the heart, the heart rate during submaximal exercise decreases, and therefore the cardiac output remains fairly stable. The VO_2 tends to decrease, because of the body's improved biomechanical efficiency. Blood flow to the working muscles also decreases, because the muscles are able to extract increased amounts of oxygen from the blood.

(3) Training effects evident during maximal exercise

(See Figure 20.2.) The VO_2 maximum increases,

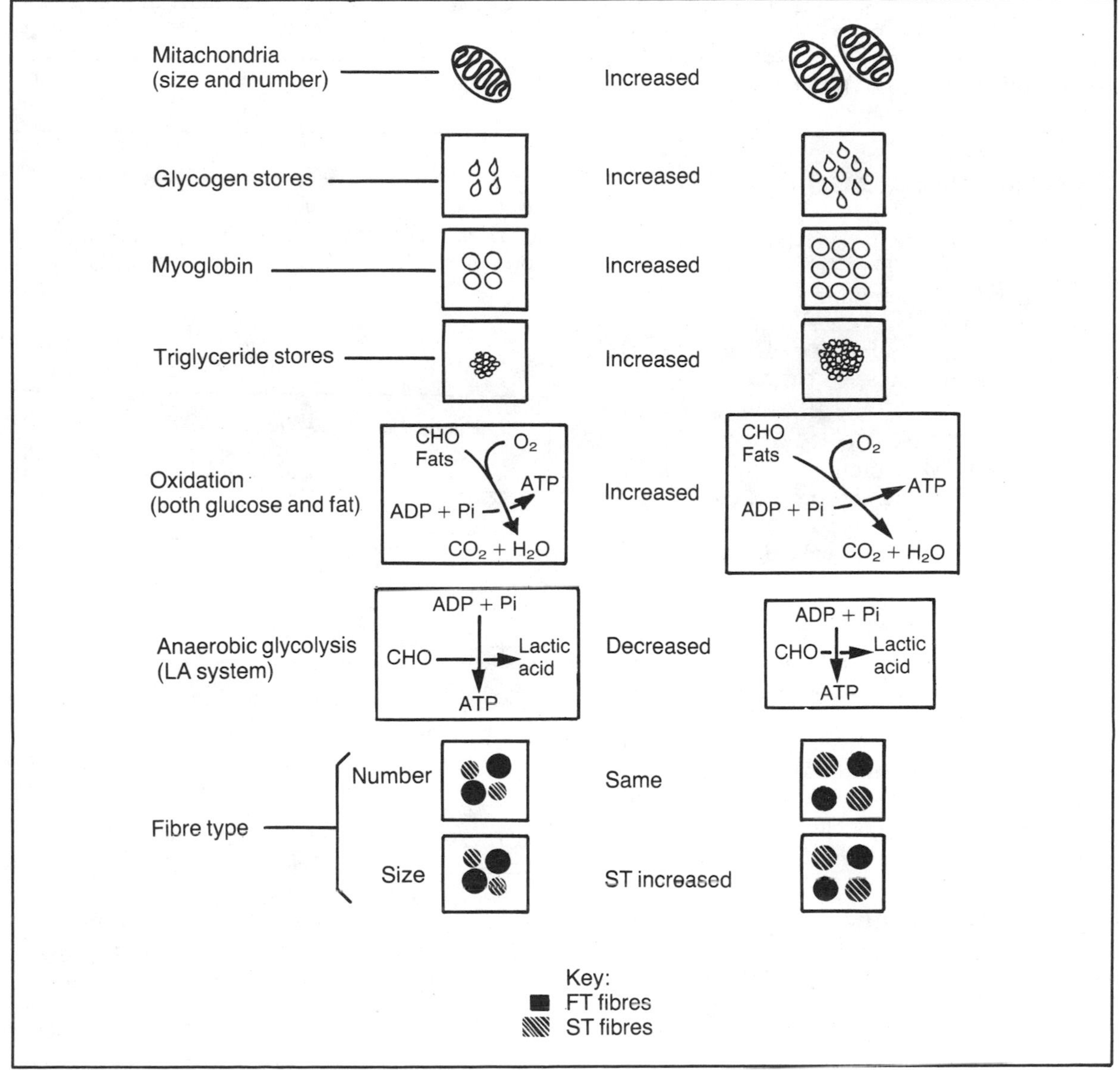

Figure 20.4 Summary of the effects of endurance training on skeletal muscle. The muscle before training is on the left and the muscle after training is on the right.

because of increased cardiac output and the improved oxygen extraction by the muscles. Since training reduces the maximal heart rate, increases in cardiac output are caused solely by the increased stroke volume.

(4) Overall effect of cardio-respiratory training

Cardio-respiratory training effects lead to improved, more efficient delivery of oxygen to the working muscles which, in turn, improves performance on aerobic tasks. These cardio-respiratory training effects are best developed by continuous, circuit and interval training methods.

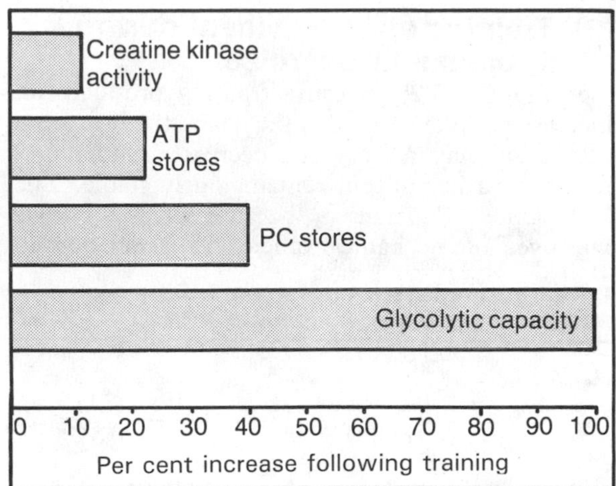

Figure 20.5 The effects of training on the anaerobic potential of skeletal muscle include increases in creatine kinase activity, muscular stores of ATP and PC, and in glycolytic capacity.

Skeletal muscle training effects

Changes occur inside the skeletal muscle as a result of chronic training. These changes are highly specific to the training method being used. The two main classifications of effects are:

- Endurance muscle training effects
- Non-endurance muscle changes.

(1) Endurance training effects in skeletal muscle

These adaptations increase aerobic energy production:

- Lead to an increase in fuel stores of glucose and triglycerides.
- Increase oxygen extraction by increased concentrations of myoglobin.
- Increase oxygen delivery through vascularization — that is, increase the number of capillaries within the muscles.
- Increase the energy production sites by increasing the size and number of mitachondria.
- Lead to improved ATP production via the aerobic system, because of vast increases in oxidative enzymes.

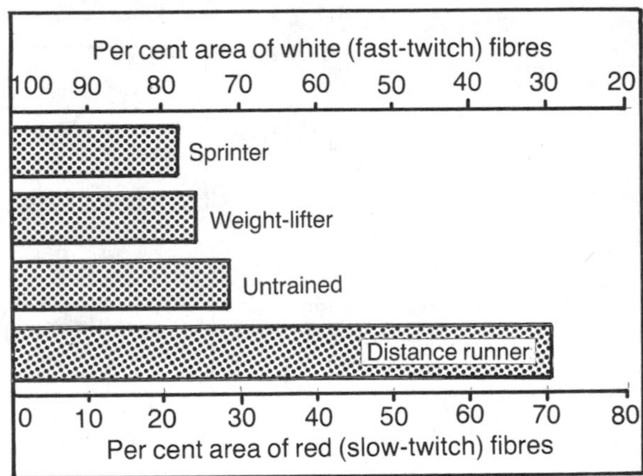

Figure 20.6 Training produces a selective hypertrophy of red and white skeletal muscle fibres. The red fibres of endurance athletes occupy a greater area of the muscle than do the white fibres. However, the white fibres occupy a greater area in weight-lifters and sprinters.

(2) Non-endurance training effects in skeletal muscles

(See Figure 20.5.) These changes are best produced through weight, calisthenic and sprint training, where the aim is to increase anaerobic power and strength. These changes include:

- Increased capacity of the ATP-CP system because of increased muscle stores of ATP and PC and increased levels of ATP turnover enzymes.
- Increased glycolytic capacity resulting from increased muscle glucose stores and increased levels of glycolytic enzymes.
- Increased speed of muscle contraction.

- Muscle hypertrophy (mostly of the fast-twitch fibres) (see Figure 20.6), resulting in:
  - An increased cross-sectional area, and therefore increased muscle force
  - Increased number and size of myofibrils per fibre
  - Increased amounts of myosin and actin
  - Increased fibre size and (possibly) number.
- Increased capillary density per fibre.
- Increased strength and amounts of connective tissue, including the tendons and ligaments.
- Increased ability to recruit motor units to produce more forceful contractions.
- Increased lean body weight.
- Flexibility training effects:
  - Increased resting length of the muscles, tendons and ligaments
  - Increased joint range of movement
  - Decreased resistance to joint movement.

Laboratory work 31: Measuring training effects

Perform the following tasks using class members as subjects:

(1) **(a)** Measure the resting pulse rate of a class member who has a current background in distance running.
(b) Measure the resting pulse rate of a class member who has no background in distance sports.
Discuss the reasons for the variations in the above readings.

(2) **(a)** Measure the hip flexion of a class member who is involved in gymnastics or calisthenics.
(b) Measure the hip flexion of a distance runner.
Discuss the reasons for any variations in these measurements.

(3) **(a)** Measure the arm girth of a class member who trains with weights.
(b) Measure the arm girth of a class member who has never trained with weights.
Discuss the reasons for any variations in these measurements.

Worksheet 19: Physiological training effects

Choose the correct response for Questions (**1**)–(**5**).

(1) A sedentary individual decides to undertake a regular jogging programme. Which of the following would indicate an increased level of cardiovascular endurance fitness?
(a) Increased resting heart rate
(b) Decreased submaximal heart rate
(c) Increased maximal heart rate
(d) Increased submaximal heart rate.

(2) After a programme of long-term aerobic training, which of the following adaptations will occur in skeletal muscle during exercise at submaximal intensity?
(a) Increased utilization of carbohydrate
(b) Increased utilization of fat
(c) Increased production of lactic acid
(d) Increased utilization of protein.

(3) As an adaption to long-term training, you would expect stroke volume at submaximal work to:
(a) Remain the same
(b) Decrease
(c) Increase
(d) Both increase and decrease.

(4) Which of the following is not a muscular endurance chronic training effect?
(a) Increases storage of ATP
(b) Increased number of mitachondria
(c) Recruitment of motor units
(d) Asynchronous firing of motor units.

(5) Which of the following are both acute and chronic responses to exercise?
(a) Increased stroke volume
(b) Increased blood flow to the muscles
(c) Increased $a-vO_2$ difference
(d) All the above.

(6) Identify the changes brought about within a muscle by a weight training programme designed to increase muscle strength.

(7) Describe the training effects that occur in the heart and circulatory system when an individual trains for an extended period of time (at least three months) for an endurance event, such as the marathon or the 1500-metre swimming race.

21. The elite athlete

Elite athletes are generally physically superior humans who have fulfilled their athletic potential by performing the necessary training. Below is a list of factors that contribute to elite performance. Aim to add details to these items, relying on discussion, material found in this book, and information to be gained from further research.

Physiological factors

- Proportions of fast-twitch or slow-twitch fibres in muscles
- VO_2 maximum (93 per cent of which is genetic)
- Anaerobic capacity (81 per cent of which is genetic)
- Maximum strength
- Nerve impulse velocity
- Reaction time
- Functional flexibility
- Body composition.

Psychological factors

- Mental capacity (especially for memory and decision-making)
- Co-ordinated movement
- Learning ability
- Motivation
- Temperament
- Mental preparation and rehearsal.

Environmental factors

- Coaching
- Reinforcement
- Facilities
- Nutrition
- Ergogenic aids
- Money.

Worksheet 20: What makes an elite athlete?

(1) Study in detail the background of several elite athletes in different sports. Try to identify the factors that have contributed to their success. List these factors.

(2) 'Champions are born, not made.' What evidence is there to defend this statement?

22. Factors affecting performance

Even after all the training and preparation in the world, the athlete's final performance still depends on a number of extra factors:

- Biomechanical efficiency
- Effective equipment
- Mental preparation
- Prevention and treatment of injury
- Dietary manipulation and ergogenic aids
- Environmental conditions.

Biomechanical efficiency

Any activity requires the correct technique to use the available force and effort to maximum advantage. (This area is further explored in Part 3 of this book). For instance, the swimmer who employs a straight-arm recovery and slaps the arm into the water produces a bobbing motion that wastes effort. However, the biomechanically efficient swimmer uses a high, bent-elbow recovery and spears into the water. In this way he or she maintains a more efficient constant body position in the water, maximizing forward movement.

Effective equipment

Equipment might limit performance by failing to perform its appropriate function during competition — for example, a cracked mast during a yachting regatta. Similarly, athletes who do not use the appropriate safety equipment may limit their own performances through injury — for example, soccer or hockey players who do not wear shin guards.

Mental preparation

Despite all the skill and fitness training performed, if an athlete has not mentally practised and rehearsed a forthcoming competition, he or she is unlikely to justify that training.

Prevention and treatment of injury

Injury, either during training or competition, is the bane in the life of the athlete, and usually the most important and most frequent limitation to performance. The following information is designed to assist in injury prevention, treatment and recovery.

(1) Pre-season fitness testing

Undergo pre-season fitness testing to identify physical deficiencies.

(2) Pre- and in-season training

Aim to develop fitness in specific body areas that you need for your sport. Emphasize the areas of deficiency, as identified in the pre-season test.

(3) Warm up and flexibility exercises

By increasing muscle temperature and resting muscle length, you can greatly decrease the risk of injury.

(4) Protective equipment and safety gear

- Mouthguards, shin pads, helmets and goggles can prevent injury and pain, give confidence and enhance performance. It is worth remembering that 'the macho hero is a thing of the past'.
- Strapping and taping is also important in preventing new injuries or aggravating old injuries. In particular, ankle taping can be useful.
- Rings, sleepers, worn stops and long fingernails may all be safety hazards if worn while playing sport.
- Wear the correct clothing and gear for the specific sport. For instance, footy shorts used for distance running cause severe chafing and cheap heavy runners are not good for jogging, as they can lead to foot and lower-leg injuries.

(5) Umpiring (refereeing)

Good umpiring or refereeing is needed to enforce the rules of the game, therefore ensuring that each player is protected during play.

(6) Balanced competition

Examples include:

- Modified rules for juniors in some sports, such as no contact in junior football
- Gradings for height and weight rather than for age.

(7) Intelligent coaching

Intelligent coaches can:

- Emphasize winning by the rules
- Make sure that players are well trained — that is, given the skill and fitness needed to avoid injury
- Make sure that players are aware of the rules
- Make sure that injured players do not play; and apply rigid post-injury fitness tests to players before they return to the field.

(8) The field or training track

On the field or training track, make sure that fixed structures are safe. Check such features as padded goalposts and covered sprinklers.

(9) Allow for environmental conditions

- Make sure that drink stations provide plenty of fluid replacement during hot weather
- Arrange protection from rain and cold wind in very cold weather — for example, weatherproof coats and gloves.

(10) Play all out

A half-baked, unenthusiastic mental approach usually results in errors and injury.

Types of sports injury

(1) External violence

This includes contact injuries, such as a corked thigh and a broken nose.

(2) Internal violence

These include sprains, strains and tears — that is, usually soft-tissue injuries. Internal injuries may be of two types:

(a) Acute injuries

They occur immediately and spontaneously.

(b) Chronic injuries

They reappear at regular intervals because of a continuing weakness. Chronic inflammation and pain may be associated with the *overuse* or incorrect use of a body part.

RECOGNITION AND DIAGNOSIS OF INJURIES

[To avoid worsening an injury, it is essential to follow a plan of action in dealing with an injured player. For this reason all sports people should memorize the diagnosis plan presented by Dr Russell Gibbs in his booklet *Sports Injuries*.]

SALTAPS

Follow the detailed procedures represented by the above letters:

- **S — Stop play**

Stop play immediately an injury occurs. Either examine the player on the spot or remove him or her from the field or court for this purpose. In many cases, if this is done as soon as injury occurs, the player will be able to finish the game after first aid treatment has been given. This procedure is the most important in decreasing the effects of any injury and speeding the return to sport.

- **Ask**

Ask the player what happened, how, when or why. Get this information while it is fresh in the player's mind and make a note of it. (Besides, asking this information also takes the player's mind off the pain.)

'Describe in detail what actually happened:
'What were you doing before the injury?
'What did you go to do?
'What actually happened?
'How did it happen?
'Were you hit or not?
'If you were, where, and from what direction?
'What happened afterwards?
'Did you clear the ball?
'Could you stand, move, etc.?
'Did you play on?

'What does the pain feel like?' (A throbbing pain usually means that the blood circulation has been affected; a burning pain means the injury is neural; a stabbing pain means that it has affected the muscles or ligaments; and a gnawing pain usually shows it is an aggravated old injury.)

Then add some reassurance. 'Don't worry' helps the player who thinks he or she has a broken leg, whether it's true or not. We all need reassurance and comforting words when injured.

- **L — Look**

Now look at the injury very carefully before touching it. Carefully observe the injured area for change in colour, shape, size and resting position, and compare it with the opposite limb or part of the body. With recent injury, paleness or blanching may indicate arterial damage, while blueness can indicate obstruction to the veins draining the injured area. Redness in an old injury means inflammation. Obvious change in shape or resting position can be from fracture, dislocation or both. An increase in size occurring very suddenly or immediately after the injury will indicate rapid bleeding under the surface, compared with swelling increasing slowly over an hour or more. With joints, sudden swelling almost certainly comes from haemorrhage, whereas swelling coming on after two to four hours will probably be from an increase of joint fluid.

- **T — Touch**

Only when you have thoroughly looked at the injured area and its opposite limb or equivalent part should you touch the injured person to further assess the injury.

Begin by feeling the appropriate area of the opposite side of the body, taking particular note of the bone shapes, contours and landmarks, looking for obvious differences indicating bone injury. Next feel for variations in the amount and distribution of tissue over the bones and around the joints, checking any difference in tissue thickness, joint contents, lumps, bumps or collections of fluid under the surface. Difference in temperature may indicate the inflammation of infection.

- **A — Active movement**

With acute injuries, the next step is critical. Can **the injured person** move it? Not: can **you** move it? If the injured person cannot move the area around the injury, **do not try to do so for him or** ▶

her. Test for a full range of movement in the limb as a whole and the joints above and below the injury. With old injuries, restriction of range of movement is important.

Feel the injured area during movement through the full range for clicking, grating or creaking, and the alteration in tension of both soft tissue and joints.

- **P — Passive movement**

Only when you have established the degree and extent to which active movement is possible can you gently move the part through its range of movement without forcing movement in any way. This will give you the final information before proceeding to the next step.

- **Stand up, play on**

Can the injured person stand, can he or she bear weight on the injured leg or hold an arm against pressure? Can he or she walk? Can he or she run? Is he or she fit to play on? In cases of head injury or suspected concussion, check that the player knows what is going on and what to do next.

These methods will give you a good idea of the situation in both acute and old injuries. Remember that the decision to play on is *not* made by the athlete or coach but by the trainer. It does take the needs of the coach and the opinion of the athlete into account.

If you learn this method of procedure and apply it to all the injuries you see, you will soon begin to have a very good idea of the situation in both acute and old injuries. Experience plus feedback from the doctor who ultimately sees the injury will enlarge your knowledge and improve your judgement. You will have been of much use and will have done no harm if you have proceeded according to the plan outlined.

SUMMARY — SALTAPS
Stop play
Ask
Look
Touch
Active movement
Passive movement
Stand up, play on.

Note: Do not progress through the whole SALTAPS formula if you cannot complete each step in order.

— Dr Russell Gibbs, *Sports Injuries*, Macmillan, 1977

Treatment and rehabilitation

Immediate first aid

(1) Head injuries (concussion)

For head injuries, apply the '**ABC**' formula:

- **Airways**
  Place the person in the coma position, and clear the airways.
- **Breathing**
  Give mouth-to-mouth resuscitation if breathing cannot be detected in the injured person.
- **Circulation** (external cardiac compression)
  External cardiac compression (ECC) must be applied if the injured player does not have a pulse.

(2) Spinal injury

In case of spinal injury:

- Clear the area around the player
- Ring for an ambulance immediately
- Never move the patient, as further damage is likely to be caused.

(3) Soft tissue injuries (muscles, ligaments, skin)

Use cryotherapy, which relieves pain by decreasing circulation, and hence internal bleeding and swelling, and decreases muscle spasms. The main elements of this therapy are:

RICES:
Rest
Ice
Compression
Elevation
Stretch.

- **Ice**

Use crushed ice, cold pack, cold water or frozen food for:

— 0–12 hours: 20 minutes on, 20 minutes off
— 12–48 hours: 20 minutes on, 40 minutes off
— 48–72 hours: alternate hot and cold, such as a bucket filled with each
— 72+ hours: hot only, via ultrasound, hot water or diathermy.

Monitor the swelling. If it reappears, start the process again.

- **Compression**

Apply direct pressure to the area via tape or bandage.

- **Elevation**

Raise the body part so that the blood must work against gravity to reach the injured area. This will decrease circulation to the area.

- **Stretch**

For muscle injuries, maintain the muscle in a lengthened position during treatment so that the scar tissue or repair does not shorten the resting length of the muscle, and so that clotting blood can be removed easily later.

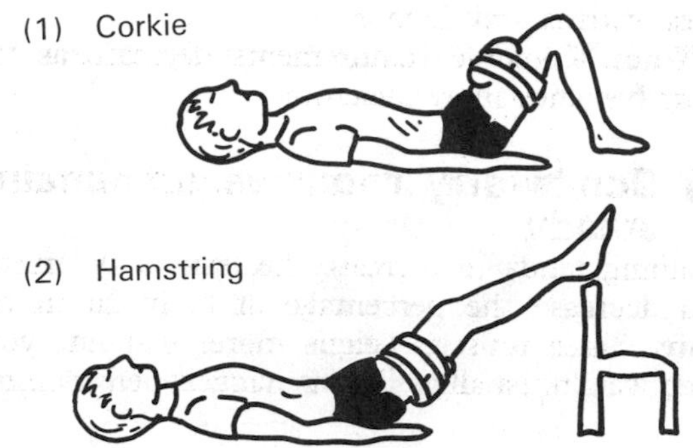

Figure 22.1 Dealing with muscle injury.
(1) Corkie
(2) Hamstring tear.

Rehabilitation of the injured player

The main principle of rehabilitation is: 'Increase activity within the limits of pain'.

(1) Flexibility exercises

Static, or PNF methods:

- Restore flexibility to previous level
- Improve on that level because it was inadequate in the first place; otherwise the injury probably would not have occurred.

(2) Strength and endurance exercises

They may include weights and calisthenics:

- Restore to previous level
- Then aim to improve on that strength level.

(3) Balance exercises

For joint injuries to restore the correct functioning of proprioceptors.

An example of rehabilitation

For instance, an athlete has suffered ankle ligament damage, and is rehabilitated using the following exercises:

- Flexibility exercises: ankle circles; sit on heels; heel drops
- Strength exercises: weighted ankle circles; calf raises (toes in, straight, out)
- Balance exercises: wobble or skate board.

A summary of treatment

Objective	Method
0–48 hours	
Ice and compression plus elevation	
Control bleeding	Crushed ice
Prevent oedema (tissue swelling)	Cryogel packs Bandages
Decrease tissue irritation	Air splints
After 48 hours	
Increasing activity within limits of pain	
Resolution of oedema	Cold Heat/cold Heat
Absorption of blood	
Resolution of blood clot	
Increase blood supply for tissue repair	Do not massage
After 5 days	
Stretch and strengthen to prevent recurrence or secondary injury	
Firstly	
Regain full flexibility to minimize fibrosis	Gentle passive and active stretching, progressing to full range movement
Later	
Restore strength and endurance to muscles	Correct graduated work load and training back to full power.

Dietary manipulation and ergogenic aids

Many misconceptions surround the usage and effect of dietary supplements and ergogenic aids. The following information is designed to guide you through the maze of available information, both factual and fictional.

(1) Balanced diet

Athletes require a balanced diet — that is, you need to choose from each of the food classifications.

(2) Prevention of overweight

You need to monitor your weight to see if your diet is fulfilling or exceeding your kilojoule needs. Your calorie intake might be too high if your weight is increasing.

(3) Body fat and lean body weight

A far more accurate measure of dietary effectiveness than weight is a measure of the percentage of weight that is actually lean body weight. That is:

- If your increased body weight is caused by an increased percentage of body fat, you need to reduce your calorie intake.
- If your increased body weight is caused by an increased percentage of lean body weight, you can maintain your calorie intake.

(4) Useful kilojoules versus 'empty calories'

Athletes usually require a high carbohydrate diet — that is, a high-kilojoule intake — because of their high kilojoule expenditure. However, these extra kilojoules should be taken in through useful nutritional foods, such as fruits, rather than through 'empty calories', such as junk foods, chocolate and sugar, which have no nutritional value and often contain toxic chemicals in their preservatives and flavour.

Note: Kilojoule requirements decrease as the sport becomes more anaerobic.

(5) Don't worry if your weight remains steady

Training tends to increase the lean body muscle and decrease the percentage of body fat in the body. Since muscle weighs more than fat, your body weight usually will not change when training.

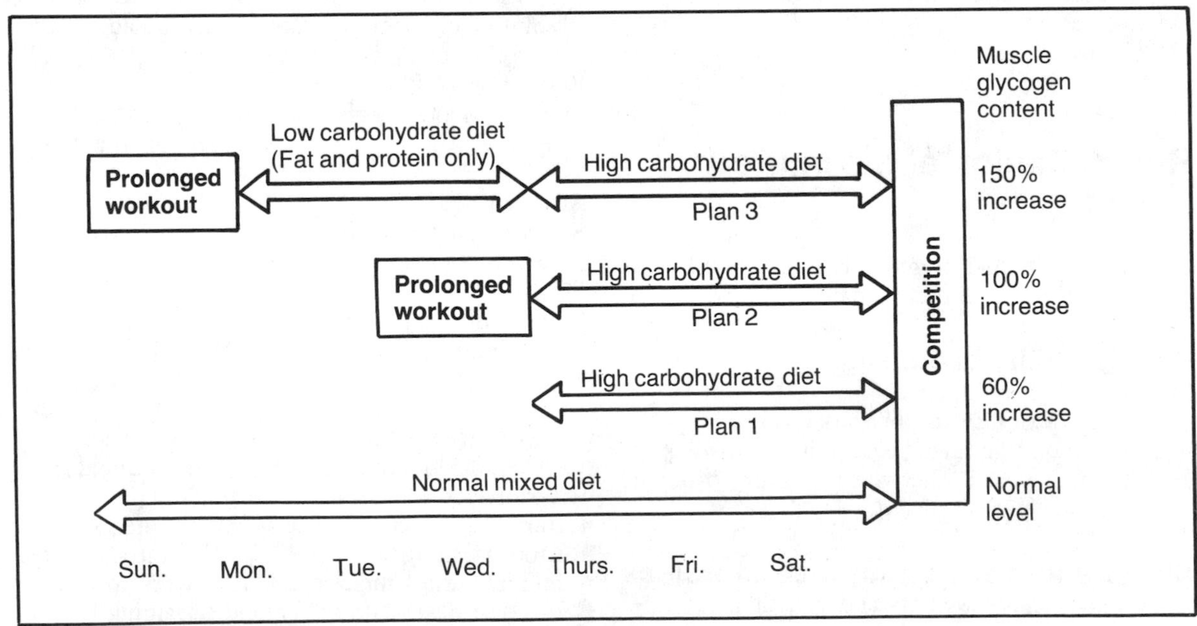

Figure 22.2 Three different muscle glycogen loading plans.

(6) Ways in which exercise does assist weight reduction

Exercise assists weight reduction by:
- Burning up stored carbohydrates and fats
- Acting as an appetite suppressant for several hours after training.

(7) Muscle glycogen levels

The higher the level of muscle glycogen, the better the performance during endurance events. Therefore a high-carbohydrate diet increases muscle glycogen levels (see Figure 22.2). Muscle glycogen levels are restored faster after exercise when you are on a high-carbohydrate diet.

(8) Carbohydrate loading

(See Figure 22.2.) Carbohydrate loading relies on the **glycogen supercompensation phenomenon** — that is, with repeated bouts of daily exercise, the repletion phase does not stop at pre-exercise levels of glycogen, but increases stores in anticipation of future exercise. By manipulating the diet and the frequency of exercise bouts just before a big competition, and relying on the glycogen supercompensation phenomenon, you can greatly increase your muscle glycogen levels and increase your endurance performance.

However, there is a problem with carbohydrate loading. For every gram of carbohydrate stored, you store 3.5 grams of water. When you increase your storage of muscle glycogen, you store more water in the muscle, and this leads to a feeling of stiffness or heaviness. Carbohydrate loading is useful only for events of 60 minutes or more.

(9) Use of fatty acids

Training improves the body's ability to use fatty acids for energy production, therefore slowing the usage of glycogen stores, and delaying fatigue.

(10) Protein loading

A certain amount of protein is required in the diet, because protein is the building block of most tissue, especially muscle. However, most Australians overdose on protein anyway, so protein loading is unnecessary, even if you are involved in a weight-training programme.

Protein loading greatly increases the chances of cardiovascular disease, because it increases the intake of saturated fat and cholesterol.

(11) Vitamin and mineral supplements

A well-balanced diet provides more than adequate vitamin and mineral requirements. Boosting your vitamin and mineral intake with tablets:
- Can only have a placebo effect
- Can lead to disorders of the liver and the bones (especially from excess Vitamins A and D)
- Produces expensive multi-coloured urine and stresses the kidneys (especially from excess Vitamins B and C).

Vitamins and mineral supplements should be taken in very small quantities only if an athlete does not eat a balanced diet.

(12) The pre-game meal

Use the pre-game meal to:
- Boost your carbohydrate intake, especially if you are facing an endurance event
- Eat carbohydrates anyway — at least two hours before a competition
- Eat fats, at least three to four hours before a competition
- Drink water up to 30 minutes before a competition
- Eat bowel-elimination foods, such as wholemeal bread, bran and fruits.

During the pre-game meal, avoid fatty, distasteful or gas-forming foods, since these can cause nausea and gastric disturbances.

Ergogenic aids

An ergogenic aid is any substance that improves performance. Some of the more common ergogenic aids are:

(1) Amphetamines

Amphetamines are used to improve endurance performance. They are stimulants that:
- Increase mental and physical alertness
- Decrease fatigue
- Increase one's metabolism
- Increase heart rate and blood pressure.

However, they have harmful side effects, especially if taken in excess. These effects include:

- Insomnia and depression
- Unwanted weight loss
- Abdominal cramps
- Blood in the urine
- Collapse and coma because of cardiovascular problems.

(2) Blood doping

This is the removal and reinfusion of a person's blood to improve the aerobic capacity by increasing the numbers of red blood cells. This increases the blood's oxygen-carrying capacity. There is a danger of increasing the viscosity of the blood, leading to heat stroke.

Blood doping seems to have little effect on the performance of trained athletes.

(3) Anabolic steroids

Anabolic steroids are artificially produced male hormones. They:

- Emphasize the anabolic (protein-building) properties of the hormone
- Minimize the androgenic properties of the hormone — for example, male characteristics such as facial hair
- Promote muscle growth and, therefore, increase the lean body weight.

Any benefits from taking anabolic steroids appear only after several weeks. They can cause such problems as:

- Liver damage
- Decreased sperm count
- Decreased libido (sex drive)
- Acne.

(4) Caffeine

Caffeine is a stimulant that:

- Increases the activity of the central nervous system
- Increases the athlete's strength by increasing recruitment
- Gives increased endurance by improving the release of fatty acids within the body, and therefore slowing the use of muscle glycogen and postponing fatigue.

Caffeine may be useful in the form of two cups of coffee just before a competition.

However, caffeine:

- Is a drug of addiction. If you are drinking more than two cups of coffee or more than a can of Coca-cola per day, you probably suffer from caffeinism (addiction).
- Causes increased fluid loss, so straining the kidneys and increasing the danger of dehydration
- Leads to acidic stomach and feelings of heartburn
- Increases irritability
- Can lead to withdrawal symptoms, such as headache and nausea.

(5) Aspirin

Aspirin is a drug that does not directly improve an athlete's performance, but may allow performance during periods of tendonitis or other inflammations by:

- Reducing the inflammation itself
- Blocking the transmission of pain caused by swelling tissue.

Taken in excess, aspirin can cause:

- Hyperventilation
- Nausea
- Dizziness and trembling.

(6) Anti-inflammatory drugs

Anti-inflammatory drugs include cortisone, which is a catabolic steroid. They can decrease the pain and inflammation caused by injuries by increasing the atrophy of muscles. They do this by hastening the breakdown of muscle protein (catabolism). Therefore if you use cortisone you become more susceptible to injury if you continue to train.

Environmental conditions

The three environmental conditions that affect performance are the extremes of wind, heat and cold.

(1) High wind

Problems associated with high wind cannot be avoided short of moving a competition indoors. However, the other environmental extremes require specific safety precautions.

(2) Extremes of heat

Once the temperature reaches 28°C, you need to take precautions to avoid dehydration and potential heat stroke and exhaustion:

- Drink small amounts of liquid frequently
- Wear light clothing

- Pour water over yourself
- Whenever possible, wear a hat.

If the temperature reaches 35° or above, abandon strenuous exercise.

(3) Extremes of cold

Similarly, on cold days, particularly when the wind is strong and it is wet or raining, take precautions to avoid hypothermia:

- Whenever possible, wear windproof or waterproof garments
- Wear warm and dry clothing, such as a track suit
- Whenever possible, wear a hat and gloves to control heat loss.

Laboratory work 32: Treatment of sports injuries

(1) Choose six students to act out the following injuries:
  (a) Torn ankle ligaments
  (b) Broken arm
  (c) Concussion
  (d) Spinal damage
  (e) Torn hamstrings
  (f) Corked thigh.

(2) Choose a different class member to diagnose and treat each of these injuries, whilst the remainder of the class critically assesses his or her procedure.

Workshop 21: Avoidance and treatment of sports injuries

(1) Decide whether each of the statements (a)–(p) is true or false.
  (a) Shin splints is an example of an acute, internal injury.
  (b) A burning injury signifies a chronic injury problem.
  (c) A dislocation is a soft tissue injury.
  (d) Cryotherapy is a method of administering heat via diathermy apparatus.
  (e) When treating soft tissue injuries, ice should be applied for 40 minutes on, 40 minutes off, after 12 hours.
  (f) If you know your percentage of body fat, you should by using your bath scales be able to calculate your lean body weight.
  (g) If an athlete's weight increases, he or she must be eating too much.
  (h) Empty calories are non-nutritional carbohydrates.
  (i) High-carbohydrate diets make little difference to muscle glycogen levels, but increase percentage body fat.
  (j) Carbohydrate loading is an excellent practice for any sports person.
  (k) Protein loading is a necessary practice for athletes involved in weight training.
  (l) All ergogenic aids require athletes to take something orally.
  (m) Steroid manufacturers emphasize the protein-building properties and minimize the anabolic properties of the artificial hormones.
  (n) Cortisone is a type of steroid.
  (o) A corked thigh is an example of an acute injury.
  (p) It would be of no value to apply ice to an injury caused by internal force.

Choose the correct response for each of Questions (2)–(16).

(2) Which of the following is an overuse injury?
  (a) Tendonitis
  (b) Hamstring tear
  (c) Bruising
  (d) Strained ligaments.

(3) A broken nose would be classified as:
  (a) Internal violence
  (b) External violence
  (c) Chronic injury
  (d) Soft tissue injury.

(4) If an injury throbs, it is likely to be:
  (a) Neural
  (b) Muscle damage
  (c) A chronic injury
  (d) None of the above.

(5) A marathon runner will be best able to sustain speeds close to his maximum if his pre-race diet (two to three days before the race) is:
  (a) High in carbohydrates; low in fats
  (b) Low in carbohydrates; low in fats
  (c) High in carbohydrates; high in fats
  (d) Low in carbohydrates; high in fats.

(6) A player tears a hamstring during a game and is taken off the field. Which of the following constitutes the correct first aid management?

(a) Ice pack applied over the muscle for approximately 20 minutes
(b) Massage the injured part
(c) Compression bandage applied around upper leg
(d) Both (a) and (c) above.

(7) Active movement in injury examination refers to:
(a) A player attempting to get up and play on
(b) A player moving the injured part himself
(c) The examiner moving the injured part
(d) Both (b) and (c) above.

(8) The use of heat in treating soft tissue injures should not be applied for:
(a) 12 hours
(b) 48 hours
(c) About an hour
(d) 5 days minimum.

(9) Which of the following is not directly aimed at reducing blood flow to the injured area?
(a) Ice
(b) Stretch
(c) Elevation
(d) Compression.

(10) Which exercise below would not be advisable for rehabilitation of an ankle injury?
(a) Weighted boot ankle circles
(b) Heel drops
(c) Wobble board work
(d) Agility runs.

(11) Which of the following would not be classified as an injury due to external force?
(a) Corked thigh
(b) Dislocated finger
(c) Sprained ankle
(d) Bruised skin.

(12) Pre-game meals:
(a) Should be eaten within two hours of the event so that the food is used to provide energy
(b) Should be high in both carbohydrate and fat
(c) Should not contain bowel-elimination foods
(d) Should contain fruits or bran.

(13) Which of the following are stimulants?
(a) Blood doping
(b) Amphetamines
(c) Anabolic steroids
(d) All of the above.

(14) The dangers of using anabolic steroids are:
(a) Acne
(b) Liver damage
(c) Decreased libido
(d) All of the above.

(15) Which of the following are physically addictive?
(a) Caffeine
(b) Money
(c) Cortisone
(d) Hypnotism.

(16) Anabolic steroids are taken to:
(a) Increase muscular strength
(b) Increase aerobic power
(c) Increase the body's resistance to lactic acid
(d) Increase heat acclimatization.

(17) What precautions should you take to lessen the risk of suffering:
(a) Heat problems?
(b) Hypothermia?

(18) You tear your hamstrings in a match. Describe what you would do from the time it occurs until six weeks later, when you resume playing.

(19) You find a player collapsed on the ground, conscious but in considerable pain. What do you do?

(20) You are planning to run in the Big M Marathon. How, in the week before the race, could you adjust your diet to improve your performance?

(21) List five ergogenic aids. For each, describe:
(a) How they improve performance
(b) The dangers of their use.

Part Three

Biomechanical factors involved in human movement

23. Human and projectile motion

Introduction to biomechanics

Biomechanics is the science that examines the internal and external factors acting on a human body, and the effects produced by these forces.

In other words, biomechanics studies what makes a body move and the results of that movement.

Once you have found out how your body actually moves, it is possible to work out scientifically how your body *should* move in order to perform a given task more efficiently. In this way, you can work out the various techniques needed to participate successfully in particular physical activities — for example, the Fosbury flop, the hitch kick and the handstand.

Motion

Motion is subject to the laws of the universe. If you understand the laws, you can improve the efficiency of your movement.

Motion is defined as the 'continued change of position of an object in space'. In order to analyse motion accurately, you need to describe the position of a body, and the time between its successive positions. Some concepts used when describing motion include **speed**, **velocity** and **acceleration**.

Definitions used when discussing motion

Some definitions you will need when discussing motion include:

- **Mass**

Mass is the amount of material of which an object is made. Mass does not vary from place to place.

- **Weight**

Weight is the force of attraction between an object and the earth. It can vary from place to place — for instance, objects weigh less on the moon, but retain the same mass that they have on earth. However, weight depends very much on the mass of a body (m), and its gravitational attraction. This is expressed as an equation:

$$W = m \times g.$$

- **Inertia**

Inertia is a body's resistance to change in motion, and is proportional to the body's mass. For instance, a medicine ball has greater inertia than a ping-pong ball.

- **Velocity**

Velocity is the rate at which a body moves from one location to another.

- **Acceleration**

Acceleration is the rate at which velocity changes with respect to time.

Movement of the body

Movement of the human body can take place only at a **joint** — therefore body motions are described in relation to **joint actions**. These include terms already defined in Part One of this book — terms like **flexion, extension, adduction** and **abduction**.

Types of motion

There are two basic types of motion:

- Translatory
- Rotary.

Translatory motion

During translatory motion, all points in a body describe parallel lines that are either straight or curved. Translation takes place when a body moves so that all parts of it travel exactly the same distance, in the same direction, in the same time.

(1) Linear or rectangular motion

Linear motion occurs when the points in a body describe **straight parallel lines**, as in tobogganing.

(2) Curvilinear motion

Curvilinear motion occurs when the points in a body describe **curved parallel lines**, as in skydiving, during the flight of an arrow, or as the earth orbits the sun.

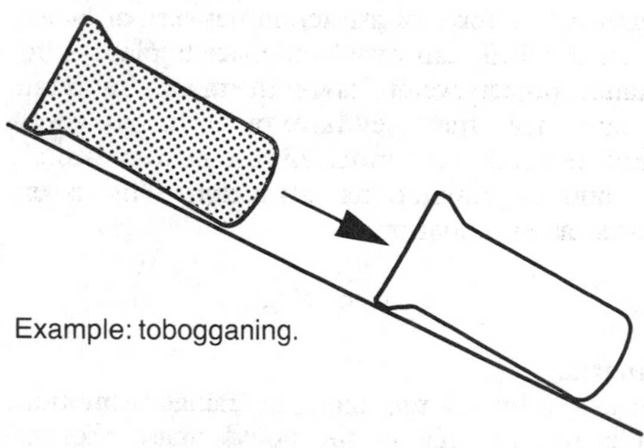

Figure 23.1 **Translatory movement: (1)** Linear or rectangular movement.

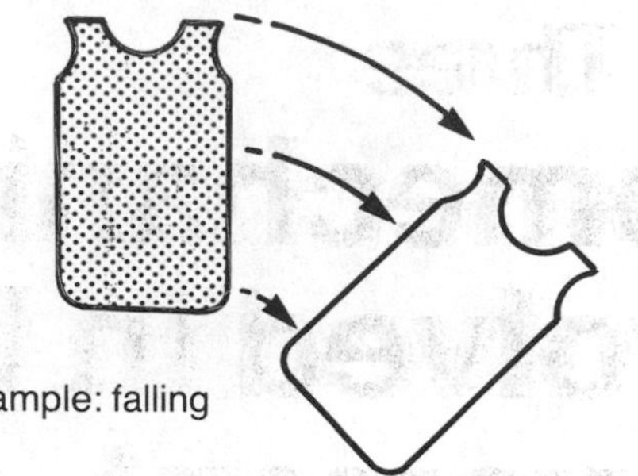

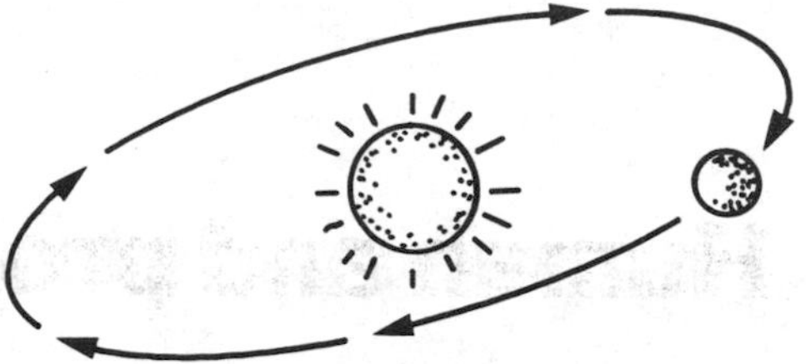

Figure 23.2 **Translatory movement: (2)** Curvilinear movement.

Angular, or rotary motion

Angular motion .is a common type of motion, during which a body moves about an **axis** — for example, as a record spins on a turntable, or a wheel turns. Angular motion often depends upon levers, where one part of the body is fixed (the axis) and the rest turns about the axis.

- **Internal axis**

This axis may pass through the body, usually at a joint. When it does, it is called an **internal axis** — for example, the arm action in bowling, or the earth spinning around its axis.

- **External axis**

The axis may be outside the body — that is, an **external axis**. An example is the giant swing in gymnastics, where the high bar is the axis, and the gymnast's body rotates around this.

General motion

In physical activity, angular motion is more common than linear motion, but more common still is motion that is a combination of the two. This is sometimes called **general motion**.

General motion may be described as **linear movement of the whole body that is achieved by the angular motion of some parts of the body**.

When walking, for example, your whole body

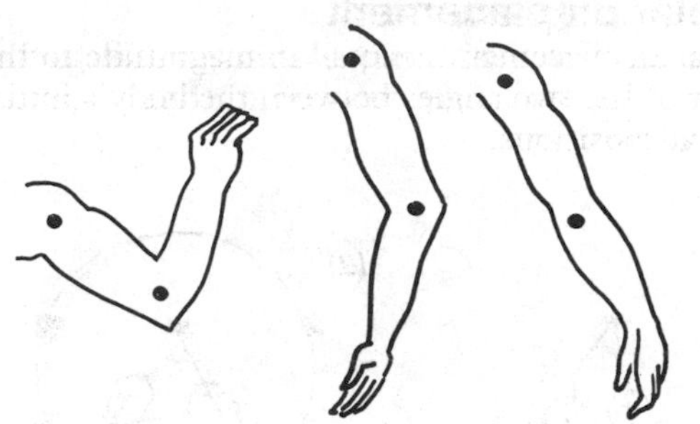

Example: arm movement. The shoulder and elbow joints act as internal axes to arm movement.

Figure 23.3 Rotary or angular movement.

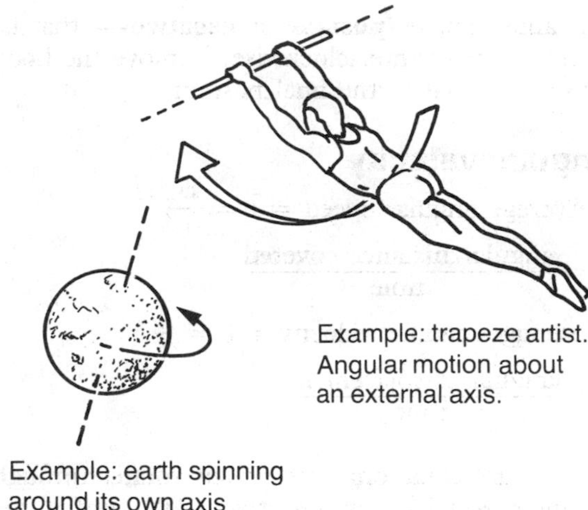

Example: trapeze artist. Angular motion about an external axis.

Example: earth spinning around its own axis

Figure 23.4 Angular motion.

experiences linear motion. However, this is achieved by the angular motion of the legs. In another example, a car moves linearly as a result of the angular motion of its wheels.

Some athletic events involve the combination of translatory and angular motion. For instance, rotational movements can give translation to a hit, thrown or held object, as in racquet sports, baseball, and hammer and javelin throwing.

When cycling, both the bicycle and the rider experience linear motion. The bicycle achieves this through the angular motion of its wheels, while the cyclist uses the angular motion of his legs. When cycling, your leg movement involves at least three simultaneous examples of angular motion:

- Your thigh rotates around the hip joint
- Your lower leg rotates around the knee
- Your foot rotates around the ankle.

Figure 23.5 General motion: translation and rotation combined.

Concepts of motion

Linear velocity

Linear velocity is the rate at which a body moves in a straight line from one location to another. It differs from average speed.

$$\text{Average speed} = \frac{\text{distance covered}}{\text{time taken}}$$

whereas

$$\text{Average velocity} = \frac{\text{displacement}}{\text{time taken}}$$

'Displacement' includes the idea of distance, but also infers the idea of direction. Here are a few examples:

Travel from A to B

A B

20 m in 5 seconds

Distance covered = 20 m

Speed $= \frac{20}{5} = 4$ m/sec.

Displacement = 20 m

Velocity $= \frac{20}{5} = 4$ m/sec.

Travel from A to B to A

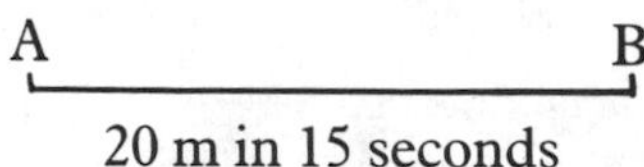

Distance covered $= 40$ m

Speed $= \frac{40}{30} = 1.33$ m/sec.

Displacement $= 0$ m

Velocity $= \frac{0}{30} = 0$ m/sec.

Travel from A to B to C

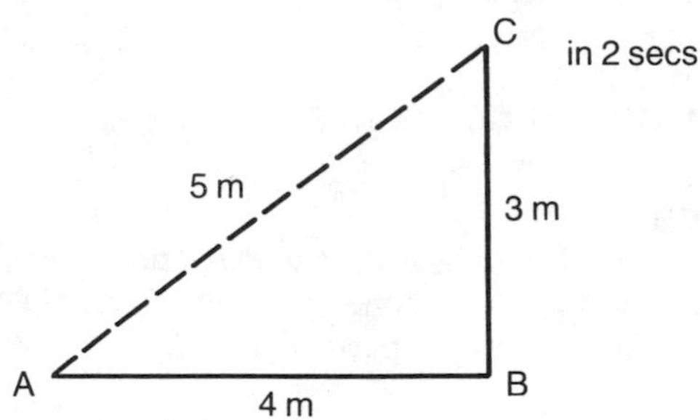

Distance covered $= 7$ m

Speed $= \frac{7}{2} = 3.5$ m/sec.

Displacement $= 5$ m

Velocity $= \frac{5}{2} = 2.5$ m/sec.

Angular distance

Angular distance is the angle between the initial position and the final position measured, following the path taken by the body. An example:

$\phi = 75°$

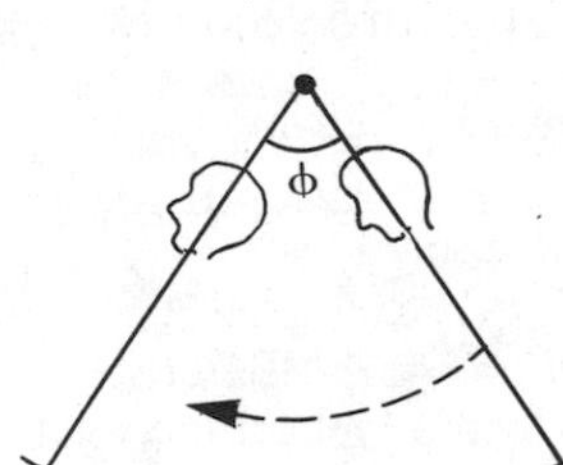

Angular displacement

Angular displacement is equal in magnitude to the smaller of the two angles between the body's initial and final positions.

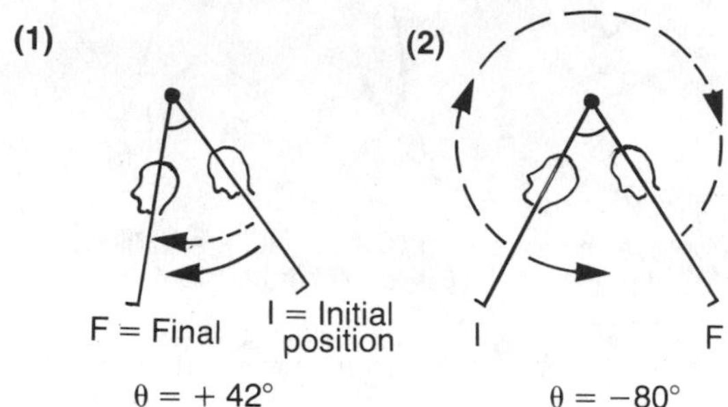

The angle can be **positive** or **negative** — that is, clockwise or counter-clockwise, to move the body from the initial to the final position.

Angular velocity

Average angular speed $= \bar{\theta} = \frac{\phi}{t}$

$= \frac{\text{angular distance covered}}{\text{time}}$

Average angular velocity $= \bar{\omega} = \frac{\theta}{t}$

$= \frac{\text{angular displacement}}{\text{time}}$

$\bar{\theta}$ and $\bar{\omega}$ are equal only if the body rotates through an angle equal to, or less than 180°, and if the rotation is in one direction.

Linear acceleration

Linear acceleration can be expressed as the following equation:

$$\bar{a} = \frac{v_f - V_i}{t} = \frac{\text{final velocity} - \text{initial velocity}}{\text{time}}$$

If $\bar{a}$ is a negative value, the object is 'decelerating', 'retarding' or 'slowing down'. This can be seen when blocking in volleyball.

Acceleration changes during a jump. If you are performing this action, you show negative acceleration in the air when going up; zero acceleration at the height of the jump; and positive acceleration when coming down (disregarding direction of movement).

Figure 23.6 Linear acceleration. Example: blocking in volleyball.

Angular acceleration

Angular acceleration is the rate at which the angular velocity of a body changes with respect to time.

$$= \alpha = \frac{W_f - W_i}{t} = \frac{\text{final ang. velocity} - \text{initial ang. velocity}}{\text{time}}$$

Projectile motion

Any body that is released into the air becomes a projectile. As a human body, you and the objects you propel can be considered as projectiles. Examples include:

- **Throwing:** discus, cricket fielding, softball and lacrosse
- **Striking:** tennis, football and cricket
- **Projecting of the body itself:** jumping, diving, skiing and gymnastics.

The striking or throwing can be done either by a body part or by an implement held by a body part.

The initial velocity can also be supplied *indirectly* by moving an object which, in turn, causes another object to be projected. This happens when firing a gun or drawing a bow.

Whether projectiles are inanimate (such as a baseball, tennis ball, shot put, javelin or discus) or human (such as a vaulter, a long jumper or a hurdler), they are governed by the principles of:

- Velocity
- Vertical displacement (height)
- Horizontal displacement (distance).

The projectile's predetermined path of flight is influenced by:

- The force applied to it, establishing its velocity at release
- The angle of release
- The height of release
- Impact
- Spin.

Propelling force

The most important of the forces applied to the projectile is propelling force. All things being equal, the greater the propelling force, the further the projectile will travel.

Opposing this force are the forces of:

- **Gravity**, which acts on vertical motion
- **Air resistance**, which acts on horizontal motion.

These two forces cause the formation of a **parabolic** flight path.

(1) Gravity

Gravity's influence depends on the weight of the object. The heavier the object, the greater the acceleration towards the ground.

(2) Air resistance

Air resistance causes a projectile to fall to the ground before it has completed its parabolic path. For many activities, air resistance is of little consequence, but it is obvious that in some sporting activities, its force plays an important part.

- The lighter an object and the larger its surface area, the more it is affected by air resistance — for example, a shuttlecock is affected more than a tennis ball.
- Air resistance also increases with speed so that, for instance, a golf ball drive is more affected than a golf ball lifted gently onto the green.
- Air resistance is also increased by any motions in a direction other than the direction of flight — for example, a spinning football or a quivering arrow.
- Since air resistance acts on the horizontal component, you need to increase that component by lowering the angle of release in order to compensate for the effects of air resistance. The greater the air resistance, the lower the angle of release should be.
- The surface covering of a projectile influences the degree of air resistance. For instance, a cyclist should wear a smooth outfit to reduce frontal and surface drag.

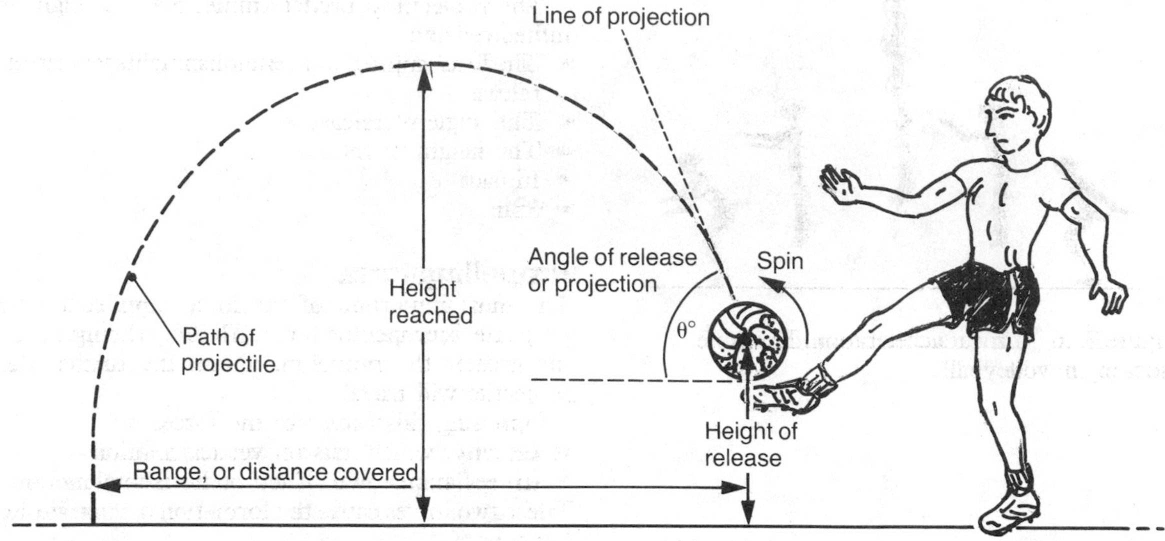

Figure 23.7 Projectile motion.

Centre of gravity

(Discussed further in Chapter 24.) In Figure 23.7, the parabolic flight path traced by the object's centre of gravity *cannot* by altered after takeoff.

When you are in the air without support, your centre of gravity cannot be raised or lowered, although movement may raise or lower your body parts around the centre of gravity. This can be seen clearly in these high jump styles:

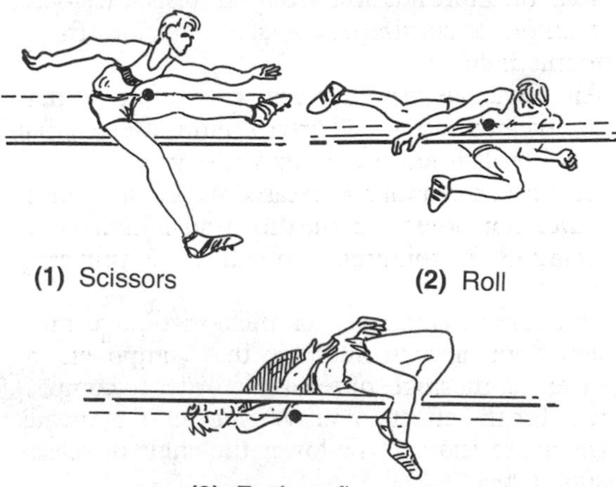

Figure 23.8 High jump styles. For the same height reached by the centre of gravity (•), differing heights can be jumped.

In this way it is possible to jump differing heights, although the centre of gravity (•) reaches the same height.

Vertical projection

In vertical projection — as when throwing up a ball 90° to the ground — the speed decreases gradually to zero at the maximum height of the throw. After that, **gravity** causes the body to return to the ground.

Vertical height and the **time** of the flight are determined solely by the **vertical velocity** at release or takeoff. The [downward velocity, distance and time] = [upward velocity, distance and time].

Horizontal projection

For any projection, other than straight up or down, a horizontal component is involved. Figure 23.9 shows the relative magnitude of the horizontal and vertical components of a given force, applied at various angles.

If the propelling force is constant, the angle at which the object is projected — **angle of release** — determines the **height** that it reaches, assuming that the take-off and landing levels are the same. Different sports need differing angles of projection. For instance:

- A high angle of projection — about 80° — is needed in a badminton serve and a volleyball set

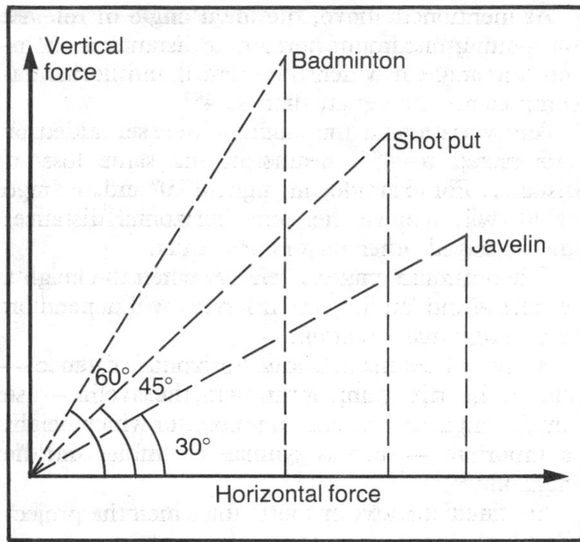

Figure 23.9 Relative magnitude of horizontal and vertical components of a given force, applied at various angles.

- Medium angles — about 45° — are needed for shot putters
- Low angles are needed for baseball pitchers and long jumpers.

The horizontal range depends on:

- Speed
- Angle
- Height of release.

In general, **the greater the speed of release, the greater the distance covered.**

Factors affecting projectile motion

(1) Speed or velocity of release

The greater the speed of release, the greater the range. Generally, the speed of release has a greater influence on the range of a projectile than the angle or height of release.

The greater the initial vertical velocity, the greater the flight time and the greater the height reached. Conversely, the greater the initial horizontal velocity, the greater the horizontal distance able to be covered.

In many activities, the speed of the projectile is

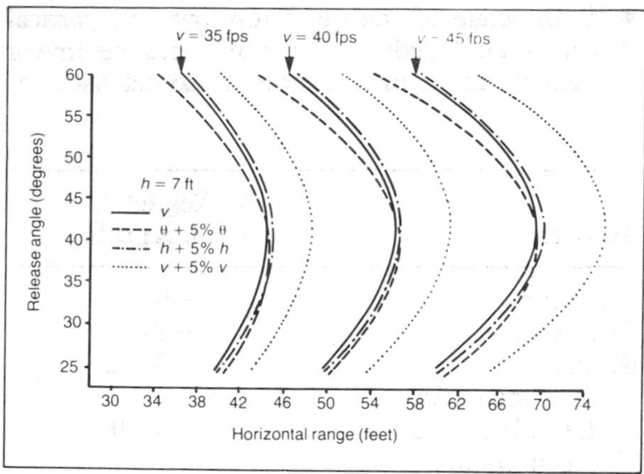

Figure 23.10 The effects of 5 per cent changes in the speed, height and angle of release of a shot, on the total distance the shot is thrown.

more important than gaining the maximum distance (for instance, in basketball or archery). Since a low angle increases the horizontal component, the lower the angle of release, the faster the projectile will reach its destination. However, if the angle is too low, the vertical component will reduce the time of flight, thereby reducing the horizontal distance — in other words, the projectile will hit the ground before reaching its target. To compensate for this, the velocity of release must be increased.

So, **the lower the angle of release, the greater the release velocity** must be if the projectile is to travel the required distance.

(2) Angle of release

For any given speed of release, the **optimum angle** at which you need to project a body in order to obtain the maximum horizontal range is 45°. This applies **only where the release and landing occur at the same level**, and where there is no spin and no air resistance.

In sporting situations, the angle is almost always less than 45°; 35° to 45° is the most common range of angles, taking into consideration the height of release and the presence of air resistance.

The angle of release influences the trajectory of a projectile in the following way:

- If the angle of release is too high, the horizontal component is reduced, thus reducing the horizontal distance.

- If the angle of release is too low, the vertical component is reduced, thus reducing the time of flight which, in turn, reduces horizontal distance.

Activity	Angle* (degrees)
Ski jumping	−4
Tennis serve	−3–15
Racing dive	5–22
Triple jump (step)	11–13
Volleyball float serve	13–20
Triple jump (hop)	16–18
Triple jump (jump)	16–21
Long jump	17–22.5
Javelin throw	25–34
Discus throw	35–38.5
Shot put	33.7–40
Hammer throw	40
High jump (Fosbury flop)	40–48
High jump (straddle)	42–53
Handspring vault (board)	52
Front somersault (tuck)	53
Round-off, back somersault (layout)	58
Round-off, back somersault (tuck)	63.5
Standing back somersault (tuck)	75

*Angles above the horizontal are considered to be positive and angles below the horizontal to be negative. Where one number is given, this is the mean of all the values obtained. Two numbers indicate the range of the recorded values.

Figure 23.11 Angles of take off and release used in selected activities.

As mentioned above, **the ideal angle of release** for gaining maximum horizontal distance is therefore the angle at which the vertical and horizontal components are equal, that is, **45°**.

Any variation in the angle of release, added or substracted to 45°, results in the same loss of distance. For example, an angle of 50° and an angle of 40° will achieve the same horizontal distance, given that all other factors are equal.

The optimum angle of release, when the heights of release and landing are different, will depend on each individual situation.

Activities requiring a large horizontal distance — such as the triple jump or throwing the javelin — use smaller angles of release than those for which height is important — such as gymnastic tumbles and the high jump.

As stated already, in sports for which the projectile takes off and lands at the same level, as in soccer, the optimum angle is 45° theoretically.

When the projectile lands at a lower level than at takeoff — as in the shot put and long jump (as determined by the body's centre of gravity at takeoff and landing) — the optimum angle is always less than 45°, and depends on the height and speed of release.

When the projectile lands at a higher level than at takeoff, as in golf, the optimum angle is greater than 45°.

(3) Height of release

For a given speed and angle of release, as the height of release increases, the horizontal range is increased — see Figure 23.12 (2). If the landing height is higher than the release height, the horizontal range is decreased — see Figure 23.12 (3).

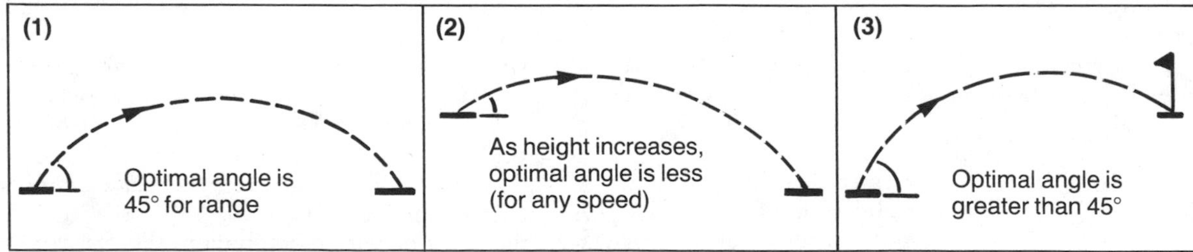

Figure 23.12 Optimal angles.

Activity	Speed of release	Angle of release	Height of release	Air resistance
shot put	Most important	35°–40°	Taller athletes have the advantage	Negligible
Hammer throwing	Most important	Approx. 45° (released close to ground)		Negligible
Discus	Most important	32°–40°	Taller athletes have the advantage	Important to use lift. Lift proportional to the square of the speed. (Discus and Javelin)
Javelin	Most important	Less than 35°	Taller athletes have the advantage	

Figure 23.13

A note on spin

The range of a projectile is decreased with top spin — for instance, during passing shots in tennis — and increased with back spin — as during the defensive stroke in tennis. Hooking and slicing — as in golf and soccer — alter the projectile's flight path so that it can veer to either the right or the left.

Laboratory work 33: Determine the influence of speed, angle and height of release on the distance of an arrow's flight

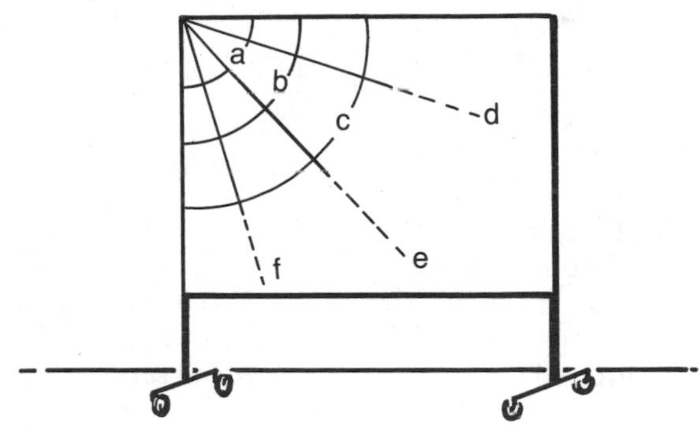

Figure 23.14

Height (1)

Speed of release	Angle of Release		
	30°	45°	60°
(a)			
(b)			
(c)			

Height (2)

Speed of release	30°	45°	60°
(a)			
(b)			
(c)			

Method

(1) Set up a drawing board on coasters in an open area.

(2) Draw lines on the drawing board as shown:
   (a) Small drawback of a bow string
   (b) Moderate tautness of a bow string
   (c) Limit of a bow string.
   Examples (a)–(c) create increasing speeds of release for the arrow.
   (d) 30° to the horizontal
   (e) 45° to the horizontal
   (f) 60° to the horizontal.
   Examples (d)–(f) establish the angle of release of the arrow.

(3) To vary the height, set up (a) to (f) on a board held higher and/or lower than the original drawing board. Record the distances reached, as shown in Figure 23.14.

Laboratory work 34: Demonstrate the influence of air resistance on the distance of an arrow's flight

(1) Keeping the height, speed and angle of projection as constant as possible:

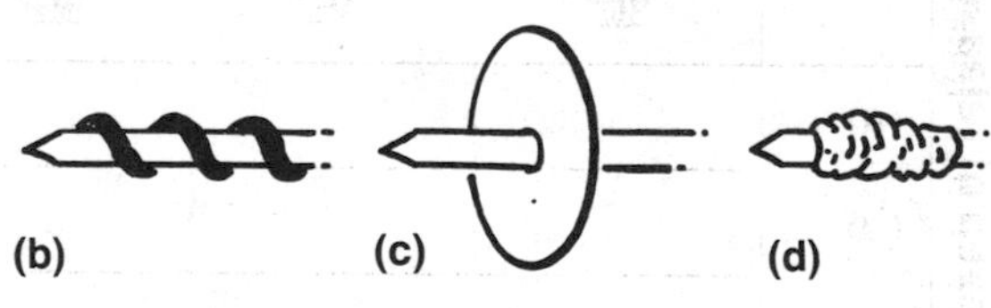

   (a) Shoot an arrow
   (b) Place a piece of plasticine around the arrow — that is, increase its mass
   (c) Place a circle of cardboard around the arrow — that is, increase its frontal area
   (d) Place rough paper around the arrow — that is, increase its surface area.
   Make the alterations to the arrow near its tip so that its release will not be interrupted.

(2) Record the distances reached after (a), (b), (c) and (d). Do the results align with theory?

Worksheet 22: Linear, angular and projectile motion

(1) Linear motion is:
   (a) Movement in a straight line
   (b) Movement in a straight or curved line, so that all parts of the object travel exactly the same distance in the same amount of time
   (c) Movement in a straight line that enables an object to cover as great a distance as possible in as short a time as possible
   (d) None of the above.

(2) Write this table into your notebook. Indicate with a tick the type of motion(s) occurring:

	Recti-linear	**Curvi-linear**	**An-gular**
Earth orbiting the sun			
Elbow flexion			
Running home from third base			
Rounding a bend in track			
Free flight in ski jumping			
25 m freestyle swim			
The path of a thrown ball			
The twist in a dive			
The path of a diver			
A 'hook' in bowling			

(3) **Torque**
Torque, or twist, can be rotary (angular) movement in any plane about an axis of motion. Torque occurs when bones move around each other at joints which serve as axes of movements.

From the table, write into your notebook the activities that give an example of torque.

Working a woodscrew into a plank Pulling a nail from a plank (no aids) Wringing out a wet towel Extending the elbow Stepping on the accelerator Riding down a roller coaster Turning on the TV Standing at attention Shoulder action in forehand tennis stroke Chewing gum Drinking through a straw	

(4) 'The inertia of a body is its ability to move when a force is applied.' Is this statement true or false?

(5) What is another name for linear motion? Give an example.

(6) Define angular motion. What is another name for angular motion? Give an example.

(7) What is general motion? Give an example.

(8) For each of the following, state what type of motion is undergone by the *whole* body:
  (a) A 400-metre runner on a running track
  (b) The discus in the hand of the thrower
  (c) A drag-racing driver
  (d) A weight-lifter
  (e) A baseballer running from home to first base.

(9) For each of the following instances, say whether acceleration is positive, negative or zero:
  (a) A high jumper at the top of the jump
  (b) A tennis ball nearing the highest point of its flight
  (c) A diver about to hit the water
  (d) A trampoliner immediately after leaving the mat
  (e) A skydiver just after opening the parachute.

(10) What is the difference between weight and mass?

(11) Complete the following statement: 'Inertia is best described as ....'

(12) The optimal angle of projection is 45°, all things being equal. However, for the following events, would the angle have been better if it were greater than, or less than 45° from the ground?

Event	Greater/less than 45°
Pole vault Outfielder's baseball throw Field goal kick Long jumper	

(13) All things being equal, if you were elevated 1.5 metres above the ground and throwing for distance, what would your optimal angle of release be?
  (a) 85°
  (b) 65°
  (c) 45°
  (d) 35°.

(14) Why is the optimal angle for the long jump around 22°?

(15) Name three factors that might influence the distance a projectile moves.

(16) A person is pushing a heavy box across the floor. Muscular force is exerted in the direction indicated by the arrow.

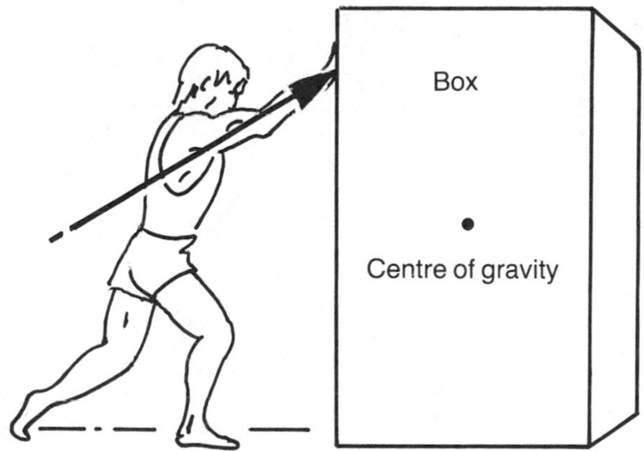

  (a) Draw dotted line arrows indicating the two components of force.
  (b) Which component represents unnecessary work and, in turn, increases the difficulty of the task?
  (c) Indicate by a solid line arrow the direction in which the person should have applied his force.

(17) You are playing a volleyball match. Compare the desired release velocities of the dig volley and the spike:

(a) How do the different aims of these strokes influence the ideal release velocity of the ball?

(b) How does the release velocity of the player affect his jump?

(18) Why is it important to gain maximum height in performing the spike?

(19) Compare the angles of release of the dig, the volley and the spike:

(a) From your knowledge of biomechanics, what influence will the angle of release have on the flight of the ball?

(b) How does a player's angle of take off influence his performance in a spike? How can he achieve the optimum angle of take off?

(20) Revise the section in this chapter on projectile motion. List the outlined factors that are important considerations when playing badminton. Give reasons for your answer.

(21) Why is a Fosbury flop style of high jump more effective than other methods?

(22) Give three instances in sport where the speed of the projectile is more important than the distance it travels.

(23) Give three examples from sporting situations where the distance a projectile travels is more important than the speed at which it travels.

(24) Why is this statement not accurate? 'The lower the angle of projection, the faster the projectile will travel to its destination.'

(25) What factors increase the effect of air resistance on a projectile?

(26) How would you adjust your throw of a javelin in order to compensate for a high level of air resistance? Give reasons for your answer.

(27) Why will the distance of a throw be reduced:

(a) If the angle of release is too high?

(b) If the angle of release is too low?

(28) Under what circumstances is the ideal angle of release 45°?

(29) All Olympic shot putters are over 180 centimetres tall, weigh at least 100 kilograms and can run 100 metres in 10 seconds. How do these factors contribute to longer throws?

24. Force and body levers

Force

Force can be described as 'a push or a pull' or 'the effect that one body has upon another'. Force can:
- Cause a body at rest to move
- Cause a moving body to slow down, stop, increase its speed or change its direction.

Force can produce three types of movement, either separately or together:
- **Deformative movement:** a force that changes the shape of the body
- **Translational movement:** a force that moves the body from one place to another
- **Rotational movement:** a force that causes the body to rotate.

When you kick a football, you produce the three types of movement at one time:

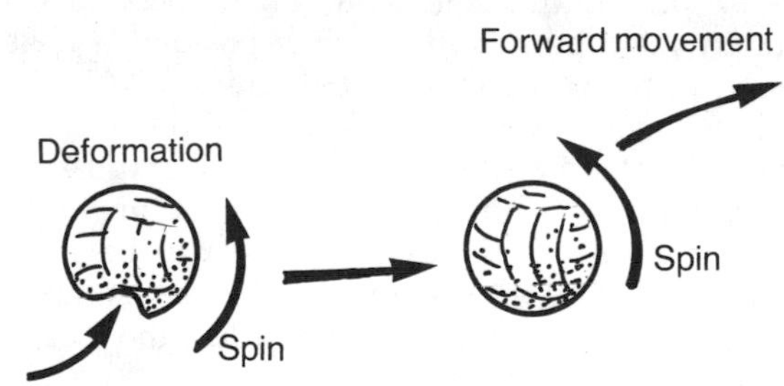

Figure 24.1 Kicking a soccer ball.

The magnitude of acceleration caused by a force will depend on the mass of the body being moved. For a given force, the larger the mass, the smaller the acceleration. (Which is why, for example, sprinters would aim not to carry excess weight.)

Measuring force

Force can be measured in terms of:
- Magnitude
- Direction
- Point of application
- Line of action.

Magnitude of force

The magnitude of muscular force is in direct proportion to:
- The **size and number** of muscle fibres exerting tension
- The speed at which active fibres are forced to lengthen.

Maximum tensions occur when the **active muscles are stretched quickly**. For instance, if you are performing the high jump, you quickly lower your body on ground contact, and quickly check your horizontal motion before jumping, in order to stretch the quadriceps before take off. (Remember from Part One that more tension — 120 per cent — can be produced in a muscle that is stretched slightly beyond its resting length.)

Direction of force

To measure the direction of a force, you need to consider the total resultant body force. For example:
- When high jumping, first lower yourself, to enable more vertical force to result
- When running, concentrate on maximal horizontal movement, and avoid lateral movement.

Point of application of force

You need to take advantage of the point where the force is applied — for example, the spot where you place your feet prior to a high jump.

Line of action of force

The line of action of a force can be described as the body's point of application, plus the direction of the force (or line of force, applied in a straight line).

If you want to apply spin or curve to a moving body, apply a force outside the centre of gravity. This eccentric (off-centre) force will give extra rotation to the object.

Inertia and force

When you want to set in motion a body, or a segment of a body, you need to overcome the tendency of the body to remain at rest. This tendency is called **inertia**, which the force overcomes.

Sometimes a force may not be enough to alter the state of motion of an object — for example, when a small child tries to lift a heavy weight. Scientifically speaking, however, the force applied by the child has brought the weight nearer to the point at which it will move. In other words, the child *tends* to move the weight.

Therefore it is more accurate to define **force** as **'that which alters or tends to alter a body's state of rest or uniform motion in a straight line'**.

- **Force without motion**

If a force is applied — as when the child tends to move the weight, but no movement is observed — this is described as a **force without motion**. Isometric contractions are examples of this type of force — for example, when gripping a javelin or shot put.

- **Submaximal force, or optimal force**

Other actions require only a submaximal force or optimum force — for example, where accuracy is more important than speed: putting in golf, lay up shots in basketball, or bunting in baseball.

- **Maximal force**

(See 'Force summation' later in this chapter.)

Forces that act on the body

Forces that act on the body may:

- Originate within the body
- Originate outside the body.

Forces originating within the body

Usually a force originating within the body is provided by concentric, and at times eccentric muscle contraction, which acts upon bones with sufficient force to set them in motion.

A muscle creates pull by contracting along its long dimension. Typically, a muscle contracts up to one-half of its resting length. The amount of pull produced by a muscle is proportional to its cross-sectional area (3 kilograms per square centimetre of muscle at optimal length).

Forces originating outside the body

Gravity is the most persistent of the outside forces acting on the body. All objects within the earth's gravitational field are constantly subjected to the force of gravity, which is exerted in a vertical direction downward toward the centre of the earth. The magnitude of the force of gravitational attraction that the earth exerts on an object is called its **weight**.

Centre of gravity

Gravity acts on all points of any object. It is the distribution of these points in space that determines the location of the centre of gravity. The centre of gravity is defined as **'the point of concentration of mass'** or, more simply, **'the point in relation to which all parts of the object are in balance'**.

In the case of a symmetrical body with uniform density, such as a ball or a block, the geometrical centre is also the centre of gravity.

The human body, however, is irregularly shaped, and has many moveable parts. Therefore its centre of gravity cannot be defined so easily. Also, it changes with every change in position of a body part. When you are in standing position, your centre of gravity is located at a distance, about 55 per cent of the total standing height (and is higher for males — 57 per cent). In general, then, the centre of gravity for a human in standing position is considered to be in the region of the hips.

If an external weight is added to a body part, the weight of that body part changes. There must be a corresponding shift in the centre of gravity to balance all body parts. This shift will be in the direction of the external weight. Similarly, amputations and congenital deformities affect the location of the body's centre of gravity.

Newton's First Law: The law of inertia

Newton's First Law states that **'An object at rest tends to remain at rest unless acted upon by some external force'**. A barbell lying on the ground is said to have **stationary inertia**.

The law also expresses that **'an object in motion tends to remain in motion and to travel in a straight line with uniform velocity unless acted upon by some external force'**. Train passengers tend to lurch forward after the train stops, because their bodies are said to possess a certain amount of **moving inertia**. Their bodies are reluctant to change the direction in which they are travelling.

Dyson puts it this way: '. . . everything in the universe is lazy, so lazy that force is necessary to get it on the move, when it then travels in a straight line with constant speed; . . . once in motion, further force must be applied to slow it down, stop it, speed it up or change its direction.'

Once a body is moving, it takes less force to keep it moving at a constant speed than it does to change its speed. A fast-travelling baseball is not easy to stop or have its direction changed.

Here are some examples of **forces that:**

- **Slow down objects:** ground and air friction, gravity, and contact with other players
- **Speed up objects:** implements for hitting, such as racquets, and body parts that apply force.

Overcoming inertia

For movement to occur, the force applied must be sufficient to overcome inertia. **The greater an object's mass and any resistive force**, such as friction, air or water resistance, and gravity, **the greater is the force necessary to move it**.

When a force is applied to a body that is moving, the body moves in the direction in which the force acts. This may not be obvious, since the body may retain some motion in its original direction.

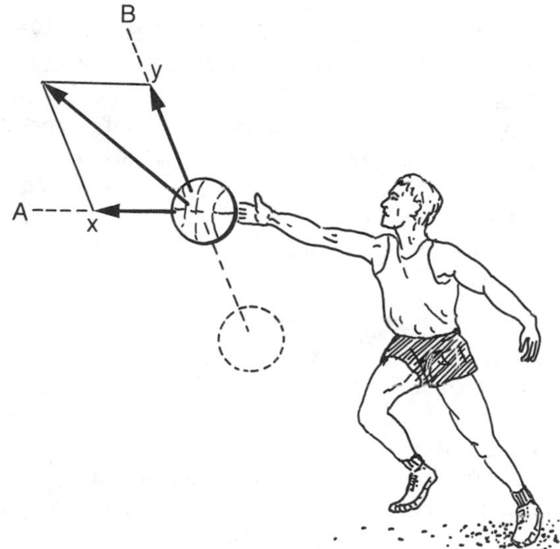

Figure 24.2 A deflected pass in basketball—the applied force accelerates the ball in the direction in which the force acts.

In Figure 24.2, the ball is on its way up, and the basketballer just manages to reach it with his outstretched hand in order to apply a horizontal force. The resultant direction of the ball depends on the sum of the two forces. In order for the direction of the ball to be changed completely to the direction in which the second force is applied, the second force must be much greater than the first.

Because of every object's tendency to maintain its state of motion (inertia), it takes more force to start an object moving than to keep it moving. Sometimes, as in Figure 24.3, the starting force is so great that it is impossible to control the object's motion once inertia has been overcome.

Figure 24.3

The inertia of an object is directly proportional to its mass — the quantity of matter of which a body is composed. A body with a greater mass will need a greater force to overcome its inertia, compared with a less massive body. For instance, a medicine ball requires more force to move it compared with a volleyball, which has a lower mass, and therefore less inertia. In rugby, it is hard to stop a well-built, solid player because he has more inertia than a slight player. A weight-lifter increases the bar's mass every time he or she adds more weights to the ends, hence increasing its inertia.

Momentum

Momentum is 'the amount of motion possessed by a moving object'. Every body in motion has a certain mass and a certain velocity; the product of these two is its momentum. That is:

$$M_0 = m \times v.$$

A body's momentum can be changed by altering either its mass or its velocity (more common). Likewise:

- If the mass is constant, the momentum increases if the velocity increases
- If the velocity is constant, the momentum increases if the mass increases.

The momentum of an object increases with any increase in either mass or velocity. Since, in sporting situations, the mass of an object remains constant, **any change of momentum is synonymous with a change in velocity** — that is, **acceleration**.

Moving inertia of an object

The moving inertia of an object is proportional to its momentum. Therefore:

- If two objects of the same mass travel at different velocities, the object possessing the greater velocity is more difficult to stop.

or

- If two objects travel with the same velocity, but different mass, the heavier object is more difficult to stop.

Collisions

Momentum is important when there is a collision with another body. The greater the momentum, the greater the effect on the other bodies, and the greater is the force required to stop a body. For example, when catching a ball, the faster it is moving, the more force is required to stop it.

Striking situations

Momentum is also important in striking situations. The speed at which a baseball is hit depends on the momentum of the bat. When playing baseball, you can adjust how hard you hit the ball by either changing the velocity of the swing or by using a lighter or heavier bat (changing its mass). However, a heavier bat will slow down the swing, so you may gain little advantage.

A 'bunt' is a low-velocity swing with less momentum than a 'home run'.

Altering velocity

When performing at sport, usually you alter your own velocity (but not your mass) in order to impart greater momentum to an object, or for your own projection. For instance, if you were long jumping, you would concentrate on improving the velocity of the run up in order to increase your momentum just before take off.

The conservation of momentum

The **linear momentum** of the long jumper is said to be **conserved** while he or she is in the air. The mass and velocity cannot be altered (and air resistance is not an important factor) until the jumper lands. The landing alters the jumper's velocity.

Therefore, to conserve linear momentum, **either** the mass and velocity are constant (as in the example above); **or** the mass and velocity are inversely proportional — as one increases, the other decreases accordingly to keep momentum constant. Where two bodies collide, the sum of their momenta remains constant, while the bodies themselves either speed up or slow down as a result. Newton's First Law embodies this concept of the conservation of momentum.

Newton's Second Law of Motion: The law of acceleration

Newton's Second Law of Motion states that '**When a body is acted upon by a force, its resulting change in momentum (acceleration) is proportional to the force causing it, and inversely proportional to the mass, and the change takes place in the direction in which the force is applied.**'

This can be expressed as:

$$a = \frac{f}{m} \quad \text{or} \quad f = ma$$

In other words:

- The greater the force, the greater the acceleration
- The smaller the mass, the greater the acceleration
- The change in motion takes place in the direction in which the force is applied.

A slow-moving object (such as a train or a truck) can have great momentum because of its size, while a small object depends on its velocity for increased momentum.

Consider a golf ball, a tennis ball and a soccer ball being struck with the same force. Which has the greater acceleration? Why?

An object's reluctance to change its state of motion (inertia) depends on its mass. The greater the mass, the greater is the force required to alter its speed or direction. For a body to accelerate, a greater force must be applied to it than the force required to maintain a constant speed.

Force summation

Any desired movement is a combination of a number of forces, but it is important to note that 'whenever a sequence of movement is used to produce optimal velocity, then each segment should be moved at the instant the previous segment begins to slow down' (*Towards Better Coaching*, p. 101). **Therefore the velocity of a projectile, such as a ball or implement, depends on the speed of the last part of the body at the time of contact or release.**

The correct sequence of body movements permits the performer to attain optimal velocity at release or contact, and is especially important when **maximal force** is desired:

- When maximal force is desired — as during javelin throwing or bowling at cricket — as many body parts as possible should be used.
- In humans, the body parts that are the strongest, heaviest and with the greatest inertia (and therefore are slower) are moved first. You need to use different muscles at a time when they are capable of sufficient speed to apply full force. Although, in theory, all parts of the body should commence acceleration simultaneously, in practice, the strongest and slowest around the centre of gravity begin first — for example, the trunk and thighs move first, followed by weaker, lighter and faster extremities.

This is known as the **sequential acceleration of body parts**, resulting in **successive force summation**.

Also, to gain maximal force summation, you need the **sequential stabilization** of body parts. Examples include:

- The leading leg in a golf swing is stabilized to provide for the development of effective force by other body parts.
- Cricket bowling requires a stable lead leg for the other forces to summate and be applied effectively to the cricket ball at the moment of release.

Other examples of activities that require body parts to contribute force sequentially include:

- The hockey drive
- The soccer kick
- The baseball pitch
- The field throw in cricket
- Casting a line in fishing
- Discus throw.

Timing

The timing of the application of these forces is vital. In a well-timed volleyball spike, the forearm begins to extend at the elbow just as the upper arm begins to decelerate. If the forearm commences to extend either before or after the upper arm decelerates, the force that can be exerted is reduced. (See Figure 24.4.)

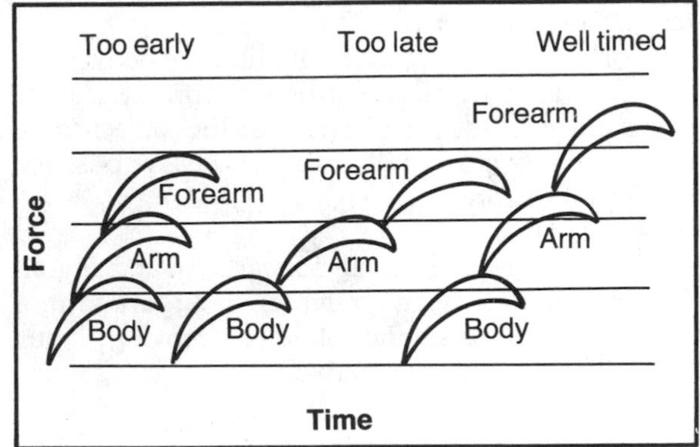

Figure 24.4

A kick in football includes the following succession of events for an effective, maximal kick. When a maximal force is applied to the football at the point of impact:

- Body weight is transferred forward with the trunk leading
- Non-kicking hip follows
- Kicking hip moves forward with leg trailing
- Thigh moves forward
- Lower leg straightens
- Foot 'snaps' at football.

Note: Because of the above sequence, muscles are stretched slightly before they are called into action. Physiologically, this provides for the development of more tension within the muscle.

Simultaneous force summation

Some sporting actions require body parts to contribute force explosively at the same time — that is,

simultaneous force summation. Examples include:

- The gymnastics vault
- The high jump take off
- The hockey push stroke
- The judo kick
- The breaststroke leg kick
- The basketball chest pass.

Take the example of the basketball chest pass. Several actions occur simultaneously to contribute to the force of the pass:

- A step in the required direction
- The rear leg push
- Trunk flexion
- Arm extension
- Wrist flexion.

Effective force

If a force is to be effective, the limb or body parts must be accelerated according to the resistance being moved. If the 'resistance' or the 'object to be moved' is moving rapidly, it is not always possible to apply full force.

For example:

- When pushing a child forward on a hanging swing, unless you straighten your arms at a faster rate than the child is moving, your pushing will be ineffective.
- At top speed, the runner is unable to exert his or her full force against the ground because there is not enough time to do so.
- On a surfboard, the paddling action to take you out to sea will be effective only if your arms move faster (and more efficiently) than the speed of the incoming waves.

General introduction to force and body levers

The rotation of a body segment is caused by a muscle, providing a force, acting in conjunction with the skeletal system as a series of **levers**.

A lever is a **'bar or some other rigid structure, hinged at one point, and to which forces are applied at two other points'** (Hay, p. 116).

It is a simple machine consisting of three components:

- A pivot point (**fulcrum**)
- A weight to be moved (**resistance**)
- A source of energy (**effort** or **force**).

There are three classes of lever, as shown below:

(1) First class of lever

The fulcrum lies between the resistance and the point of effort. Examples include a crowbar, a seesaw and scissors.

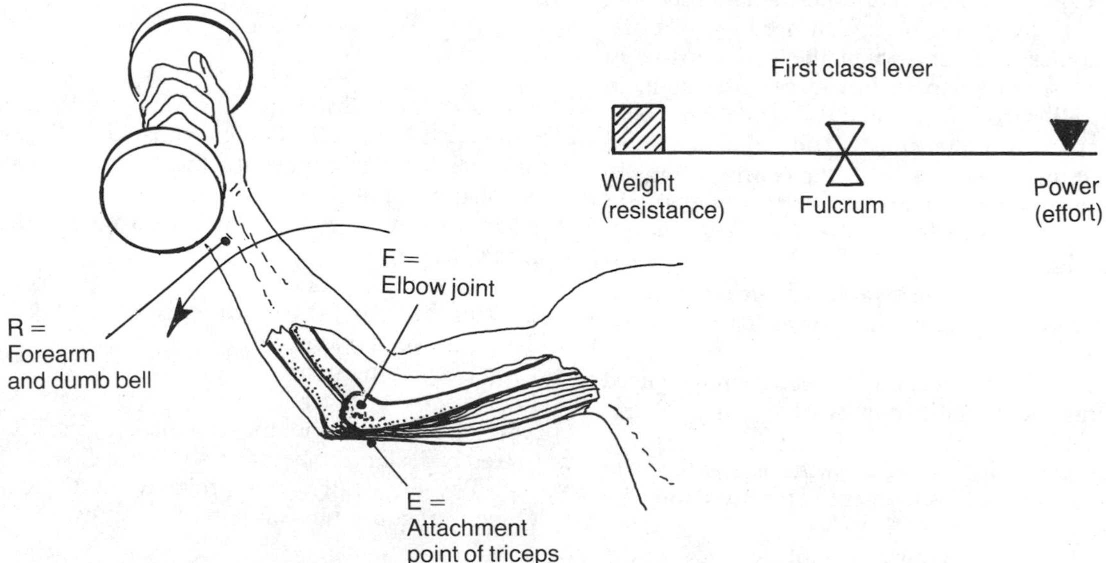

Figure 24.5 **First class of lever:** The fulcrum lies between the resistance and the point of effort. Examples: crowbar; seesaw; scissors.

(2) Second class of lever

The resistance lies between the fulcrum and the point of effort — for example, opening a door using the handle; lifting a wheelbarrow.

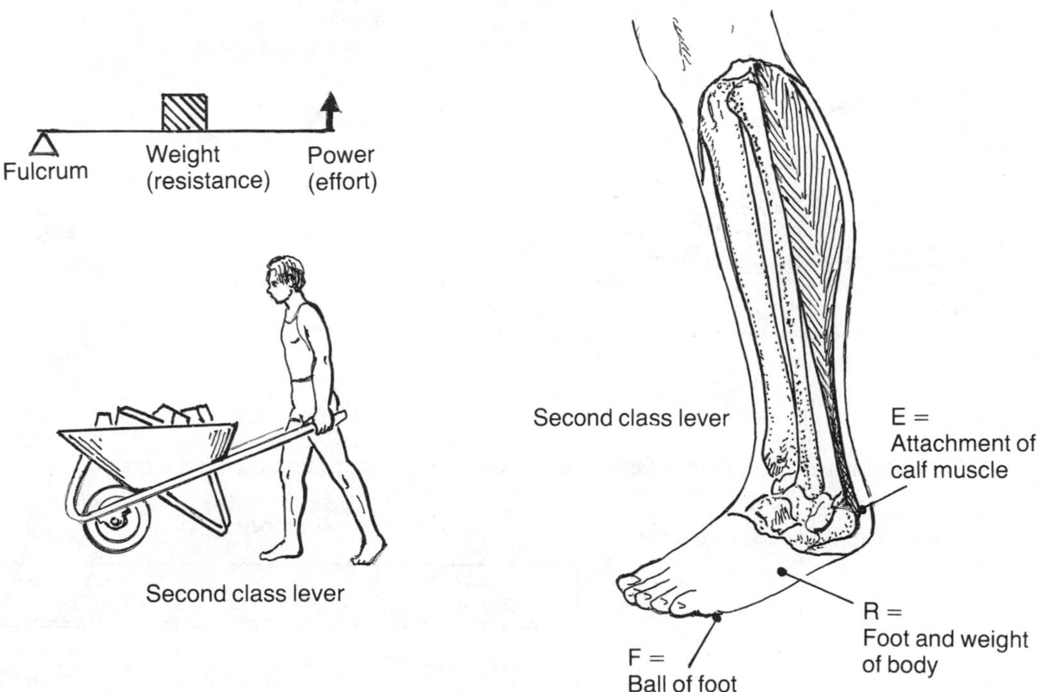

Figure 24.6 **Second class of lever:** The resistance lies between the fulcrum and the point of effort. Example: wheeling a barrow; or opening a door using the handle.

(3) Third class of lever

The point of effort is between the fulcrum and the resistance. In Figures 24.5, 24.6, 24.7 and 24.8:

- **The force arm** = the shortest perpendicular distance between the fulcrum and the application of force = **the effort arm**.
- **The resistance arm** = the shortest perpendicular distance between the fulcrum and the resistance.

Functions of levers

Levers have two chief functions:

(1) To increase the resistance moved by a given effort

This can be done only if the effort arm is greater than the resistance arm — for example, when wielding a crowbar.

(2) To increase the velocity at which a body moves

This is done by causing it to move a greater distance within a given time. This can be done only if the resistance arm is greater than the effort arm — for example, when using a golf club.

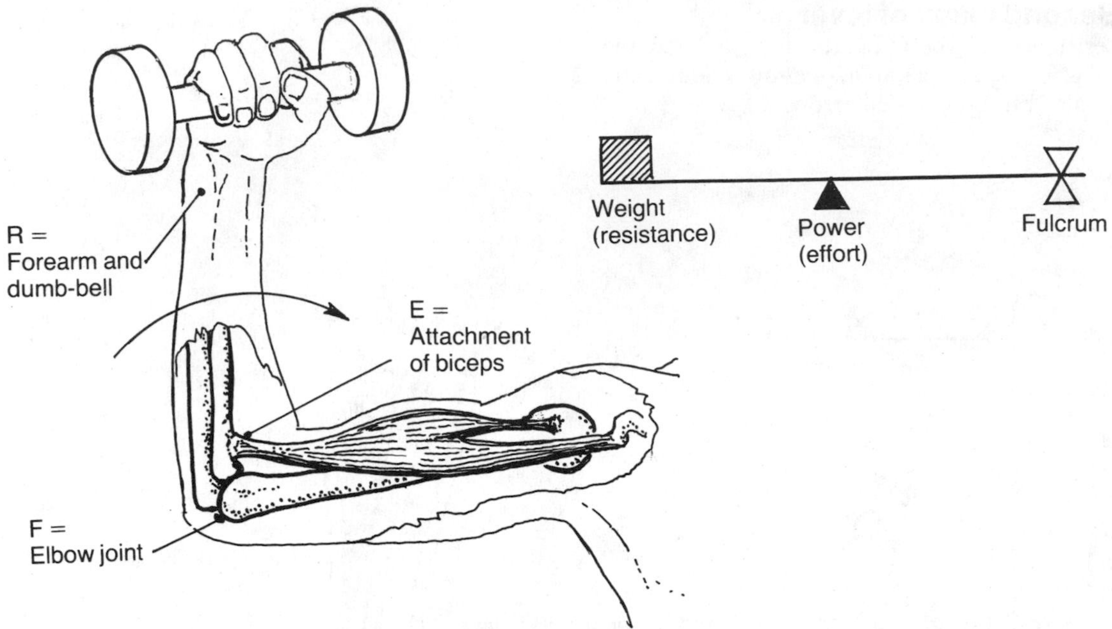

Figure 24.7 **Third class of lever:** The point of effort is between the fulcrum and the resistance.

Figure 24.8 Chief functions of levers.

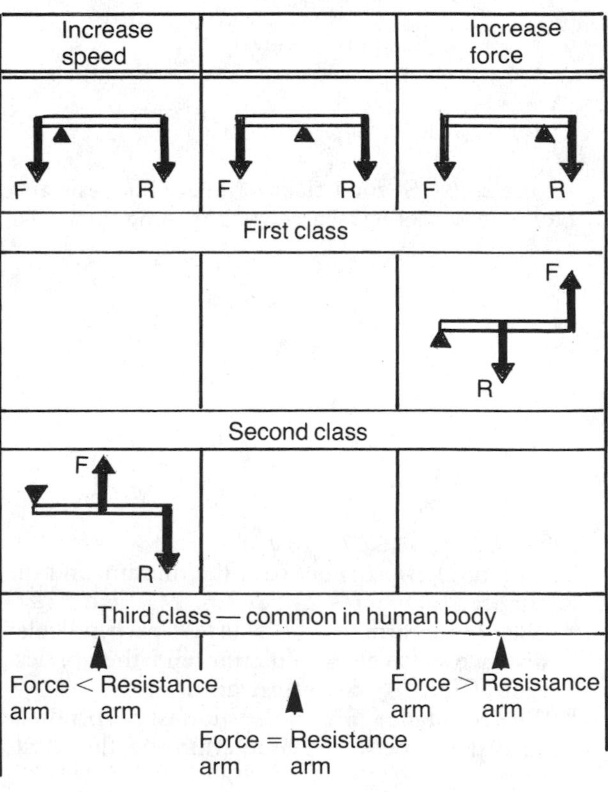

Levers in the body

Types of levers

In the body, the fulcrum of the lever is supplied by the **joint**, the resistance is represented by the **body part to be moved**, and effort is provided by **muscle pull at the muscle insertion.**

When a muscle contracts to cause motion at a joint, the resulting rotary effect (**torque**) is a product of the force and the shortest (perpendicular) distance between the force and the axis of rotation (fulcrum).

(1) **First class levers**

First class levers occur to some degree in the body, and mainly in actions of extending limbs — for example, the arm or the lower leg.

(2) **Second class levers**

Second class levers are very uncommon in the body. Two examples are:

- Standing on tiptoes
- Closing the lower jaw.

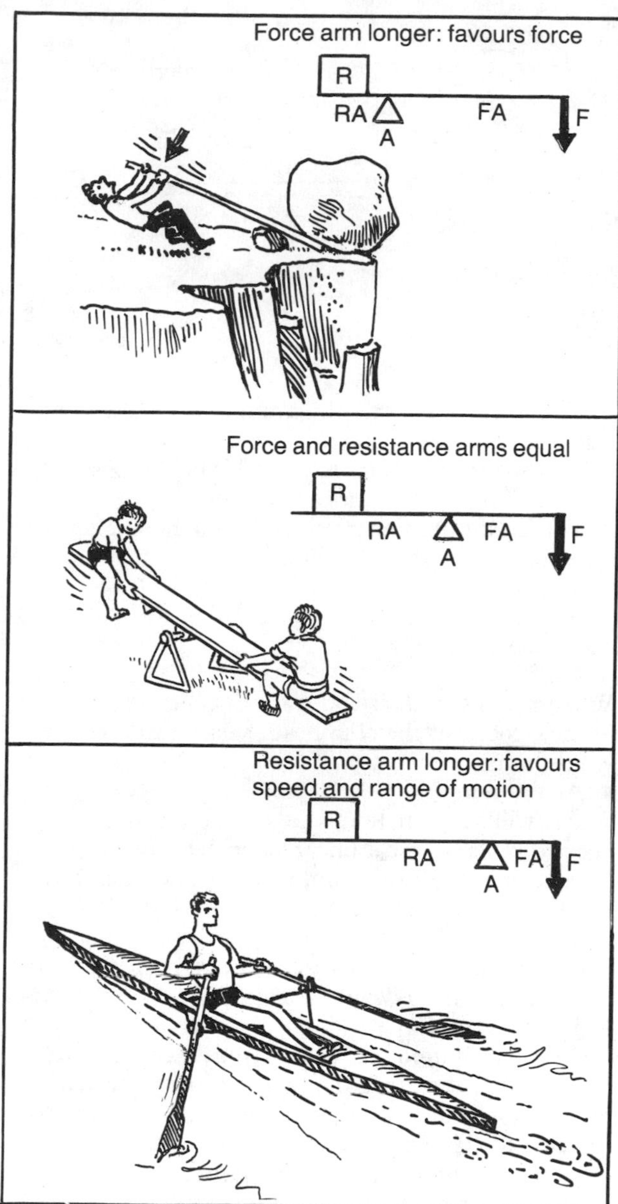

Figure 24.9 First class of levers.

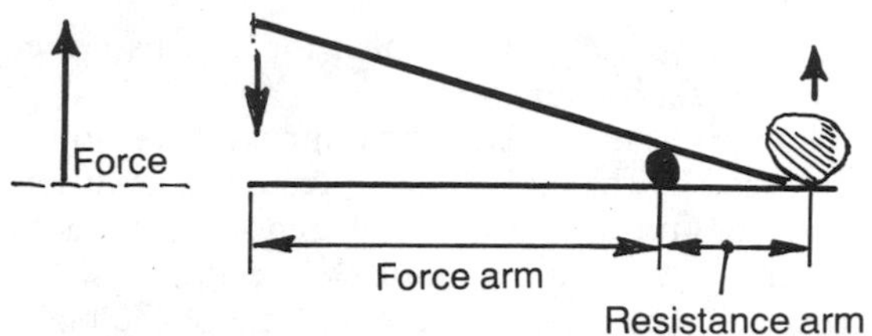

Figure 24.10 Second class of levers.

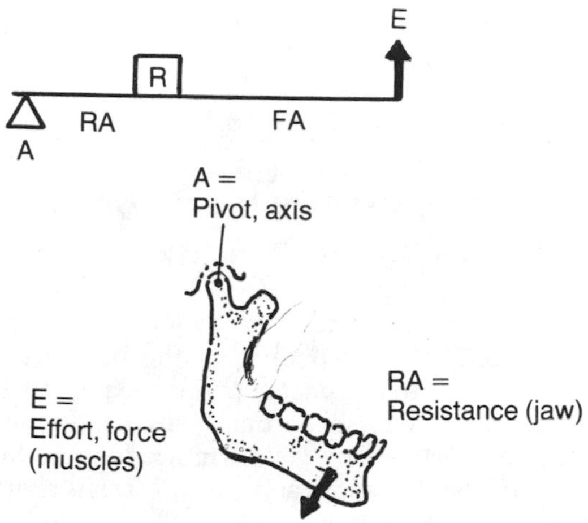

Figure 24.11 Third class of levers.

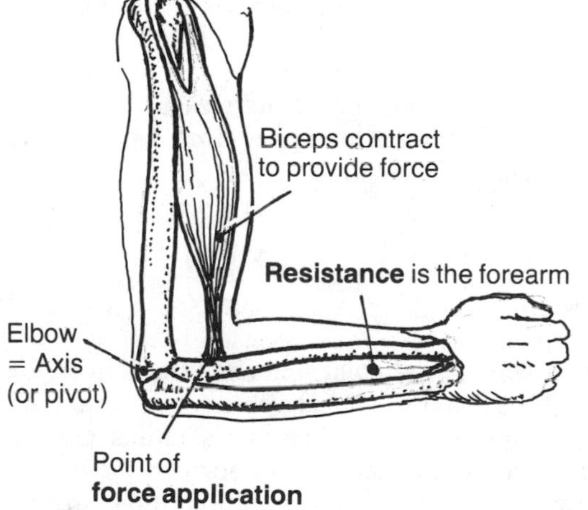

Force arm is the distance between the elbow and the attachment of biceps (point of force application)

Resistance arm is the distance between the elbow and the forearm's centre of gravity

Figure 24.12

(3) Third class levers

The body is virtually a system of third class levers. Since in third class levers the resistance arm (RA) is always greater than the effort arm (EA), it follows that most of the levers within the body are more suited to increasing the body's ability to move quickly than to increasing its ability to move heavy weights, especially since most force arms are constant in the human body.

The result is that large amounts of effort must be produced by the body to complete tasks involving a great amount of resistance, which is why it is very important to build up muscle strength. Weights should be lifted close to the midline of the body to reduce the resistance arm.

On the other hand, the human body is very effective in completing tasks requiring great speed. Its natural levers are extended by oars, ski poles and baseball bats.

The application of leverage to human physical activity

The longer the resistance arm of a lever, the greater is the speed at the end of it. If the body part is extended by a tennis racquet, the racquet strikes the ball with more speed than your hand would. This also explains why your arm needs to be fully extended when bowling, and why a 7 iron is shorter than a driver in golf.

As momentum can be transferred from a moving lever to an external object, an athlete can use angular motion to increase the linear velocity of an object — for example, in hammer throwing, golf and softball.

Linear velocity at impact or release (V)
= Angular velocity of upper limb and racquet × Radius of rotation

That is:

$$V = \omega r$$

For a constant angular velocity, the longer the radius, the greater the linear velocity. For example, a slight increase in the hammer's radius gives a sixfold increase in the distance thrown.

Note: The linear velocity of a point on a turning body is directly proportional to its distance from the axis.

In Figure 24.13:

- The hands are 33 centimetres from the axis of rotation
- The hammer is a metre from the axis of rotation.

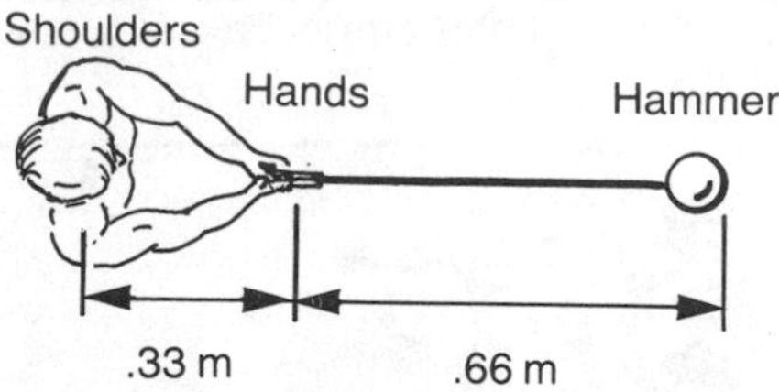

Figure 24.13

Therefore:

- The hands have one-third the linear velocity of the hammer
- The further any point is located from the axis, the greater the point's linear velocity
- The maximum linear velocity for a moving lever occurs at the distal (far) end.

Some more examples:

- **Golf**

When playing golf, if you want to generate greater linear velocity at the club head, select a club with a longer shaft.

- **At the net**

When volleying in tennis at the net, you do not need to generate great linear velocity at the racquet face. Bring the elbow into your ribs, therefore shortening the arm-racquet unit as a lever.

- **Serving**

When serving in tennis, straighten your arm to increase the linear velocity at impact.

- **Jumbo racquet**

A Prince, or jumbo racquet in tennis increases your leverage and therefore the linear velocity imparted to the ball, but the larger racquet may be more difficult to handle. It has a greater mass than an ordinary racquet, so you must overcome more inertia to move it. If you are a stronger, more experienced player, you could use its advantage to the greatest because you would have the force to accelerate its greater mass, as well as having the technique to provide the greatest amount of time in preparation for each stroke.

If there is a shortened performance time — as when a ball is directed at the player's body only a short distance from the net — it is more appropriate to use a short lever to play the shot.

What effect does a double-handed backhand technique have on the force generated, and the leverage?

Accuracy components

'An object continues to move in the direction in which it was moving at release until acted upon by some other force. If the hand is travelling in an arc, the thrown object moves in a line which is tangential to that arc at the point of release' (Broer, p. 256).

This means that **there is only a single release point that corresponds to an accurate performance in accuracy events.**
Therefore:

(1) To increase the accuracy of direction, the arc is flattened by moving the centre of the arc in the direction of the movement

Figure 24.14 is a schematic representation of the flattening of the arc of the underhand throw, accompanying a forward and downward movement of the shoulder. This is important, especially for long distance throwing, as in bowling down a lane, baseball pitching, and discus and hammer throwing.

In sports where accuracy is important, the arc of the curve must be flattened so that **more than one** release or contact point corresponds to an accurate performance. Flattening the arc increases the striking or release zone for an accurate performance.

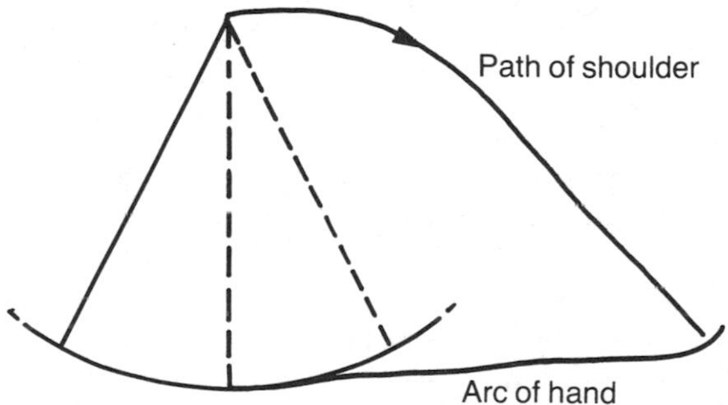

Figure 24.14 Schematic presentation of the flattening of the arc of the underhand throw accompanying a forward and downward movement of the shoulder.

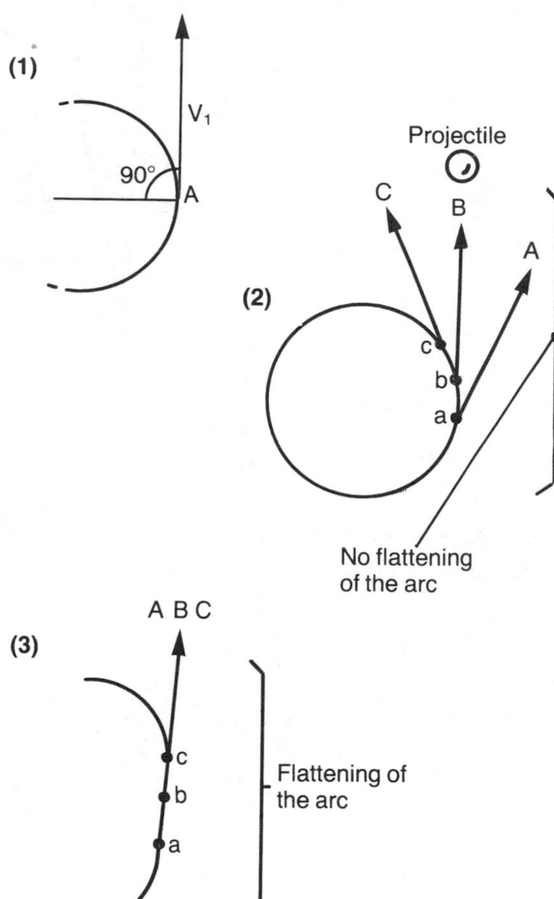

Figure 24.15 **No flattening of the arc.**

(1) The direction of linear motion of a body in rotation is 90° to the radius (or tangent to the curve) at the intersection with the radius of rotation.
(2) The point of release of a projectile is crucial in accuracy events.
(3) Accuracy can be increased by flattening the arc of the swing.

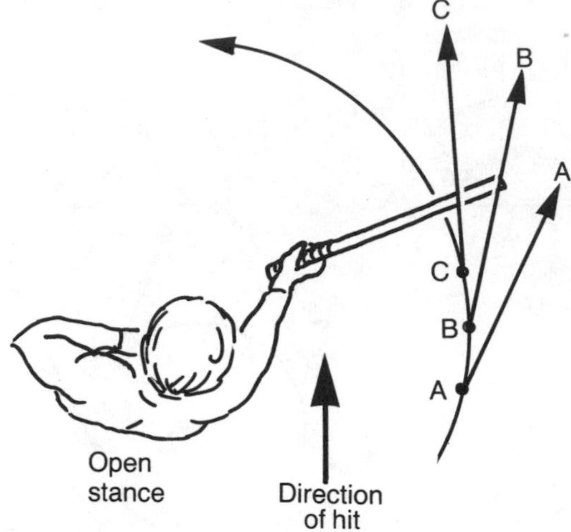

Figure 24.16 Arc is not flattened, and only contact at B will result in a straight hit.

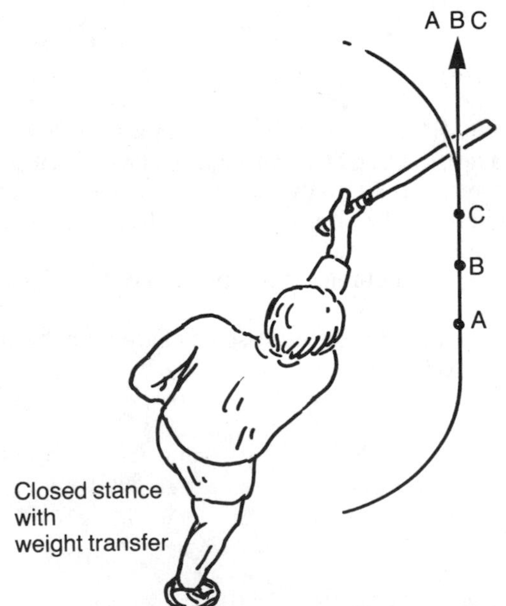

Figure 24.17 The arc is flattened, and contact at either A, B or C will result in a straight hit.

(2) There must be a balance in producing speed yet maintaining accuracy

(3) There must be a careful gauge of the factors that may influence the projectile's flight in the air

They may include wind currents and aerodynmaic factors. Gravity, on the other hand, affects the distance, not the direction of the throw.

Accuracy in track and field events is needed at points of take off. There must be minimal braking once horizontal momentum has been developed. Practice in such sports as the long jump and the javelin throw ensures correct pacing to avoid penalties.

Accuracy: summary

This chapter shows that the accuracy of a throw, catch, hit or any other movement depends on several biomechanical factors:

- The force applied overcoming inertia to the correct degree
- The force applied creating the desired momentum
- The force applied acting in the desired direction
- The force applied being correctly timed
- Complementary movements to ensure accuracy in the application of force.

Laboratory work 35: Summation of forces: the shot put

Aim

To investigate the summation of forces when throwing a shot put.

Procedure

Sum these forces together:

(1) **Arm action**
- Front stance
- Left arm by side
- *No* upper body rotation.

Distance: . . . .

(2) **Arm action**
- Front stance
- Left arm drives across body

- Rotation of upper body.

Distance: . . . .

(3) Side-on stance: shot in neck
- Shot in neck
- Left elbow high, ready to drive
- Upper body rotation.

Distance: . . . .

(4) **Side-on stance: shot in neck**
Weight transfer:
- Left elbow high, ready to drive
- Weight on back foot; drive to front foot
- Upper body rotation.

Distance: . . . .

(5) **Velocity increase: shot in neck**
Side-on stance:
- Left elbow high, ready to drive
- Weight on back foot; drive to front foot
- One hop, then step to throw
- Upper body rotation.

Distance: . . . .

Exercise

Referring to an appropriate sequence of a track and field event, use arrows and comments to identify:
- Contributing forces
- Force summation
- Height of release
- Angle of release.

Laboratory work 36: Investigation of the summation of forces

(1) Determine which body parts contribute most to throwing an object. How far (in paces) can you throw the ball using only:
- **(a)** Your hand. (Get your partner to hold back your wrist at shoulder level; grip the ball in your fingers.)
- **(b)** Your lower arm. (Get your partner to hold down your upper arm.)
- **(c)** Your upper arm (from lying on your back).
- **(d)** Your body (from a sitting position, with the ball thrown from the ear).
- **(e)** Your body (from a sitting position, with the ball thrown from an extended arm behind the body).

(So far, from which of the above positions were you able to throw the furthest?)
- **(f)** On your knees (with arm fully extended behind your body).
- **(g)** Standing. (Front-on stance; feet shoulder width apart.)
- **(h)** Standing. (Side-on stance; feet shoulder width apart, but feet may not leave the ground.)
- **(i)** Standing. (Side-on stance, feet shoulder width apart; feet may leave the ground.)

(2) From which position did you manage to throw the furthest?

(3) Did each successive throw produce a greater distance?

(4) Why do you think this happened?

(5) Can you throw the ball any further:
- **(a)** By using a few walking paces?
- **(b)** With a short run up?

(6) Did you manage to increase your throw?

(7) Why does the run up improve your throw?

(8) Why is it important to make sure that your throwing foot is planted firmly on the ground as you throw?

(9) The order in which the body parts move during throwing determines how well and how far you can throw. Here are the body actions in incorrect order. Beside each, write the correct order, using the numbers 1–8.
- Upper body turns in the direction of the throw ( )
- Run up ( )
- You fall forward after the ball leaves your hand ( )
- Arm delivers (ball with a whip-like action) ( )
- Feet placed side on, with front foot planted ( )
- Hand and finger movements ( )
- Body leans forward ( )
- Throwing arm extended behind the body ( ).

(10) Discuss the above results, further commenting on the timing of the body part movements.

(11) Apply your findings to another appropriate sporting action.

(12) Compare the above results with a sporting action that requires simultaneous force summation.

Worksheet 23: Force development and application

(1) Describe the 'summation of forces' concept in throwing a cricket ball at the stumps.

(2) Pick the correct statement from the alternatives offered:
Summation of forces in throwing for distance depends upon:
- **(a)** The use of the whole body
- **(b)** Maximizing the release velocity of the ball
- **(c)** Timing the contribution of each additional body segment
- **(d)** Full range of movement
- **(e)** All of the above.

(3) The principle of summation of forces states that: 'Whenever a sequence of movement is employed to produce an optimal velocity, each segment should be moved at the instant the previous segment begins to slow down.'
True or false?

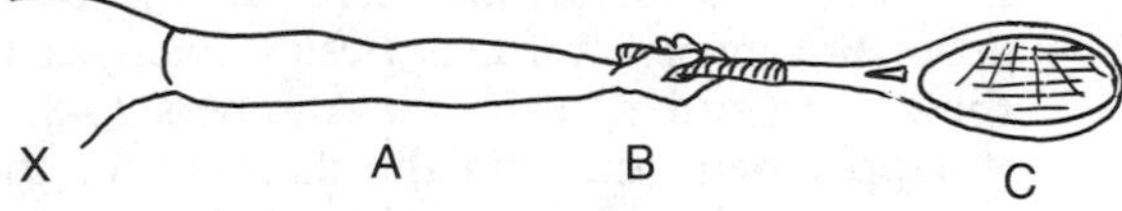

Point X = Shoulder Point B = Hand
Point A = Elbow Point C = Racquet face

Figure 24.18

(4) Look at Figure 24.18. Given an arm-racquet unit travelling through the motion of a forehand stroke in tennis:
- **(a)** Which point (**A**, **B** or **C**) has the least linear velocity? Why?
- **(b)** Which point (**A**, **B** or **C**) has the greatest linear velocity? Why?

(5) The following activities involve swinging a bat at a pitched softball:
- **(a)** The batter swings a bat. The striking surface of the bat travels 10 metres in 3 seconds. What is the linear velocity of the striking surface?
- **(b)** Using the same amount of force, the batter swings a bat of the same weight as in (**a**). The striking surface of a longer bat travels 13 metres in 3 seconds. What is the linear velocity of this striking surface?
- **(c)** If the batter wished to swing a 70-centimetre bat with the same linear velocity as an 80-centimetre bat, what would he have to provide?

(6) A long-legged man has a thigh muscle strength equal to that of a short-legged man. Which man can kick a ball further, and why?

(7) Complete the table by identifying the force responsible for the listed changes in inertia:

Change	**(Major) force responsible**
Boy falls into swimming pool	Gravity
Girl propels a bowling ball	Arm and body muscles
Rolling ball 'hooks' to right	
Bowling pin falls down	
Sprinter accelerates	
Released shot put falls to earth	

(8) Define Newton's First Law, and give two illustrations of how the law is demonstrated when playing badminton.

(9) One reason why a driver will send a golf ball further than a 3 iron is that it possesses greater mass. What is the other reason?

(10) In ten-pin bowling, what are the two factors that influence the momentum of a bowling ball?

(11) The following is a quote from a volleyball coaching manual. It refers to the 'dig' (bump).

Fault	**Reason**
The ball flies up in the air.	The player is swinging his arms as he plays the ball so that it follows the direction of his arm movement; the angle of his arms in relation to his body is too high.

What principles of Newton's First and Second Laws of Motion are illustrated here?

(12) What class of lever is illustrated in each of the following examples?
   (a) A crowbar levering a large rock
   (b) A man pushing a wheelbarrow
   (c) A drawbridge opening
   (d) A man flexing his biceps
   (e) A woman rowing a boat
   (f) Opening a door by the handle.

(13) What are the two chief functions of levers?

(14) Which type of lever is the most common in the human body?

(15) For the levers in the human body, what acts as:
   (a) The fulcrum?
   (b) The point of effort?
   (c) The resistance?

(16) From your knowledge of lever systems, explain how a body lever increases the velocity of a body part. Give an example.

(17) Why is it important to be able to increase the velocity of a body part in some sporting activites?

(18) Given your knowledge of levers in the body, why is it so important for muscle strength to be developed in order to perform heavy or strenuous tasks?

(19) Why is it difficult to throw a ball with spin as fast as a ball thrown without spin?

25. Linear motion: Impact, rebound, resistance and friction

Impact and rebound

Impact takes place when two bodies collide. In sport, players are called upon to predict the outcome of impacts. Common impacts in sport are:

- Ball against foot
- Racquet against ball
- Ball against wall or ground.

A sports player must be able to predict how a ball will rebound after it has made impact, and how to get it into a suitable position to play a shot.

Elasticity

When a ball strikes a fixed surface, both the ball and the surface are compressed to varying degrees. The ball tends to resume its former shape after rebounding from the surface, as does the surface. In other words, when two bodies collide, they both undergo '**compression and restitution**'.

Elasticity is the property of a body that causes it to tend to regain its original shape after any compression or deformation has occurred.

Coefficient of restitution

The **coefficient of restitution of an object** is a measure of its elasticity upon striking a given surface — in other words, it is a measure of a ball's ability to return to its original shape after being deformed at impact. The greater the elasticity of a ball, the greater its coefficient of restitution (e).

$$e = \sqrt{\frac{\text{height bounced}}{\text{height dropped}}}$$

An example: A ball that is dropped 16 centimetres and rebounds to 12 centimetres has a coefficient of restitution of .87.

that is:

$$e = \sqrt{\frac{12}{16}} = \sqrt{.75} = .87$$

Because some of its vertical velocity is lost during impact, no ball will have a value of 1 for e.

Coaches and umpires test the coefficients of restitution of their equipment by dropping balls onto the surface to be used.

The coefficient of restitution is affected by:

(1) Surface composition

The surface composition is the composition of the surface with which the ball makes contact. The

Type of surface	Height bounced (cm)	Coefficient of restitution
'Proturf'	104.8	0.76
Wood	103.3	0.75
'Uniturf'	102.6	0.75
Steel plating	101.6	0.74
Concrete	100.3	0.74
Tumbling mat (2.5 cm thick)	82.9	0.67
Gravel	66.9	0.60
Grass	34.3	0.43
Gymnastic landing mat (20 cm thick)	33.0	0.42

Figure 25.1 The coefficient of restitution for a volleyball dropped from a height of 18 centimetres onto various surfaces.

more 'give' that a surface has, the less the rebound. For instance, a cricket ball bouncing on a moist wicket makes a dint, causing a loss of energy at impact, and therefore less rebound.

(2) Composition of the ball

If a ball is pumped up, there is an increase in its hardness, or the pressure within, which increases elasticity. The ball, on impact, will be deformed less, and a smaller amount of energy is lost as heat, so the ball will return faster to its original shape. For example, new golf balls, tennis balls and cricket balls have greater coefficients of restitution than have aged balls.

(3) Speed of impact

The greater the speed of impact, the lower the coefficient of restitution.

(4) Temperature

Squash players, for example, make good use of the fact that warming up a ball increases its liveliness.

(5) Elasticity of the striking implement

Any deformation of the implement at impact results in a loss of energy. For example, a new tennis racquet with tight strings will have a greater amount of elasticity than one with loose strings. A cricket ball rebounds more from practice nets that are tightly strung than those that are loosely strung.

Type of ball	Dropped	Projected 80–100 kph
Baseball	.50	.44
Basketball	.75	.64
Golf ball	.60	.58
Handball	.80	.50
Lacrosse ball	.70	.60
Paddleball	.70	.45
Squash ball	.52	.40
Softball	.55	.40
Super ball	.90	.85
Tennis ball	.74	.52
Volleyball	.75	.68

Figure 25.2 The coefficient of restitution of various balls when dropped and projected to a wood surface.

Type of ball	Coefficients of restitution (The height of the bounce when each ball was dropped from a height of 183 cm is shown in parentheses.) Cooled (1 hr in freezer)	Normal	Heated (15 min. at 225°)
Baseball	0.50 (46 cm)	0.53 (51 cm)	0.55 (56 cm)
Solid rubber ball	0.57 (58 cm)	0.73 (97 cm)	0.80 (117 cm)
Golf ball	0.67 (81 cm)	0.80 (117 cm)	0.84 (130 cm)
'Super ball'	0.91 (150 cm)	0.91 (152 cm)	0.95 (165 cm)

Figure 25.3 The effect of temperature changes on the coefficient of restitution.

Mass-velocity relationships

(1) Speed of the striking implement at impact

The striking implement must be travelling at the greatest possible velocity when the impact occurs. This means that timing (and force summation) during the swing must be directed towards producing the maximum velocity of the bat, club or racquet at impact.

Remember from Chapter 24 that if you increase the lever length, you increase the linear velocity of the object hit ($V = \bar{\omega} \times r$).

(2) Mass of the implement

There is little practical gain in increasing the mass of the striking implement. There is an optimal implement weight (mass) for each person. If a performer tries to use a mass above this amount, he or she fatigues too easily and loses implement velocity.

(3) Mass of the object struck

The greater the mass of the object struck, and the lower the force imparted, the shorter the distance travelled. For example, in golf the large (American) ball travels a shorter distance for a given force than does the small (British) ball.

Rebound and rolling

When a moving object meets a resistance greater than its own, it will rebound from that resistance. The type of rebound will depend on:

- **The firmness of the surface**

The greater the firmness of the surface, the greater the rebound, as less energy is lost at impact with surfaces that are deformed only slightly.

- **The velocity of the object**

Increase the velocity of the object and you increase its rebound.

- **The mass of the object**

It is more difficult to make a more massive object rebound than a less massive object.

- **Its coefficient of restitution**

The greater the ability of the object to resume its shape after the force of the impact, the greater will be its rebound.

- **The friction involved at impact**

Increase the friction involved in the impact, and you lower the rebound of the object.

- **The angle of approach**

The angle of rebound varies with differing angles of approach.

Angle of rebound

Direct impact

There are a few examples of direct impact in sport — that is, where two bodies collide directly. In other words, they are both moving along the same straight line before impact, or one of them is at rest while the other is travelling at right angles to the surface where contact occurs. Three examples are shown in Figure 25.4.

When a ball approaches the floor from directly above, it bounces straight back up, regardless of its loss of vertical velocity at impact. This is because the ball is depressed symmetrically, making the force of the rebound the same from all parts of the bottom of the ball.

Oblique impact

If a ball approaches at an angle to the floor, the back of the bottom of the ball is depressed more than the front, and the rebound force throws the ball forwards and upwards.

If there were no 'give' (**deformation**) of the surface which an object struck (surface perfectly resistive), no friction involved in the impact, no spin in the ball and the ball had perfect restitution, a ball would rebound at an angle equal to its angle of approach. This happens rarely in reality.

Rebound angles

If the approach angle is discussed in relation to the horizontal surface, it is called the **'angle of approach'**. Conversely, if it is discussed in relation to the vertical, it is called the **'angle of incidence'**.

Likewise, the rebound angle is respectively called the 'angle of rebound' or the 'angle of reflection'.

These terms should be remembered when discussing rebound angles.

(1) Theoretical rebound

Because of gravity, a ball moving forward through the air approaches a surface in a curved path. This

Figure 25.4 **Examples of direct impact:**
(1) A soccer goalkeeper punching away a lobbed shot at goal
(2) A basketball official testing the bounce of the ball
(3) The cue striking a ball in billiards or snooker.

can be seen in Figures 25.5 and 25.6, which also show the alternative ways of talking about the angles of approach and rebound.

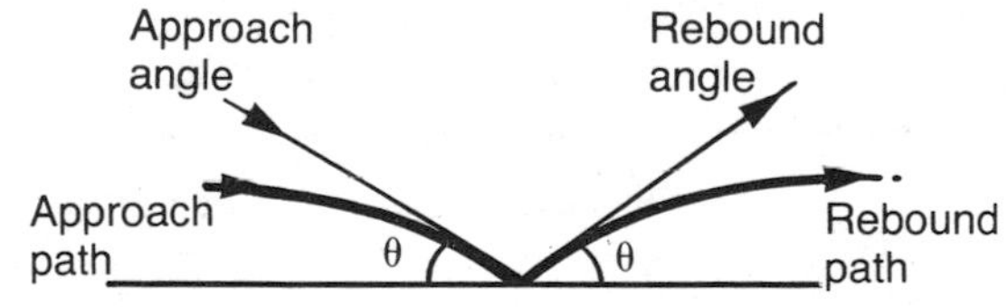

Figure 25.5

or

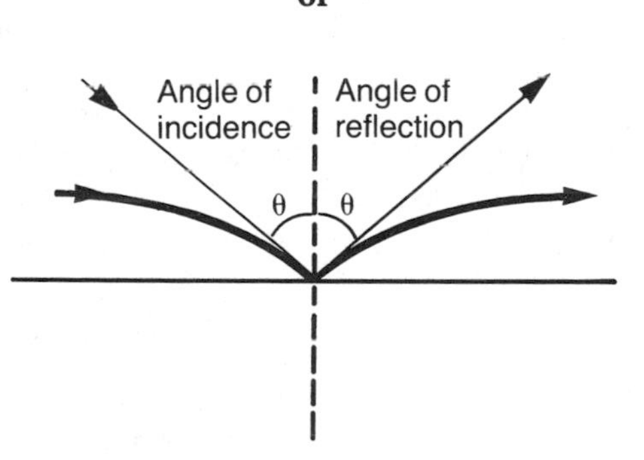

Figure 25.6

If, during the rebound, there were

- No give in the floor
- No friction
- No spin
- No consideration of the coefficient of restitution

the angle of approach would equal the angle of rebound or the angle of incidence would equal the angle of reflection.

The angle at which the ball strikes determines how far back on the bottom of the ball the greatest depression comes, and therefore how much the rebound will be forward. The smaller the angle of approach, the farther back will be the area of greatest depression, and the more forward will be the rebound.

(2) Friction

When the ball strikes the floor, the two surfaces slide against each other, and this friction reduces horizontal velocity. This acts to raise the rebound angle, or decrease the angle of reflection. In Figures 25.7 and 25.8, TR means theoretical rebound.

TR = theoretical rebound

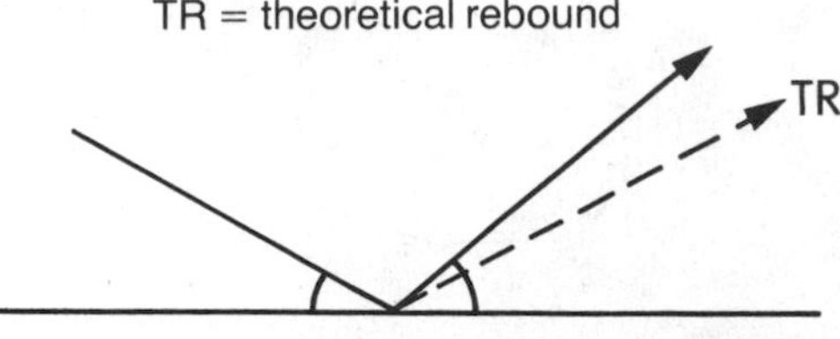

Angle of rebound > angle of approach

Figure 25.7

or

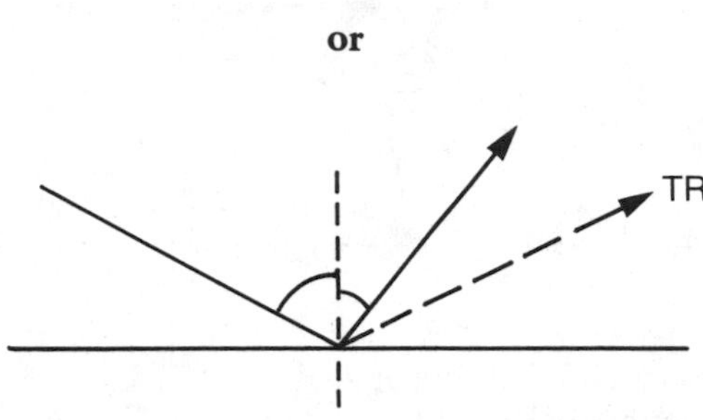

or Angle of reflection < angle of incidence

Figure 25.8

(3) Coefficient of restitution

The coefficient of restitution causes a loss of vertical velocity which decreases the angle of rebound, or increases the angle of reflection.

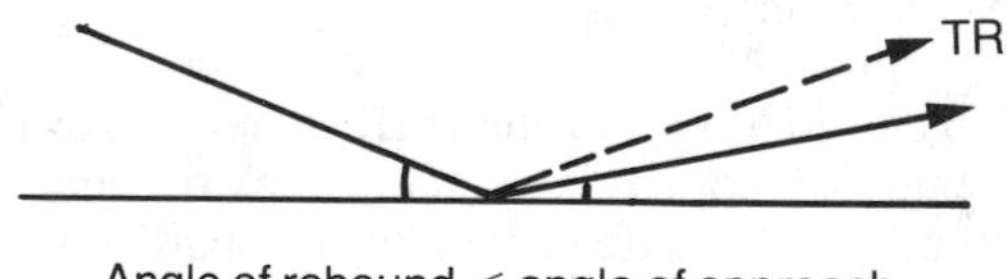

Angle of rebound < angle of approach

Figure 25.9

or

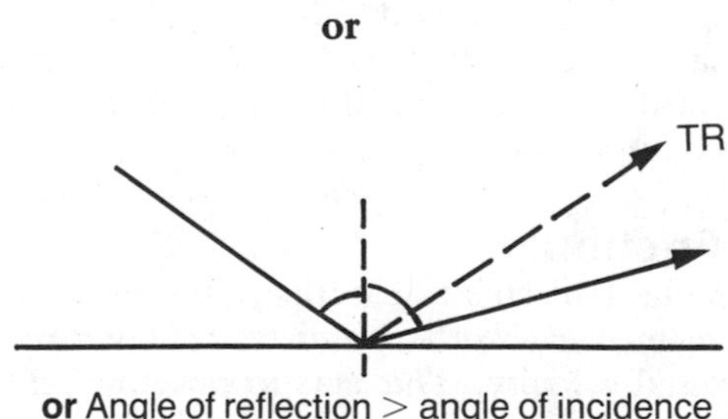

or Angle of reflection > angle of incidence

Figure 25.10

(4) Back spin and top spin

During spin, according to the rate and direction of the spin on impact, the force caused by friction is modified. Friction is increased in the direction opposite to that of the motion of the bottom of the ball.

During **back spin** (the bottom of the ball moving forwards), the friction force acts to propel the ball backwards — that is, increases the angle of rebound.

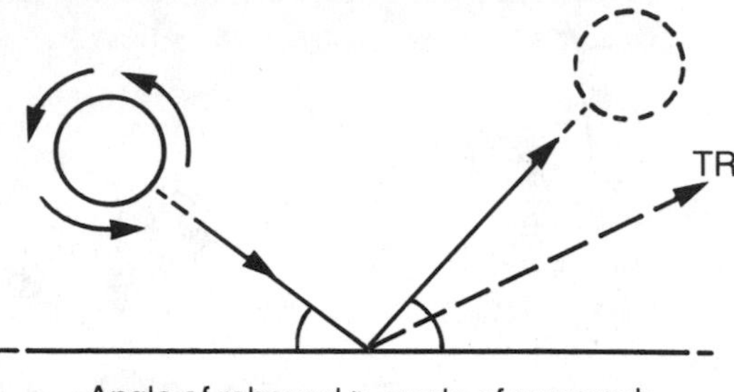

Angle of rebound > angle of approach

Figure 25.11

or

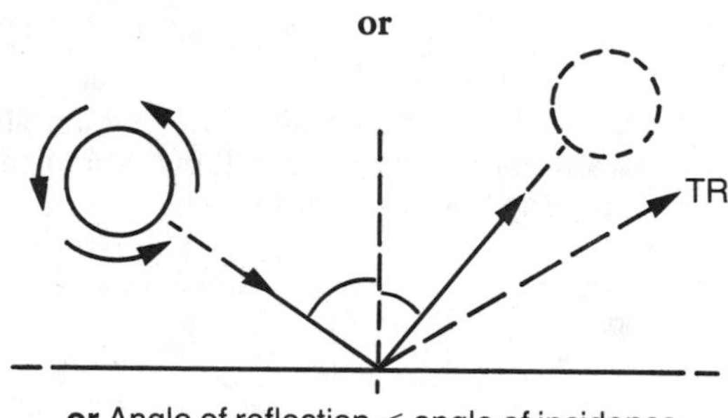

or Angle of reflection < angle of incidence

Figure 25.12

During **top spin** (the bottom of the ball moving backwards) the friction force acts to propel the ball forwards — that is, decreases the angle of rebound.

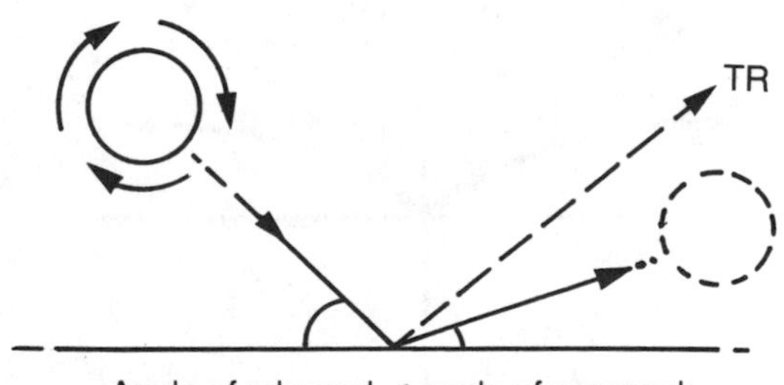

Angle of rebound < angle of approach

Figure 25.13

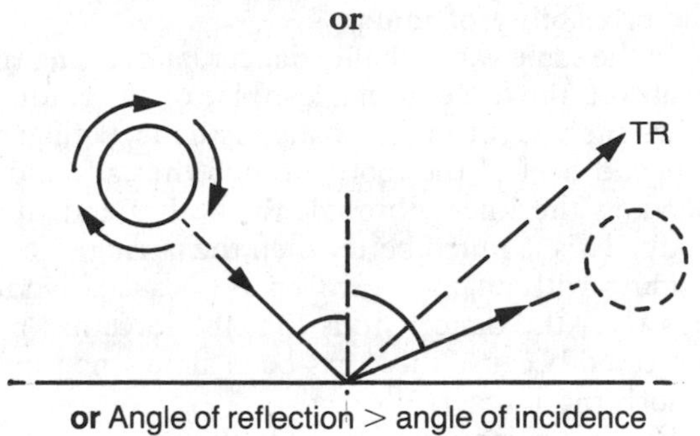

Figure 25.14

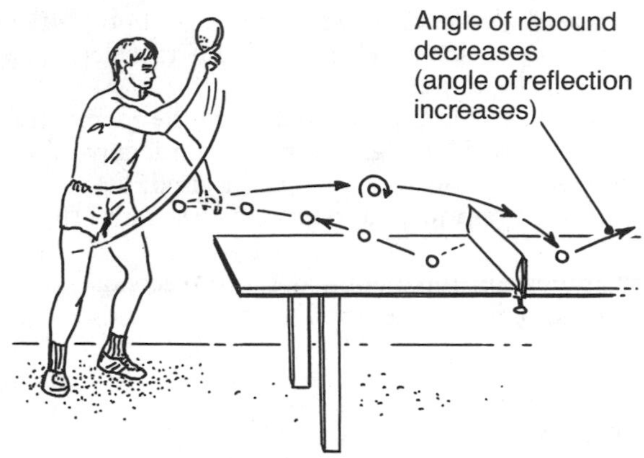

Figure 25.16 **A forehand top-spin drive in table tennis.** The application of top-spin to the ball ensures that it will come off the table **fast and at a low angle** and thus be difficult to return.

(5) Side spin

With side spin, the friction force is greater on the back of the ball, so a ball with right spin will rebound to the right, and a ball with left spin with rebound to the left. These effects will occur only during an oblique impact.

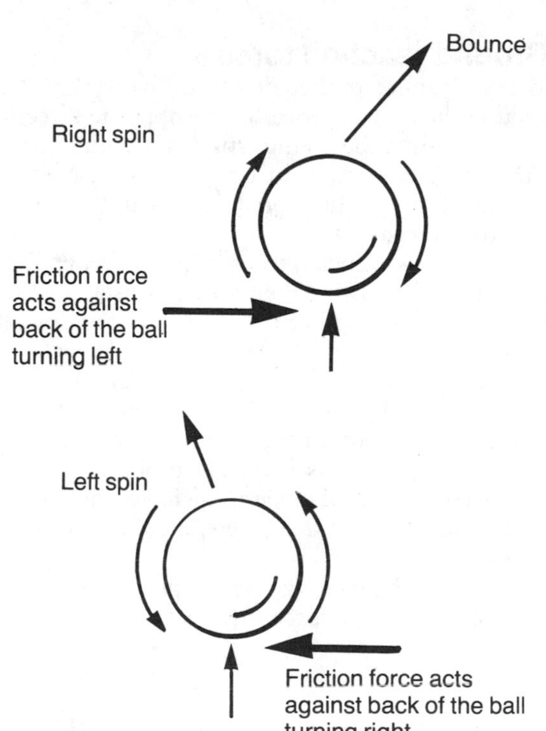

Figure 25.15 Right spin and left spin, viewed from above.

Impulse

The greater the amount of time for which a given force is applied, the greater will be the acceleration of the body to which it is applied. It follows that the greater the force applied, the less the time it needs to be applied for, and vice versa, in order to achieve a given level of acceleration (such as stopping a ball).

Therefore the change in speed of a discus, shot, javelin or hammer thrown does not merely depend upon the force applied, but also upon the time for which it operates — that is, its impulse.

Impulse = product of the force applied over a period of time

$= F \times t$

Since $F = m \times a$ (that is, mass × acceleration)

$$F = \frac{m \times (v_f - v_i)}{t}$$

So $Ft = mv_f - mv_i$

(that is, impulse = change in momentum)

$F \times t$ = change in momentum

$Ft = \chi mv$ i.e. χ units of momentum.

The impulse of an object is equal to the change in momentum that is produced. Therefore, the greater the force, and the longer the time the force is applied to an object, the greater the change in the momentum of the object.

To speed up an object, the impulse must be

increased (by increasing F or t or both). This results in a change of momentum (acceleration), the object's impulse.

For example, in order to change the momentum of a ball by 50 kilograms per second, any of the following combinations could be used:

- 10-kilogram force applied for 5 seconds ($10 \times 5 = 50$)
- 5-kilogram force applied for 10 seconds
- 25-kilogram force applied for 2 seconds.

Impulse and particular sports

Impulse is important in starting track or swimming events, and in football and other sports. An athlete can increase his or her impulse by increasing force (that is, his or her personal strength) or time (range of motion).

Take the following examples:

- **The bunch start**

The bunch start is a start made when there is the smallest possible distance between the feet. This gets the athlete out of the block more quickly than any other start. However, the horizontal impulses are limited by the short time the feet are in contact with the blocks, and this limits the runner's horizontal velocity.

- **Throwing events**

In throwing events, the best techniques are those in which the maximum muscular force is exerted for the longest possible time. In the shot put, it is more useful to carry out the circular run before throwing than to throw from a standing position.

- **Tennis**

While carrying out a tennis serve, bend your elbow at the back in order to gain a longer swinging time for the racquet before hitting the tennis ball.

Force reception

Conversely, **the faster an object is moving and the less time involved in stopping it, the greater is the force that must be applied**. Thus the force required to catch a given ball is less when the force is applied over a longer period of time.

A good example of this is an outfielder who catches a cricket ball — that is, **force reception**. If you are an outfielder catching a cricket ball, you will put out your arms. The ball reaches your hands, which carry it to your chest. This increases the time over which you can stop the ball, reducing the force required by your hands, and also reducing the probability of injury.

In the same way, a ballet dancer takes a long time to absorb the force from a leap. He or she gradually takes the weight on the balls of the feet, then the sole and heel of the foot, through the calf, and by bending the knee, through to the hip and upper body. This is much better than the jarring effect of landing without any 'give' in the legs. If landing this way, the dancer finds that the force has been increased because there has been almost no time to absorb the impact.

For any given impulse, as in this example, force and time are inversely related.

Newton's Third Law

Newton's Third Law of Motion states that **'for every action there is an equal and opposite reaction'**. Some results of this law are:

- A force acting anywhere always has a force equal to that acting in the opposite direction
- Forces work in pairs opposing one another
- The initial force (**action force**) is opposed by a second force (**reactive force**).

Ground reaction force

When a runner pushes down and back against the ground the athlete moves in the opposite direction. A force must be being applied to him in that direction (see section in Chapter 24 on Newton's Second Law). This force is called the **ground reaction force**.

When a swimmer pushes back the water, he or she moves forward. When a weight-lifter performs a bench press, the barbell exerts a force down on him or her.

If these forces are equal, why isn't the earth pushed back by the runner? Remember that the change of momentum experienced by a body, when a force is applied, is inversely proportional to its mass. The greater the mass, the lower the acceleration. Also, consider the difference when you run on sand.

What is happening when two people push against each other forcefully, yet neither moves?

Implications for sporting activities

- When an object exerts a force upon a second object, the second body exerts an equal and opposite force upon the first.

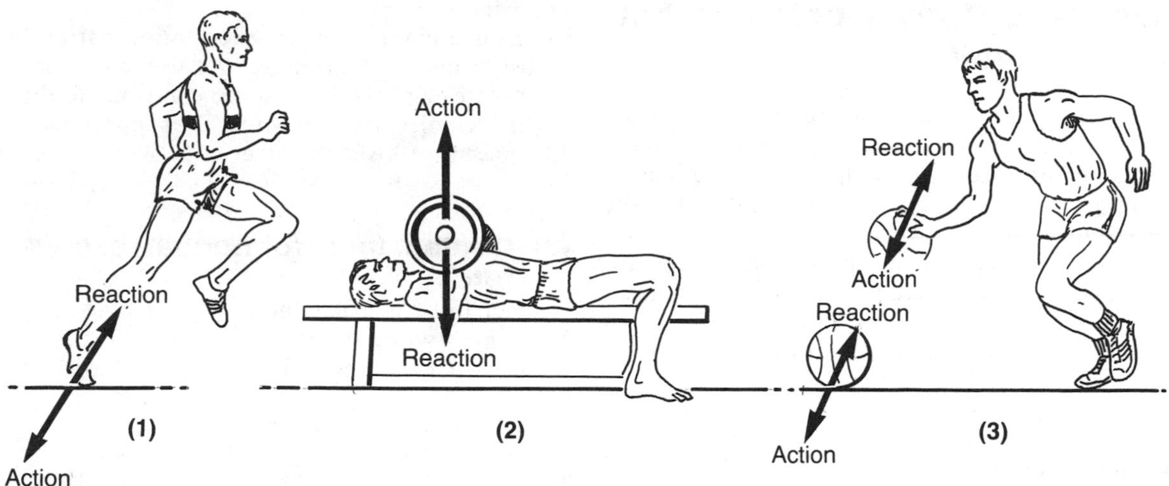

Figure 25.17 Examples of Newton's third law **(1)** in running; **(2)** in performing a bench press; and **(3)** in dribbling a basketball.

- The opposing forces cancel each other if they are from the same body, but in sport we usually find equal and opposite forces in two distinct bodies.
- Newton's Third Law embodies the concept of the conservation of momentum.

Conservation of momentum

The law of conservation of momentum states that **'when two or more bodies collide with each other, momentum is conserved'**. In other words, **the total momentum of the bodies before impact is the same as their total momentum after impact.**

When a bat meets a ball, the total momentum is equal to the momentum of the bat (mv) and the momentum of the ball. After impact, the momentum of both objects may change, but the total momentum remains constant. This means that some momentum from the bat has been transferred to the ball, or vice versa.

Take this example:

Mass of bat = 4 kg
Mass of ball = 0.5 kg
Speed of bat before impact = 10 m/sec.
Speed of ball before impact = 100 m/sec.

If the bat speed after impact equals 5 m/sec., the ball speed after impact *must* be 140 m/sec.

Momentum of bat before impact = 4 × 10
= 40 kg/sec.
Momentum of ball before impact = 0.5 × 100
= 50
Total momentum before impact = 90
Momentum of bat after impact = 4 × 5
= 20

Since total momentum must be 90, momentum of ball after impact must = 70
= 0.5 × 140

(disregarding directions).

Another way of saying this is: when two balls collide, the impulse received by ball A from ball B is equal and opposite to that received by ball B from ball A.

Another example: A high jumper's momentum at take off is equal to the change in the earth's momentum in the opposite direction, *but* the reaction of the earth is not noticeable because of its enormous mass.

Angular applications of Newton's Third Law

When a person is in mid-air and free from support, the body mass is no longer affixed to the earth's mass. During the airborne period, Newton's Third Law produces highly observable results. If the performer flexes the trunk (action), the thighs will rise toward the upper trunk (reaction). See Chapter 27.

Resistance forces, or forces that oppose motion

Forces that act to oppose the motion of a body are called **forces of resistance**. Examples of these forces include catching, stopping, or pulling or pushing against a body travelling in the opposite direction.

If a force is applied in opposition to a moving object during a sporting activity, the object's motion will be **decelerated** (slowed down).

The four most common forces acting against a performer are:

- Gravity
- Fluid resistance
- Contact force
- Friction.

(1) Gravity

For a person performing any action on the earth's surface, gravity:

- Is applied constantly
- Acts on each part of the body
- Acts in the direction of the earth's centre
- Opposes upward movement, so that you feel fatigued if you try to perform any action, such as running, away from the earth's centre of gravity.

(2) Fluid resistance

Fluid resistance comes from such substances as air or water. Fluid resistance:

- Is related to the velocity of the moving body
- Works according to the law that **'resistance increases proportionately with the square of the body's velocity'**. For example, when swimming, if you travel faster, you encounter more drag, and therefore need more energy to keep swimming.

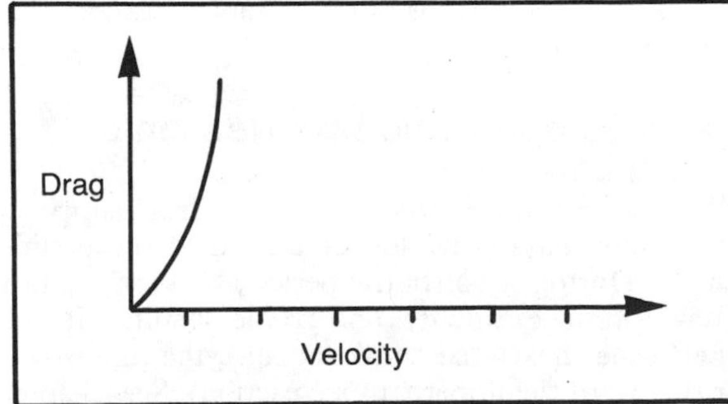

Figure 25.18

Drag force

Drag force is the **resistance to motion** felt by the cyclist, runner or swimmer. As well as velocity, frontal area and the body shape contribue to drag.

On a windless day, a sprinter uses approximately 13 per cent of his or her energy to overcome drag force.

(3) Contact force (or normal reactive force)

Contact force is experienced when a body comes into contact with a surface, and it acts perpendicular to that surface (as shown by Newton's Third Law).

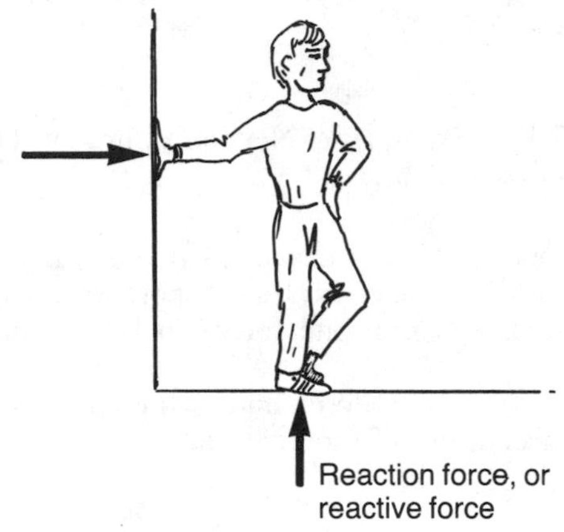

Figure 25.19

(4) Friction

Friction is the resistance to motion, or impending motion, caused by contact between two surfaces. That is, friction develops whenever a body moves or tends to move across the surface of another body. Friction always opposes motion, and acts parallel to the surfaces.

Types of friction include:

- Starting (static) friction
- Moving (sliding) friction
- Rolling friction
- Stopping friction.

The First Law of Friction

The First Law of Friction states that **'for two dry surfaces, the frictional force is proportional to the normal reaction, and is dependent on the nature of the surfaces'**. It is shown as a formula:

Friction = reaction × coefficient of friction
F = RU

$$\text{Coefficient of friction} = \frac{\text{friction}}{\text{reaction}}$$

$$U = \frac{F}{R}$$

For example, a weight with a force of 20 kg pressing down on a surface is acted upon by an equal reaction. The frictional force is 10 kg.

$$\frac{10}{20} = 0.5$$

Any increase in the force applied downwards will result in a proportional increase in the frictional force. If the reaction force increases by 10 kg, the resulting friction must be 15 kg to maintain the coefficient of friction for that situation.

$$\frac{15}{30} = 0.5$$

Factors that affect frictional forces

The factors that affect frictional forces are:

- **The magnitude of the force (weight)**

The greater the weight, the greater the friction.

- **Materials at the interface (contact surfaces)**

The rougher the contact surfaces, the greater the friction.

- **Velocity of movement**

The greater the velocity, the greater the friction. The direction of movement is also important.

- **Irregularity of the contact surfaces**

The more irregularities on the contact surfaces, the greater the friction.

Sliding friction

Sliding friction develops when one body begins to slide across another.

A coin resting on a table has no tendency to slide, and therefore has no sliding friction. If it is pushed

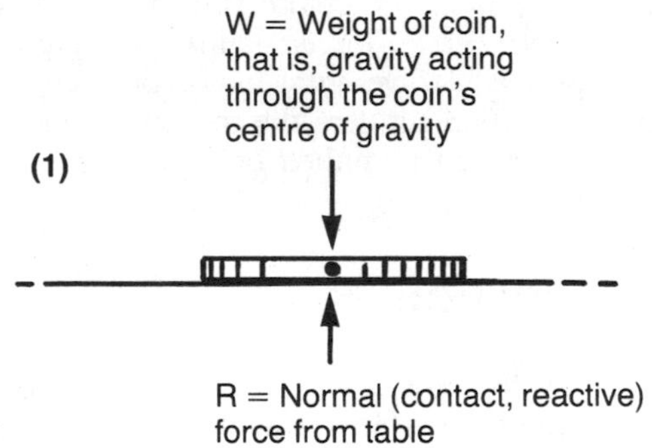

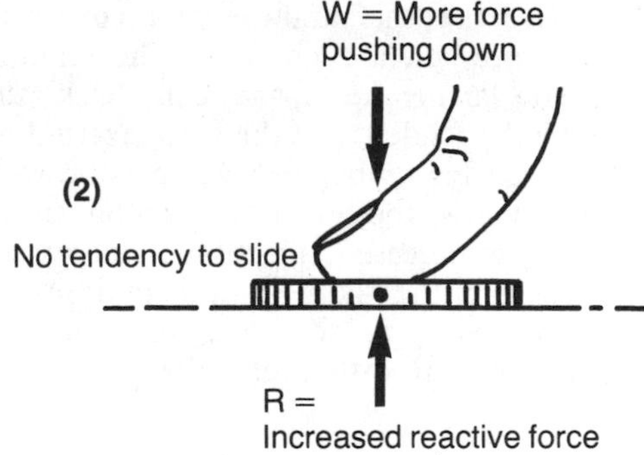

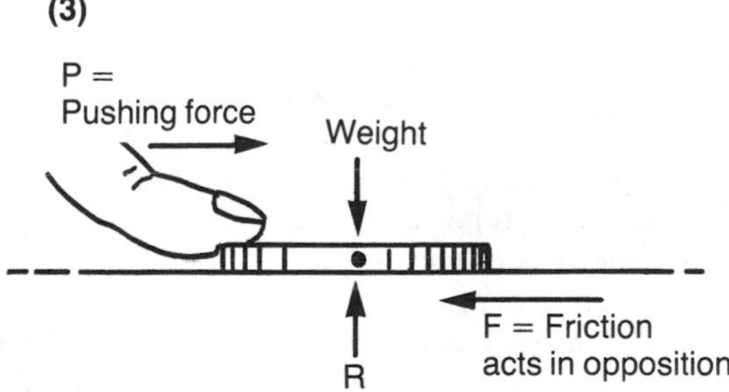

(4)

W

P

F

R

Limiting friction has been reached, once the coin starts moving, that is, friction (F) is not great enough to cancel out the pushing force (P).

Figure 25.20 Sliding friction.

down into the table with a finger, its ability to slide is decreased because the force pushing the coin downwards has increased, so increasing the reactive force from the table.

If the coin is pushed from the side, the coin will act in opposition to this tendency. Until the coin begins to slide, the magnitude of the friction is equal to the force tending to cause the coin to slide. In other words, friction cancels out the pushing force, and no movement occurs.

When friction becomes as large as is possible — that is, the coin's limiting friction — sliding is about to commence.

Adjusting friction

Friction can be adjusted in two ways:

- **By adjusting the forces with which the two bodies are pushed against each other**

For example, pushing on the coin increases friction. It will not move until a sideways push or force counteracts the friction enough to permit sideways movement.

Climbers also use this knowledge in order to increase their grip on a rock face. The climber knows that the farther he or she leans back, the greater will be the tendency of the force exerted by the rope to push his or her feet against the rock face. In other words, the horizontal component of the force will be increased. Friction is increased, and the tendency of the boots to slip is minimized.

- **More commonly, by adjusting the surfaces that are in contact with each other.**

Figure 25.21

Increasing friction

Friction can be increased by sportspeople in order to increase their grip. Examples include:

- Abrasive substances used on diving boards
- The gymnast's use of magnesium chalk to improve the grip on apparatus
- Bat handles covered in materials that increase grip
- Basketball boots with cleated rubber soles
- Table tennis bats with pimpled surfaces to increase ball control
- Shoes with stops and spikes on the soles
- Baseball pitchers who put resin on their hands.

Reducing friction

Friction can be reduced by using smoother surfaces. For example:

- Dancers wear shoes with soles of smooth leather
- Ballroom dancers use highly polished floors
- Skiers apply wax to their skis in order to reduce friction with the snow, and so increase speed and manoeuvrability.

Friction can be a help or a hindrance to sportspeople. For instance, the runner or jumper could not exert great force against the ground without slipping, if it were not for friction. On the other hand, friction hinders the movement of any object being pushed or pulled or rolled.

Rolling friction

When a ball rolls across a surface, it is constantly in contact with that surface. The two surfaces are slightly deformed in the process, so friction is a major influence on how far and fast the ball will travel. Rolling friction is very much less than sliding fiction, which explains why a heavy load can be moved much more easily when it is mounted on wheels.

The amount of friction that occurs depends on:

- The size and type of the ball
- The type of surface
- The dryness of the surface.

The harder the surface, the lower the force of rolling friction; the wetter the surface, the greater is the friction.

Sportspeople must assess the degree of friction on a surface and adjust their movements accordingly. For instance:

- When golfing, and faced with a soft, wet, uncut green, you know that you must strike your putt with greater force than you would need to do on a well-cut, hard, dry green.

- When playing soccer or hockey, you may elect to play the ball in the air in order to avoid a surface that creates a high degree of friction.

Laboratory work 37: Factors affecting the coefficient of restitution of a tennis ball

Method

(1) Establish the height from which the tennis ball is dropped, and the height to which it returns after impact.

(2) Using the figures, calculate the coefficient of restitution, using the formula:

$$e = \sqrt{\frac{\text{height bounced}}{\text{height dropped}}}$$

(3) Drop the same tennis ball onto:
- **(a)** Concrete
- **(b)** A wooden floor
- **(c)** The surface of a tennis court
- **(d)** Dry grass
- **(e)** Wet grass
- **(f)** A crash mat
- **(g)** Sand
- **(h)** A tennis racquet with tight strings
- **(i)** A tennis racquet with loose strings.

(4) Choose a tennis ball that is either newer or older than the one used so far during this experiment. Drop the ball onto one or more of the surfaces listed above. Compare the coefficient of restitution with the results already obtained for the same surfaces.

(5) **(a)** Drop a tennis ball onto a tennis court surface — that is, your hand simply releases the ball.
- **(b)** Project the same tennis ball onto a tennis court surface — that is, apply force to the ball at release point.
- **(c)** Drop the same tennis ball onto the same surface:
  - — At existing temperatures
  - — After being 'cooled'
  - — After being 'heated'.
- **(d)** Compare the results with your theoretical findings, giving explanations for your results.

Laboratory work 38: Evaluating starting positions for sprinting

Method

(1) In groups of four, complete the table, Figure 25.22, timing a 10-metre sprint:

(2) Compare each subject's average times for the four differing starts:
- **(a)** When wearing socks
- **(b)** When wearing shoes.

(3) Which starting position produced the best time?

(4) Which type of footwear produced the best times?

(5) Discuss the results in the light of what you've discovered about:
- **(a)** Newton's Third Law
- **(b)** Friction
- **(c)** Horizontal and vertical components of force.

Worksheet 24: Rebound and friction

(1) From the table of heights given in Figure 25.2, work out:
- **(a)** Which ball rebounded the most when dropped?
- **(b)** Which ball rebounded the least when dropped?
- **(c)** Which ball rebounded the most when projected at 80–100 kilometres per hour?
- **(d)** Which ball rebounded the least when projected at 80–100 kilometres per hour?
- **(e)** Does a ball have a higher or a lower rebound when it is moving at game speed?
- **(f)** Can you make a generalization concerning the differences between the rebound of soft balls and hard balls under either 'dropped' or 'projected' conditions?

		Subject							
	Trial no.	1		2		3		4	
Initial position		**Socks**	**Cleated shoes**	**Socks**	**Cleated shoes**	**Socks**	**Cleated shoes**	**Socks**	**Cleated shoes**
Feet together (1) **Upright start** (2) (3)									
Average time:									
Standing start (1) (2) (3)									
Average time:									
Crouch start (1) (2) (3)									
Average time:									
Crouch start (1) Using blocks (2) or wall to (3) push off									
Average time:									

Figure 25.22

(2) Determine the coefficient of restitution (e) for the following objects:

	Height dropped	**Bounced**	**e**
(a) Baseball	1.2 m	0.3 m	
(b) Golf ball	1.8 m	1 m	
(c) Handball	2.2 m	1.8 m	
(d) Superball	2 m	1.9 m	
(e) Volley ball	2.8 m	1.7 m	

Figure 25.23

(3) Determine which way the ball will rebound in the following diagrams:

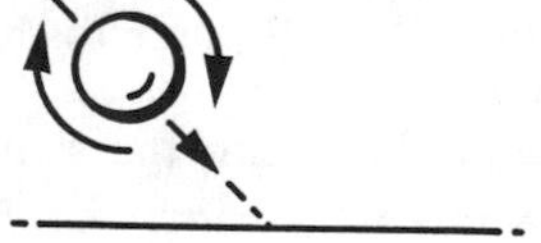

Figure 25.24

(a) Label the type of spin and rebound.
(b) Note the reason for your answer.
(c) Draw in the rebound.
(d) Give reasons for (a).

(4) From the following list, circle the letters beside the examples that increase the coefficient of starting friction:
(a) Snow tread on cars
(b) Wax on a dance floor
(c) Abrasive surface on a swimmer's starting block
(d) Paint with sand, applied to shower cubicles
(e) Dancing slippers
(f) Spikes on golf shoes
(g) Starting holes dug in a track.

(5) What component of force (or velocity) is reduced when the coefficient of starting friction is reduced for human locomotion?

(6) Give three examples of physical activity in which high frictional forces are important for enhancing performance.

(7) Give three examples of physical activity in which low frictional forces are important for enhancing performance.

(8) (a) In which direction does sliding friction operate?
(b) What is the term for the greatest amount of friction for an object?
(c) Other than changing the two contact surfaces, how can friction be increased?
(d) Define rolling friction.
(e) What kind of things does it depend on?
(f) What can increase rolling friction?

(9) Rolling friction is:
(a) Less than sliding friction, but greater than limiting friction
(b) Greater than limiting friction and greater than sliding friction
(c) Less than sliding friction and less than limiting friction
(d) None of the above.

(10) In order to decrease the amount of limiting friction between two bodies, it is best to:
(a) Lift one of the bodies
(b) Alter the nature of the two surfaces in contact
(c) Change the forces that hold together the two surfaces
(d) Lighten the load and lubricate the surfaces.

(11) Which is more important when hitting for distance?
(a) Bat weight
(b) Bat speed
(c) Bat density
(d) None of the above.

(12) What is the relationship (theoretical) between the angle of approach and the angle of rebound? How could this relationship be changed?

(13) Sliding friction occurs when:
(a) Two objects slide or tend to slide on one another
(b) You apply the brakes of your car
(c) You push off from the blocks in a sprint start
(d) None of the above.

(14) A ball that has been imparted with back spin will have a rebound angle .... its approaching angle:
(a) Greater than
(b) Less than
(c) The same as
(d) Which cannot be compared to.

(15) Using a sport or sports with which you are familiar, explain the effect of:
(a) Top spin
(b) Back spin.

(16) (a) Give three examples of impulse, where the performer is propelling an object in an overhead action.
(b) Give three examples of impulse, where the performer is propelling an object via striking.

(17) In performing a tumbling stunt, why is it easier to gain height from the surface of a small trampoline than from the surface of the floor?

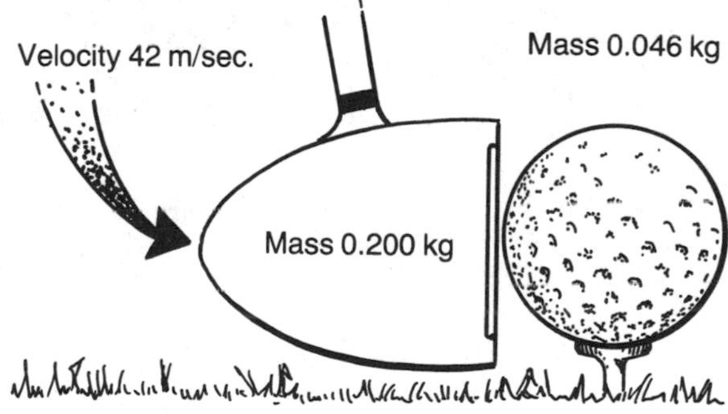

Figure 25.25

(18) (a) What is the total momentum of the club and ball in Figure 25.25?

(b) If the club slows to 19 m/sec. immediately after impact, what must the release speed of the ball be?

(19) Kicker A punts a football with the right foot, and the left foot is in contact with the earth. Kicker B punts a football with the right foot while the left foot is off the ground:

(a) Which kicker will produce the longest punt?

(b) What will happen to the body of kicker B as the kicked ball starts forward?

(c) Why will the body of kicker A not be affected in the same manner?

(d) What are the two forces that account for the additional length of kicker A's punt?

(e) Which of these forces in not available to kicker B?

(f) Why is this second force not available to kicker B?

(20) A tennis player serves a slice serve that curves away from his opponent. What will happen when the ball makes contact with the ground?

(21) What enables a footballer to kick a ball further on a hot day compared to a cold, rainy day?

(22) What are the biomechanical advantages of a crouch start?

(23) A baseballer uses a particular size and weight of bat each innings.

(a) Why does the baseballer choose a particular weight?

(b) Why use a bat, anyway?

(c) What factors may be involved in the collision between bat and ball?

(24) Why is the O'Brien Method of shot putting more effective than the original side-facing style? (See Figures 25.26 and 25.27.)

Figure 25.26 The O'Brien method.

Figure 25.27 The side-facing style.

26. Angular kinetics

Concepts in angular motion

The human body, mechanically speaking, comprises a system of levers capable only of rotational motion. Therefore most movement in sports is of an angular character. In talking about angular motion, the main concepts discussed in this chapter are:

- Eccentric force
- Couple
- Moment
- Moment of inertia
- Angular momentum
- Conservation of angular momentum
- Transfer of momentum.

Planes of motion in the human body

Human movements are often described in terms of the plane in which they occur. Three planes (flat surfaces) of motion pass through the human body (see Figure 26.2):

(1) The sagittal plane (anteroposterior)

The sagittal plane passes through the body from front to back, dividing the body into left and right portions.

(2) The frontal plane (coronal)

The frontal plane passes through the body from left to right, dividing the body into anterior and posterior portions.

(3) The horizontal plane (transverse)

The horizontal plane passes through the body in a line parallel to the floor, dividing the body into superior and inferior portions.

For example:

Action	Plane
Softball pitch	Sagittal
Sidearm throw	Transverse
Flutter kick in swimming	Sagittal
Pirouette	Transverse
Long jump	Sagittal
Star jumps	Frontal

Figure 26.1

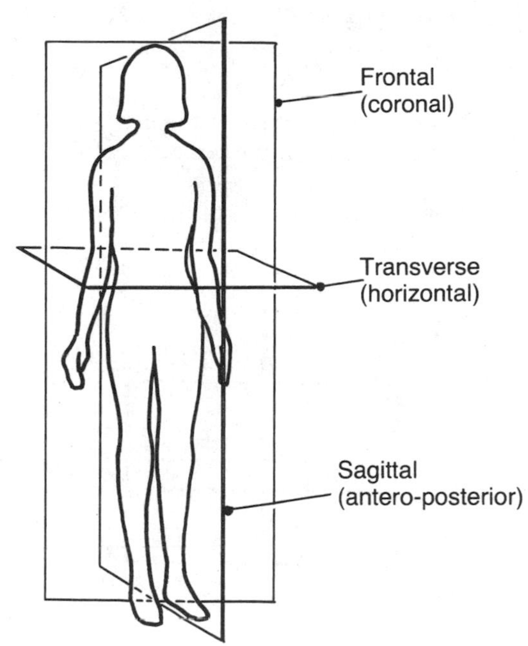

Figure 26.2

Eccentric force

Eccentric force is a force whose line of action *does not* pass through the centre of gravity of the body on which it acts.

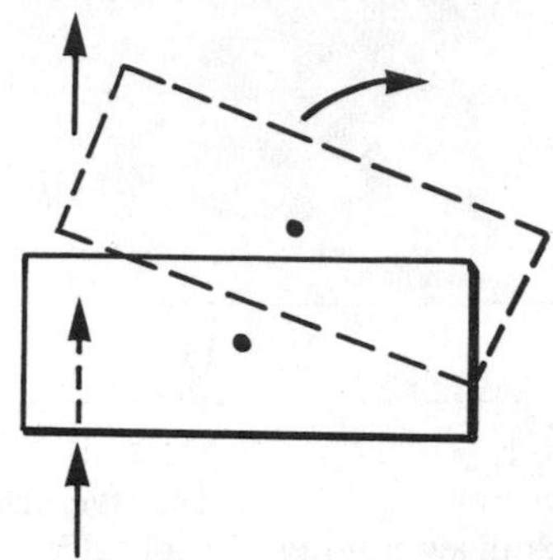

Figure 26.3

The result is **translation and rotation**. The direction of movement depends on which side of the centre of gravity the line of action passes.

Eccentric force can be most clearly compared with:

Direct force, or Concentric force

Direct (concentric) force is a force whose line of action *does* pass through the centre of gravity of the body on which it acts.

The result is **translation**, in the direction of the force.

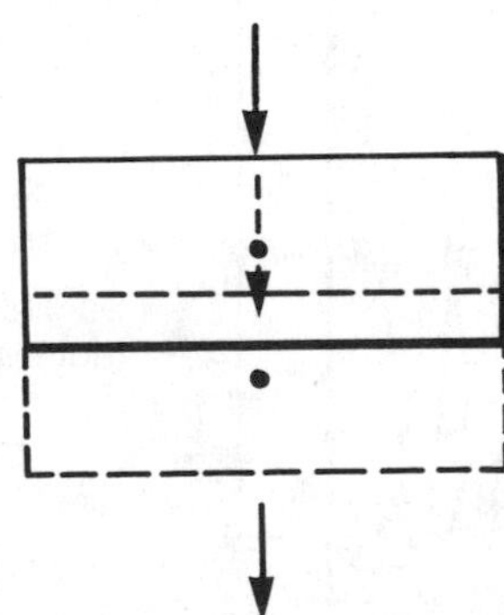

Figure 26.4

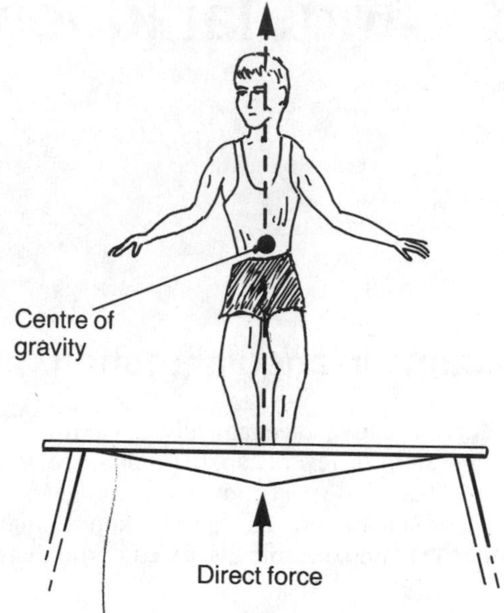

Figure 26.5 Translation.

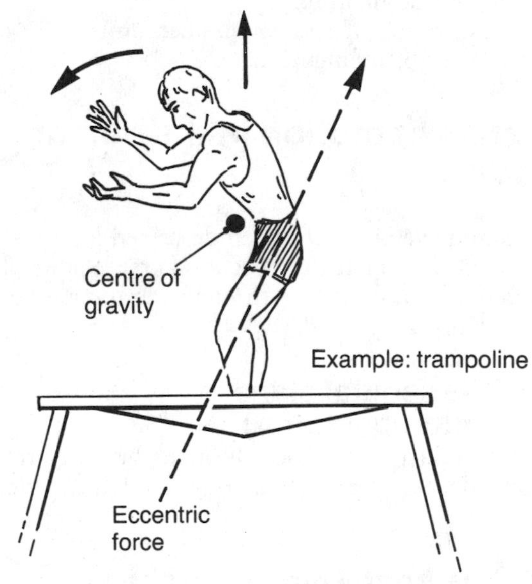

Figure 26.6 Rotation and translation.

Force couple

In the human body, rotary motion is often achieved by means of force couples. Authors differ on the exact definition of a force couple.

Hay's definition

For example, Hay defines a force couple as consisting of **two equal forces, equidistant from the centre of gravity, acting in parallel but opposite directions**. Such a force couple can only produce rotation, as the translatory effects of the two forces are cancelled out.

Hay gives the illustration of two gymnasts, on opposite sides of a pommel horse, equidistant from the centre and both pushing forward with equal amounts of force. As a result, the horse rotates.

Another example: Sitting in a rubber tube, if you push forward with one hand as hard as you push back with the other, on either side of the tube you will create a force couple that causes the tube to spin in the same spot.

Figure 27.7

Figure 26.8

Other examples are rarely found in sporting situations, because it is so difficult to establish two equal and opposite forces.

Dyson's definition

Dyson (and others) uses a less stringent definition of a force couple. Dyson provides the following illustration, which shows a couple of forces creating both rotation and translation.

In diving, 'the diver's rotation off the board is brought about by a single couple':

- One force is the **'reaction to his leg thrust'** — that is, 'the force of the springboard acts vertically upward'.
- The second force is **'the sweep of his arms'** — that is, 'the force of his weight, acting through his centre of gravity, pulls vertically downward'.

'He obtains this eccentric or sideways thrust about the Centre of Gravity by bringing his head and arms (i.e. just under a fifth of his total body mass) forward beforehand.' (See Dyson, p. 80.)

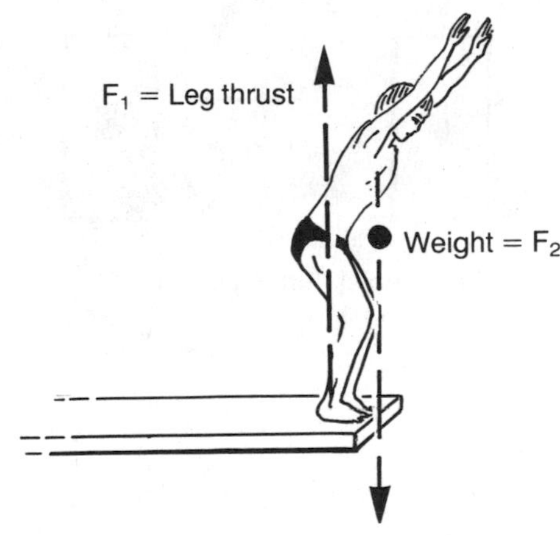

Figure 26.9

Other illustrations of force couples include:

- **In softball:** the grip of the right and left hands opposite each other create a couple. As one hand pushes forward, the other pulls back, turning the bat.
- **In hockey:** the push shot is governed by a couple created by the upper hand pushing back and the lower one moving forward.
- **In paddling (and tightrope walking)** the hands act as a couple on the paddle (or balancing stick).

Translation and rotation: summary

- A force directed through a body's centre of gravity causes translation.
- A force couple causes rotation only, if the two forces are opposite and equal. If not, some translation will occur.
- An eccentric force causes both translation and rotation.

The turning effect of an eccentric force

The turning effect of an eccentric force is directly related to the distance of the point of application of the force from the centre of gravity. An equal force applied further from the centre of gravity has a greater turning effect than one applied nearer to the centre of gravity.

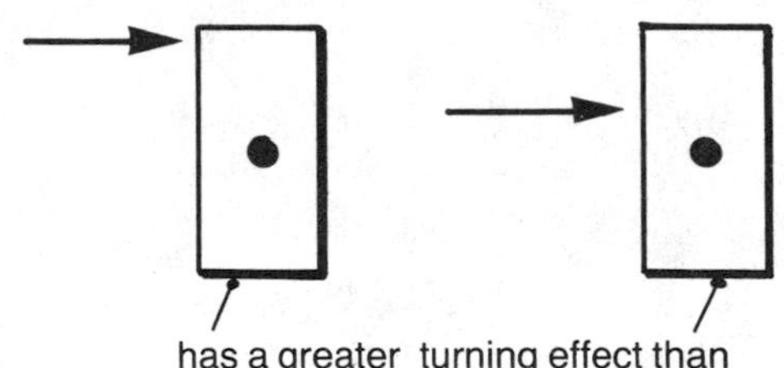

Figure 26.10

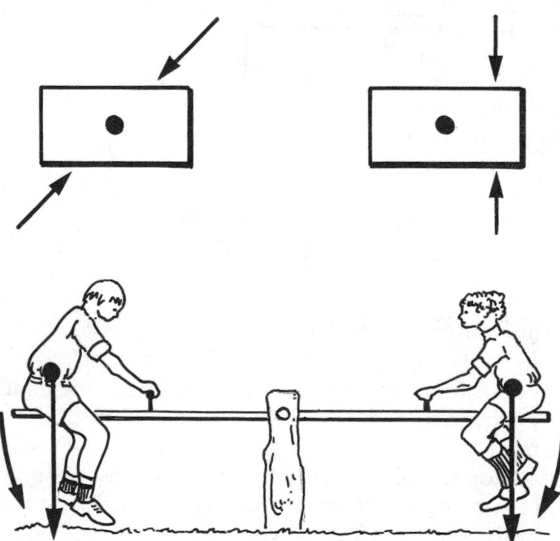

Figure 26.11

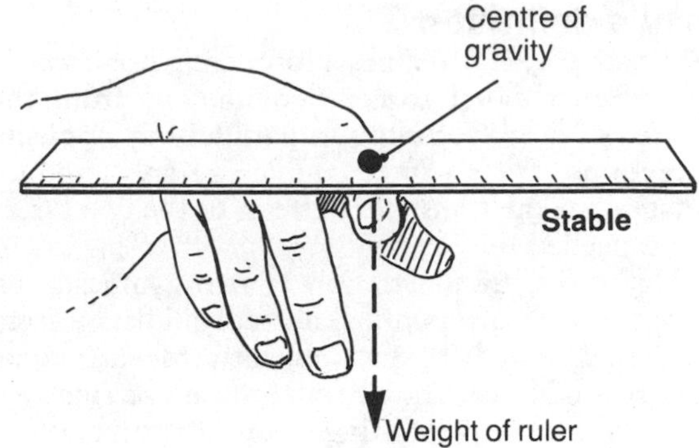

Figure 26.12

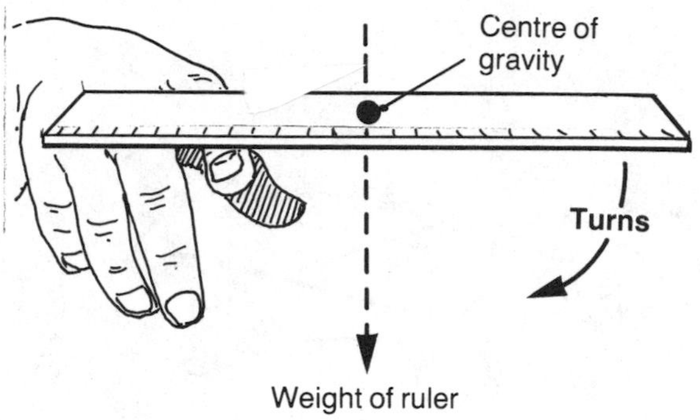

Figure 26.13

When two equal forces are applied against each other, they cancel out each other and no movement occurs.

Moment of force, or torque

The moment of force, or torque, is a measure of how much turning effect that force will have when applied.

Hold a classroom ruler in the centre (Figure 26.12). Compare this with holding it further down its length, or at the tail end (Figure 26.13). You will find it increasingly difficult to hold the ruler, because of its tendency to rotate. This tendency increases as the horizontal distance between the force of its weight (acting through the centre of gravity) and the hand increases.

Wheels, revolving doors and clothes lines are easier to turn when they are pushed as far away as possible from their axes (the hub, the hinge, the centre pole) or when greater force is applied. In other words:

- Greater rotation occurs with a greater lever arm.
- Greater rotation occurs with a larger force.

The lever arm is the shortest perpendicular distance from the axis of rotation to the point where force is applied.

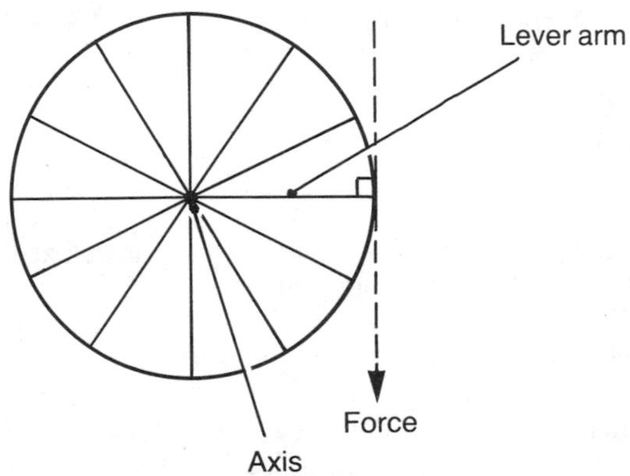

Figure 26.14

The **product of the force and the lever arm** is called the **torque**, or **moment of force**. It is a **measure of the turning effect**.

M = F × MA
Moment of torque = Force × moment arm (lever arm)
= Magnitude of the force × the shortest perpendicular distance between the axis and the line of action of the force.

In the following example, which wheel — **A, B, C** or **D** — has the greatest 'turning effect', 'moment' or 'torque'?

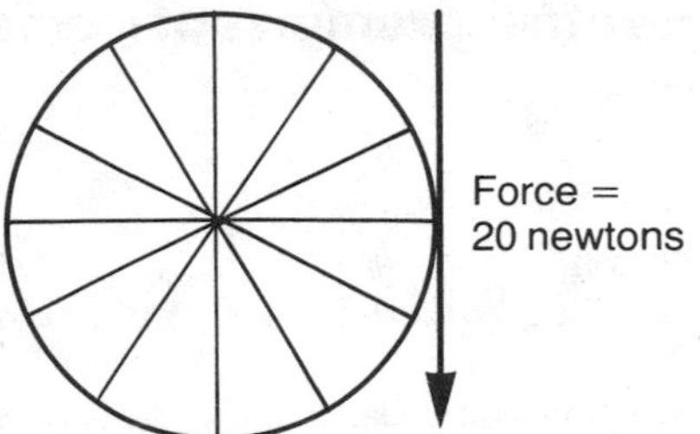

(**A**) Radius of the wheel = 10 centimetres

M = F × MA
M = F × MA
= 20 × 10
= 200 units.

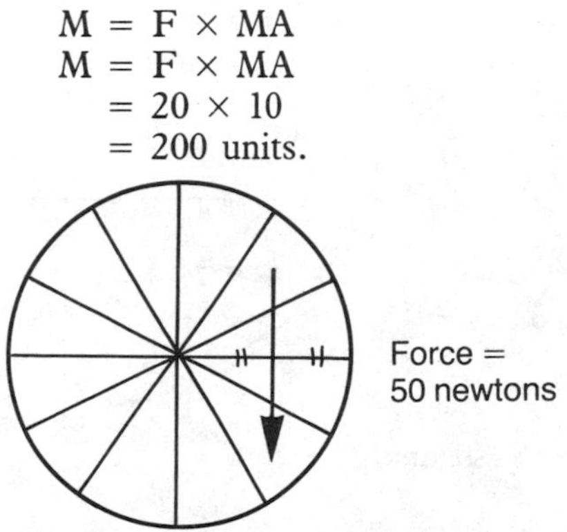

(**B**) Radius of the wheel = 10 centimetres.

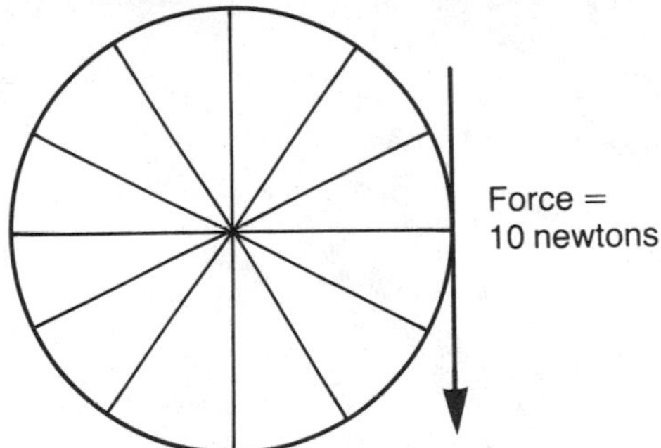

(**C**) Radius of the wheel = 15 centimetres.

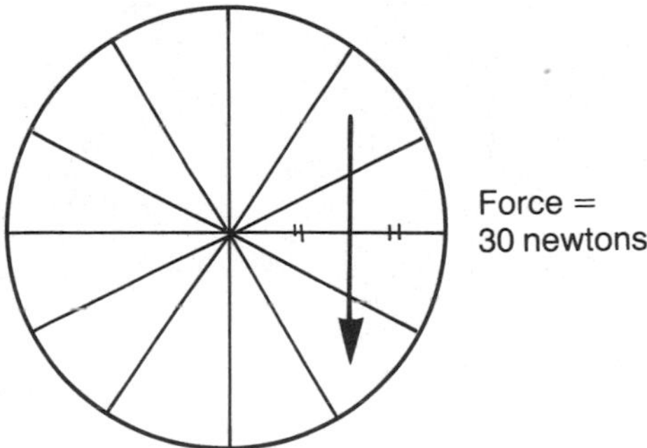

Figure 26.15 (**D**) Radius of the wheel = 15 centimetres.

Some other examples of moments of force

• Rowing

When rowing, you can alter your action on the oar by:

(1) Altering the magnitude of the force exerted

(2) Adjusting the length of its moment arm.

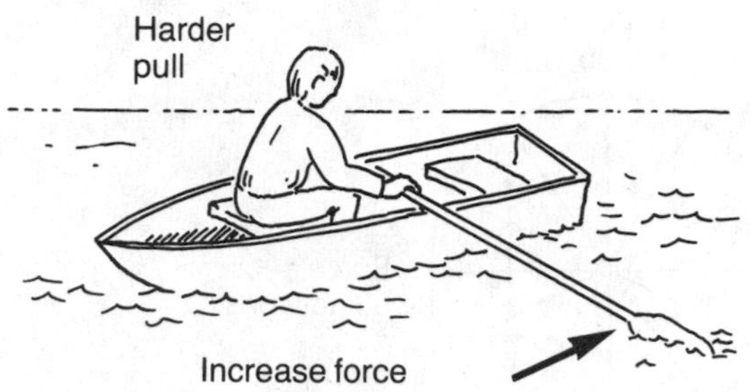

Harder pull

Increase force

Figure 26.16

or

Figure 26.17

You gain a greater turning effect with either a harder pull or a longer moment arm.

• Diving

When diving you can alter the length of your moment arm by leaning out further before diving. This gives a lot of 'turning effect'. In this example:

- The force is the weight of the diver's body — that is, the line of gravity acting through the body's centre of gravity.
- x_2 is the longer moment arm.
- Therefore M = F × MA will be greater for (2).

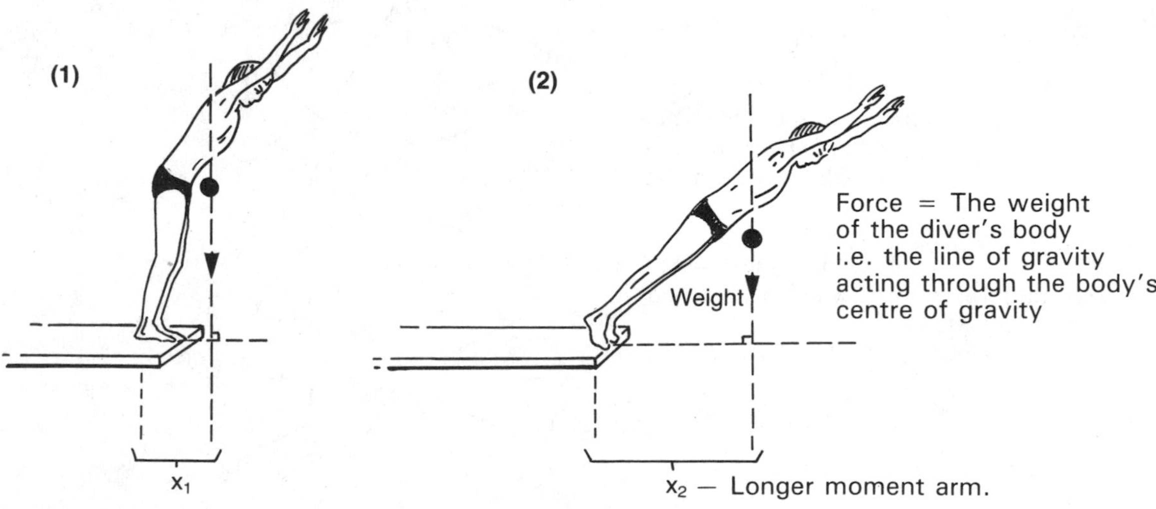

Figure 26.18

• **Running**
When running, you need to lean forward in the early stages of a race to counteract the tendency of the upper body to rotate backwards. This tendency is caused by an eccentric force being applied to the balls of your feet — that is, the ground reaction force. As your speed increases later in the race, this force decreases, and the body is more upright.

• **Long jump**
At the take-off board in long jump, you need to give an eccentric thrust that, in conjunction with gravity, tends to rotate the body forward in flight. The hang technique and the hitch kick both are aimed at counteracting this forward rotation.

Equilibrium

An object is at rest, or in a state of equilibrium, when the resultant of all the forces acting on it is zero — in other words, **when a force from any given direction is balanced by an equal force from the opposite direction**. An imbalance of forces will cause **either** a **linear** or a **rotary motion**, according to the point at which the force is applied.

The equilibrium of a body is said to be **stable** if, when being slightly displaced, the body tends to return to its original position.

The equilibrium is **unstable** if the body tends, instead, to move further from the original position.

Equilibirum relies on:

- The location of the centre of gravity in relation to the base of support
- The direction of the forces involved.

Static equilibrium

When a body is in static equilibrium, it is static or stationary — for example, when performing a headstand, or in the ironcross position in gymnastics.

Dynamic equilibrium

During dynamic equilibrium, the body is not stable but in motion, moving with constant linear and angular velocities that balance out each other. For example, running involves 'unbalancing' and 'rebalancing'.

Centre of gravity

The stability of a body therefore depends on its being in a state of equilibrium. Equilibrium and stability are closely related to the centre of gravity — the one point of the body where the force of gravity is concentrated.

Principles of equilibrium

Principle 1: The nearer the line of gravity falls to the centre of the base of support, the greater the probability of maintaining balance

If the centre of gravity moves outside any margin of the base of support, stability is lost.

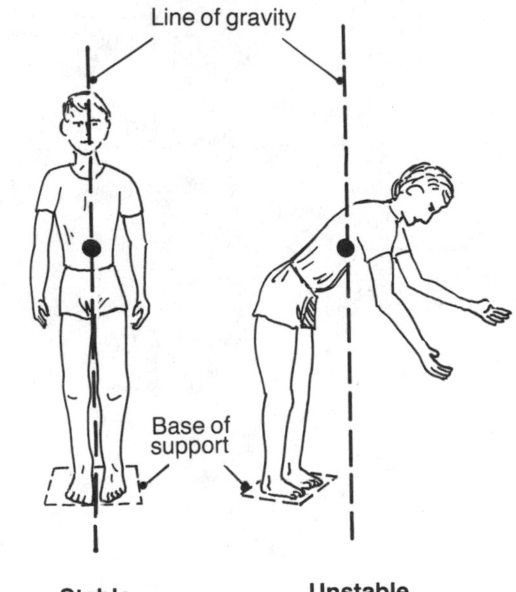

Figure 26.19

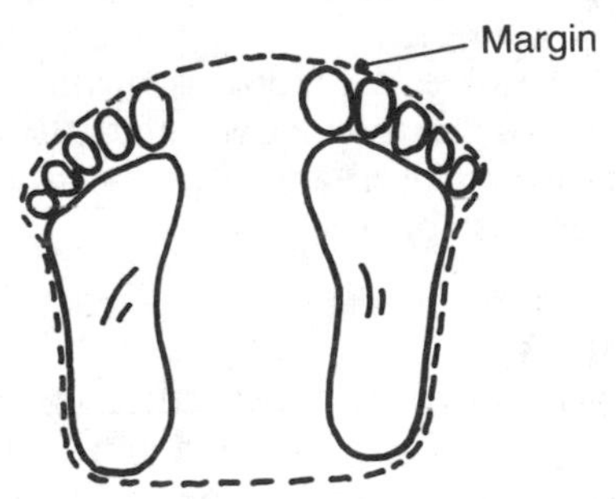

Figure 26.20

Note: The base of support involves the points of contact with a supporting surface and the area between these points of contact.

Principle 2: The broader the base of support, generally the better the probability of maintaining balance

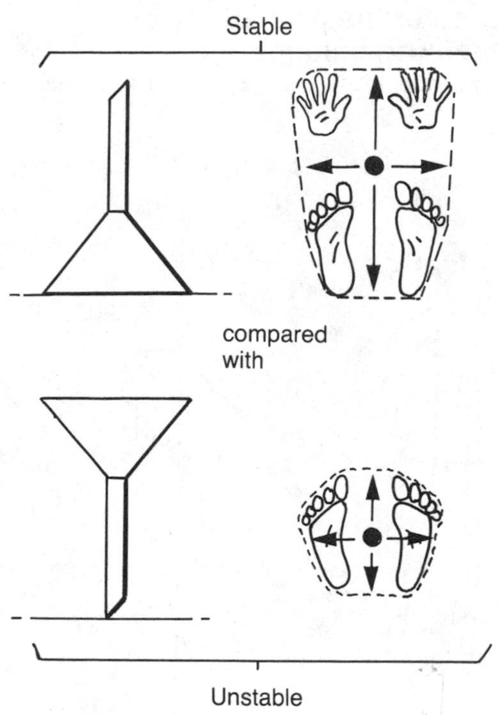

Figure 26.21

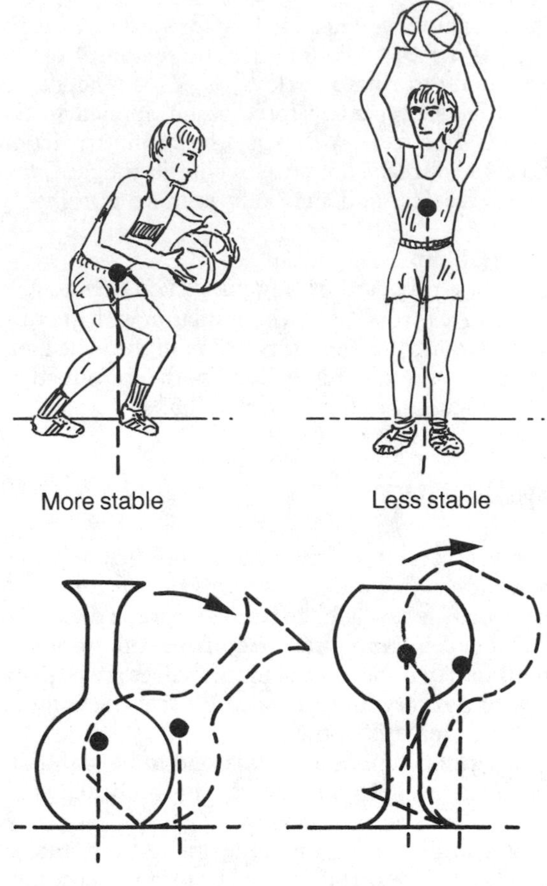

Figure 26.22

For example, a wrestler on hands and knees is more stable than a wrestler who is standing. Since the margin of the base of support is further from the centre of gravity in the first wrestler, the centre of gravity must be moved a greater distance to make the wrestler unstable.

Principle 3: The probability of maintaining balance is increased and when the centre of gravity is lowered in relation to the base

Raising the centre of gravity within the base of support decreases stability. This is because the distance that the centre of gravity needs to be moved before the object becomes unstable.

Principle 4: The further one body segment moves away from the line of gravity, the greater the probability of losing balance, unless another segment moves to compensate for it

Whenever one body part moves, the centre of gravity moves in the same direction. Also, if the centre of gravity shifts towards an oncoming force while still within the base of support, stability is increased. This is because the centre of gravity would have to be shifted a greater distance before making the person unstable.

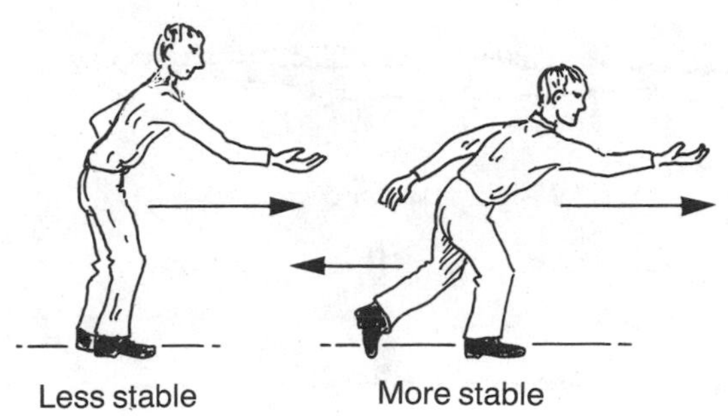

Figure 26.23

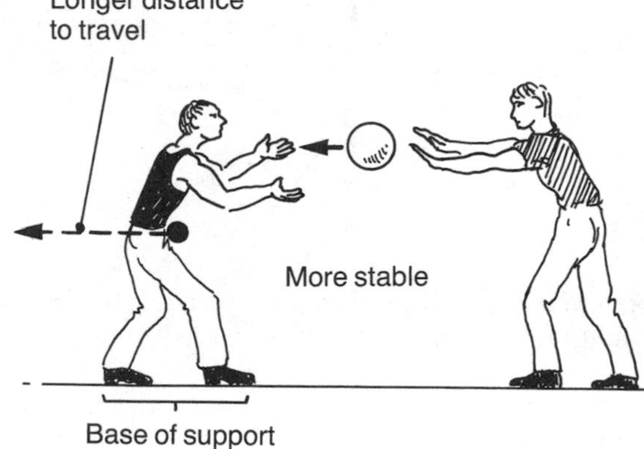

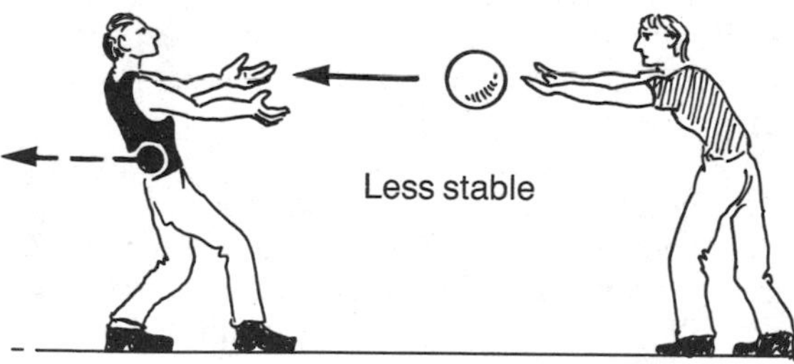

Figure 26.24

Principle 5: Rotating movement increases stability

It is much more difficult to balance on a still bike than on one with rotating wheels. Likewise, when ice-skating, rotation increases stability.

Other conditions affecting stability

Other conditions affecting stability include:

- Any external weight added to the body becomes part of the total body weight and causes the centre of gravity to move towards the position of the external weight.
- Any increase in friction between surfaces increases stability.
- Any increase in mass increases stability, because of increased inertia. For example, a sumo wrestler has a large mass, stands squat with his feet apart placed in the direction of the oncoming force, and leans towards that force. Therefore he establishes a very stable position.

Stability: a summary

(1) Increasing stability

To achieve greater stability you need:

- To maintain a large supporting base, in line with the oncoming force
- A lower centre of gravity
- A line of gravity close to the centre of the base of support
- To lean into the oncoming force
- To increase rotation.

(2) Reducing stability

To reduce your stability, you need:

- A narrow supporting base, perpendicular to the oncoming force
- A high centre of gravity
- A line of gravity moved in the direction of the edge of the supporting base
- To lean away from the oncoming force
- To decrease rotation.

Body movement and centre of gravity

When a body moves, the centre of gravity moves in the same direction — for example, when extending an arm to the right, crouching down, or extending one leg behind you. This can be particularly useful in activities where extra height is an advantage. In Chapter 23 and Figure 23.8, we saw how high-

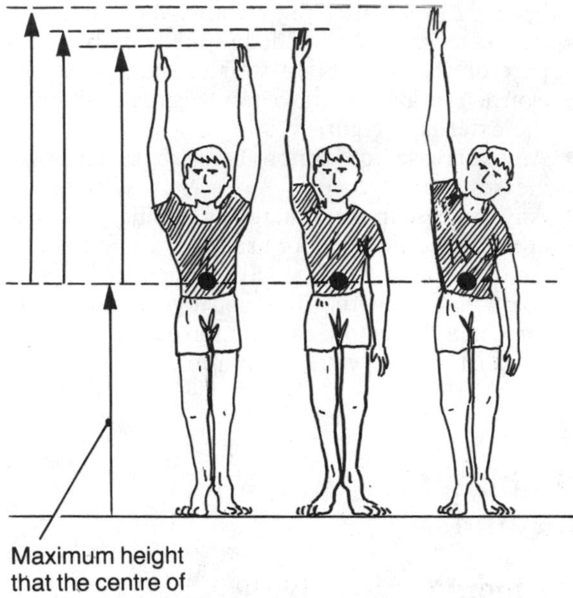

Figure 26.25

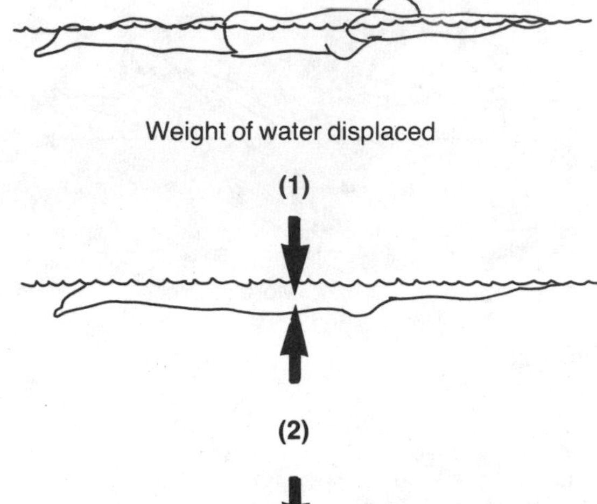

Figure 26.26 The buoyant force is equal to the weight of the water displaced.

jump styles vary in the actual height jumped, even though the centre of gravity was lifted to the same height.

When playing basketball, and you leap into the air, your centre of gravity reaches a certain height. If you stretch up with both your arms you reach a given height. If, however, after you have left the floor, you stretch one arm downwards, you cause your centre of gravity to move downwards. Your centre of gravity will still rise the same distance. However, since it is lower in the body, there will be more of your body above your centre of gravity, and therefore you can reach higher.

Buoyancy and specific gravity

Athletes move through the fluid environment of air. Skindivers move through the fluid environment of water. Swimmers operate in a combination of fluid environments — water and air. A watery environment creates more obvious effects on bodily movements than air does.

The following areas apply particularly to the swimmer:

- Buoyancy and specific gravity
- Centre of buoyancy.

Specific gravity

(See Figure 26.26.) In the vertical direction, the only forces acting on the swimmer are:

- His or her weight
- Any upward vertical forces exerted by the water.

For horizontal flotation, the upward vertical forces (buoyant force) must be equal in magnitude to the swimmer's body weight. In other words, a body will float if the body weight is less than the maximum buoyant force.

Archimedes' Principle states that a body that is wholly or partly submerged in a fluid is buoyed up by a force equal to the weight of the displaced fluid. In other words, the buoyant force is equal in magnitude to the weight of the water displaced by the body.

The maximum volume of water that the swimmer could displace would be a volume equal to that of his or her own body — that is, if she or he were immersed.

Therefore the maximum buoyant force is equal to the magnitude of the weight of water with the same volume as the volume of the body.

Therefore a body will float only if:

Weight of the body ≤ Weight of an equal volume of water

$$\Rightarrow \frac{\text{Weight of body}}{\text{Weight of an equal volume of water}} \leq 1$$

Specific gravity is the above ratio, and is a measure of a body's capacity to float. (If specific gravity equals 1, the body will be suspended in water.)

If the specific gravity is greater than 1, the body will sink.

Body composition is the main factor that determines a person's specific gravity. The less dense a body, the more buoyant it is. Bones and muscles, because they are more dense than other parts of the body, have a higher specific gravity. For instance, muscles have a specific gravity of 1, and bones of 1.5–2, but adipose tissue or fat has a specific gravity of 0.8. The chest cavity, with the lungs, is the most buoyant part, especially when filled with air (specific gravity of 0.0012). Therefore:

- Males are more 'dense' than females
- Males generally have greater difficult than females in floating
- The very young and the very old have lower specific gravities, and therefore find it easier to float than do other people.

Centre of buoyancy

On land, rotary motion is a result of the body's rotation around the centre of gravity. In water, rotary motion is a result of the body's rotation around the centre of buoyancy. **The centre of buoyancy** may be defined as **'the centre of gravity of the displaced water'**.

In a symmetrical object with a uniform density, the centres of buoyancy and gravity are the same, and the object remains balanced when placed in water. (Whether it floats or not depends on its weight.)

When a body is irregular in shape, and consists of parts of varying densities — for example, a human body — the centre of buoyancy may be in a position that is different from the centre of gravity. In the human body, this is generally higher than the centre of gravity — that is, at chest level (the human body's usual centre of gravity is at hip level).

The closer the centre of gravity and the centre of buoyancy, the more buoyant the body. Because they are generally separate, rotation occurs about the centre of buoyancy until the centre of gravity falls in a vertical line below the centre of buoyancy. When this happens, the swimmer can achieve motionless floating.

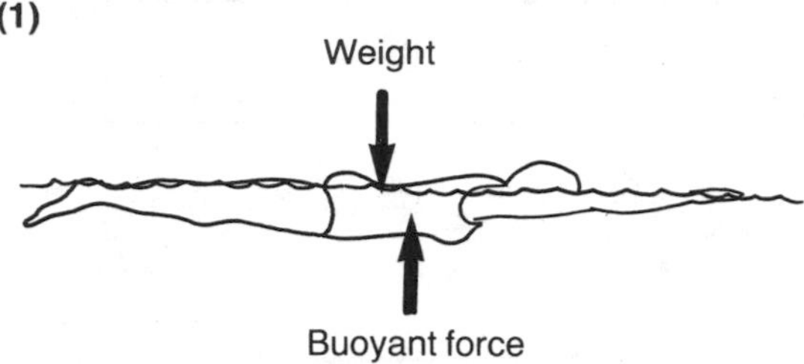

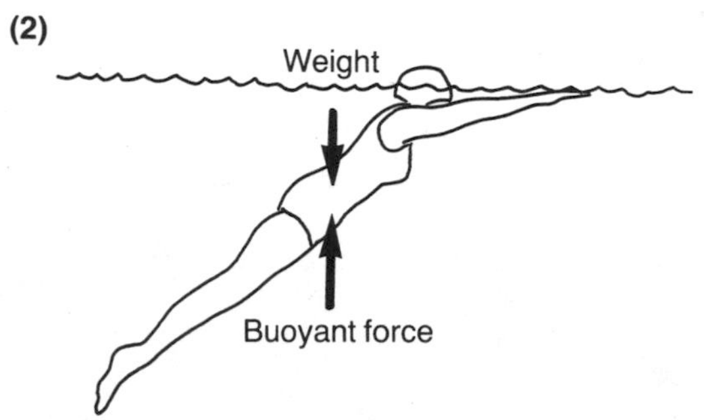

Figure 26.27 Whether a body floats horizontally or rotates to some inclined position is governed by the relative positions of the lines of action of the weight and the buoyant force.

Buoyancy in people is determined by three main factors:

- Lean body weight (heavier than water)
- Body fat (lighter than water)
- The amount of air in the lungs.

In the human body, the chest filled with air is usually the centre of buoyancy, because it is very light for its size and therefore very buoyant. For most people, the legs, having a higher percentage of bone and muscle, tend to sink during floating.

Buoyancy can therefore be increased by redistributing the body weight around the centre of buoyancy. In the jellyfish float position, all the body parts are as close to the centre of buoyancy as possible. Raising the arms above the head, arching the back, and laying the head back in the water all tend to raise the centre of gravity towards the centre of buoyancy. This counteracts the tendency of the legs to sink, since they do not need to drop very far before the centre of gravity and the centre

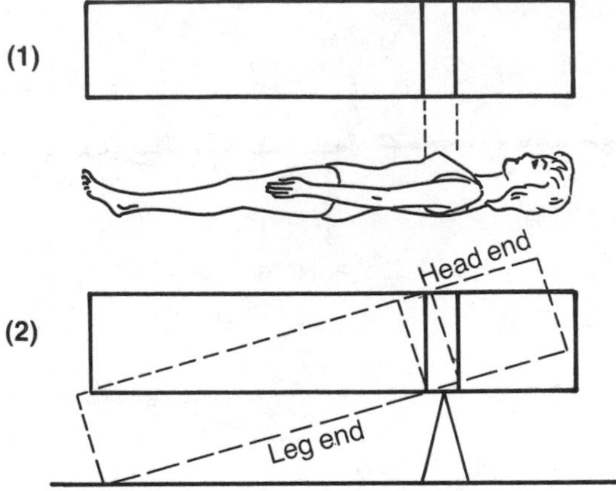

Figure 26.28 Tendency of a body to rotate around the chest area.

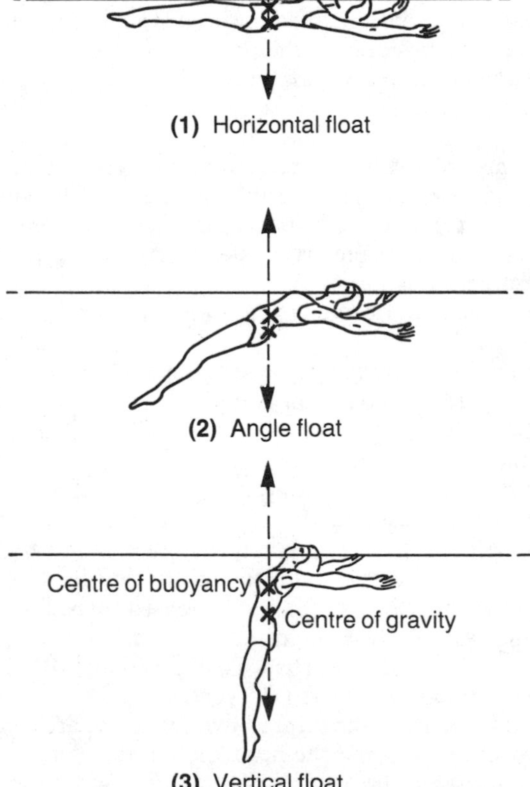

Figure 26.29 Floating positions resulting from various locations of the centre of buoyancy.

of buoyancy are vertically aligned.

This position also tends to expand the chest and increase the volume of the upper body, thus reducing its density.

The greater the amount of air in the lungs, the greater is an individual's buoyancy. Buoyancy can, therefore, be influenced by:

- Body shape
- Body position
- Body density
- Uniformity
- Amount of lean weight in the body
- Amount of fat in the body
- Amount of air in the lungs.

Laboratory work 39: Stability: conditions of minimum supported and inverted positions

Method

In your notebook, comment 'biomechanically' on your position and stability in each of these examples:

(1) **Principle 1: The relationship of the line of gravity to the base of support**
  (a) Feet on beam
  (b) Body bending forward
  (c) Balance on one foot:
    (i) Front foot with back leg extended as high as possible
    (ii) Back foot with front foot brought to the back knee.

(2) **Principle 2: The size of the base of support**
  (a) Pivot on the beam with feet .33 metre apart
  (b) Pivot on the beam, with feet close together.

(3) **Principle 3: The centre of gravity in relation to the base**
  (a) Pivot standing on the beam
  (b) Pivot squatting on the beam
  (c) Sitting astride the beam
  (d) Lying with upper torso on the beam.

(4) **Principle 4: Body segments moving away from the line of gravity**
  (a) Ball is bounced alongside the low beam, an arm's length away (while walking along).
  (b) Ball is bounced alongside the low beam, close to the beam.

(5) (a) Swan balance on the beam or bar
(b) Then lift your head and shoulders, with no other movement.

Laboratory work 40: Stability

Task 1

(1) Push your partner, who takes the following stances:
(a) Standing on one foot
(b) Standing feet together
(c) Standing feet apart perpendicular to force
(d) On hands and feet, spread.

(2) Which support is the most stable? Why?

Task 2

(1) Try to balance a series of objects on the floor.
(2) Compare objects with the same base of support but different heights.
(3) Compare objects with the same height but different sized bases.
(4) Which are the easiest/most difficult to knock over? Why?

Task 3

Stand against the wall with your back touching it. Touch your toes. What happens? Why?

Task 4

Why do toys with a curved base and a weighted base return to upright when pushed over?

Task 5

Balance on the narrow side of a bench:
(1) Arms by side
(2) Arms out
(3) Holding a stick across your body
(a) Up high
(b) Down out
(4) Holding a weighted pole
(a) Up high
(b) Down low
(5) Repeating (4)(a) above, with knees bent.
Which is the easiest? Why?

Laboratory work 41: The centre of gravity in the human body

Aim

To illustrate methods for determining the location of the centre of gravity of the human body.

Introduction

When a body is acted upon by gravity, every particle of mass of which it is composed is attracted towards the earth. The resultant of all these attractive forces is the weight of the body. This resultant force acts in the same direction as the individual particle forces, and acts through a point at the centre of the body's mass distribution. This point, called the body's 'centre of gravity', 'centre of mass' or 'gravicentre', often needs to be calculated if you want to investigate the mechanics underlying the body's motion or stability.

Method 1: Reaction board

For this method, the apparatus used is a reaction board, and the calculations are based on the **principle of moments** — that is, **when a system of forces is in equilibrium, the sum of their moments about any point in the plane of the forces must be zero.**

Single plane method (one scale)

(1) Obtain the subject's body weight: W = ... kg.
(2) Arrange the reaction board so that it is level, with one knife edge resting across the centre of the set of scales (see Figure 26.30).
(3) Record the scale reading: R_1 = ... kg.
(4) The subject lies supine in front of the reaction board, with feet at the end away from the scales.
(5) Record the new scale reading: R_2 = ... kg.
(6) Record the subject's height: H = ... cm.

Calculations

To calculate the location of the transverse plane in which the subject's centre of gravity lies, we apply the principle of moments. Taking moments about Point A:
where x is the horizontal distance of the subject's centre of gravity from Point A or the soles of the feet.

Taking moments about point A =

$$W \times x = (R_2 - R_1) \times 210 \text{ cm}$$

$$\therefore x = \frac{(R_2 - R_1) \times 210 \text{ cm}}{W}$$

$$x = \frac{\ldots \times 210}{\ldots}$$

$$x = \underline{\qquad\qquad} \text{ cm}$$

What is this as a percentage of the subject's standing height?:

That is:

$$\frac{x \text{ cm}}{H} \times \frac{100\%}{1} = \frac{\ldots}{\ldots} \times \frac{100}{1}\%$$

$$= \ldots \%$$

Questions

(1) Find the mean value of the centre of gravity for
  (a) The male members of the class
  (b) The female members of the class.
(2) Account for any difference between these mean values.
(3) Is this supported by the literature?
(4) If time permits, ask the subject to lie on the reaction board, varying his or her body position. Calculate his or her centre of gravity, and compare this to the position of the centre of gravity in the supine position. Comment.

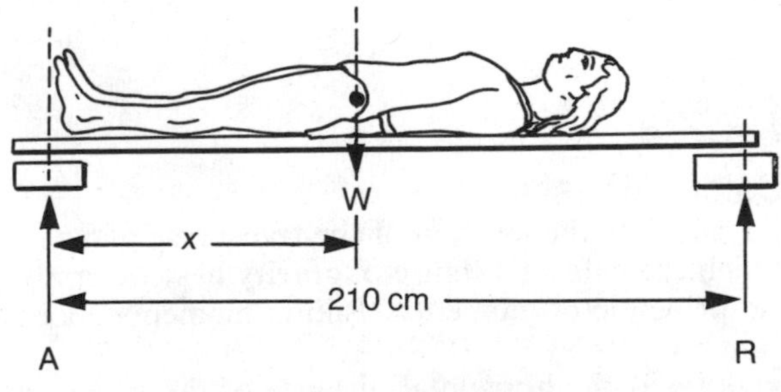

Figure 26.30 Method 1: Single plane method.

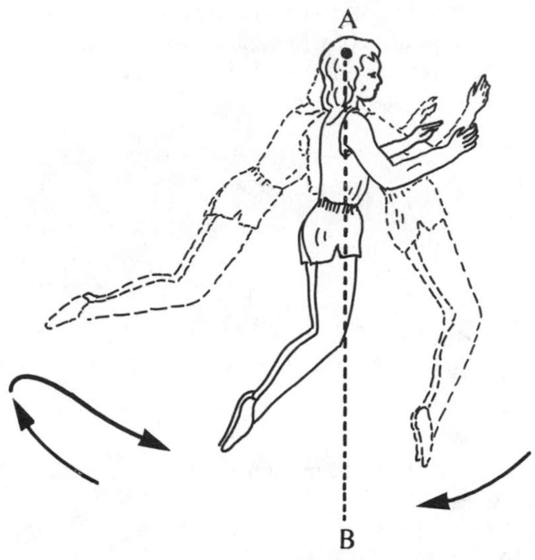

Figure 26.31 Method 2: Suspension method.

Method 2: The suspension method

The centre of gravity of a body can be found by suspending it:

(1) A cardboard cutout of a body in a sporting action is suspended from Point A (the top of the head), as in Figure 26.31. A plumb line (a weight attached to a piece of cotton) is also suspended from this point.
(2) Move the cutout so that its centre of gravity lies to the right of the vertical through A (that is, the line AB). Now there is a clockwise moment that will cause the cutout to rotate in that direction. When its centre of gravity crosses the line AB, a new counterclockwise moment reverses the direction of the swing. Eventually, after oscillating back and forth this way, the cutout comes to rest. When this occurs, the moment of the weight about the pivot at A must be zero, and the centre of gravity must lie on a line directly below this point.
(3) Mark the direction of the line AB on the cutout.
(4) Suspend the cutout from another point (for instance, the cutout's knee), and make it oscillate again. When it comes to rest once more, a second vertical line (corresponding to the plumb line) is drawn through the point of suspension.
(5) The point at which the two drawn lines intersect is the centre of gravity of the cutout.

Worksheet 25: Centre of gravity, forces, stability, buoyancy

(1) (a) What percentage of the height from the floor is the centre of gravity for:
— Men?
— Women?
(b) A male athlete stands at 185 centimetres tall. How far above his feet is his centre of gravity?
(c) A female athlete stands at 170 centimetres tall. How far above her feet is her centre of gravity?
(d) Why do you think that a man's centre of gravity is higher than a woman's?

(2) An athlete swings a 15-kilogram weight around his body — for example, during a hammer throw. What is the effect of this action upon his centre of gravity?

(3) The centre of gravity in a man is about:
(a) 55 per cent of his height
(b) 60 per cent of his height
(c) 50 per cent of his height
(d) 65 per cent of his height.

(4) What is the centre of gravity? What would be the effect on the centre of gravity of a person if he or she raised both arms above the head?

(5) Why do you lift a heavy object, such as a barbell, as close to your body as possible?

(6) The moment of a couple, or torque, is:
(a) The turning effect
(b) The product of the forces involved and the length of the moment arm
(c) The distance through which an object is moved about its axis
(d) None of the above.

(7) The difference between a force couple and an eccentric force is that:
(a) One causes translation only, and the other causes rotation only
(b) A force couple is stronger and it consists of two eccentric forces
(c) One causes translatory movement and rotation, whilst the other causes only rotation
(d) Both (b) and (c).

(8) Forces applied through the centre of gravity of an object tend to cause:
(a) Translation
(b) Rotation
(c) Translation and rotation
(d) Curvilinear motion.

(9) (a) Draw a simple diagram to illustrate how a force couple can cause rotation alone
(b) Explain why only rotation occurs.

(10) If the weight of a body is greater than the weight of an equal volume of water, the body will:
(a) Float
(b) Sink
(c) Be buoyant
(d) Both (a) and (c).

(11) Generally the centre of buoyancy and the centre of gravity are:
(a) The same position
(b) Located at the sciphoid process
(c) In different positions within the body
(d) Found near the hip region.

(12) Which of the following specific gravities would allow a person to float?:
(a) 1.1
(b) 1.2
(c) 0.9
(d) 1.05.

(13) (a) In tumbling, why is the handstand a more difficult position to maintain than a head-stand?
(b) You've suffered a knee injury. The doctor provides crutches so that your body's weight will not be supported by the injured leg. How do crutches provide a useful by-product of increased total body stability?
(c) Why is it difficult to walk on stilts?
(d) Why is it safer to kneel in a canoe than to sit on the seat?

(14) For each of the stances below, give an example of a different, but specific sports activity:
(a) Four-point position (for base of support)
(b) Three-point position
(c) Two-point position
(d) One-point position.

(15) A baseball catcher is attempting to tag a runner at home plate. The runner is about to collide with the catcher. List three adjustments the catcher can make to increase stability just before the collision.

(16) A body said to be in an unstable equilibrium:
(a) Has no tendency to move farther away from its original position
(b) Will show no response to a slight displacement from its original position
(c) Can never be in a state of balance
(d) Has been displaced from its original

position by a force couple.

(17) The stability of a volleyballer about to perform a dig depends on:
  (a) The width of the base of his support
  (b) The position of centre of gravity in relation to the base of support
  (c) Height of the volleyballer
  (d) All the above.

(18) 'The larger the base of support, the greater the stability.' True or false?

(19) Name two relationships between centre of gravity, base of support and stability.

(20) A man jumps as high as he can three times, but varies the shape of his body each time. In which of the three positions listed below would you expect him to reach (**a**) the highest?; and (**b**) the lowest? Give reasons for your answer.
- **Position 1:** Both arms stretched straight up and both legs stretched straight down
- **Position 2:** Both arms stretched straight up and one knee lifted high
- **Position 3:** Both arms stretched straight up and both knees lifted high.

(21) (**a**) What two factors contribute to the production of rotation? (**Example:** Using a hinged door, work out where it is best to push the door to open it — that is, rotate it.)
  (**b**) Define:
    (**i**) Concentric force
    (**ii**) Eccentric force.
  (**c**) What type of force is required to produce rotation of a body?
  (**d**) What is the relationship between rotational force applied (the torque) and the subsequent rotation produced?

(22) The diagram below is of a diver on a springboard at takeoff.

  (**a**) Copy the diagram into your notebook, and draw on it the eccentric force that will produce rotation.
  (**b**) Draw a cross where you might expect the centre of gravity to be for the diver in this position.
  (**c**) Draw on the diagram the expected direction of rotation.

(23) When long jumping:
  (**a**) Where is your centre of gravity, when landing, in relation to your base of support?
  (**b**) What must you do to maximize the distance jumped?

27. Angular momentum

Moments of inertia

Linear momentum

Remember that:

- A body's inertia is its resistance to change in motion
- With linear movement, mass is the only measure of that inertia.

In other words, the greater the mass, the greater the resistance to change, and therefore the greater the inertia.

With angular motion, resistance to change in motion depends not only upon mass, but also on the **distribution of the mass around the axis**. This is called the **moment of inertia (I)** of the object.

The closer the mass is to the axis (centre of gravity), the easier it is to turn.

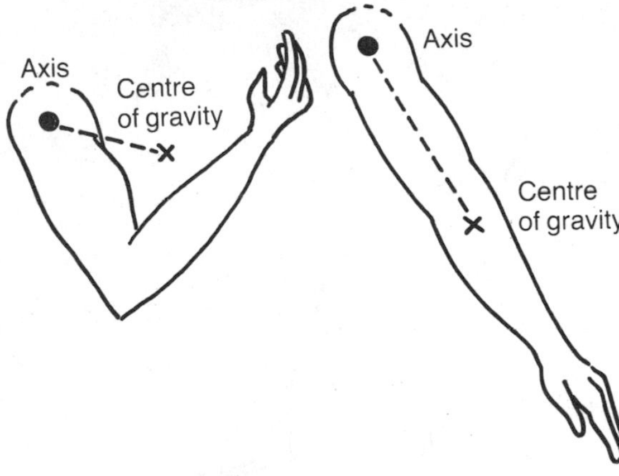

Figure 27.1

With a bent arm, the moment of inertia is lower — that is, there is a less resistance to turning motion. This can be shown as a formula:

$I = mr^2$
Moment of inertia
= how much mass there is × (General distance from the axis of rotation) squared.

Moment of inertia: examples

(1) Running

It is easier to run by bending the legs on recovery, because it is easier for the quadriceps to lift a bent leg (lower moment of inertia) than one that is straight.

Figure 27.2

(2) Pole-vaulting

When pole-vaulting, flex the legs well on the swing up to make rotation easier.

(3) Cricket

The moment of inertia of a junior cricket bat is far lower than for the senior bat, which requires a lot more effort to control. The junior bat has a lower moment of inertia because it has a lower mass.

(4) Woodchopping

If you hold an axe at its handle, it has a high moment of inertia, because you are holding the head away from the pivot point. The moment of inertia varies according to the distribution of the mass. Handling an axe would be a lot easier if you were able to hold the head when swinging the axe. The moment of inertia is lower because most of the axe's weight is close to the point of rotation. Why is this not desirable for chopping wood?

(5) Baseball

Small children will 'choke up' on a full-sized

Figure 27.3 High moment of inertia.

Figure 27.4 Low moment of inertia.

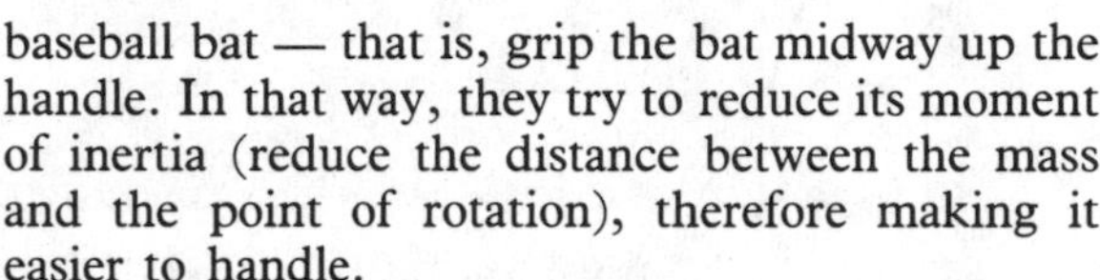

baseball bat — that is, grip the bat midway up the handle. In that way, they try to reduce its moment of inertia (reduce the distance between the mass and the point of rotation), therefore making it easier to handle.

(6) Racquet sports

Children often use smaller racquets when playing games such as tennis. The child can swing the smaller racquet more easily than a larger one, and can learn strokes more easily with it. The hitting surface of a 'jumbo' or 'Prince' racquet is 30–50 per cent larger than that for an ordinary racquet. Therefore it has more mass, and a greater distribution of that mass, giving it a higher moment of inertia.

Comparative moments of inertia

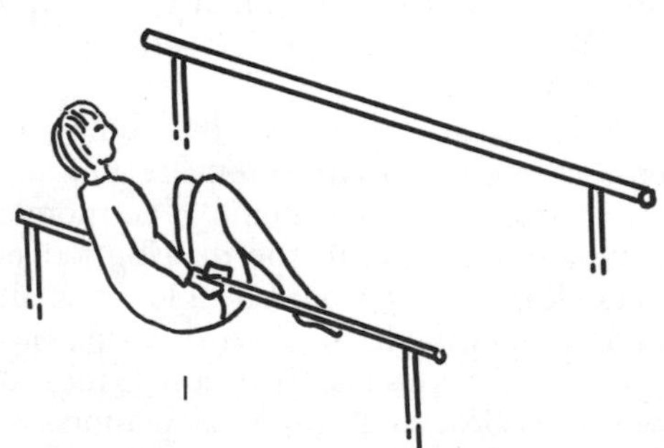

Figure 27.5

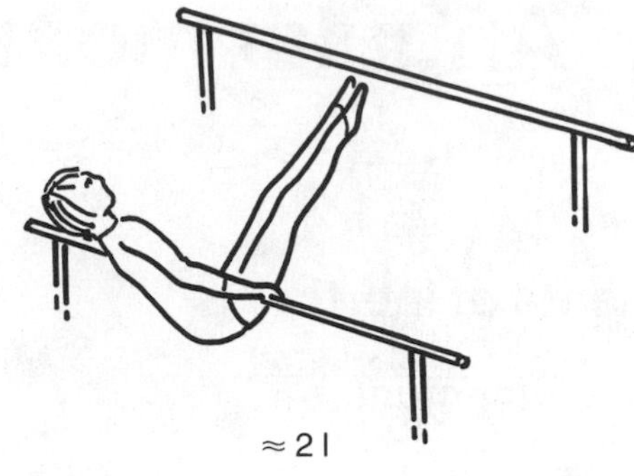

Figure 27.6

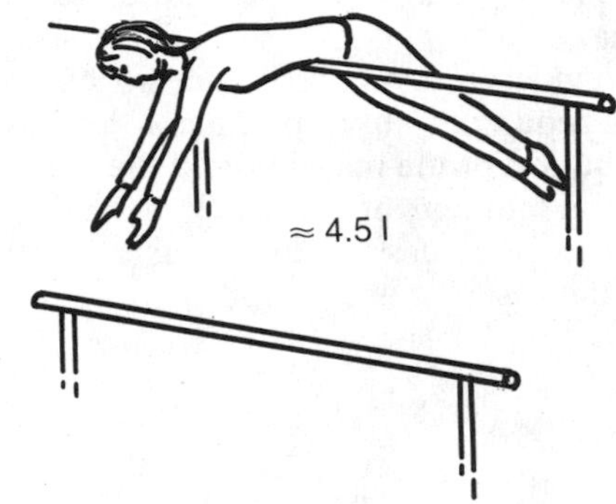

Figure 27.7

Figure 27.8

Figure 27.9

Figure 27.10

Conservation of angular momentum

Remember that in linear motion, when one moving body strikes another, the momentum involved is said to be 'conserved'. In other words, the total momentum after the collision of the two bodies is exactly equal to the total momentum of the two moving bodies before the impact.

$$M = mv$$

that is:

Momentum = mass × velocity.

For example, if a heavy man is tackled by a light man, he may be slowed down, but still keeps moving. His loss of velocity is offset by the fact that he has gained in mass — that is, the addition of the tackler to his moving body.

What, then, would happen if two men of the same mass ran head on at the same speed? Both of them would halt — they had equal momentum but in opposite directions.

Angular momentum

Angular momentum depends not on mass and linear velocity, but on moment of inertia and angular velocity:

Angular momentum ('rotary motion') = $I \times \omega$
= moment of inertia × angular velocity

Conservation of angular motion

The **conservation of angular motion**, which is an analogue of Newton's First Law, states that: '**A rotating body will continue to turn about its axis of rotation with constant angular momentum, unless an external couple or eccentric force is exerted on it.**'

This law can be seen most clearly in sports that feature the spin, the pivot, the twist, the somersault or the pendulum swing.

This definition implies that, **given a constant angular momentum, moment of inertia and angular velocity are inversely proportional** — that is, as one increases, the other decreases, and vice versa. Take an example:

If angular momentum is constant, say 100 units:

$100 = 1 \times \omega$
= moment of inertia × angular velocity

Example: $100 = 5 \times \mathit{20}$

If I decreases, ω must increase:
Example: $100 = 2 \times 50$

If I increases, ω must decrease:
Example: $100 = 25 \times \mathit{4}$.

Examples

(1) Swinging a weight

If you place a weight on the end of a string, and swing it around your head, you establish a certain angular momentum. If you draw in the string — that is, decrease the moment of inertia — you increase the angular velocity, so the weight spins faster.

Figure 27.11

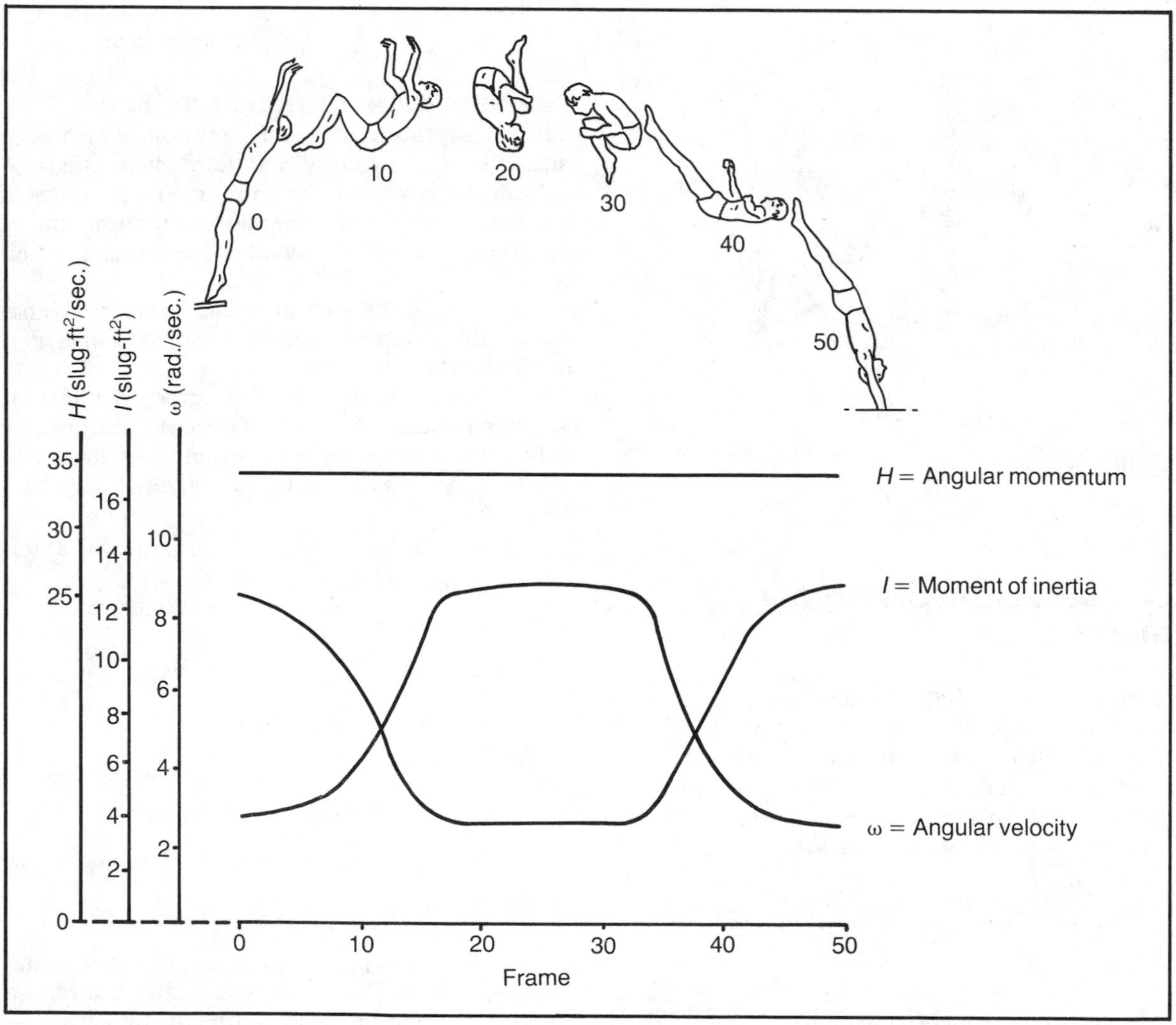

Figure 27.12 A tucked backward one-and-a-half dive well illustrates the interplay between angular momentum, moment of inertia and angular velocity.

(2) **Figure skating**
When spinning, if your arms are outstretched initially, bringing them into the body increases the speed of rotation. Since the moment of inertia depends on the distribution of mass around the centre of gravity, outspread arms give a greater moment of inertia than spinning with your arms tucked in.

(3) **Diving**
When diving, you gain initial rotation (angular momentum) by leaning off the take-off board (force couple and torque), and this is conserved until your body enters the water. In a **tucked** position, the diver spins faster than in a **layout** position, because the moment of inertia decreases, causing a proportional increase in angular velocity. The angular momentum remains constant, but:

- A tuck gives decreased moment of inertia (I) and increased angular velocity (ω)
- A layout gives increased I and decreased ω.

(4) **Basketball and netball**
How can basketballers or netballers increase their bluffing and pivoting speed? By keeping their limbs close to the centre of the torso — keeping a bunched-up position (moment of inertia is decreased, therefore increasing angular velocity).

(5) **Gymnastics**
A beginner gymnast, when performing a handspring, often tucks quickly at the end of the movement (therefore decreasing the moment of inertia), which increases his or her angular velocity in order to avoid landing on his or her back.

Analogue of Newton's Second Law

An analogue of Newton's Second Law is that **'the rate of change of angular momentum of a body is proportional to the torque causing it, and has the same direction as the torque'**. In other words, **a greater turning effect will result in greater angular momentum, in the direction of the turning effect.**

In this example (Figure 27.14), the diver is undergoing angular acceleration about an axis (———) through her feet. The torque causing this is:

$$T = \text{diver's weight} \times \text{horizontal distance } x$$

that is:

$$T = F \times \text{moment arm.}$$

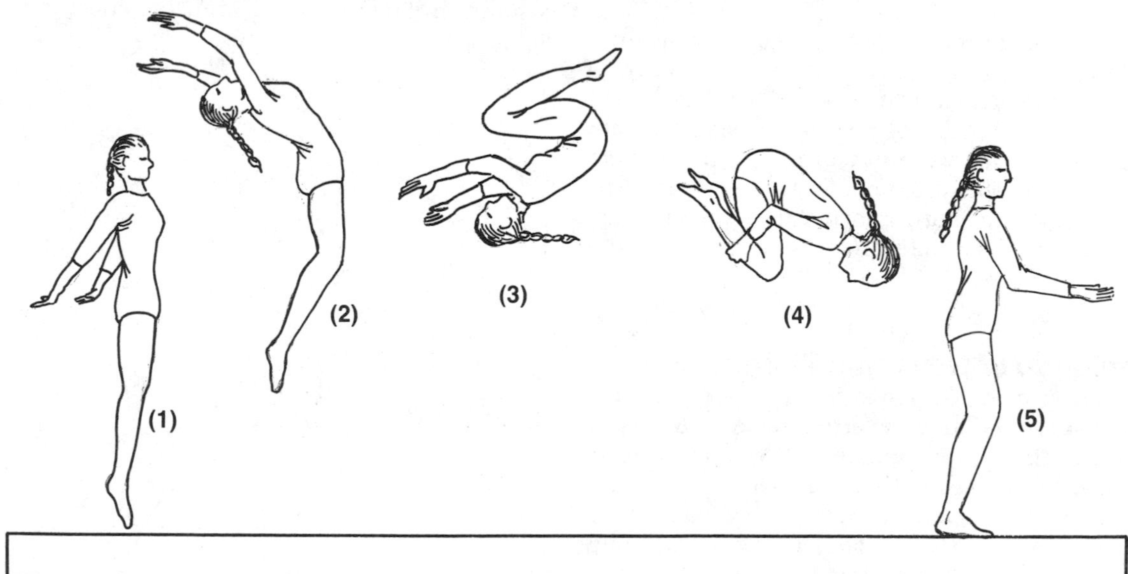

Figure 27.13 **Back somersault** on a beam.

- Angular momentum: established at **(1)** and altered at (5)
- Angular velocity: greatest at **(3)**
- Moment of inertia: greatest at **(1)** and **(2)**, and at (5).

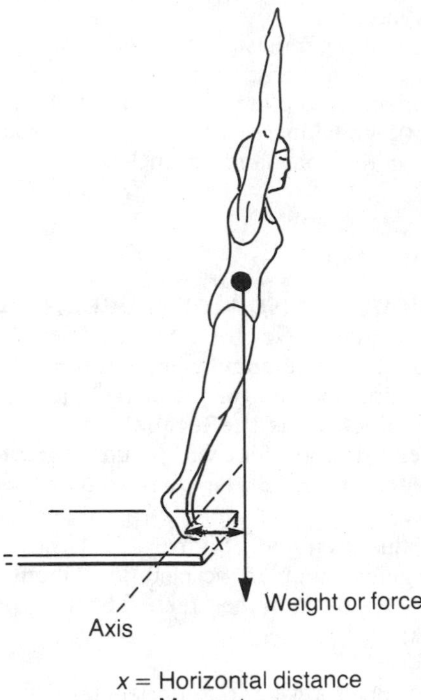

Figure 27.14

The diver would gain more angular momentum if she leaned out further, as the torque is larger — that is, the distance is larger. She has leaned forward more, and will be able to perform more rotation. If she were performing only a plain forward dive, she would not lean out very far. This would reduce the horizontal distance from the axis, and hence reduce the torque.

Analogue of Newton's Third Law

An analogue of Newton's Third Law is that '**for every torque that is exerted by one body on another, there is an equal and opposite torque exerted by the second on the first**'.

The most common example is when one part of the body twists, by contracting a muscle or a group of muscles. The equal and opposite reaction causes some other part of the body to rotate or tend to rotate in the opposite direction.

The opposite directions of rotation around the axis of rotation are called clockwise and anticlockwise.

Examples

(1) Long jump

When long jumping, swing your legs forward and upward for landing (anticlockwise). This creates an opposite reaction, which can be seen in the remainder of the body moving forward and downward (clockwise).

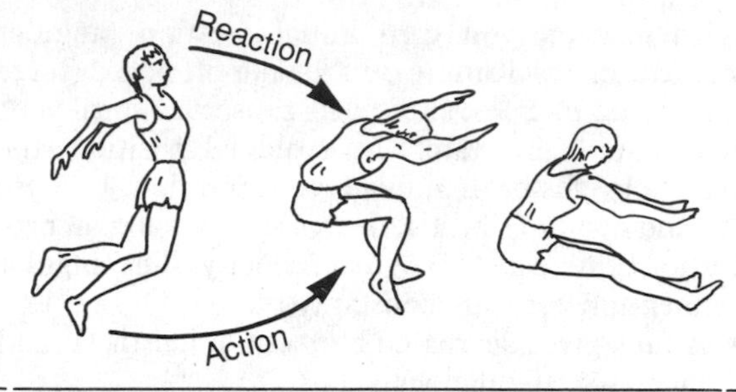

Figure 27.15

(2) Basketball

When playing basketball, you propel the ball towards the basket by extending your elbow and wrist. The rest of the body is acted upon with an 'equal and opposite torque' but, because the body is so much larger than the arm, the effect is very slight.

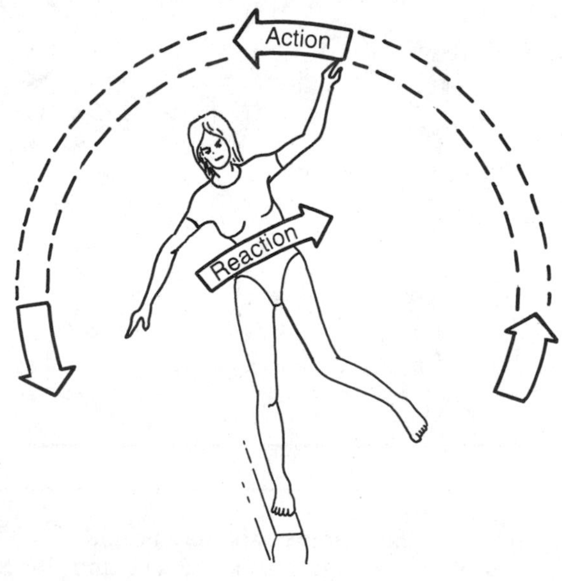

Figure 27.16

(3) Gymnastics
If you find yourself overbalancing while doing gymnastics, rotate your arms and legs in the direction in which you are falling. This causes the rest of your body to rotate in the opposite direction, probably overcoming your tendency to fall.
(4) Tennis
When playing tennis, you can use torque to produce a forehand stroke (anti-clockwise direction). The equal and opposite torques that have been created tend to cause the rest of the body to rotate in an opposite direction (clockwise). You can best see how these reactions work by trying them out on a swivel chair.

Note: Because your feet are in contact with the ground, this tendency is tranferred to the ground. This means that the equal and opposite effects hardly matter, because of the earth's large moment of inertia. When playing tennis, keep both feet in contact with the ground, so that reactions that accompany strokes can be absorbed by the earth and not cause instability.

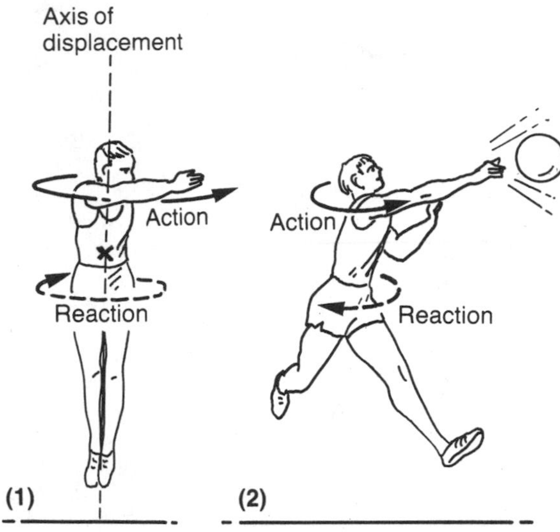

Figure 27.18

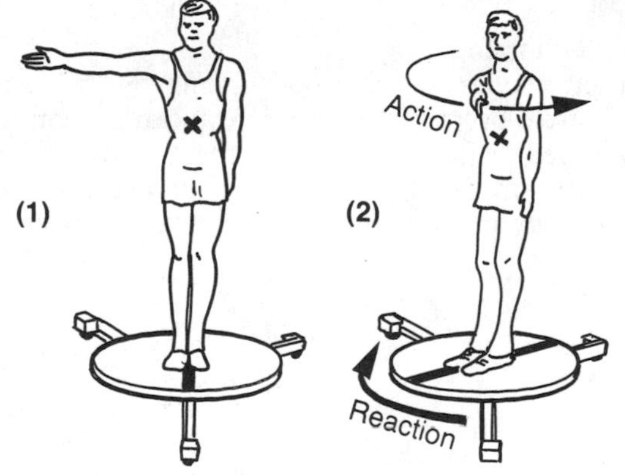

Figure 27.17

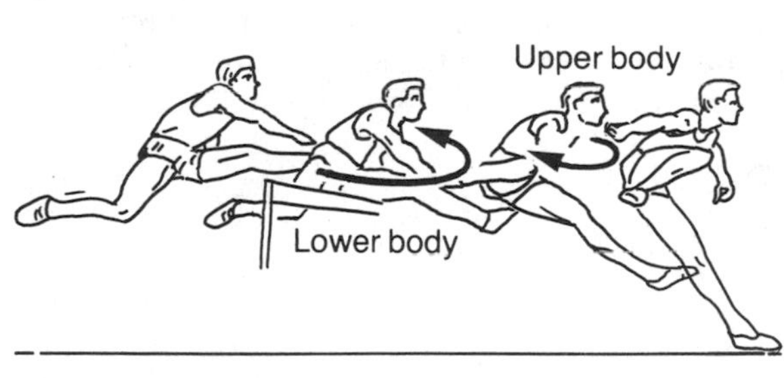

Figure 27.19

(5) Use of arms
When on a frictionless board, if you swing your right arm across the body, the turntable will move to the left.

If you jump and fling your right arm across your body, your body turns to the left — for example, during a mid-air pass shot. Again, if you want stability, keep both feet in contact with the ground.
(6) Hurdling
When you pull your rear, trailing leg over the hurdle rail, you create an opposite and equal torque to the contraction. The upper leg twists the trunk towards that leg.
(7) Swimming
When swimming, if you make any arm rotations that are too wide from the line of the body alignment, you create reactions in the legs and feet in the opposite direction. This increases resistance to forward movement, and should be avoided.

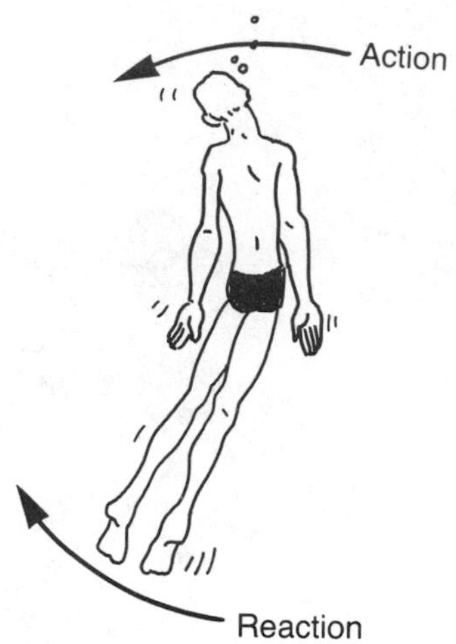

Figure 27.20

Transfer of momentum

Remember that **linear momentum** is transferred and conserved, as when a racquet strikes a ball. Likewise, if the total **angular momentum** is to be conserved or held constant, when a body is in the air and one part of that body slows down, another part (or all) of that body must increase in angular momentum. This process of **redistribution of momentum** is called a **transfer of momentum**, and is very common in diving and gymnastics.

Examples

(1) Locked hips

If you lock your hips while swinging your legs forward, you transfer the momentum to your upper body.

(2) Diving

On the springboard, you develop angular momentum by swinging your arms, which in turn help to rotate your body in the air.

While in the air, you have constant angular momentum:

- When you pike, the momentum of your legs is reduced to zero, while your upper body moves forward to bend.
- As you enter the water, this is reversed. The legs swing upward, while the upper body does not rotate.

(3) Long and triple jump

When landing for the long and triple jump, you place your arms behind you, so that when you land you can throw your arm forward. As you transfer momentum to the rest of your body, it rotates forward. This stops you falling back behind the landing position of the feet, which penalizes distance.

(4) Swimming

In some styles of racing start, swing your arms in a full circle backward just before locking them outstretched in front. This helps them to transfer the momentum developed by the arm swing to your total body mass, giving you a good start from the blocks.

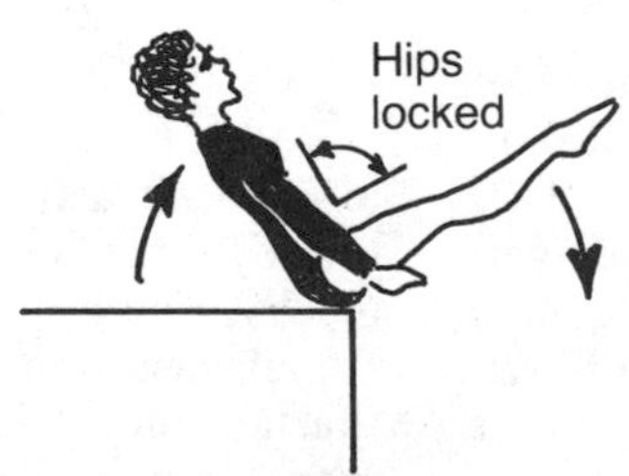

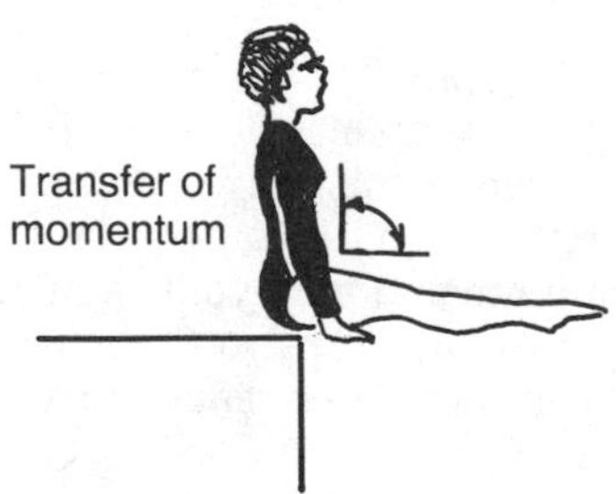

Figure 27.21

Figure 27.22 Momentum developed in the swing is transferred when the swinging arms are locked.

(5) **Dancing**
When dancing, if you perform a pirouette in the air, you develop angular momentum by twisting your body, with the feet fixed to the floor. As your legs drive the body into the air, the twisting effect of the upper body transfers to the whole of the body, causing rotation in the air.
(6) **High jumping**
When high jumping, swing your free leg at take-off so that you can build up enough angular momentum to perform the layout over the bar at the height of the jump.

Laboratory work 42: Rotary action

Aim
To examine the effect of changing body position on rotation.

Procedure
Work with a partner on a polished floor. One student sits on the floor with knees bent up his chest and his feet *off* the floor. His partner gives him the following pushes and observes the rotation that takes place.

(1) Push him in the small of the back, from behind.
(2) Push his feet from the side and count how many revolutions he makes.
(3) Repeat (2) with the same force, but this time your partner straightens his legs.
(4) Repeat (3), but this time push at a point near the top of your partner's legs — that is, at a similar distance from the centre of gravity as in (2).

Conclusions
(1) Compare the speed of rotation in (2) and (4).
(2) Compare the number of rotations in (2) and (3).

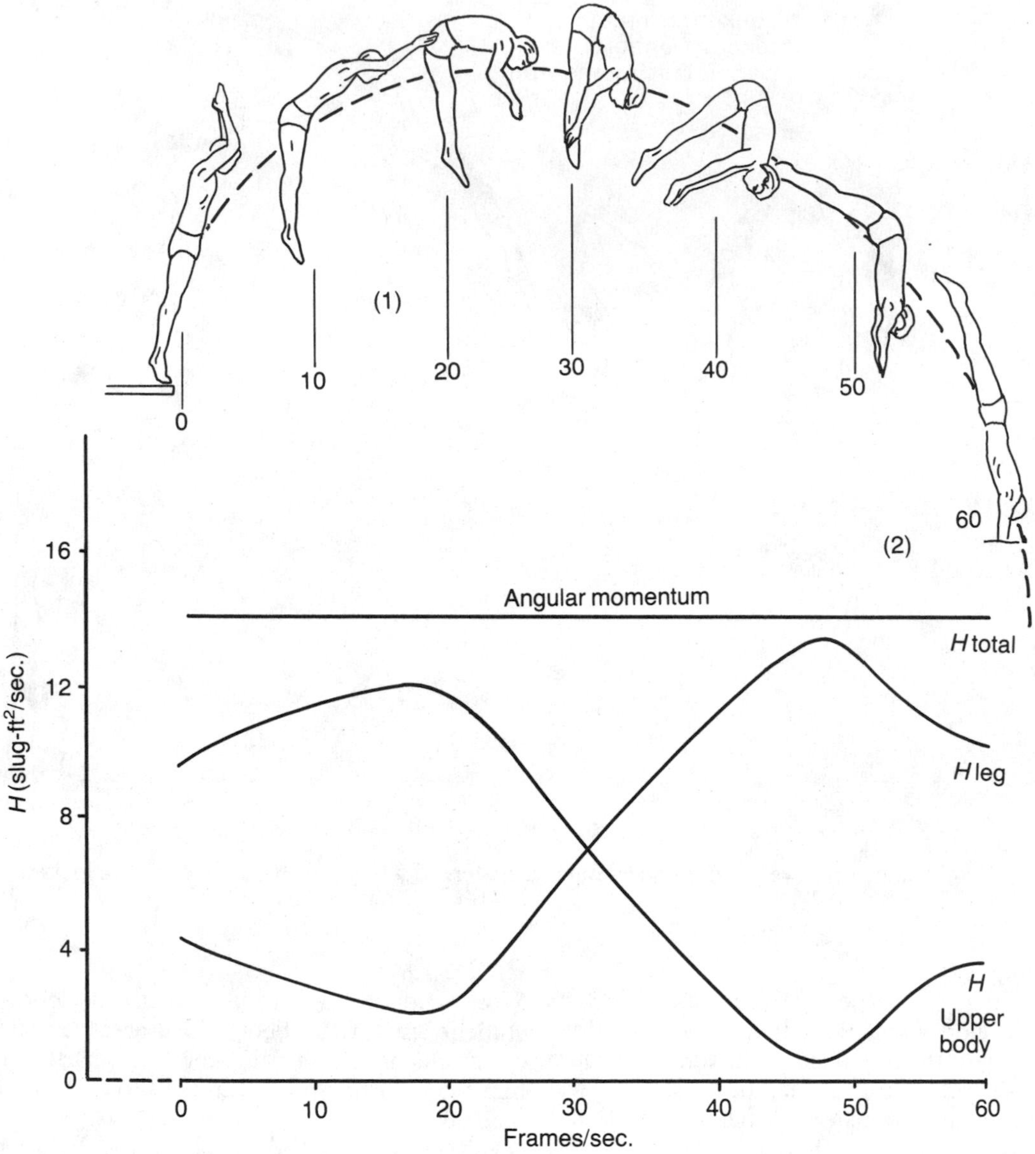

Figure 27.23 The angular momentum of a diver performing a piked front dive is first localized in his upper body and then in his legs.

Figure 27.24 Feet stay fixed to the floor while the upper body twists.

(3) What differences can you observe in the rotation of the subject on these four occasions. What do you think causes these differences?

Figure 27.25

Laboratory work 43: Newton's Third Law

Aim
To determine the effect of swinging the legs forward on the upper half of the body.

Procedure
Take a good run and jump as high as possible in the air. Keep your legs straight and together, and swing them forward and up.

Conclusions
What happens to the upper part of the body, and why? (Explain the words 'equal' or 'opposite' fully.)

Laboratory work 44: Moment of inertia

Aim
To assess appropriate rolling techniques.

Procedure
Perform a forward roll:
- In tucked position
- Piked.

Conclusion
In which position is it easier to regain your feet. Why?

Laboratory work 45: Transfer of momentum

Aim
To examine jumping techniques.

Procedure
(**1**) Perform a standing vertical jump from a crouched position with one arm extended above the head. Do not use either arm during the jump. Measure the height of the jump.
(**2**) Perform a standing vertical jump, using your arms. Measure the height you reached.

Conclusion
Did you jump higher when performing (**1**) or (**2**)? Why?

Laboratory work 46: Conservation of momentum

Aim
To demonstrate the interrelationship between moment of inertia, angular velocity and conservation of momentum.

Equipment
- Frictionless base
- Bicycle wheel, weighted at the rim if possible.

Method and results
(**1**) Why is it preferable to use a low-friction base to illustrate conservation of momentum?
(**2**) In what plane does the turntable operate?
(**3**) When the rim is weighted, what does this do to the wheel's moment of inertia? Why?
(**4**) Hold two shot puts in extended arms while standing on the turntable.
 (**a**) Have your partner rotate the turntable
 (**b**) Bring your arms into your chest.
 Comment on your angular velocity, momentum and moment of inertia.
(**5**) Stand on the turntable:
 (**a**) Have your partner spin the wheel and hand it to you while it rotates horizontally
 (**b**) Keep the wheel clear of the body, then check its movement against your body.
 Explain the results.

(6) Have your partner spin the wheel and hand it to you while it is spinning horizontally and you are on the base. Turn the wheel to let it spin vertically. Explain the result.

(7) Have your partner spin the wheel in the vertical plane and hand it to you while you are on the base.
(a) Turn the wheel so that it spins horizontally
(b) Turn the wheel again so that you are holding it in the vertical plane.
Explain the results.

(8) Have your partner spin the wheel in the vertical plane. You are on the turntable.
(a) Rotate the turntable
(b) Turn the wheel horizontally so that it rotates in the same direction as the turntable.
Attempt three variations:
(c) Give the wheel an angular momentum less than that of the turntable.
(d) Give the wheel an angular momentum equal to that of the turntable.
(e) Give the wheel an angular momentum greater than that of the turntable.
(f) Describe, and attempt to explain the results. Bear in mind the major principle of the experiment: the conservation of the system's total angular momentum.

Worksheet 26: Angular momentum, moment of inertia and angular velocity

(1) Use stick diagrams to answer the following:
(a) A trampolinist, while airborne, extends the spine. Which way will the legs and feet move?
(b) If you extend your spine while standing on the ground, what happens to your legs and feet? Why?
(c) A trampolinist, while airborne in a sitting pose, rotates the head and shoulders to the right. Which way do the legs move? Why?

(2) Why do you swivel faster on a swivelchair with legs tucked in compared with your speed when you extend your legs?

(3) When performing a piked front dive, and you go into the piked position:
(a) The angular momentum of your arms and legs is decreased
(b) The angular momentum of your arms and legs is increased
(c) The angular momentum of your legs is reduced to near zero
(d) Both (b) and (c).

(4) 'For every torque that is exerted by one body on another, there is an equal and opposite torque exerted by the second on the first.' Explain what is meant by the above statement, using an example to illustrate your

Figure 27.26

(5) Explain the interplay of angular momentum, moment of inertia and angular velocity in the diagram.

(6) The extended position in the long jump is used to:
(a) Minimize rotation
(b) Increase the moment of inertia
(c) Decrease the angular velocity
(d) All of the above.

(7) The bent knee, flexed thigh position during the recovery phase in running:
(a) Increases the leg's moment of inertia
(b) Increases angular velocity
(c) Decreases the moment of inertia
(d) Both (b) and (c).

(8) The moment of inertia does *not* depend upon:
  (a) The mass of the object
  (b) The distance from the axis of rotation
  (c) The acceleration of the object.

(9) In the giant swing on the horizontal bar:
  (a) How could you decrease your moment of inertia?
  (b) What effect would this have on your angular velocity?
  (c) What effect would this have on your angular momentum?

(10) An innovation in tennis equipment is the Prince (oversized) racquet. What are the biomechanical advantages and disadvantages of this racquet?

(11) Why is it easier to raise a stubborn window by standing close to it?

(12) Greg Chappell uses a heavy bat and holds it near the top of the handle, compared with small children, with heavy bats, who often hold the bat nearer the bottom of the handle. Explain this difference.

(13) (a) Why does the long jumper adopt various body positions during the flight phase?
  (b) What path does his centre of gravity follow?
  (c) In Figure 27.27, what is changed at (1), (3) and (8)?
  (d) When is the angular velocity greatest? Why?

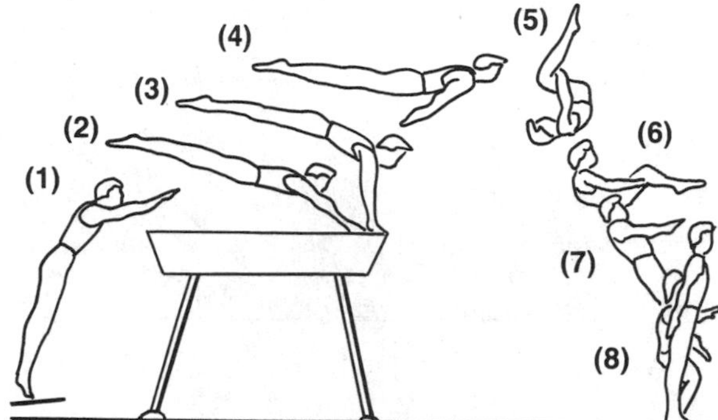

Figure 27.27

28. Review: Biochemical principles in selected activities

Running

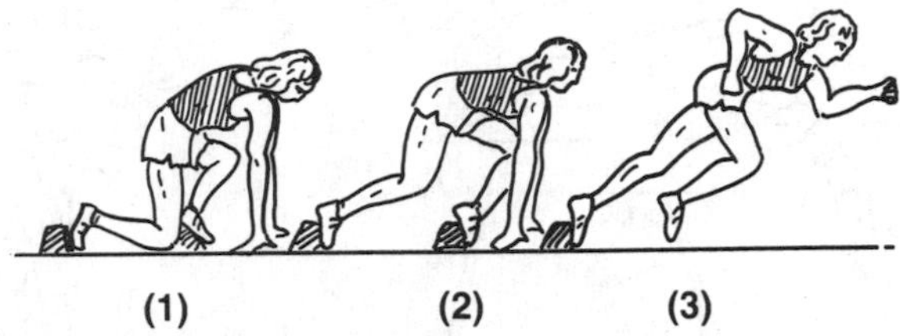

Figure 28.1

Crouch start

At the beginning of a race you need to overcome maximal inertia — that is, your body's resistance to change in motion. The body's initial momentum is zero (mv).

Impulse

Impulse is the change in the body's momentum, and is the product of the force exerted by the legs against the blocks (in the horizontal direction) and the time that this force is applied.

Impulse = F × t
= change in momentum
= for the runner, a change from zero momentum to the momentum of your body at any point in the race.

For a top sprinter, weighing (with a mass of) 70 kilograms, and at top speed running at 11 m/sec., his momentum would be:

$$m \times v = 70 \times 11 = 770 \text{ units}$$

At his top speed, his impulse would be:

$$mv_f - mv_i = 770 - 0 = 770.$$

Where:

- mv_f = momentum at top speed (final)
- mv_i = momentum at start (initial).

Time of force application

The time when the force is applied is crucial in overcoming the body's inertia:

- The medium start is theoretically recommended as providing the best velocity after 50 metres
- The bullet start gets the runner out of the blocks the quickest, as the time for force application is minimal
- The elongated start provides the greatest impulse at the blocks, as the time for force application is maximal.

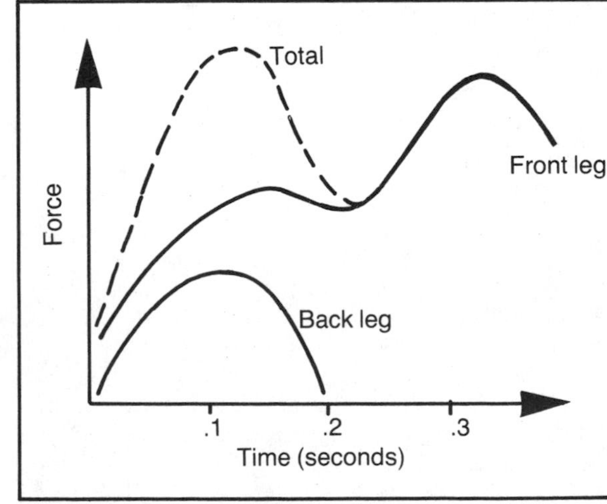

Figure 28.2

Impulse in the blocks

Impulse in the blocks is gained from both legs, with the front leg providing the greatest impulse (see Figure 28.2).

Forward movement

Forward movement is possible because of the horizontal ground/reaction force. Remember Newton's Third Law: the ground exerts an equal and opposite force to the athlete's body.

The reaction is greatest in the periods of acceleration, because at these times the legs are driving hardest back against the ground.

Stability

- Your stability is greatest at the call of 'on your marks' — your centre of gravity is low and you have a four-point base of support.
- Your stability is decreased at the call of 'get set' — your centre of gravity is raised, and therefore there is a decreased distance for it to travel before it falls outside the base of support.
- At the call of 'go', your body is unstable, as the centre of gravity is outside the base of support. You would undergo forward rotary action if your legs did not drive hard to come under the centre of gravity. This process results in forward horizontal movement.

Figure 28.3

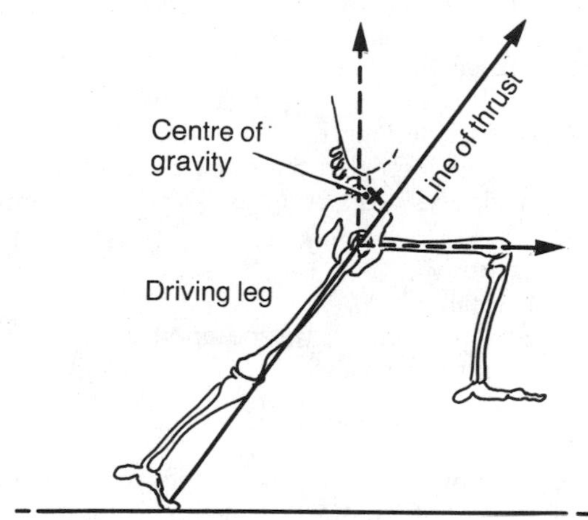

Figure 28.4

Note:
(1) 90 per cent of maximum acceleration is achieved during the first 15 metres of a race.
(2) 45 per cent of maximum acceleration is achieved during the first 20 metres of a race.
(3) 100 per cent of maximum acceleration is achieved by the 40-metre mark.

Figure 28.5

Friction

Friction is:

- Enhanced by the use of spiked shoes
- Decreased in wet conditions
- Essential for an effective ground/reaction force.

Friction ensures that you can exert maximal force back down into the ground, and that you can minimize lateral forces (slipping). For instance, when running in mud, you waste some of your effect in displacing the mud, and therefore lose force-reaction.

Speed

Speed may be expressed as stride length × stride frequency. (Taller, long-legged athletes have the advantage.) While running, you pump forward your arms and legs to decrease lateral movement.

(1) Arm swing
Arm swing absorbs the opposite reaction in the upper body, caused by hip rotation. Remember the analogue of Newton's Third Law — that for every torque there exists an equal and opposite torque.

The bent arm swing (90-degree angle) has a lower moment of inertia than the straight arm recovery, and is therefore easier to rotate about the shoulder joint.

(2) Leg recovery
A bent leg decreases the moment of inertia, enabling easier rotation about the hip joint.

(3) Centre of gravity
The centre of gravity should be held:

- Above the landing foot, to decrease any backward forces
- Ahead of the driving foot, to enable horizontal movement.

(4) High thigh lift
High thigh lift:

- Increases stride length
- Increases the force that can be exerted against the ground via the supporting leg (Newton's Third Law).

(5) Upper body
Hold the upper body:

- Relaxed, to minimize wasted energy
- Upright, to aid balance.

Motion

During running, rotary motion exists at the shoulders, elbows, hips and knees. The body also experiences two types of linear motion:

- **Rectilinear** (or **translation**), when the body is moved forward in a straight line
- **Curvilinear**, when the body moves around the bend of the track.

Long jumping

The run up

When long jumping, the run up contributes up to 90 per cent of the total performance, because it enables you to develop horizontal momentum:

(1) Centre of gravity

Your body is a projectile, with the path of the centre of gravity forming a parabola. After take off, you cannot alter the path of the centre of gravity.

Note: If the centre of gravity remains behind the take-off foot, it has a braking effect.

(2) Transfer of momentum

You achieve transfer of momentum from the fast driving of your shoulders and arms at take off. Their movement stops at about shoulder height, resulting in a transfer of momentum to the lower part of the body. This helps to lift the body.

(3) Impulse

When jumping, the centre of gravity starts behind the take-off foot, and moves forward, providing

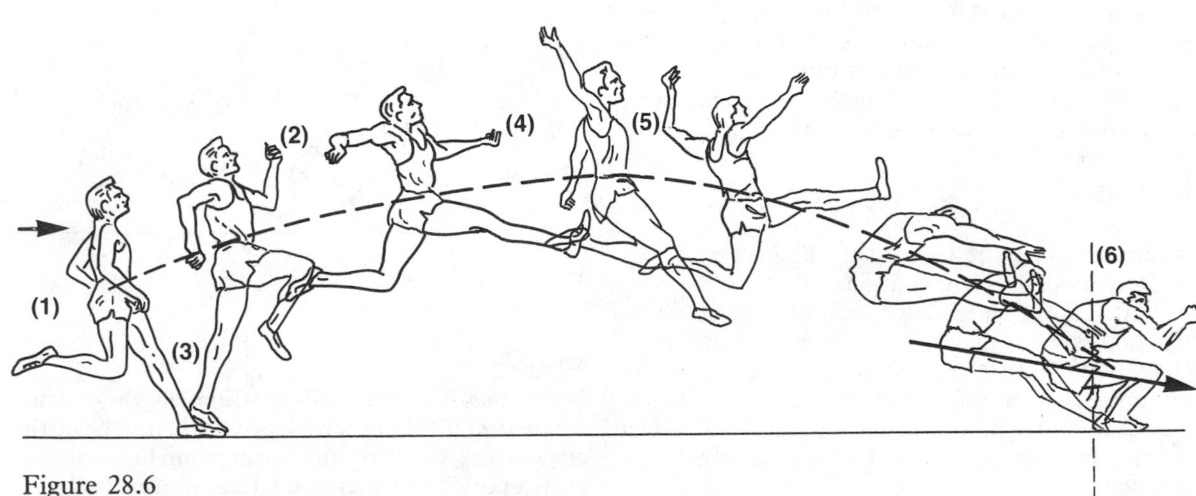

Figure 28.6

more time for force to be applied through this foot. This effect increases the body's impulse for vertical drive. (However, you have very little time to achieve this effect.)

(4) Your arms

You use your arms to counterbalance the rotation of your lower body (taking advantage of the analogue of Newton's Third Law).

(5) Your body

Your body, in flight, has a constant amount of angular momentum. The main problem is to overcome the body's tendency to rotate forward. You counteract this by:

- **The hang technique**

(See Figure 28.7.) This technique increases the body's moment of inertia, therefore decreasing its angular velocity — that is, its forward rotation.

- **The hitch kick**

The hitch kick technique results in backward rotation (and is the preferred technique).

Figure 28.7

(6) Range of flight distance

You determine the range of your flight distance by:

- **The speed at take off**

Your speed at take off must not decelerate too much at the board. Therefore you need to develop your accuracy of pacing and taking off.

- **Angle of take off**

The angle at take off should be 15–25°. Even though the optimal angle is near 45° for a projectile that takes off and lands at nearly the same level (the centre of gravity is higher at take off), you have developed a very fast run up that gives a very quick take off and therefore a very short time to develop vertical lift. Horizontal momentum should not be sacrificed for height.

- **Height at take off**

Your height at take off depends on the height of your centre of gravity. Lifting your legs, arms, head and trunk raises the centre of gravity.

- **Air resistance**

Air resistance has little effect on the long jumper.

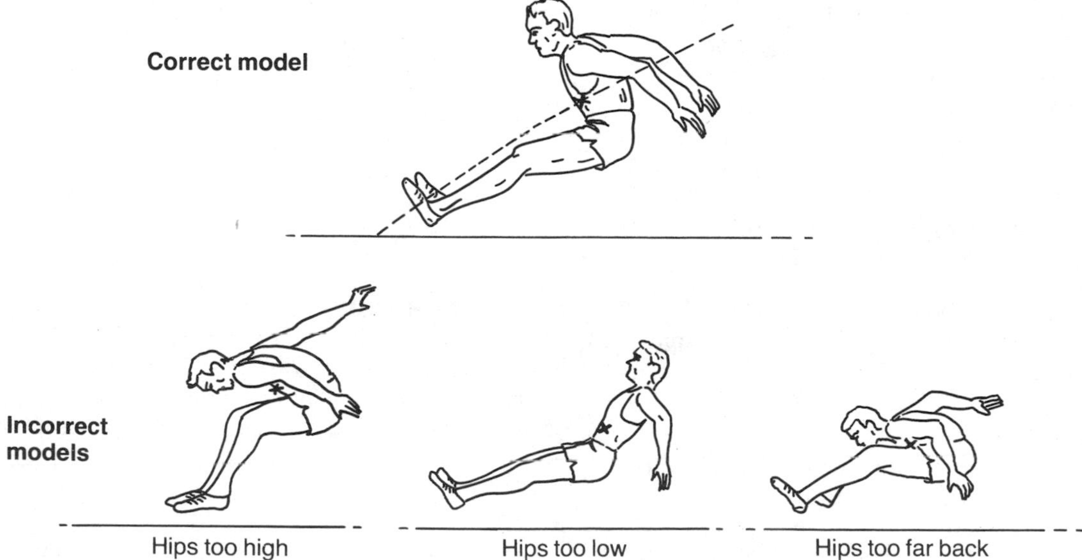

Figure 28.8

(7) Landing

(See Figure 28.8.) When landing:

- Extend your legs in front of you, and bring down your arms (since an equal and opposite torque exists).
- Flex your knees, so that your hips follow through horizontally (force reception) and you avoid 'sitting down'.

Figure 28.9

Striking

Principles

Striking is guided by the following principles:

- **Newton's First Law**

You need to overcome the inertia of the object, which tends to stay at rest unless it is acted upon by external forces. In other words, you strike with your hand or the racquet.

- **Newton's Second Law**

The ball will be propelled with an acceleration proportional to the force hitting it and in the direction in which it is hit. The larger the mass, the less the deceleration for a given force. Follow through is important for accuracy.

- **Newton's Third Law**

When the ball is bounced, or hits a side wall, there is an equal and opposite reaction from the floor or wall.

Stability

You enhance your stability when you place both feet in contact with the ground. This applies particularly to racquet sports, where the earth's mass can absorb the turning effect exerted on it by the player's upper body rotations (an analogue of Newton's Third Law).

Friction

Friction is increased by the rubber cleating on the soles of your shoes.

Angular motion

The angular motion of your arm and racquet imparts linear motion to the ball. This can be seen as:

$$\text{Linear velocity} = \begin{matrix}\text{radius of arm/racquet} \times \\ \text{angular velocity.}\end{matrix}$$

To increase the speed of the ball, either increase the length of the racquet or golf club or increase the angular velocity of the arm or racquet — that is, swing faster.

Figure 28.10

Angular velocity

The angular velocity of a body's part or implement is proportional to its distance from the axis of rotation — that is, an extended elbow enables greater angular velocity to be generated at the club head.

Momentum

A ball will have greater momentum if you transfer greater linear velocity (M_0 = mass × *velocity*) from the striking implement.

Figure 28.11 Throwing.

Angle of rebound

Theoretically, the angle of rebound equals the angle of approach. Top spin decreases the ball's flight through air, and decreases the angle of rebound. Bottom spin increases the flight through air, and increases the angle of rebound.

Coefficient of restitution

The coefficient of restitution:

- Increases with a warmed-up squash ball
- Decreases with an old tennis ball played on a muddy court.

Torque, or turning effect

Torque is increased if either:

- Force is increased — that is, if you use a greater force or a heavier implement

or

- You place the point of contact further from the pivot, as with oars.

Throwing

The distance thrown equals:

(a) The horizontal distance of the shot in front of the inside edge of the stopboard at release

plus

(b) The horizontal distance it travels while in the air.

Note that the distance thrown:

(a) Is affected by the athlete's physique and body position

(b) Is affected by:

- The speed of release
- The angle of release (slightly less than 45°).

If you decrease the speed of release or increase the height of release, you need to decrease the optimal angle.

Height of release

Fully extending your arms and legs increases the height of release, and will increase the range (all other things being equal).

Speed of release

Speed of release depends on:

- The magnitude of the forces applied, and the direction of those forces (the muscular strength and the ground/reaction force that you need)
- The distance and time over which these forces act — that is, impulse.

Exercise

Draw illustrations and make notes to describe the following principles in throwing:

- Aerodynamic factors
- Flattening the arc
- Friction
- Spin
- Force summation
- Leverage
- Follow through
- Newton's Laws
- Stability
- Impulse
- Rebound/rolling.

Worksheet 27: Biomechanical slide test

Take this test in conjunction with slides from J. C. Harmer and G. T. Hosford, *Biomechanics in Physical Education: Slide Teaching Kit*.

		Marks
(a)	**Football: Drop punt**	
(1)	How is the arc flattened?	**(1)**
(2)	Why is it flattened?	**(1)**
(3)	Where is the kicking leg's moment of inertia?	**(1)**
(4)	Why is it decreased?	**(1)**
(b)	**Soccer: Dive header**	
(5)	Force summation is successive or simultaneous. Why?	**(2)**
(6)	The amount of rotation the player has depends on what?	**(2)**
(c)	**Volleyball: Spiking**	
(7)	State the angular analogue of Newton's Third Law.	**(1)**
(8)	How is it seen in this action?	**(2)**
(9)	Force summation is successive and simultaneous in this slide — where do these occur?	**(2)**
(d)	**Cricket: Bowling**	
(10)	Where is the 'Direction of force application' for this action?	**(2)**
(11)	Discuss 'Force summation' for this action.	**(4)**
(12)	Comment on the 'leverage' of the bowling arm.	**(2)**
(13)	Compare a cricket ball's coefficient of restitution to that of a pingpong ball.	**(2)**
(14)	What type of force causes spin?	**(1)**
(e)	**Softball: Pitch**	
(15)	How is impulse increased?	**(2)**
(16)	What is done to improve the pitcher's stability?	**(3)**

Part Four
Skill acquisition

29. Characteristics of skill

Skill acquisition

Skill acquisition in physical education involves the learning of motor control. In studying skill acquisition, therefore, we are concerned with:

- The motor control itself
- How it is learned.

What is a motor skill?

What is a motor skill? What is the difference between a skilled movement and an unskilled movement?

A skill satisfies certain criteria:

- The task involves sequences of movements that are reasonably complex to the individual performing them.
- The individual must undertake a period of learning.

Compare the complexity of the action of standing up for a ten-month-old baby, and the same action for a normal healthy teenager.

In terms of the learning period, compare the actions of jumping out of a window to escape a fire and performing a long jump.

Skill is relative to the individual. For example, the best player in a school football team might appear skilled compared with the rest of the team, yet, when placed in a team of professional players, he might appear to be a poor performer. However, in each case the player has the same degree of skill.

Definitions of skill

The following definitions of skill should be considered:

- **Knapp:**

'Skill is the learned ability to bring about predetermined results with maximum certainty, often with the minimum outlay of time or energy, or both.'

- **Robb:**

'While the task can be physical or mental, one generally thinks of skill as some type of manipulative efficiency. A skilled movement is one in which a predetermined objective is accomplished with maximum efficiency with a minimum outlay of energy. A skilful movement does not just happen. There must be a conscious effort on the part of the performer in order to execute a skill.'

- **Welford:**

'An organized, co-ordinated activity in relation to an object or a situation which involves a whole chain of sensory, central and motor mechanisms.'

Learning

Skills acquisition implies learning. Learning can be defined as 'a more or less permanent change in behaviour that is reflected in a change in performance'.

The only way we can be certain that learning has occurred is to observe and/or measure the change in behaviour over the learning period. Is the change more or less permanent, and does it result from practice or past experience in the situation?

Three types of learning

There are three types of learning:

(1) Cognitive learning
This is learning brought about by the use of mental processes, such as problem solving, concept formation, reasoning and gaining knowledge. It might apply to school subjects like mathematics or geography, or skills such as working out tactics for a game.
(2) Affective learning
Affective learning is brought about by changes in attitudes and values from influences such as home, friends and school. Sportsmanship is developed through affective learning.
(3) Effective learning
Effective learning applies to learning through physical actions — for example, kicking, hitting, walking and catching a ball.

Learning of motor skills

Motor skill learning involves a reorganization of basic movement patterns resulting in a permanent change in large muscle group behaviour, this change being brought about as a result of practice.

Note that **not all learning produces skill.** Sometimes inefficient actions may be learned, and this makes it much more difficult to learn correct actions. For example, it is easier to teach a beginner to hit a tennis ball correctly than it is to teach the same skill to someone who has already learned an incorrect grip. This grip must be 'unlearned' first. A badminton player, for instance, may find it difficult to learn to play a game like tennis, which requires a 'stiff' wrist.

Motor skill does not depend solely on physical ability, but also on an individual's ability to:

- **Think**
- **Interpret** the conditions of his or her environment
- **Select**, accordingly, the correct course of action.

Terms such as perceptual motor skills, sensory motor skills and cognitive motor skills are therefore commonly used.

Skilled performance

Skilled performance, therefore, involves:

- **A goal:** the action is performed with a specific purpose in mind
- A complex **sequence of activity**
- **Organization** of time, space and muscular movement

Figure 29.1

- Learning through **practice**.

Skilled performance is also characterized by:

- The performer seeming to 'have all the time in the world'
- The performer having smooth, perfectly timed movements
- The performer doing 'the right thing at the right time'.

Motor performance

We need to distinguish between motor performance and skill learning:

- **A motor performance**

A motor performance is simply the action of a large muscle group, an action that may be temporary in nature. It is any change in behaviour that is not permanent — for example, jumping over a puddle in the street (see Figure 29.1).

- **Skill learning**

Skill learning is affected by factors that influence efficient communication between the sense, the brain and the muscles.

Factors in motor performance

Motor performance is influenced by:
(1) Physiological factors

They include fitness, strength, endurance and flexibility.

(2) **Age**

These factors include bodily growth, and development and deterioration as a person grows older. For example, a child at ten years old can jump three metres in the long jump, and when thirteen can jump four metres. This improvement may be attributed to growth and not to an increase in the required skill.

(3) **Requirements of the task**

Physical requirements of a task may promote or limit motor performance. They include:

- Limits of the rules of a game
- Weather conditions
- Equipment needed
- The design of modern equipment — for example, the advantages and disadvantages of a fibreglass pole compared with a wooden one in pole-vaulting
- Condition of the equipment — for example, a worn grip on a tennis racquet or a poorly inflated ball.

(4) **Motivation**

The greater the level of motivation, the more likely it is that performance will be at its best. Although the same could be said for skill learning, there are many examples of performers who excel on one occasion because they are highly motivated, but cannot repeat the performance. An example is Bob Beaman's famous long jump at the Mexico Olympic Games.

Organization of a skill

A skilled act may be seen as a whole plan that specifies the temporal and sequential properties of the total movement. This is known as an executive programme or motor programme.

Subroutines

Motor programmes are made up of a number of related parts called subroutines:

When you have already learned particular subroutines, it makes it much easier to learn a motor programme. For example, the high jump involves such subroutines as running, jumping and landing. The more subroutines that you learn in childhood, the more resources you will have as an adolescent or adult to perform motor programmes.

Motor programme	**Subroutines**
Tennis serve	• Grip • Footwork • Backward swing • Forward swing • Follow through • Angle of racquet head • Watching the ball • Contact
Swimming backstroke	• Arm movement • Leg kick • Breathing • Start • Turn

Figure 29.2

Many individuals are prevented from performing particular skilled movements because they do not have enough subroutines on which to draw.

Co-ordination of subroutines

Although subroutines can quickly become automatic when practised in isolation, all motor programmes depend on the proper co-ordination of all the subroutines in relation to each other. In other words, you cannot successfully perform an executive programme if you have not already mastered any one of the necessary subroutines.

For example, you cannot be a successful footballer unless you can efficiently perform the subroutine of running.

Relegating executive programmes to subroutines

As you become more skilful, you relegate motor programmes to the subroutine level. For instance, holding a cricket bat correctly is an executive programme for the beginner, but becomes an automatic subroutine to the experienced player.

Compare the way in which a five-year-old child bounces a ball compared with the bouncing action of a basketball player.

When an executive programme has been relegated to the subroutine level:

- You can concentrate on the wider range of activity around you — for example, a basketballer can take his eyes off the ball and pay attention to the actions of other players.

- You can attempt to increase the complexity of the motor programme — for example, when you have become reasonably proficient at hitting a tennis ball over the net, you can work on hitting it with top spin.

Correct sequence of subroutines

To perform a motor skill successfully, you need to perform all the subroutines in the correct sequence and with the correct timing. If you perform any of the subroutines incorrectly, in the wrong order or with the wrong timing, you affect the whole movement. For example, when performing a tennis drive, you must place the foot across the body *before* the forward swing begins.

Pacing and anticipation

Skilled movement requires that *all* the subroutines should be joined together smoothly and with continuity. This is called temporal patterning. You can recognize that a person is unskilled because he or she shows jerky or poorly timed movements.

This continuity of movement is influenced by pacing and anticipation:

- **Pacing**

Pacing refers to how you time the whole movement. In some activities, you have no control over pacing, and must time your moves in relation to external factors. For example, a basketballer times his or her moves in relation to the movements of other players and the ball. A gymnast, however, can completely control the pace of his or her movements.

Very skilful performers can control the pace of the opposition by slowing down the game or speeding it up. A good example is the pacesetter in a race.

- **Anticipation**

If you can anticipate what is going to happen next in a game, you have an added advantage in terms of timing your movements.

The human as an information-processing system

Between the presentation of a stimulus and the resultant response, the learner takes in a lot of information and tries to make sense out of it — that is, you process information in order to make a response.

This is the essence of the **information-processing theory of learning.**

Several models have been developed to try to illustrate this theory. Despite the differences between these models, they all emphasize three major components:

- Input
- Central processing
- Output.

Figure 29.3 shows the simplest model of the human information-processing system.

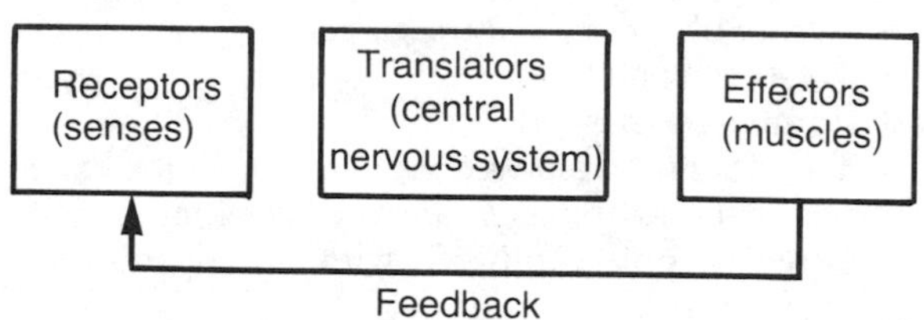

Figure 29.3

Expanded model of the human information-processing system

Figure 29.4 shows how the basic model of an information-processing system can be expanded. The components of this model are:

- **Display**

This is the physical environment — for example, the football field, players, goals and the crowds.

- **Stimuli**

These are specific parts of the display that stimulate the sense organs.

- **Sensory system**

These include visual, auditory and tactile information receptors.

- **Perceptual mechanism**

— The interpretation of sensory input
— Discrimination between stimuli
— Coding of input.

- **Decision mechanism**

Here, the input is perceived, recognized, coded and a decision on the action to be taken is made — that is, a motor plan is formulated.

- **Effector mechanism**

Motor plans are expanded to give an overall framework into which old and new subroutines and movement patterns are fitted.

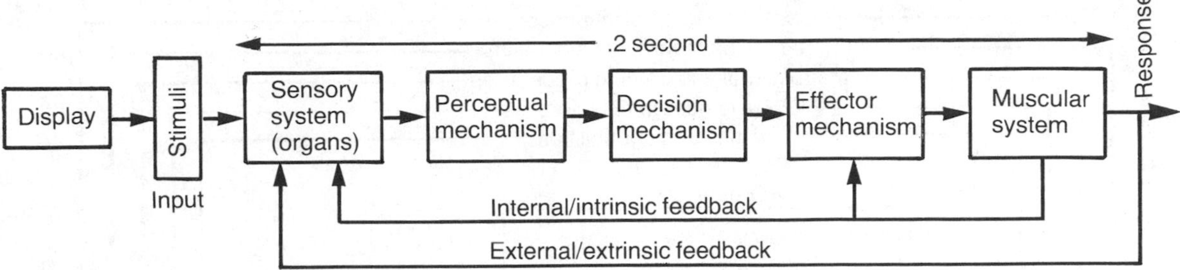

Figure 29.4

- **Muscular system**

Impulses are received from the effector mechanism so that the skill may be executed.

- **Response**

The action performed.

- **Feedback**

For smooth, accurate performance, knowledge of results (extrinsic feedback) is required. For precision control of an action, intrinsic (**proprioceptive**) feedback is required.

Whiting's model

Whiting's model is a popular illustration of the theory:

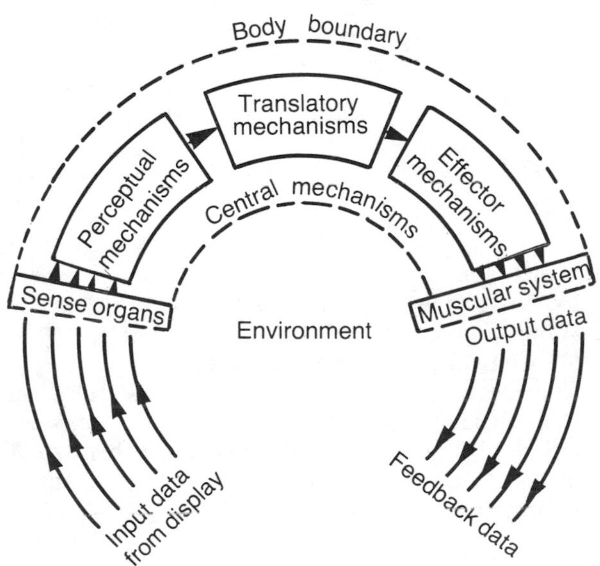

Figure 29.5 Systems analysis of perceptual-motor performance.

Complex model

Some models illustrate information processing in more detail (see Figure 29.7):

Magill's model

Here is a closer look at Magill's model:

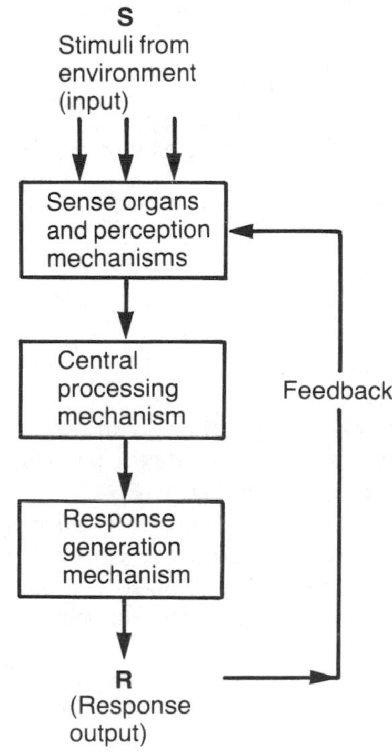

Figure 29.6

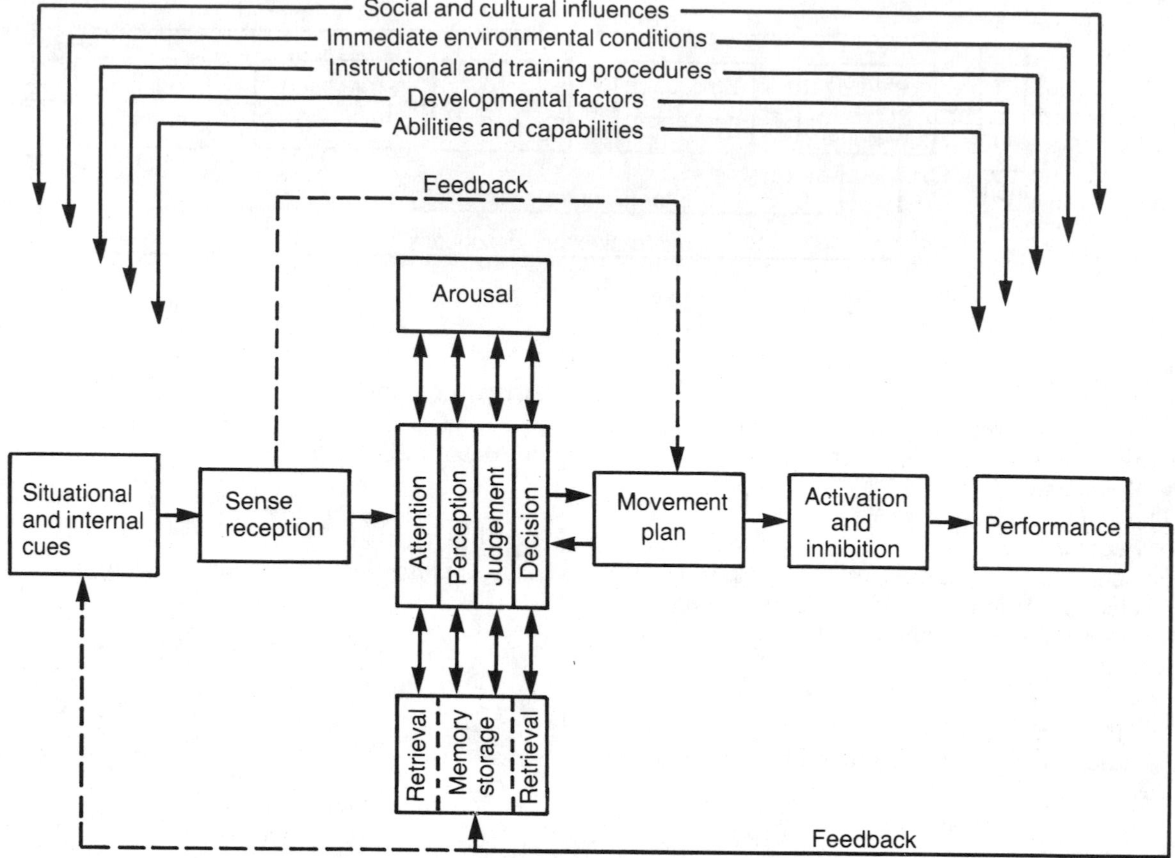

Figure 29.7 A systems model of human motor behaviour (the human as a subsystem).

The model is made up of the following parts:

(1) Stimuli

Input elements that occur in the environment. In a game, they may include the ball and the opponent's racquet, eyes and arm.

(2) Sense organs and perception mechanisms

- Information from the **external environment** is received through the five senses: seeing, smelling, touching, tasting and hearing.
- Information from the **internal environment** is received through the **proprioceptors** — that is, the sensory nerves from the muscles, nerves, tendons and joints. This information results in a **kinesthetic sense** — that is, a knowledge of the position and movement of body parts.

Which stimuli deserve the most attention? **Selective attention** is **attending to the appropriate stimuli**, which is vital for skilful movements.

(3) Central processing mechanism

This mechanism is also called the **'translator'** — it translates incoming information for the effectors or muscles. The central processing mechanism is made up of the **brain**, which codes, organizes information and stores data.

The **memory** is used for information storage and retrieval, and for strategy making.

(4) Response generation mechanism

When the learner has made a decision concerning the appropriate strategy, the components of the response must be organized and sent on to the muscles.

(5) **Response**

The response is performed by the 'effectors' — that is, the entire muscular system of the body. (Sometimes coaches give too much attention to just this one part of the information-processing system.)

(6) **Feedback**

Feedback is information about how the effectors have performed. This information is sent back to receptors and the central processing system. Feedback:

- Motivates the performer
- Changes the immediate quality of the performance
- Reinforces learning.

Differences in the skill learning of individuals can be accounted for by differences within the information-processing system. These differences can occur at any of the processing stages or at any point between them.

Feedback control

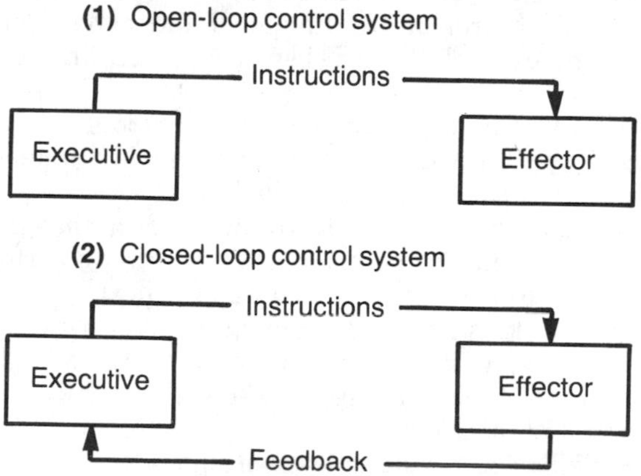

(1) Open-loop control system

Executive	— Instructions →	Effector

(2) Closed-loop control system

Executive	— Instructions →	Effector
↑	← Feedback —	

Figure 29.8 Schematic diagram of open-loop and closed-loop control.

Closed loop or open loop?

Information-processing systems can be either closed loop systems or open loop systems.

- **Open loop system**

This is a simple type of system with two separate components (see Figure 29.8). The 'executive' makes decisions and transmits instructions to the 'effector', which carries out the commands. A good example of an open loop system is a traffic light, which progresses through its sequence as ordered by preset commands.

- **Closed loop system**

This is a much more flexible system, because it includes a feedback mechanism. The appropriateness of the effector's actions can therefore be monitored, and changes made accordingly to the commands sent by the executive. An example is the automatic pilot on a plane. It can adjust its actions according to whether or not the plane is on course, and can make corrections to take into account weather conditions.

Human information-processing system

- **Closed loop**

Generally speaking, the human information-processing system is closed loop — that is, it uses a feedback mechanism to monitor effector behaviour and can adjust its future actions accordingly.

For example, when serving a tennis ball, you do not throw it up high enough. Your central processing system receives this information through the feedback mechanism. You then adjust your movement in order to serve the ball successfully.

- **Open loop**

However, there seem to be two bases for applying the open loop theory to human information processing:

(1) Results of some laboratory experiments indicate that subjects can make adjustments to their movements in a time that is less than the time it takes signals to be transmitted via the feedback mechanism — that is, in less than one proprioceptive reaction time.

(2) Some movements appear to be completed without the aid of feedback. It seems that humans have the ability to programme a complete movement beforehand and carry it out without the need for feedback during performance. This can be seen in tasks involving very fast movements, when the time between successive actions is extremely short — for example, when playing a rapid piece of music on the piano.

Some theorists argue that this is what happens during the performance of closed skills of short duration, such as the golf swing. The performer can go through a preplanned movement pattern without the need for feedback during performance.

Skill classification

There are several different ways of classifying skill types:

(1) Discrete, continuous and serial skills

- **A discrete skill** is one with a distinct beginning and an end. Examples include:
  - — A baseball throw
  - — A football kick
  - — Switching on a light.
- **Continuous skills**
  When a motor skill has no distinct beginning or end, it is said to be **continuous**. Examples include driving a car, running or basketball dribbling — all activities that can continue for an unspecified time.
- **Serial skills**
  Serial skills are those that string together several discrete tasks to form an apparently continuous performance. They include a number of distinct elements, the order of which is very important. Examples include:
  - — Starting a car: sequence of ignition-clutch-accelerator
  - — Playing a tennis stroke on the run
  - — A complete football move: sequence of mark, run, and handball.

Fine and gross motor skills

This is a common type of classification that is based on the amount of movement and force required to perform a skill:

- **Gross motor skills**

They are skills that involve large parts of the body or the movement of the whole body — for example, a somersault, or kicking a ball.

- **Fine motor skills**

They involve the movement of small muscle groups — for example, writing or painting. They are generally not included in the field of physical education.

A problem with this classification is that some skills undoubtedly employ both large and small muscle groups. For example:

- Balancing on a beam with one foot requires the strength of the muscles of the whole body as well as the fine adjustments of the foot and ankle muscles.
- Bowling a cricket ball employs great force from the whole body but requires skilful manipulation of the fingers.

Open and closed skills

This classification, suggested by Poulton (1957) and Knapp (1964), distinguishes between open skills and closed skills. It is based on the extent to which a performer needs to adjust to the environment.

- **Open skills**

Open skills are **externally paced** — the timing of them depends on factors external to the performer. For example:

- — The skill of fielding a cricket ball varies according to the speed and height of the ball, the positions of fellow fieldsmen, and whether the batsmen are running or not.
- — The timing of a football tackle depends on the opponent's speed and direction and his ability to change either or both.

- **Closed skills**

Closed skills are **internally paced** — performer is in full control of the timing of the movements. Examples include the handstand and the golf swing.

- **Skills for unpredictable environments**

Skills performed in an unpredictable environment are **open skills**. Examples include:

- — Team games are played in an ever-changing environment that makes it difficult for a performer to predict what will happen next.
- — The skills needed for sailing in rough weather.

'At every instant the motor activity must be regulated by and appropriate to the external situation' (Whiting).

- **Skills for predictable environments**

Skills performed in predictable environments are **closed skills**. In such an environment, the performer can go through a prelearned motor programme without having to consider environmental changes — for example, diving, archery or the shot put.

'Conformity to a prescribed standard sequence of motor acts is all important' (Whiting).

Learning open or closed skills

Knapp's view is that all skills lie on a continuum

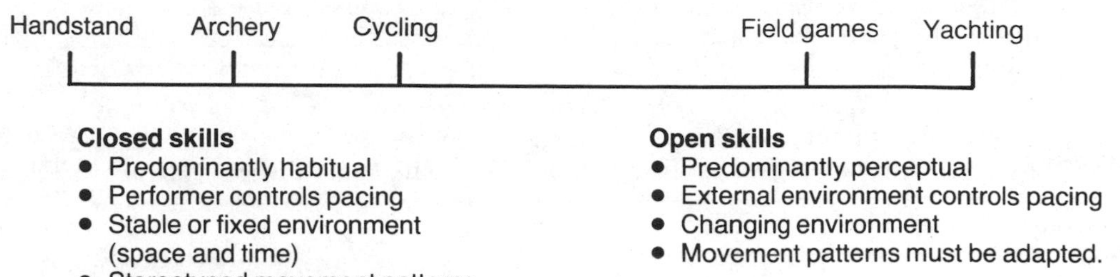

Figure 29.9

Figure 29.10

between open and closed, and that some skills are more open or closed than others (see Figure 29.9).

The main consideration for learning skills under these classifications is that **closed skills** can be learned more easily because it is simply a matter of mastering, through practice, a specific movement pattern and repeating it.

Open skills, however, are not so easy to master, because they are rarely repeated exactly, and their performance depends on the circumstances of the time.

Therefore a beginner will learn the skill of kicking a ball more quickly if he or she learns it as a closed skill. Once the closed skill has been mastered, the player can learn to adapt it to an open environment.

Sometimes the same skill can be open or closed, depending on the circumstances. For example:

- When playing tennis, your forehand drive against a wall is a closed skill because the return is predictable, but it becomes a very open skill when you are matched against a skilful opponent.
- Skiing down a constant slope and with no one in sight is a closed skill, but skiing on a crowded slope in varying weather on rough terrain is very much an open skill.

Phases of skill learning

According to Fitts and Posner, there are three main phases through which an individual progresses in learning a skill:

- Cognitive phase (plan formation)
- Associative phase (practice)
- Autonomous phase (automatic execution).

Phase (1) Cognitive phase

During this phase, the individual learns what is to be done. In other words, you *find out* what is expected in order to perform a skill. During this phase, you must identify the subroutines involved

	Sports						
Classification	**Archery target shooting**	**Skeet shooting**	**Gym-nastic vault**	**Track-race 50-metre dash**	**Bowling**	**Tennis forehand drive**	**Race car driving**
Type of environmental regulation							
• Closed (spatial control)	X		X	X	X		
• Open (temporal/spatial control)		X				X	X
Pacing of movements							
• Externally paced		X		X		X	X
• Self-paced	X		X		X		
State of system prior to movement							
• Object and body at rest	X		X	X	X		X
• One of the two moving		X				X	
• Both moving							
Type of movement							
• Postural-stability	X	X					
• Transport							
—Limb					X	X	
—Body			X	X	X	X	
• Object manipulation	X	X			X	X	X
Main feedback sources							
• Internal	X	X	X	X	X	X	
• External	X	X			X	X	
• Intrinsic (task)							X
Objective							
• Judge's rating of form			X				
• Points scored	X	X			X	X	
• Speed (time)				X			X

Figure 29.11

and their correct sequence. You need to see and experience the feel of the movement required.

The exploratory nature of the **cognitive phase** leads to a large number of errors, and a great deal of very specific feedback is needed in order to recognize and correct these errors.

The best way to achieve Phase (**1**) is through demonstration. Your teacher or coach can show you what is required, either by carrying out the action personally, asking another person to show what is required, or by showing videos or films.

On the other hand, you could achieve this phase by reading information or listening to a description of the skill. Phase (**1**) is usually completed in a short time.

Phase (2) Associative stage

After you, as the learner, have received and understood information about what is required in performing a given skill, you must **practise** in order to become familiar with the sequence of subroutines and the timing required.

The amount of practice needed will depend on the complexity of the activity, your abilities and past experience, and how ambitious you are.

Demonstrations and coaching can be very useful for correcting errors during Phase (2). As you refine your skills, you make fewer and smaller errors, and your ability to recognize errors and make the necessary adjustments improves.

Phase (2) usually takes place over a long period of time. Some performers remain within the associative stage for many years, and never reach the autonomous stage.

Phase (3) Autonomous stage

During the autonomous stage, the skill becomes much easier to accomplish, and your level of anxiety is reduced. Practice has enabled you to reach a stage where you can organize the required movements into the correct sequence, and time your movements without thinking. The skill can be relegated to a lower level, leaving the central nervous system to deal with skills that have not yet reached Phase (3).

Having reached the autonomous stage:

- The temporal and sequential patterning of subroutines becomes automatic
- The likelihood of being distracted by interference from the environment is reduced
- Less cognitive control is required
- Your speed and efficiency is increased.

Once having reached this stage, you can concentrate on more detailed aspects of the skill. For example:

- When playing tennis, if you have mastered the forehand drive you can work on placing your shot.
- Once you have perfected your shooting at basketball, you can work on ways of evading opponents in order to get into a better shooting position.

Note: In order to maintain a skill at Phase (3) level, you must bring Phase (2) repeatedly into operation, and it might even be necessary to go back to Phase (1) to check that you are performing a skill correctly.

Laboratory work 47: Tennis ball throw and bounce with the non-dominant hand

Hypothesis

Learning can be distinguished from performance.

Apparatus

- Tennis ball
- Target.

Procedure

(1) Stand facing a target on a wall. Hold a tennis ball in your non-dominant hand. Between you and the target is a restraining line on the ground.

(2) Bounce the ball on your side of the restraining line so that it hits the target.

(3) You don't score any points if the ball lands on the floor between the line and the target.

(4) Do not practise before the commencement of the task.

(5) Follow the sequence of 10 test trials — 20 practice trials — 10 test trials.

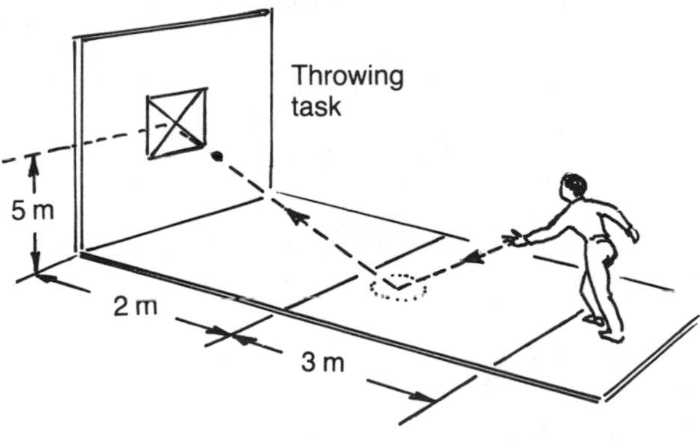

Figure 29.12

Results

(1) Add up each column in Figure 29.13. Find the average score in each column.

(2) Plot the averages on the graph, Figure 29.14:

Conclusions

(1) Has learning occurred?

(2) Why, or why not?

	Trials A											**Trials B**									
Subject	**1**	**2**	**3**	**4**	**5**	**6**	**7**	**8**	**9**	**10**	20 practice trials	**1**	**2**	**3**	**4**	**5**	**6**	**7**	**8**	**9**	**10**
1																					
2																					
3																					
4																					
5																					
6																					
7																					
8																					
Average per trial																					

Figure 29.13

Laboratory work 48: Agility movement

Hypothesis

That learning can be distinguished from performance.

Apparatus

- Two cones
- Stop watch.

Procedure

(1) Place two cones five metres apart.
(2) Sit alongside one cone facing the other.
(3) On a given signal, move and touch the other cone as fast as possible.
(4) Record the time with a stop watch.
(5) Note that no practice is allowed before beginning the task.
(6) All subjects should follow the sequence of five timed trials — two minutes rest — five timed trials.

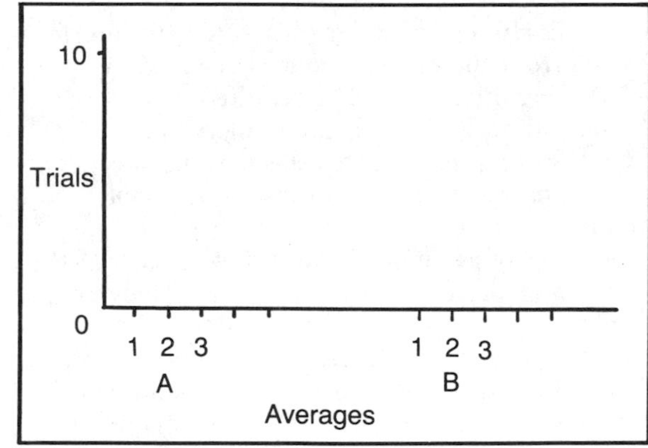

Figure 29.14

Results

(1) Record the results on Figure 29.15.
(2) Plot a graph of your own results.

Conclusions

(1) Has learning occurred?
(2) Why, or why not?

	A						B				
Subject	**1**	**2**	**3**	**4**	**5**	2 minutes' rest	**1**	**2**	**3**	**4**	**5**
(1)											
(2)											
(3)											
(4)											

Figure 29.15

Laboratory work 49: Open and closed skills

Hypothesis
Open skills are more difficult to perform than closed skills.

Apparatus
- Bin, or bucket
- Tennis ball
- Soccer ball.

Procedure
Perform each of the following skills five times:

(1) (a) Throw a tennis ball into a stationary bin.
  (b) Throw a tennis ball into a bin being held by your partner, who runs in a straight line.
  (c) Throw a tennis ball into a bin held by your partner, who is running in all directions.

(2) (a) Kick a stationary soccer ball against a wall. (No opponents should be present.)
  (b) Kick a stationary soccer ball against a wall while your opponents try to intercept it.
  (c) Kick a moving soccer ball against a wall while your opponents try to intercept it.
  (d) Kick a moving soccer ball against a wall. (No opponents should be present.)

Results
Tabulate how many times you successfully performed each task.

Conclusions
(1) Place the seven skills described above on a continuum between open and closed.
(2) Discuss this continuum in relation to the difficulty or ease of each skill.

Worksheet 28: Skills acquisition

(1) How is learning measured?
(2) How can a computer be compared with the functions of a human?
(3) Which of the following is *not* a characteristic of skilled performance?
  (a) It is goal directed
  (b) It consists of complex sequences of activity
  (c) The skilled player must attend to everything very carefully
  (d) During skilled performance, complex movements are organized both spatially and temporally.
(4) Figure 29.16 represents the human being as a simple information-processing model.

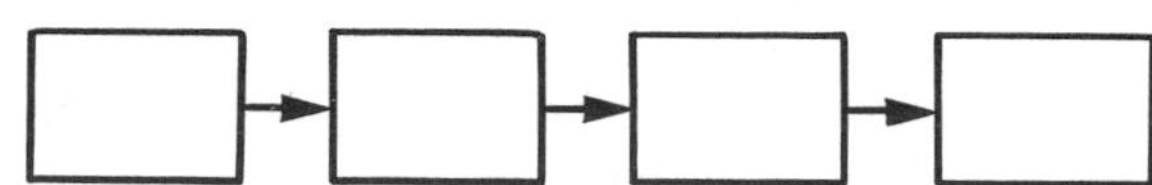

Figure 29.16

Place the following in the correct sequence:
(a) Central mechanism
(b) Information
(c) Muscular system
(d) Sense organs.

(5) Fitts and Posner showed that there are three phases of learning for the acquisition of complex skills. Name and briefly describe these phases.

(6) Which one of the following phases is characterized by the performer becoming increasingly independent of attention demand?
(a) Hierarchical phase
(b) Associative phase
(c) Contemporary phase
(d) Autonomous phase.

(7) During the autonomous phase of learning:
(a) Less cognitive control is required
(b) There must be a reaction time between each subroutine
(c) Errors are gradually eliminated
(d) Players begin to understand the demands of the task.

(8) Figure 29.17 illustrates a continuum on which various 'open' and 'closed' skills may be placed. For example, a skill classified as being extremely open would be placed in the '10' category.

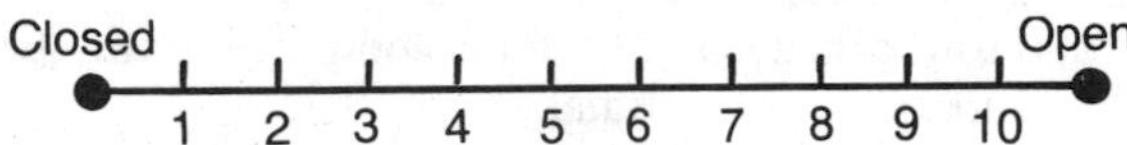

Figure 29.17

Indicate where you would place the following activities on the continuum by giving an appropriate number to the particular activities chosen:
(a) Driving a golf ball
(b) Running a 1500-metre race
(c) Playing wing attack in netball
(d) Batting in softball.

(9) In what significant ways do closed skills differ from open skills?

(10) Classify the following skills as 'open' or 'closed':
(a) Shooting an arrow in archery
(b) Batting in cricket
(c) Bowling in cricket
(d) The backhand defensive stroke in table tennis
(e) Ten-pin bowling.

(11) Open skills:
(a) Require spatial and temporal patterning
(b) Require spatial awareness only
(c) Are used in golf
(d) Both (b) and (c).

(12) A closed skill utilizes:
(a) A stereotyped movement pattern
(b) An environment in which objects are relatively stable
(c) None of the above
(d) Both (a) and (b).

30. Receiving information

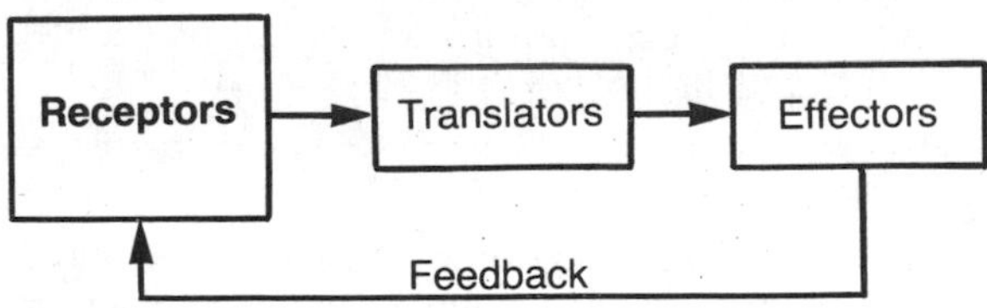

Figure 30.1

Perception

Perception is the interpretation of sensory information. A human being cannot perceive all the stimuli coming from all of the various receptors. We must select certain stimuli from among all the possibilities. This selection process involves a series of coding operations. An example is shown in Figure 30.2.

If a dog begins to bark and growl — that is, provides new visual and auditory input — a new response results — that is, 'turn and run'. If you do this promptly, it implies that you have already learned and familiarized yourself with this stimulus.

Perceptual styles

People can be classified into two types, according to their perceptual styles:

(1) **Field-dependent**

Field-dependent people tend to experience objects as **fused with the background**. Therefore they find it difficult to pick out specific objects in a display.

(2) **Field-independent**

Field-independent people can experience items as separate from their backgrounds. Therefore they can overcome an **embedding context** (the background in which the objects are set, or 'embedded'). Superior athletes tend to be more highly field independent — that is, they can distinguish the important cues from the whole display.

Interpretation

People can perceive the same thing differently, and there are often conflicting reports about the same event. For example: If you say that you don't understand what the coach wants you to do in order

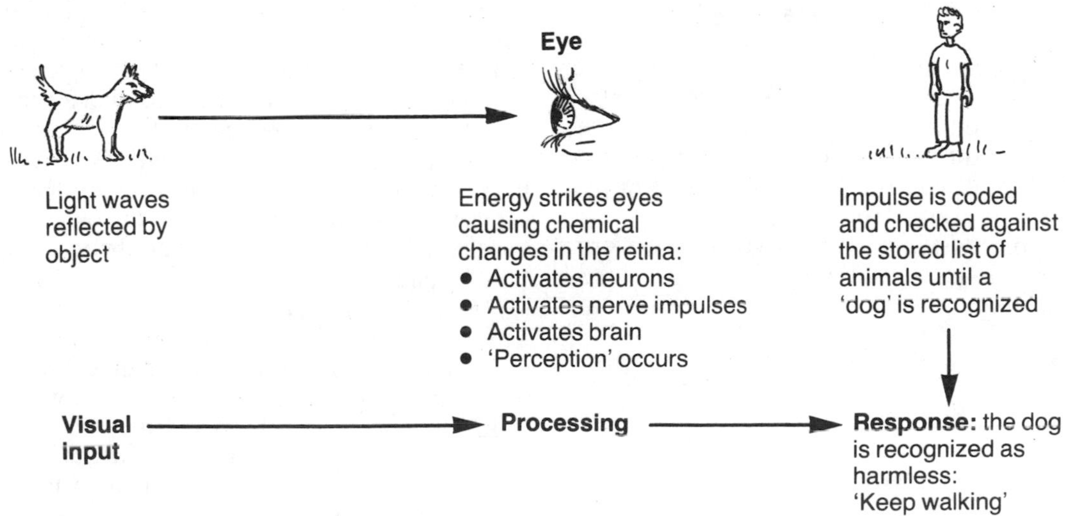

Figure 30.2

to perform a skill, it is obvious that you are not interpreting the information from the coach in the way he or she anticipated. For example, a teacher may be demonstrating how to pass in netball while the student is concerned only with whether or not the pass is successful.

Sensory systems

Information comes from:

- **External stimuli** — for example, the presence of a friend
- **Internal stimuli** — for example, the bodily systems that tell you whether or not you have a full stomach or bladder, or whether you have muscle pain.

Information from such stimuli is conveyed by the sensory nerves from the sense organs or receptors, which act as receiving instruments, or indicators:

- Information from the external environment is received through the five senses of seeing, hearing, smelling, touching and tasting (**exteroceptors**)
- Information from the internal environment (within the body) is received through the **proprioceptors** (that is, the muscles, tendons, joints and nerves).

The senses and motor skills

- **Taste and smell** rarely play a part in motor skills.
- **Hearing**
  Hearing plays an important part in some motor skills — for example, responding to a starter's gun, the sound of an opponent coming from behind, or the sound of a cricket ball striking the bat. Also, of course, you must be able to hear performance instructions clearly.
- The three most important senses in the performance of motor skills are:
  (1) **Vision**
  (2) **Equilibrium**
  (3) **Proprioception** (kinesthesis, and touch).

Vision

Vision has many functions, including:

- Following a moving projectile
- Judging the distance and direction of an object (spatial relations)
- Detecting colour and brightness.

Specific examples include:

- A batsman, who must have keen eyesight in order to detect a ball bowled at 140 kph
- A footballer who, when going for a mark, must judge the distance of the ball from him and its speed in order to time his leap correctly
- A fieldsman in cricket, who must often separate a small red sphere from a background of people, stands and lights.

Equilibrium

Your organ of balance (equilibrium) is located in the vestibular apparatus of the inner ear. Equilibrium is the internal sense that tells you when your body is balanced and under control. It is very important for all skills, particularly those involving sudden changing movements (such as team sports) where balance and control must be maintained. Equilibrium is very important for divers, trampoliners and gymnasts, since in these activities the body takes on many unaccustomed positions, and loss of control can be dangerous.

Proprioception

This is the provision of information from within the body itself about the position of the whole body or its parts in space. The nerves and muscles are the proprioceptors that provide a rich source of stimuli to which a performer may respond:

(1) Kinesthesis

'Kinesthesis is a consciousness of muscular movement and effort' (Singer). If you are learning how to swing a golf club for the first time, the instructor will probably tell you to get the 'feel' of the movement. A good performer can judge the success of a performance by how the movement 'feels'.

Experimenters have shown that if they cut off the blood flow to a limb so that it 'goes to sleep', the subject finds it difficult to control the movement of the limb, because his or her kinesthetic sense has been impaired.

(2) Touch (tactile sense)

The tactile sense enables us to feel pain, temperature and changes of pressure. For example:

- You can tell from the feel of the ball when you kick it how hard you kicked it.
- Your motor performance in catching a hard cricket ball has to be adapted in order to catch a soft tennis ball.
- Touch lets you know whether or not you are holding a racquet, shot or bow correctly.

Efficiency of the sense organs

The process of identifying stimuli is called **signal detection**, and the ability of the sense organs to receive information depends on:

- The intensity of the stimulus
- The effectiveness of the sense organs themselves.

(1) The intensity of the stimulus

For example:

- A strong smell is more likely to be noticed than a faint one.
- A large ball, or a ball with a colour that contrasts with the background, is more easily seen than a small ball or a ball of a non-contrasting colour.
- The slower the event, the easier it is to recognize cues. During a fast event time of exposure to the cues is less.
- Unusual displays are more easily recognized than ordinary expected displays — for example, a blinking light is more easily seen than a steady one; and a very loud noise attracts attention quickly.

(2) The effectiveness of the organs themselves (sensory acvity)

Limited ability to perceive, see or hear can greatly reduce the ability to learn and perform a skill.

Improving the functioning of sense organs

Limitations in the functioning of sense organs cannot be corrected through practice — for example, continually looking at an object will not improve your ability to see it. That can be achieved only by using artificial aids.

However, **practice can make you more aware of your sensory capabilities**. For example, it has been found that peripheral vision improves with training, while task-related warm-up exercises improve the visual acuity needed in games.

Certain sense organs are more useful than others for detecting stimuli. For example, auditory alarm systems are more efficient than visual ones, because hearing is non-directional.

Signal detection

The human sensory system can:

- Detect
- Compare
- Recognize

a stimulus.

For you to be able to sense a stimulus, it must be within the range of one of your sense organs. Therefore, for example:

- Some lights are too dim to be seen.
- You cannot hear some tones, as they have too high a frequency.
- Some pressures are too weak to be felt.

Therefore a stimulus is useful only when you can detect it.

A stimulus can be defined as a 'change in the magnitude of energy impinging upon a sense organ'. Stimuli do not occur alone, but instead must be separated from the continual background of sensory stimulation ('**noise**'), of which the stimulus is a part. Once you have detected the stimulus, you must compare it with the background noise. The stimulus must then be recognized. The human capacity to compare is great, but the capacity to recognize is limited.

Signal detection

Signal detection is determining whether or not a stimulus or cue is present. For example:

- A radar monitor must work out whether there is a blip on the radar screen
- A batter must work out whether or not the oncoming ball has spin on it or not before deciding how to meet it.

'Noise'

'Noise' can create uncertainty and make decision-making difficult. As noted already, 'noise' is the cues in the environment that are not relevant or of interest. In a competitive situation, noise comes in the form of such distractions as crowds, opponents' off-putting tactics or looking into the sun at a ball.

The need for accurate signal detection

The ability to detect signals, or cues, determines whether you, as a performer, can take the necessary action in response to a signal. Some physical factors that influence signal detection are:

(1) **Visual**

- Size of the object

- Distance from the object
- Colour and brightness of the object
- The background against which it is seen
- The amount of illumination of the object and its surroundings
- The speed of the object
- Visual exposure time.

(2) **Auditory**
- Loudness
- Pitch
- Interfering noises
- Duration.

(3) **Tactual**
- Location on body surface
- Movement against body surface
- Area of body surface contacted
- Intensity of feeling.

Figure 30.3

Figure 30.4

Early signal detection

The earlier you detect a signal, the more efficient will be your reaction.

- **Example 1**

Goalkeeper 1 has his view blocked by a defender, and he catches his first sight of the ball as it speeds past his head into the net.

Goalkeeper 2 has a clear view of the attacker shooting. He also determines that, from the body position of the attacker, the ball will travel into the righthand side of the goal. Therefore he can take the appropriate action to save the ball.

Goalkeeper 1 did not detect the signal early enough, and therefore could not respond in time. Goalkeeper 2 not only detected the earlier signals but interpreted what they meant. Therefore he could respond correctly.

- **Example 2**

A skilled player will rely on *earlier* cues to give him or her more time to get into position to play a stroke.

In Figure 30.3, Player (**a**) has played her shot and notices the feet position and racquet angle of her opponent. From this 'display' she can read the play and move in to position earlier.

In Figure 30.4, Player (**a**) is unsure of whether to move until she actually sights the ball on her side of the net.

Improving signal detection

We can be trained to increase our ability to detect signals, and to make decisions more rapidly in response to stimuli.

Compared to average athletes, highly skilled athletes have superior sensory systems, and can detect information that average players may not. Also, the experience of the more skilled performers increases the accuracy of the judgements they make about the signals they detect.

When learning skills, signal detection can be practised and improved by:

- Using larger objects — for example, catching using a softball rather than a tennis ball
- Using contrasting colours — for example, yellow footballs at night
- Slowing down the object — for example, throwing rather than hitting a tennis ball to a learner
- Becoming exposed by practice over longer periods of time.

Anticipation greatly increases your ability to detect signals. Good anticipation comes from learning and experience.

Arousal

Arousal, or activation, is 'the degree of preparedness, alertness and excitement present in a performer who is about to take part in skilful activity'. For most complex motor skills, average or moderate levels of arousal usually result in the best performance and optimum effort. Experiments have shown that, if an individual is either under-aroused or over-aroused, that individual's performance will be below his or her best.

Arousal can often be measured by monitoring changes in heart rate, muscular tension, respiration and other factors indicating that an individual is preparing for a task. Also it is possible to measure functions that cease to operate if not needed for a task. For example, the digestive movements of the stomach often slow down or cease if a person is aroused.

Under- and over-arousal

Under-arousal often shows up as over-relaxation or lack of interest. **Over-arousal** can be seen as excessive tension and nervousness. Under- or over-arousal can affect your ability to detect signals. For example, if you are tired or over-excited you might:

- Believe that you have detected a signal that is not actually there

or

- Miss the signal entirely.

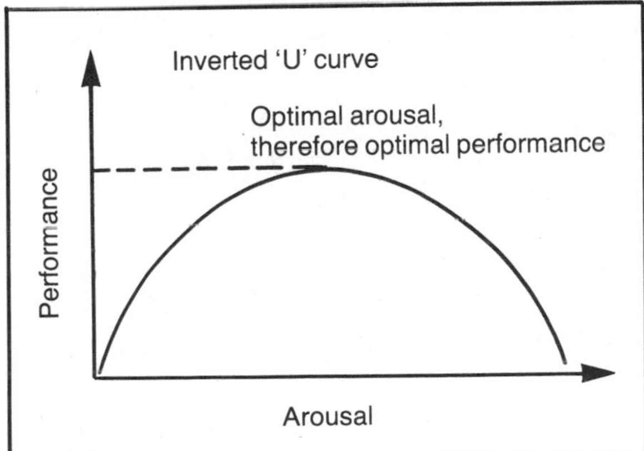

Figure 30.5

As Figure 30.5 shows, when you are at low levels of arousal (that is, drowsy or bored), your performance, both mental and physical, is very poor. As you increase your arousal, performance improves.

Eventually you reach an **optimum level of arousal**. At this point you can give your best performance.

After you pass your optimal arousal, you become over-aroused (tense and highly excited), and your performance drops off.

Note: The optimum arousal level varies from person to person and, for the same person, from task to task.

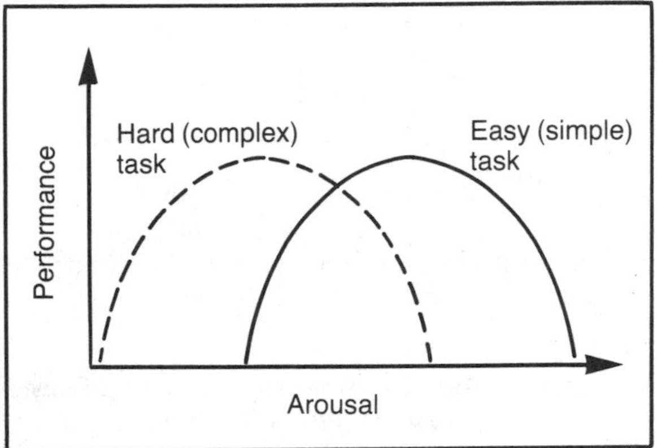

Figure 30.6

Arousal, performance and the type of task

For complex tasks, the optimum arousal level for optimum performance is lower than for simple tasks (see Figure 30.6), and a greater arousal level is needed to perform well in simple tasks. Therefore the stress and added arousal of competition might be too much for a beginner trying to master complicated skills.

Once you have learned a complex skill, practise it in competitive situations so that during performance the pressure of competion does not lead to over-arousal.

Personality, arousal and performance

Each performer has a different natural arousal level. As Figure 30.7 shows, introverts have far lower normal arousal levels than extroverts. Therefore

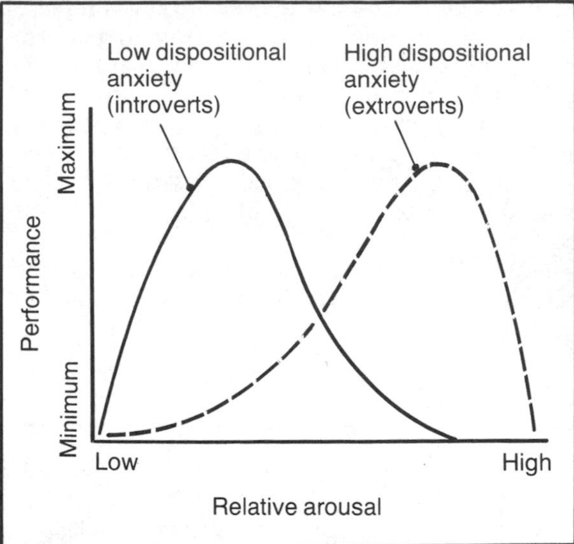

Figure 30.7 A stylized depiction of the performance-arousal curves of low and high dispositional anxiety persons under similar, relative amounts of arousal.

introverts perform better under conditions of lower arousal and worse under conditions of higher arousal. Extroverts perform better under conditions of high arousal, and worse under conditions of low arousal.

Exercise (kinesthetic feedback) leads to improved information processing by producing optimal arousal levels. Since this has been discovered, some industries have introduced 'pause gymnastic' breaks, during which workers engage in mild exercise programmes, which lead to improved performance and fewer accidents. This can be compared to the wicket keeper running up the pitch between overs, thus boosting arousal.

On the other hand, the beginner should not be stressed while learning basic skills, as it has been found that skill performance deteriorates under unfavourable conditions that lead to states of excessive arousal. When the learner has reached the autonomous stage, he or she needs to simulate the stresses of competition — for example, pressure training — that is, experience much higher levels of arousal.

Achieving optimum arousal

It is important to realize that arousal is 'infectious' — that is, it can spread from one person to another. An over-aroused coach may over-arouse the players, making them tense and edgy. A player who does not try hard, because he or she is under-aroused, can spread this negative attitude to the whole team.

To obtain optimal performance, a coach must make sure that each player is at his or her optimal arousal level just before a match. Some players may be over-aroused, and may need some relaxation — for instance, before the first quarter of a Grand Final. Others may need motivational talks, films or even abuse just before a match to increase their level of arousal.

Cratty suggests some techniques that can be used to adjust the arousal levels of performers:

- **Adjust the importance of the contest**

If the players are over-aroused, suggest that the outcome of the match is 'not all that important'. If, however, they are under-aroused, make them realize that it is the most important match they will ever play in.

- **Adjust the social conditions**

Over-aroused athletes might have to be separated from the rest of the team, while those who are under-aroused might be encouraged to mix with those performers whose level of arousal is ideal.

- **Keep their minds off the contest**

Activities that distract the attention of participants from the approaching performance can help to control their level of arousal.

- **Relaxation training**

Teach performers relaxation techniques that can reduce muscle tension, respiration and heart rate. These techniques can not only calm down the over-aroused athlete but also help the under-aroused athlete to attain higher levels of arousal. This is done by first calming down him or her and then forcefully (often vocally) urging him or her to greater arousal.

- **Help the performer to understand signs of arousal**

Some performers panic, for example, if their palms are sweating. However, if they understand the signs of arousal, they will know that sweating palms is normal and therefore they will not worry.

Selective attention

Our senses are bombarded continually by signals. However, we do not pay attention to every cue present in the environmental display. For example, in class, while you are working or listening to your teacher, birds may be twittering close by or a car may have passed. Your sense of hearing would have picked up these signals, but you were probably unaware of them.

Consider what happens when a tape recorder is left on in a crowded room. The microphone cannot distinguish between the sounds it should pick up and those it should ignore. However, if you were talking to someone in that room, how would your attention to cues vary from the tape recorder's?

You do not process every available cue. You can filter out irrelevant information and attend only to relevant stimuli. This ability is known as **selective attention**.

Selective attention effectively cuts down the amount of information in the display and so reduces processing time.

Information overload

The human processing system can cope with only a small number of items at once. If you are confronted with too many cues requiring attention, you are said to suffer from information overload. A good example is giving too many instructions to a beginner at one time.

The ability to select only relevant information is influenced by three main factors:

- Arousal level
- Experience
- Quality of instruction.

Arousal level and selective attention

The more alert you are, the more likely you are to attend to relevant cues and to recognize the irrelevant ones. For example, when batting in cricket you need a high level of alertness to pick the type of spin imparted by a bowler. You need to be able to ignore such irrelevant cues as the movements of fielders.

Alertness during the learning of a skill is important. For example, when a teacher is directing a student as to what to look for, the student who is not alert may not pick up any of the relevant information.

Experience and selective attention

From past experience you 'know what to look for' — that is, you know which particular stimuli you need to react to in order to carry out a skill correctly. Experience also tells you which stimuli can be ignored as they are irrelevant to your performance. A great deal of experience is gained from **practice**.

Instruction and selective attention

In learning a skill, a beginner does not always know to which stimuli he or she must respond. The performer therefore needs instruction that directs attention. The coach must know which information in the display is worth attending to and teach a player to attend to it. For example:

- In cricket, the coach directs attention to the bowler's arm and hand, or teaches the batsman to follow the rule: elbow up — leg break; elbow down — offbreak.
- In volleyball, when instructing how to receive a serve, the coach directs attention to server then ball.

Instructions may take the form of a verbal description. However, the student gains a much clearer idea of what is required from a visual demonstration or from being manipulated by the coach so that he or she can 'feel' what is required.

Improvement of selective attention

Selective attention can be improved by:

- Making the stimuli stand out — for example, by using a white cricket ball
- Using language suited to the level of the performers
- Emotionally charging the explanation in order to motivate and arouse performers
- Basing explanations on demonstrations or on the past experience of performers
- Directing attention to one or two significant points at a time. If the performer is instructed to look for a certain stimulus subset, then his or her attention is more likely to be directed towards it.

Often the best way to learn the selection of relevant information is to undergo a great deal of practice, during which you gradually learn which stimuli have relevance or no relevance to your performance.

Successful selective attention, therefore, requires you, as performer, to respond only to stimuli relevant to the performance of your task and to reject irrelevant information. For example:

- When playing football, your kicking for goal should not be influenced by the efforts of your opponent to put you off
- When playing tennis, you should not be in-

fluenced by remarks from the crowd when placing a difficult shot
- When playing cricket, you should not worry whether or not the batsmen are running while you are attempting to catch the ball.

Redundancy

Redundant signals are those signals that are relevant to skilled performance but to which the performer need not attend. The more skilled performer will be faced with more redundant signals than the beginner. For example:
- **Early signals**

The skilled player will react to early signals, such as the opponent's footwork, and decide a course of action before later signals occur. The later signals are therefore redundant to him, whereas the beginner might not decide a course of action until after the ball has bounced his way.
- **Certain signals**

When signals can be predicted with **certainty** they become redundant — for example, bouncing a basketball, or the position of a soccer goal. Signals that are reasonably predictable or expected are less redundant, and require some attention. Totally unexpected stimuli are not redundant at all, and require full attention.

Task vigilance

Many motor activities require the performer to monitor what is going on until the occurrence of a predetermined cue to which he must react. This is task vigilance. Examples include:
- Pressing a button only when a light flashes
- In a shooting gallery, firing the gun only when a target pops up
- When playing as a soccer goalkeeper, acting only when the ball is played in your direction.

Influences on task vigilance

Task vigilance is influenced by:
- **The number of sources from which signals can occur**

The fewer the possible sources, the easier the task becomes. For example, the soccer goalkeeper can expect the ball to come from any one of several players, whereas the service receiver in tennis need face only one possible source of relevant stimuli.
- **The rate of incoming information**

The slower the rate of incoming information, the easier it is to attend to the signals. Also, cues that occur at regular intervals are easier to attend to than those occurring at a random rate (**temporal uncertainty**). For example, the target shooter can expect to score better when targets pop up at regular intervals.

Laboratory work 50: Verbal arousal

Hypothesis
That the level of arousal affects the performance of gross motor tasks.

Apparatus
Stop watch.

Method
(1) Divide students into two groups:
- Group A: control group
- Group B: experimental group.

(2) The task is to perform the maximum number of sit ups in a 15-second trial. Five trials are performed, with 1.5 minutes' rest between trials.
(3) After the third period, the members of Group B are told that they are under the average of Group A, and are encouraged to do better.

Results
Tabulate the results for both groups.

Conclusions
(1) Is there a significant difference between the groups in trials **1**, **2** and **3**?
(2) Is there a significant difference between the groups in trials **4** and **5**?
(3) What application do these results have for human performance?

Laboratory work 51: Performance and arousal

Hypothesis
An individual who is highly motivated is more likely to perform well.

Apparatus

- Handball
- Handball target.

Method

(1) Perform 10 hand passes against a wall.
(2) Repeat on a marked handball target. How many points can you get?

Results

Record the results and draw a graph to compare the performances in both trials.

Conclusions

(1) Which exercise was the most enjoyable or interesting?
(2) In which case do you feel the standard of handball was better?
(3) To what do you attribute the improved standard of performance?

Laboratory work 52: Signal detection and background

Hypothesis

Background colour influences signal detection.

Apparatus

- Coloured tennis balls
- Yellow or white tennis balls
- Tennis racquets.

Procedure

Play two games of tennis:
(1) Use balls that blend with the court colour, such as red on en tout cas, or green on plexipave.
(2) Use yellow or white balls on the same surfaces.

Conclusions

(1) How did the colour of the balls affect performance?
(2) What implications do your findings have in relation to the design of sports equipment?

Laboratory work 53: Selective attention

Hypothesis

That the ability to attend selectively to a sensory cue affects performance.

Apparatus

- Five yellow tennis balls
- One white tennis ball (or a colour different from yellow).

Method

(1) The catcher stands two metres from the line of six throwers.
(2) The throwers hold the ball in their hands so it cannot be seen.
(3) On the command of 'ready', the throwers hold the ball in one hand ready to throw it softly to the catcher.
(4) On the command of 'throw', all balls are thrown. The catcher attempts to catch the designated ball.
(5) Rotate the balls so that the odd colour is held by a different person.

- **Task 1**

Designated ball is odd colour. Score is number caught in 10 trials. Average the scores for five subjects.

- **Task 2**

Designated ball is a yellow ball thrown by a nominated student. Score is number caught in 10 trials.

- **Task 3**

All balls are yellow. The teacher gives the commands: 'ready'; 'throw'; name of thrower. The catcher must try to catch the ball thrown by the named player. Score is number caught in 10 trials.

Results

Record scores and draw a graph to show difference between tasks.

Conclusions

(1) What is selective attention?
(2) Which of the three tasks is the easiest to attend to selectively? Why?
(3) What are some examples of selective attention in your favourite sport?

Laboratory work 54: Signal detection

Hypothesis
That performance improves the earlier that signals are detected.

Apparatus
- Volleyball
- Volleyball net.

Procedure
(1) Three players take up position on one side of the net, while one player performs a series of 10 serves from the other side.
(2) Another player acts as coach and gives instructions.
(3) When the ball is served, the three receivers have their eyes closed until the coach shouts, 'Now!'
(4) For successive serves, the coach will call 'Now!' at various points along the trajectory of the ball.
(5) Another series of 10 serves is performed, with the receivers keeping their eyes open all the time.

Results
Graph the successful attempts to reach the ball against the timing of the 'Now!' signal.

Conclusions
Discuss the influence of early signal detection on performances.

Laboratory work 55: Motor performance and information reception

Hypothesis
That successful motor performance depends on adequate stimuli being received by the brain.

Apparatus
Soccer ball.

Procedure
(1) (a) Hold your arms straight out in front of you with the backs of your hands together.
 (b) Cross wrists and clasp fingers.
 (c) Moving your hands down and away from you, curl them under your wrists and up in front of your chest.
 (d) **Move the index finger of your left hand.**
(2) (a) Close your left eye and hold your left arm straight out in front of you, with your index finger pointing up.
 (b) Hold your right arm straight out to the right, pointing with the index finger.
 (c) Keeping both arms straight and your left eye closed, swing the point of the right index finger quickly round to hit the left index finger.
 (d) Repeat with both eyes open.
(3) (a) Hold the soccer ball with both hands.
 (b) Close both eyes.
 (c) Throw the ball up high and catch it.

Conclusions
Describe the results of (1), (2) and (3), and say why each skill was difficult to perform. In making your answer, use your knowledge of information processing.

Worksheet 29: Receiving information

(1) If all outside information (that is, external cues) was eliminated, on which information could a human being rely?
(2) (a) Which sense organs receive information?
 (b) Which are more important for motor skills?
(3) (a) Which can be processed faster — visual or proprioceptive information?
 (b) What significance does this have for performance in motor skills? — that is, compare the beginner to the skilled player.
(4) Compare the beginner and the skilled player in terms of:
 (a) Signal detection
 (b) Selective attention.
(5) Selective attention deals with which one of the following?

(a) Adjustment of subroutines
(b) Adjustment of schema programmes
(c) Attending to relevant information
(d) Teaching the whole skill at once.

(6) Which of the following is an example of selective attention?:
(a) Watching your team-mates block an opponent's spike
(b) Listening to music in the background while you study
(c) Watching an opponent's hand as he spikes
(d) Looking at the crowd watching you play a big game.

(7) Describe three techniques that you could use to alter the arousal level of players in your charge.

(8) The 'inverted U' hypothesis is a relationship between:
(a) Speed and anxiety
(b) Activation and performance
(c) Knowledge of results and knowledge of performance
(d) Input and output.

(9) Activation theory states that:
(a) For every given task there is a level of activation that is optimum for performance
(b) Simple tasks are best carried out at a low level of activation
(c) The ability to process information increases with an increasing state of arousal
(d) None of the above.

(10) For complex tasks the optimal arousal level is:
(a) The same as for simple tasks
(b) Higher than for simple tasks
(c) Lower than for simple tasks
(d) Of no real significance, unlike the level needed for simple tasks.

(11) 'Grand Final nerves' are said to cause players to make mistakes. Why is this so?

(12) Describe a sporting situation that illustrates 'redundancy'.

31. Storing and processing information

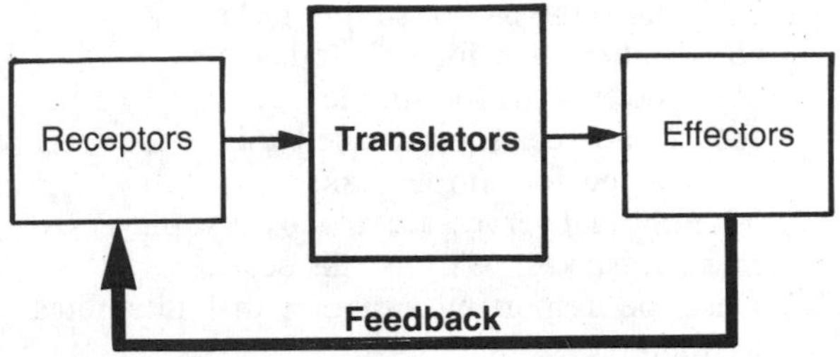

Figure 31.1

Timing mental processes

Your ability to make a response is limited by the speed with which you can react to stimuli.

(1) Reaction time

Reaction time is the amount of time between a stimulus and the first movement initiated in response to it. In other words, it is the period of time taken to process the stimulus information. For example, it is:

- The time between a ball being passed and the first movement of the receiver
- The time between the gun being fired and the first movement of a sprinter.

(2) Movement time

Movement time is the time taken to complete the task after it has been initiated. Movement time begins when movement of the body has actually started — not when the stimulus is applied — and ends when the movement of the body terminates the task.

(3) Response time

Response time is the addition of reaction time to movement time. In other words, it is the total time from the presentation of the stimulus to the completion of the task.

In the example shown in Figure 31.2:

If **reaction time** is 0.2 seconds, and **movement time** is 11 seconds, **response time** (the time taken for the 100-metre sprint) is 11.2 seconds.

The importance of reaction time

Reaction time and sport

In ball games, the player with the faster reaction time can let the ball travel further towards him or

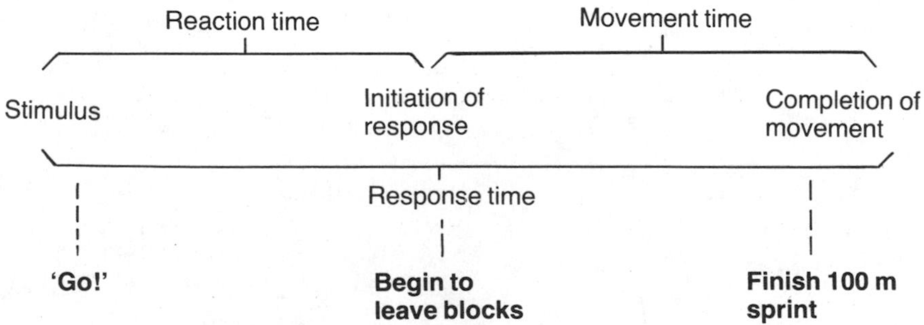

Figure 31.2

her before initiating an action. The same player has extra time in which to monitor the movements of players or the flight of the ball. Some examples include:

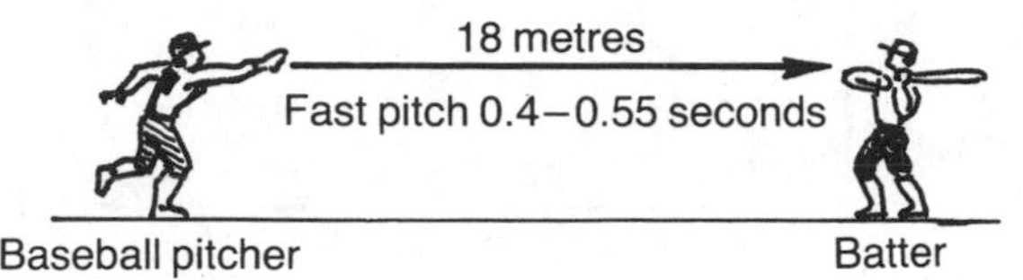

Figure 31.3

- **Baseball**

When playing baseball, players with a fast or normal reaction time can allow the ball to travel to within 5.5 metres from the plate before they begin to strike the ball, while players with a slow reaction time must begin when the ball is 9 metres from the plate. Players with better reaction times therefore have up to 3.5 metres extra to monitor the flight of the ball.

- **Cricket**

— The movement time in playing forward or back is about 0.3 seconds.

— The flight time of a ball bowled at 45 metres per second (100 miles per hour) is about 0.45 seconds.

— A player with a reaction time to a visual stimulus of 0.18 seconds has a total response time of 0.48 seconds (0.3 + 0.18). Therefore he needs to begin his shot before the ball is released by the bowler.

- **Muhammed Ali**

The time taken for Muhammed Ali to move his fist 40 centimetres was measured at 0.06 seconds — therefore he can hit you twice before you can react.

Reaction time is most influential when a response must be completed in a very short time. Compare the influence of reaction time for:

- A 100-metre sprinter
- A 5000-metre runner
- A chess player
- A netball player
- A batsman facing a cricket ball
- A batsman facing a tennis ball.

Reaction time and open skills

Reaction time is more influential in the performance of open skills than in the performance of closed skills. Compare the importance of reaction time when:

- Taking a penalty in soccer
- Attempting to save a penalty in soccer
- Addressing a golf ball
- Playing as a guard in basketball.

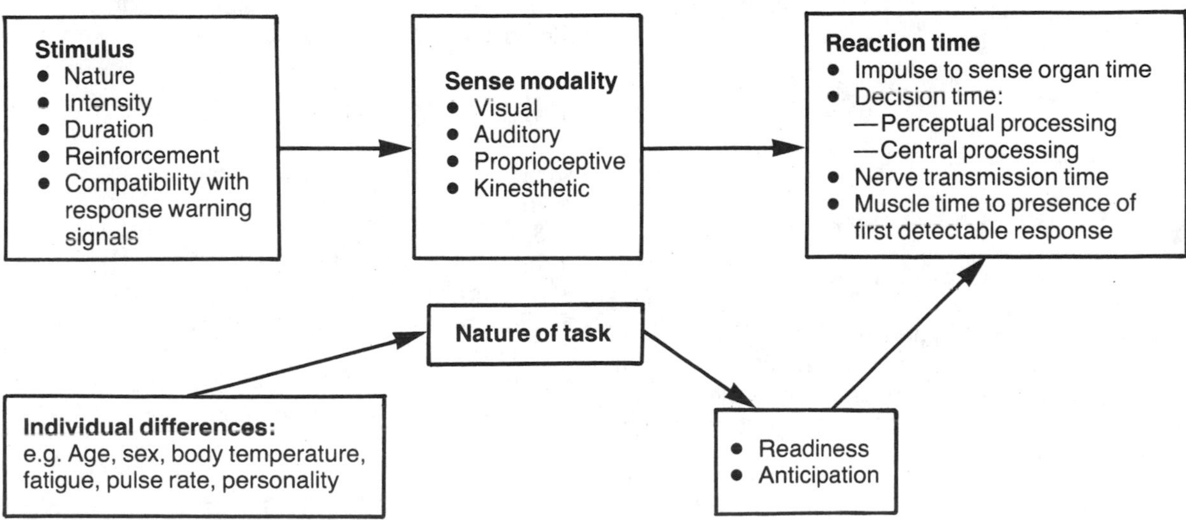

Figure 31.4 Factors affecting reaction time.

Types of reaction time

There are two general classifications for reaction time:

- Simple reaction time
- Choice reaction time.

(1) Simple reaction time

Simple reaction time occurs when a subject is asked to respond to a stimulus by making a specified response. There is one stimulus and only one correct response. Examples include:

- Pushing a button when a light comes on
- Reacting to a starter's gun.

(2) Choice reaction time

Choice reaction time involves either:

- A subject responding to several stimuli, each requiring a different response, where the subject must learn the proper response for each stimulus.

or

- A subject being presented with several stimuli and only one possible response. The subject must learn *when* to respond to a specified stimulus (see Figure 31.5).

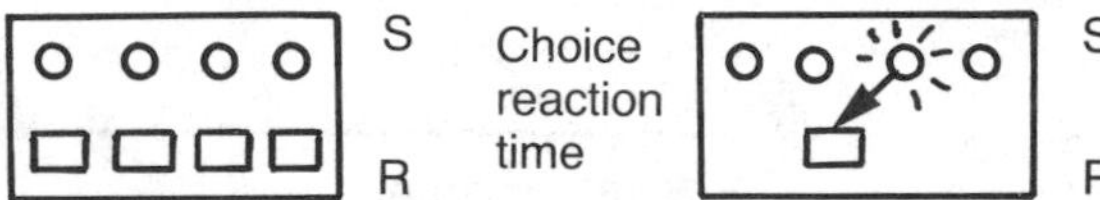

Figure 31.5

The more choices that you have, the more information you must process and the longer your reaction time (see Figure 31.6).

The complex motor performances required in ball games very often involve more than simple reaction time responses. The performer must make choices as to which response to make or which stimulus to respond to. For example, when playing basketball — you have just received the ball; will you dribble, shoot or pass? Which player will you pass to and which type of pass will you use?

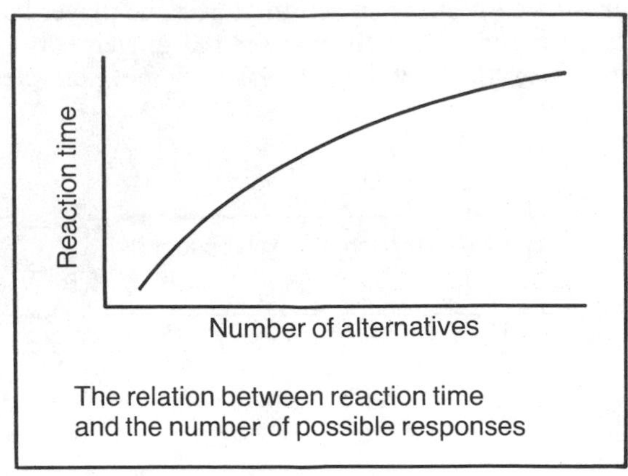

The relation between reaction time and the number of possible responses

Figure 31.6 Hick's Law.

Specificity of reaction time

(1) Task-specific reaction times

Reaction time is **specific to the task.** For example, your reaction time to a pass in basketball is unlikely to be the same as your reaction to a cricket ball bowled at you.

(2) Sense-specific reaction times

Reaction time is also **sense specific**. For example, you see things faster than your hear them. Sometimes you can see the smoke from the starter's gun before you can hear its bang. Which stimulus should the timekeeper respond to?

Influences on reaction time

Some influences on reaction time are:

- Age
- Sex
- Intensity of stimulus
- The probability of a stimulus occurring
- The presence or absence of warning signals
- The psychological refractory period
- The stimulus-response compatibility
- The type of instructions given
- The length of neural pathways.

(1) Age and reaction time

Reaction time decreases as a person matures. The reaction time of a five-year-old is almost double that of a 24-year-old. The difference is attributed to learning and experience. However, reaction times again increase in older people. (See Figure 31.7.)

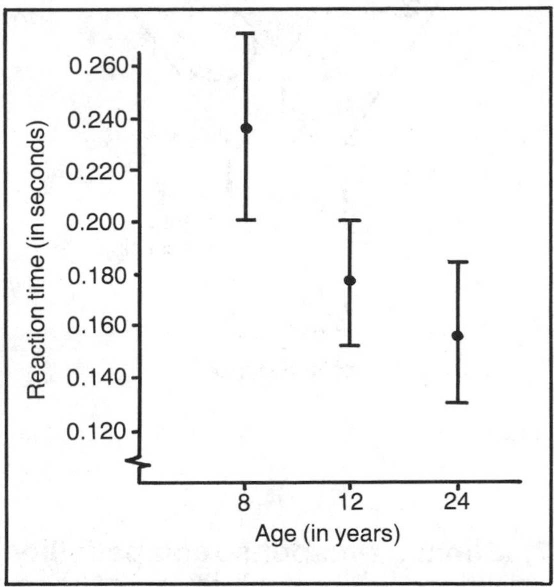

Figure 31.7 Mean reaction times and standard deviations, showing decreases in reaction time and variability with increasing age.

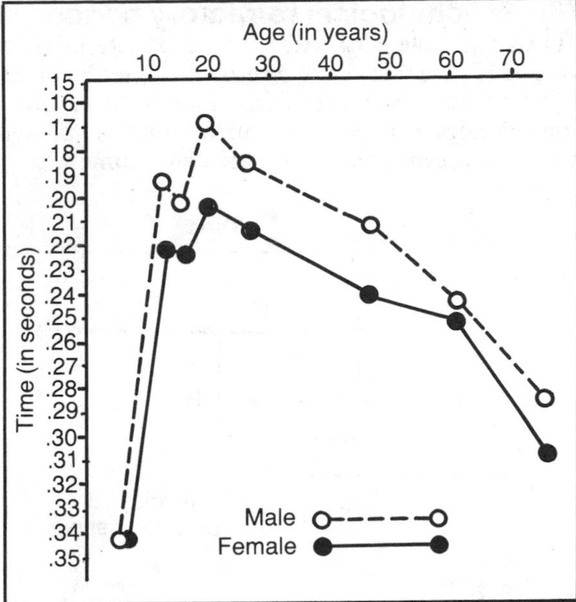

Figure 31.8 A comparison of reaction times of males and females.

(2) Sex and reaction time

Most studies show that males have shorter reaction times than females, but the increase because of age is slower in females. (See Figure 31.8.)

(3) Stimulus intensity

As the intensity of the stimulus increases, the reaction time decreases. For example, you take a shorter time to react to brighter colours, louder noises and larger balls than to ordinary stimuli.

(4) The probability of a stimulus occurring

If you know when a stimulus will occur, your reaction time might approach zero because you can anticipate the event. When you cannot predict the occurrence of stimuli, your reaction time is longer than when stimuli occur at regular intervals. (This is called **temporal uncertainty**.)

In volleyball, for example, the stimuli are much more predictable when the ball is volleyed back and forth during practice than when anticipating a spike during a game.

In sports where reaction times are faster, it is important if the probability of an event occurring is known. Is the bowler, for example, likely to bowl a bouncer, or is he completely unpredictable? Does your opponent always shoot and never pass?

It is important that drills simulate the game situation so that you can learn when an event is most likely to occur.

(5) The presence or absence of warning signals

You can reduce your reaction time by recognizing signals that indicate that movement is about to take place. Examples include:

- The good starter, who gives the ‘On your marks — set — go’ instructions at regular intervals
- The use of amber in a traffic light sequence so that the red signal does not take drivers by surprise
- The formulation by a team of a pre-game plan that a specific tactic will be employed on a given signal.

(6) Psychological refractory period

When a muscle is caused to react to a stimulus, a period of time (of up to 0.5 seconds) lapses before it can react to a second stimulus. This is the **psychological refractory period**, which limits the rate at which you can respond to successive stimuli.

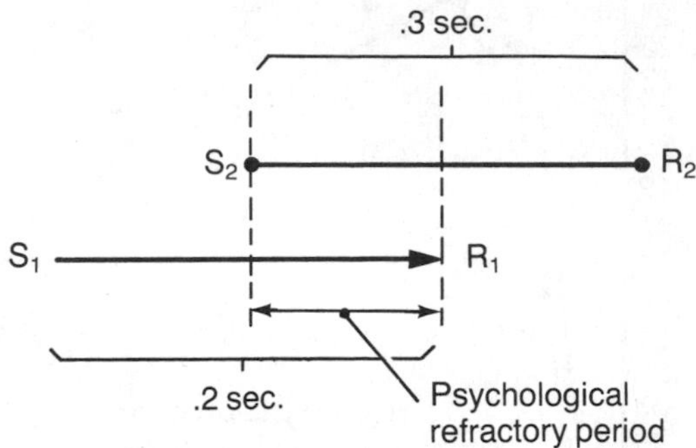

Figure 31.9

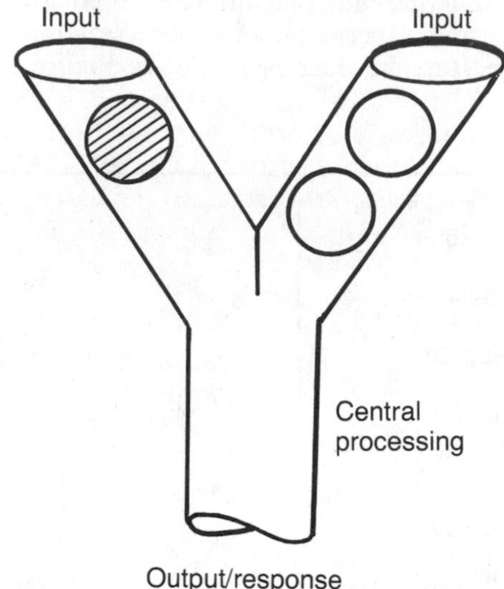

Figure 31.10

That is, the time elapsed between S_1 and R_2 is less than that elapsed between S_2 and R_2, if S_2 is between S_1 and R_1.

The psychological refractory period is caused by the increased processing time needed in the brain for the second signal. This added delay to a normal reaction time must occur before a modification to a committed course of action can be initiated.

The single channel hypothesis

The human uses a single channel for organizing responses from environmental signals. Therefore one signal must be cleared before another can be dealt with. This is what creates the psychological refractory period, and it is known as the single channel hypothesis (see Figure 31.10). Examples of the psychological refractory period include (see again Figure 31.9):

- **Table tennis**, where:
  - — S_1 = ball coming from opponent
  - — R_1 = decide to play a certain shot
  - — S_2 = ball hits top of net
  - — R_2 = must carry out the first shot before you can modify your shot.
- **Defending in soccer**, where:
  - — S_1 = opponent advancing with ball moving to right (fake)
  - — R_1 = you decide to move in that direction
  - — S_2 = opponent moves left quickly
  - — R_2 = you move right, then left.

(7) Stimulus-response compatibility

Stimulus-response compatibility is the degree of correspondence between a stimulus and its correct response. **The greater the compatibility, the shorter is the reaction time** (see Figure 31.11). If the

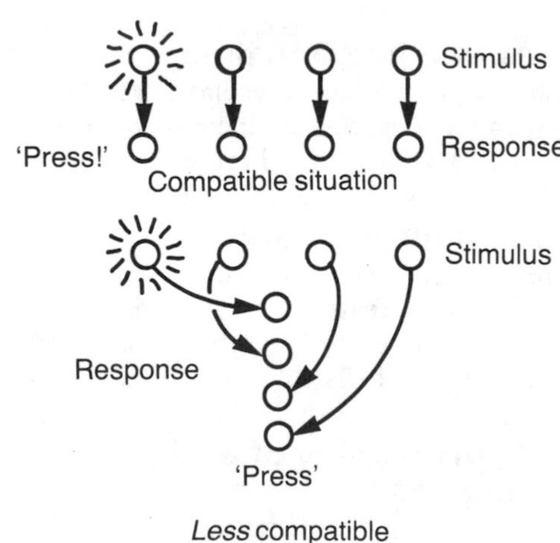

Figure 31.11 Light panel. A particular button must be pressed when a certain light flashes. Arrows link lights with the button to be pressed.

response required is the one that you are expecting or are used to, your reaction time decreases. If, however, the required response is not the one you would expect, your reaction time will be longer.

For example, the normal response to the stimulus of a dark room is to switch on the light — that is, push down the light switch. If, however, you go into a building where the lights are turned on by pushing the switches up or sideways, you may think twice before reacting.

Similarly, if suddenly you are placed in a situation where a red light signal means 'go', your reaction time to this stimulus will be slower than in a situation where green means 'go'.

When using a typewriter, the letter 'E' is usually printed when you press 'E' on the keyboard. However, if you put a maths symbol 'golf ball' in the typewriter, pressing the letter 'E' might produce something quite different. This would slow down your typing speed greatly.

In sporting situations, you can slow down the reaction time of an opponent by doing what he or she least expects. If, for example, an opponent in tennis sets herself in position to play a lob and then plays a passing shot, you could say that you were a victim of stimulus-response incompatibility.

(8) Type of instructions given

The directions given to a performer can affect reaction time. If you know what will happen, you can plan ahead. A coach can be particularly useful in providing such directions. For instance, a coach might alert you to an opponent's characteristic of pretending to pass but running on with the ball.

You can shorten your reaction time if you know what to look for. This is helped by instruction, which includes strategies aimed at developing good **signal detection** and **selective attention**.

(9) Length of neural pathways

Delays in reaction time are caused mainly by delays in central processing. Since nerve impulses travel at a particular speed (about 100 metres per second), the longer the neural pathways, the longer it takes for the impulses to travel. Short people, therefore, have a potential for faster raction times than tall people.

Short-term and long-term memory (STM and LTM)

Definitions

- **Short-term sensory storage**

Short-term sensory storage is the first 'compartment' into which information passes. This lasts about one second. If the information is not rehearsed, it is lost. Otherwise it passes into:

- **Short-term memory**

Information can be retained in the short-term memory for about 60 seconds. If the information is not further rehearsed, it is lost. Otherwise it passes into:

- **Long-term memory**

Long-term memory is the permanent retention of information through repetition or rehearsal, and is transformed into the permanent memory code (see Figure 31.12).

Short-term sensory storage

All the information coming in from the environment can be stored by the receptors for a very brief time — up to about one second. Within this brief time-scale, your short-term sensory storage capacity is limitless. However, much of that information will not be remembered because, by the time some of it has been processed, the rest has disappeared

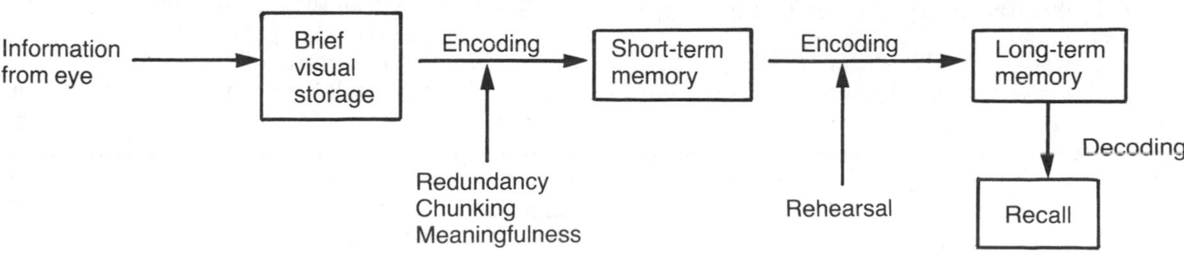

Figure 31.12

from sensory storage. Therefore the receptors have up to one second to select the stimuli to be relayed to the processor (selective attention). Therefore, the greater your ability to selectively attend and the quicker you can do so, the more efficient will be your short-term sensory storage.

Short-term memory

The short-term memory has a limited capacity, and is easily distracted. Your short-term memory is therefore measured by your ability to repeat information almost immediately after you have been exposed to it.

The short-term memory has a capacity for storing between five and nine items of information (Miller, 1956). However, this number of items can be increased by '**chunking**' the information so that you can remember between five and nine groups (chunks), representing perhaps 40 separate items.

For example, the sequence 1, 7, 6, 4, 3, 8, 2, 2, 9, 1, 3, 0, 6, 5, 2 can be more easily remembered if 'chunked' into 176, 438, 229, 130, 652.

Short-term memory and motor skills

The capacity of your short-term memory influences the learning of motor skills:

(1) Immediate information storage

In order to improve during practice, you must be able to store information about the performance you have just carried out, and compare it with information about your current performance. For example, when playing football, you might be practising a series of marks, but miss one. In order to take the next mark, you must be able to remember what you and your opponent did last time so that you can improve your performance.

(2) Giving of instructions

Take into account the capacity of the short-term memory when giving or receiving instructions. You cannot remember too many instructions given too quickly, and any interference or irrelevant information can distract your short-term memory.

Instructions should be brief, to the point, and should be given when the learner's attention is guaranteed.

After information has been handled in the short-term memory (STM), either it is released from the system or transferred into long-term memory (LTM) for future usage.

Long-term memory

Long-term memory is a store of past experiences that enables you to:

- Recognize and compare new stimuli
- Store subroutines and movement patterns to be used in constructing new responses.

Most importantly, the long-term memory stores response plans that, through practice, have become almost completely automatic.

Influences on long-term memory

Retention and retrieval of information from the long-term memory is influenced by:

(1) Rehearsal

If you do not use or rehearse information, you may forget it or take a long time to retrieve it.

(2) The meaningfulness of the information

You will find it harder to remember information that has little meaning or interest for you. For example, you are less likely to remember the sequence CPT, CAO, IWG, GDO, than the sequence CAT, DOG, COW, PIG.

(3) Speed of learning

The more quickly you learn a skill, the less likely you are to retain it.

(4) Degree of learning

Once you have learned a skill in the first place, you need to practise it in order to be certain of retaining it. This continued practice is called **overlearning**.

For example, you are able to score from a set shot in basketball. Why should you continue to practise this skill? As a skill becomes more automatic through practice, the conscious control of retrieval of information from the long-term memory decreases.

Feedback

Feedback refers to all the information that a performer receives about the performance of a skill, either during the performance (**continuous feedback**) or after the skill has been completed (**terminal feedback**). This information permits you, the performer, to profit from your experience. As you learn from your experience, you store feedback information in your memory, with the ability to recall it if necessary.

Functions of feedback

Feedback serves three functions:

(1) **Motivation**

When errors are pointed out, you are motivated to change your behaviour and correct your action. For example, you might want to improve your swimming time. Your coach says that your hand is coming out of the water first when your elbow should emerge first. You are therefore motivated to change your arm action.

(2) **Changing immediate performance**

For example, when practising archery, you receive feedback through your sense of vision, which tells you that the last arrow finished to the right of the bullseye. You realize that you must aim more to the left to improve your performance.

(3) **Reinforcement of learning**

For example, when playing soccer, you learn that you can make the ball rise by leaning back when kicking. You try this, and the feedback received tells you that the information is true.

The importance of feedback

Feedback provides information about your own performance; information that can be compared to a standard reference or yardstick — in other words, **how something should be done**.

Feedback is essential in the early learning stages of any skill, and the standard of performance that you reach eventually depends greatly on the quality of the feedback and how well you use it. At the beginning you depend greatly on **external feedback (knowledge of results)**. Also, in the early stages feedback is used more for making gross motor adjustments. Later you use feedback to make fine motor corrections to your performance.

Types of feedback

(1) **Continuous (concurrent) feedback**

Continuous feedback is that provided during the execution of the skill — for example, the information you gain from the 'feel' (kinesthesis) as you extend your arm to shoot.

(2) **Terminal (discrete) feedback**

This is feedback provided *after* the response has been completed — for example, the fact that the ball missed the goal.

(3) **Knowledge of results**

Knowledge of results and feedback are often used to mean the same thing. In fact, **knowledge of results is feedback that comes from some external source**, such as a teacher, coach, film, video or other performer. For example:

- The coach tells you that you need to tuck more in your somersault
- Watching a successful rugby tackle on video gives you feedback on the right way to tackle.

(4) **Internal (kinesthetic) feedback**

As shown already, **kinesthetic** stimuli are those provided by 'feel'. For instance, when performing a handstand, you can feel whether or not your legs are straight up in the air.

(5) **External (augmented) feedback**

External feedback is provided by visual, verbal or audible **cues**. For example:

- You can tell by the *sound* when a ball hits the cricket bat in the middle
- You can *see* how many bowling pins fall
- You can be *told* your time for a 400-metre sprint.

(6) **Positive feedback**

Positive feedback occurs when a **successful outcome** shows that your skill performance was correct — for example, scoring runs or a goal during a game. Positive feedback reinforces learning.

(7) **Negative feedback**

An **unsuccessful outcome** shows that there was an error in the performance — for example, when you failed to score from a shot at goal.

(8) **Knowledge of performance**

Knowledge of performance is feedback that you receive **about the actual performance or execution of a movement**. It is based on feedback received during the performance of a skill, and can be external or internal.

The following examples show the difference between knowledge of results and knowledge of performance:

- **Long jump**
  - Knowledge of results: 14 metres
  - Knowledge of performance: not enough drive with the take-off foot.
- **Tennis**
  - Knowledge of results: ball lands out
  - Knowledge of performance: racquet face too open.

The effectiveness of feedback

Feedback is most effective when it is detailed and given without delay.

(1) **Arrival time of feedback in relation to performance**
- Learners need to be provided with the knowledge of their results, or else they lose interest.
- Delayed feedback can be very detrimental to a learner's progress.

(2) **Precision of feedback**
The more precise the knowledge of results, the more accurate the performance will become.

Choosing the correct response

When performing a skill, you must choose the correct response to the stimuli received. For example, when playing football you may master the 'closed' skill of passing the ball. However, in the real game situation, you must decide whether or not it is appropriate to perform this skill at a particular time. Your decision will be based on such factors as:
- The state of the game
- The speed and position of the ball
- The position of team-mates or opponents
- Your own location on the field.

You might, in fact, decide that carrying the ball or trying to score is a more appropriate response.

The skilled performer can not only perform the skills but can assess the real game situation and give the correct response to each individual situation that presents itself. This ability is often lacking in a beginner.

'A player may have perfected the technique to receive the ball on the chest, direct it to his feet, and either run with it or pass it. If he selects this technique when surrounded by opposition players then he is exhibiting unskilled play' (Nettleton).

The ability to choose the correct response at the correct time, in the presence of the appropriate stimuli, depends on:
- Visual acuity
- Signal detection
- Perceptual ability
- The setting in which the stimuli occur.

Laboratory work 56: Meaningful labels

Hypothesis
That the short-term memory can cope better with meaningful information.

Apparatus
A set of 10 cards, each labelled with three letters. On five cards, the letters are meaningful — for example, CAT, DOG. On five cards, the letters are meaningless — for example, JRW, PPT, ZLB.

Procedure
(1) Flick through all the nonsense cards, allowing 30 seconds to recognize each one.
(2) Try to memorize the first label. Write it down. Look at it. Do the same for each label in turn.
(3) Repeat this process until you can memorize the whole series.
(4) Repeat the whole procedure for the set of meaningful cards.

Results
How many attempts did it take you to memorize:
(1) The nonsense series?
(2) The meaningful series?

Conclusion
Which list was easier to learn? Why?

Laboratory work 57: Organized stimuli and the short-term memory

Hypothesis

That the short-term memory can cope better with organized stimuli than with disorganized stimuli.

Procedure

(1) Write 12 letters on a piece of paper in a jumbled form.
(2) Show them to your partner for 10 seconds only.
(3) Wait 30 seconds. Then ask your partner how many letters he or she can remember.
(4) Now write the same letters in a straight line in alphabetical order.
(5) Repeat Procedures (2) and (3), using the line of letters in alphabetical order.

Results

In each case, how many letters did you remember?

Conclusions

Discuss the influence of organizing information on short-term memory capacity.

Laboratory work 58: Choice reaction time

Hypothesis

That the time taken to make a correct response increases with the number of stimuli that require attention.

Apparatus

- Stop watch
- Playing cards
- Pencil
- Paper.

Procedure

(1) Note the time it takes for you to separate red suits from the black (two groups).
(2) Note the time it takes for you to separate four suits — clubs, spades, diamonds and hearts (four groups).
(3) Note the time it takes for you to separate the aces.
(4) Note the time it takes for you to select the king of hearts.
(5) Note the time it takes for you to separate four suits of court cards (aces, kings, queens, jacks) and four suits of non-court cards (eight groups all together).

Results

List the time taken for each task.

Conclusions

Discuss the reasons for the differences in time taken.

Laboratory work 59: The importance of immediate feedback

Hypothesis

Immediate feedback is more effective than delayed feedback.

Apparatus

- Ruler
- Paper and pencil.

Procedure

(1) Attempt to rule (without looking) six 10-centimetre lines one above the other, without checking the result until the six lines have been ruled.
(2) Measure each line and note any errors — for example: 'line 2 = 8 cm, therefore 2 cm error'.
(3) Now rule one 10-centimetre line, without looking, but check for any errors immediately. Repeat this step five times, until you have six 10-centimetre lines.

Results

List the size of the errors made in each trial.

Conclusions

Compare and discuss the reasons for any differences in the results of Steps (1) and (3).

Laboratory work 60: Feedback and performance

Hypothesis
That feedback affects performance.

Apparatus
Volleyballs.

Method
(1) The class divides into three groups:
Group (a)
The subject receives no feedback.
Group (b)
The subject receives limited feedback — he or she is told only 'yes' or 'no' when asking about the success of the throw.
Group (c)
The subject receives as much feedback as possible — that is, complete information about where the ball went in relation to the target.
(2) The subject stands holding the ball about three metres from his or her partner, and with his back to the partner. The partner stands with his or her arms forming a circle in front.
(3) The subject attempts to throw the ball over his or her head (without looking) through the circle formed by the partner's arms. Each member of the group has 10 shots.

Results
Each member writes down the number of successful scores, using the following point system:
- Hit = 3 points
- Contact = 2 points
- Complete miss = 1 point.

Conclusions
Did the different amounts of feedback affect performance? Give reasons for your answer.

Worksheet 30: Storing and processing information

(1) How are reaction, movement and response time related?
(2) Which is shortest?:
  (a) Choice reaction time
  (b) Visual simple reaction time
  (c) Response time
  (d) Kinesthetic simple reaction time.
(3) How does the reaction time of an athlete compare with that of a non-athlete?
(4) Give examples of a sporting situation where:
  (a) There is only one possible response that can be made to the stimulus
  (b) There are several responses that can be made to the stimulus.
  How does the reaction time in (a) compare with the reaction time in (b)?
(5) 'Short-term memory is limited to three or four items at the most.' True or false?
(6) 'The short-term memory system functions more efficiently, provided that the material is meaningful.' True or false?
(7) 'The short-term memory system is not affected by interference.' True or false?
(8) When a performer learns a new skill, the information about the skill passes from the short-term sensory storage to the short-term memory. The passage of information from short-term memory to long-term memory is unlikely to occur without which of the following?:
  (a) Rehearsal of information
  (b) Retrieval of information
  (c) Masking of information
  (d) Decoding information.
(9) While you are waiting for your opponent to play a big forehand in tennis, the ball hits the wood and just drops over the net. This is an example of:
  (a) Poor visual acuity
  (b) Covert selective attention
  (c) Stimulus-response incompatability
  (d) Stupidity.

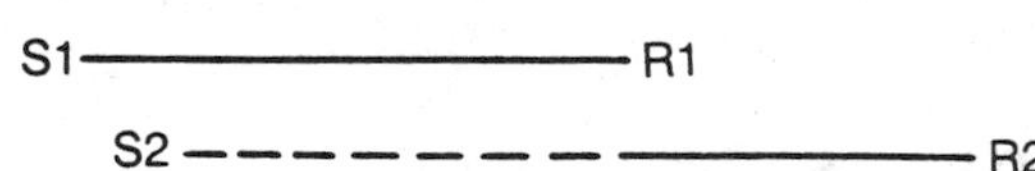

Figure 31.13

(10) In major ball games, a skilled player in possession of the ball often presents to an opponent a cue (S_1) that is closely followed by a second one (S_2). The player does this in an attempt to mask the actual intention of the second cue. This procedure is represented in Figure 31.13. The broken line indicates a central nervous system limitation, known as ....

(11) The psychological refractory period:
   (a) Is shorter than a normal reaction time
   (b) Depends on the senses used to pick up stimuli
   (c) Disappears if you use selective attention
   (d) Requires the second stimulus to be initiated within 0.2 seconds of the first.

(12) How does learning occur through feedback?

(13) What is the difference between knowledge of performance and knowledge of results?

(14) How can knowledge of performance and knowledge of results be used by the coach to improve performance?

(15) Note briefly:
   (a) Why is knowledge of results necessary for learning?
   (b) How precise should it be?
   (c) How often should it be presented?
   (d) When should it be presented?

(16) The visual feedback a basketballer receives as he watches his shot go through the basket is:
   (a) Knowledge of performance
   (b) Knowledge of results
   (c) Internal feedback
   (d) None of the above.

(17) Give examples from physical activity to illustrate:
   (a) Continuous feedback
   (b) Terminal feedback
   (c) Internal feedback
   (d) External feedback
   (e) Positive feedback
   (f) Negative feedback
   (g) Knowledge of results.

32. Motor control

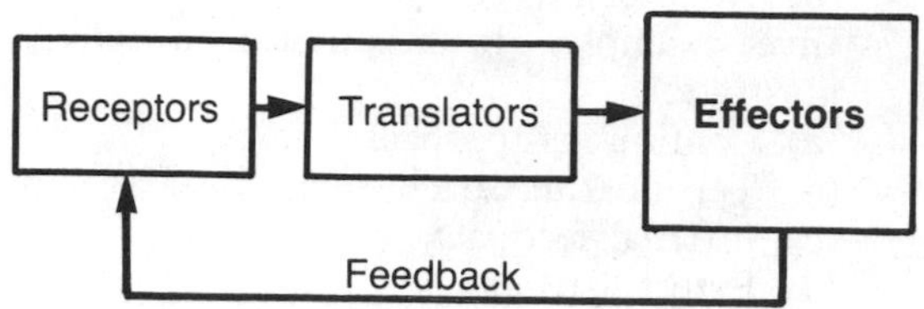

Figure 32.1

Making movements

(See Figure 32.1.) Once the central nervous system has processed all the relevant input and taken all the possible courses of action into account, appropriate signals are sent to the **effectors**.

The effector mechanism consists of the muscles that control the limb producing the desired response. Once the muscle selection process has taken place in the brain, the effector mechanism executes the movement in the proper sequence. The execution of the movement leads to **response-produced feedback**.

Co-ordinated movement involves:

- Selecting the appropriate muscles (**spatial control**)
- Activating them in the right order and at the right time (**temporal control**)
- Gradual muscle relaxation.

Skilled performance reflects just the right balance between **activated** and **inhibited** (relaxed) tissue.

Ballistic responses

Some movements have the following characteristics:

- Contraction of the muscle at the beginning of movement
- Relaxation of the muscle during the latter half of the movement which, combined with the contraction of the antagonistic muscle group, causes the limb to stop at the end of the movement.

This type of movement is called a **ballistic movement.**

According to Knapp: 'A ballistic movement is one in which the contraction of the positive muscle group relaxes long before the end of the movement so that there is a momentum phase free of muscular action.'

Examples of ballistic movement include kicking, throwing and tennis strokes. These skills rely on speed and accuracy.

The latter phase of ballistic movement depends on the build up of momentum in the limb during the first half of the movement. This momentum requires speed in the movement, so there is no value in slowing down these movements during practice. In ballistic movements, speed is vital to performance, so that the body part can be carried on by its own momentum. If you slow down in practice, you are not building up enough momentum to complete the movement and therefore you are actually practising a different motor programme.

Motor programmes: The open loop theory

When learning, you build in your memory an **overlearned** (**automated**) **plan of action** that specifies the sequential and temporal properties of a total skill. This is called an **executive plan**, or **motor programme**.

When this motor programme, stored in memory, begins to operate, it sends down a stream of motor commands that can control the entire movement independently of feedback.

As Figure 32.2 shows, motor programmes are both hierarchically and sequentially organized.

In assisting a learner to form an executive programme (motor programme), the coach should make use of previously acquired subroutines, which can be grouped under the new motor programme.

A motor programme includes many old executive programmes (now automated) and all the subroutines contained in those executive programmes.

Once you have formed a motor programme, your performance becomes rapid and co-ordinated, with feedback being used only from time to time to

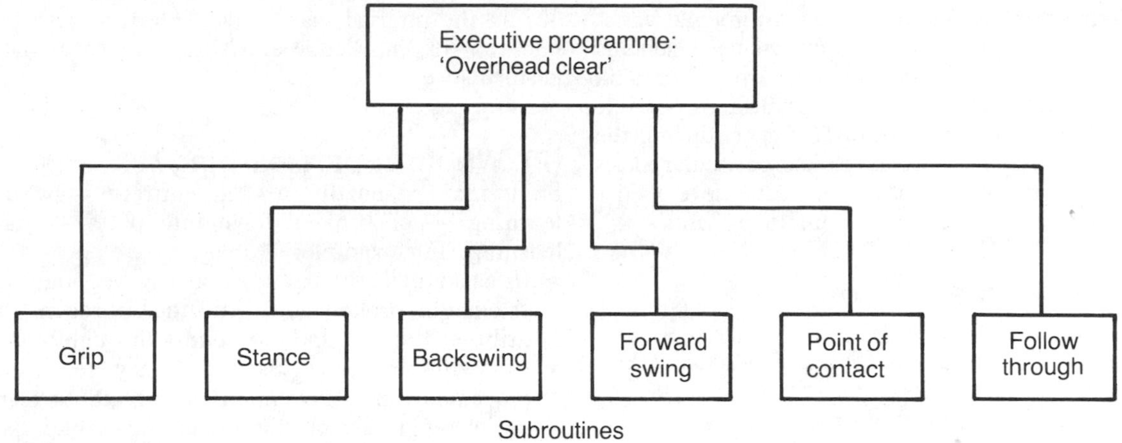

Figure 32.2 A computer analogy of the hierarchical and sequential organization of skill, using as an example the overhead clear in badminton.

correct relatively large errors in performance.

Feedback is not used to directly control movements in a sequence. However:

- Feedback gives information relevant to the starting position or the point at which to begin the programme.
- Feedback is necessary to learn new motor programmes.

The schema theory

Many skills require adjustments to be made to their performance in order to adapt to environmental changes. For example, when playing tennis you have a motor programme for the forehand drive, but you react to environmental conditions (speed and position of the ball, position of the opponent, etc.) in order to decide the exact nature of the actual stroke on each specific occasion.

The schema theory states that each possible variation of a given task does not require a brand new motor programme but that adjustments are facilitated by the development of a store of information known as **schema**.

As Martenuik puts it: 'The schema defines the general characteristics about the movement that must be organized to meet specific environmental demands as well as the goal of the performer.'

This schema is built up through practice and past experience, and can be divided into:

- Recall schema
- Recognition schema.

Recall schema

Recall schema is developed from information about the specific requirements of the task, and also about the external and internal environmental conditions that exist before the performance of the task. Recall schema **initiates** movement.

'The schema responsible for producing flexible and adaptive behaviour is based on a rich store of highly organized and integrated information developed through experience' (Martenuik).

Recognition schema

Recognition schema is developed from:

- Information received about the task by the senses during the performance of the task
- Information regarding the degree to which the task has been completed successfully.

Recognition schema **controls** the movement. 'The schema is also developed through simultaneous occurrence of information in the various sensory systems' (Martenuik).

Variability of practice

Successful performance of open skills depends not only on the **amount of practice** but also on the **variety of practice**. For example, when playing soccer, if you practise only long shots, you will have a reduced potential for adjusting your performance successfully to meet the many conditions you will meet during a match.

So that you can experience environmental variations, and so develop a comprehensive schema store, your practice in the latter stages of skill development should always be as close as possible to the competitive situation. However, during the earlier stages, you need to isolate particular skills from the environment until you have developed a basis on which to build your motor schema.

Types of instruction

The main types of instruction and practice conditions that can affect learning are:
- Massed and distributed practice
- Whole and part learning
- Drill and problem solving
- Mental and physical practice
- Serial learning
- Programmed learning.

(1) Massed or distributed practice?

- **Massed practice**

An instructor may decide to have his or her students consistently and continuously practise a skill without any breaks until the skill has been learned. This is called massed practice.

- **Distributed practice**

On the other hand, the students might learn the skill in short, frequent practice sessions interspersed with rest intervals or intervals of alternate skill learning. This is distributed practice (or spaced practice).

There has been long debate about which method provides the best results. Most of the evidence shows that distributed practice is the most effective in improving performance.

It has been suggested that massed practice is preferable for highly skilled or highly motivated performers, while distributed practice is preferable:
- In the early stages of learning
- When energy demands are high
- When the task is complex
- When motivation is low
- When the task is boring.

Knapp points out that fatigue is the greatest disadvantage of massed practice, since practising after one becomes tired serves no purpose. She puts forward the view that the opportunity to think about an activity during the rest intervals (mental practice or mental rehearsal) can improve performance, while practising another physical activity during the interval may in fact interfere with the retention of knowledge and skill, and so damage performance.

(2) Whole or part learning?

Skills may be taught in their entirety — **whole learning** — or broken down into parts — **part learning**. For example:
- In basketball, the lay-up shot may be taught all at once or broken down into the approach, the dribble, the aim and the follow through.
- In swimming, the instructor may teach leg movement, arm movement and breathing technique separately or the swimming stroke as a whole.

Some instructors combine the two methods — as **whole-part learning** — by having their students learn the whole skill at times, while at other times concentrating on parts of the skill, particularly those parts with which students are having difficulty.

There is no clear evidence about which method is best. Some researchers argue that the best method depends on which skill is being taught. Others say that whole learning is best for simple tasks and part learning gives the best results for complex tasks. The general consensus of expert opinion (for example, Knapp and Robb) seems to opt for the whole-part method.

(3) Drill or problem-solving?

- **Drill:** learning through repetition
- **Problem-solving:** learning through investigation and discovery.

There is considerable debate about the relative virtues of these methods.

Drill has been the conventional method of teaching motor skills. However Singer, while conceding that no firm evidence supports one method over another, makes the following observations:
- Closed skills are basically the repetition of movement patterns that may be better suited to the drill method.
- Open skills, that require a degree of creativity, adaptability and consideration of several possible courses of action, may be better suited to the problem-solving approach.
- In learning either open or closed skills, the problem-solving approach may lead to a better understanding of what is involved in the performance — for example: 'What caused the ball

to be hit into the net?' or 'Think about how you can increase your take-off speed'.

(4) Mental or physical practice?

Physical practice is the kind of practice with which most people are familiar: active participation in a particular activity.

However, mental practice can also be used. This is done by picturing a performance in one's mind, and involves no physical movement.

It consists of such activities as:

- Mental imagery
- Viewing films of someone else's performance
- Reading or listening to instructions.

Most evidence shows that a combination of mental and physical practice makes for the most effective learning. There is great debate about the ideal ratio between the two types of practice. However, mental practice before and interspersed with bouts of physical practice (see 'Distributed practice') is thought to best facilitate learning.

(5) Serial learning

Serial learning is the learning of the correct sequence of parts within a whole skill.

Motor skills often involve a series of discrete movements that must be performed in a particular order (see 'Serial skills').

(6) Programmed learning

Programmed learning is a modern innovation that uses special textbooks and teaching machines, and places the emphasis on self-instruction. These texts pose questions to the learner who, after answering, checks if he or she is correct. The learner then moves on to the next question, and so gradually teaches him- or herself.

Programmed learning is probably inappropriate for the learning of motor skills, but it can be useful in gaining knowledge about them. A good example of a programmed text that might be in your library is *The Mechanical Foundations of Human Motion* by Krause and Barham (see Bibliography).

Attention and motor control

In order to perform successfully, you need to be able to attend selectively to cues and to maintain attention during an activity. Attentiveness refers to your readiness to receive information and process it.

This state may fluctuate. For example, a tennis player may at times attend only to the ball, and at other times concentrate on the opponent, or even both.

When you are wide awake and interested, you are at a higher level of arousal and more sensitive to stimuli. In other words, you are more likely to pay attention and not miss out on any stimulus presented.

The skilled performer can filter out irrelevant information and choose only to respond to stimuli that are relevant to the desired response (**selective attention**).

The beginner must focus attention fully on the task in hand, and any break in concentration is bound to affect performance.

Dividing attention

The attention you require as you perform a motor task decreases with practice. As skills become automatic, you need less attention to one activity, and you are more able to perform that activity along with another. A skilled performer can therefore divide his or her attention between different tasks, and this is made easier when one or more of the tasks is regular and predictable.

For example, a skilled basketballer can bounce the ball (a reasonably predictable task) while also working out the positions of team-mates and opponents. Compare this with trying to dispossess an opponent while also attending to the positions of other players. In this case, both tasks are unpredictable.

Dividing attention is also known as **time-sharing**.

The single-channel Y theory (Figure 31.10, Chapter 31) shows that a person can attend to only one stimulus at a time. Any further stimuli are either disregarded or stored until the channel is clear to process them.

The ability to do two things at once (dividing attention) is developed from a thorough learning of at least one of the tasks so that attention to it is unnecessary.

You cannot perform several new tasks at once. Coaches need to take this into account by:

- Directing the student's attention to the relevant stimuli — for example, 'Watch the ball!'
- Transmitting only *one* new instruction at a time, as too much information cannot be absorbed by a beginner.

Anticipation and timing

- **Anticipation** is the process by which a subject prepares to initiate a particular response before the appearance of the appropriate signal. In other words, it is the ability to predict future events from early signals or past experience.
- **Timing** is the coincidence of a motor response with an external event.

Good anticipation assists the timing of a movement.

Types of anticipation

(1) Receptor anticipation

Receptor anticipation relies on **information from the external environment**. For instance, the preparation of a football player indicates that he is about to kick the ball. His team-mate uses this visual information to anticipate the flight of the ball, and this gives him more time to achieve the correct position to receive the ball.

(2) Perceptual anticipation

Perceptual anticipation relies on stored data — that is, memory. For instance, if you know your opponents' strengths and weaknesses, you can anticipate their likely moves.

(3) Effector anticipation

Effector anticipation relies on proprioceptive feedback ('feel'). For example, when batting in cricket, how hard you hit the ball allows you to anticipate how long it will take to reach the fieldsman and be returned.

Reducing reaction time

Anticipation allows you to overcome the delay caused by reaction time — that is, if you must wait for an event to occur before you begin your response, you may not be able to respond fast enough. Anticipation effectively reduces reaction time:

- Anticipation is learned and improved with practice.
- If your attention is focused on specific cues which provide you with advanced information about actions to follow, your anticipation is improved, your response time becomes faster, and your movements are made more smoothly. For example, the footwork of an opponent in tennis provides information from which you can predict the stroke he is about to play.
- You can be taught to recognize constancies in responses made by opponents so that you can predict an opponent's shots.
- If the time interval between stimuli is longer than normal, responses are usually early. If the time interval between stimuli is shorter than normal, responses are usually late. For example, you can make anticipation difficult for your opponent by:
  — Varying the pace of deliveries in cricket
  — Varying the speed of shots in tennis.
- By anticipating events, timing of responses becomes smooth and co-ordinated.

Speed and accuracy

There is a theory that, for skills requiring both speed and accuracy, it is better to slow down the movement and concentrate on accuracy while the skill is being learned. Then, once the movement pattern has been learned, it can be speeded up. For example, when fencing, practise the lunge slowly at first, then gradually speed it up.

An alternative theory says that changes of speed result in changes in the actual movement pattern, therefore slowing down a movement in practice is irrelevant to performance.

This is particularly relevant for ballistic movements, where the second part of the movement depends on the momentum built up during the first part — for example, a tennis drive.

Consequently beginners should practise skills at performance speed from the outset. Singer writes: 'When an individual practises at a high speed and then attempts to attain accuracy along with speed, he does not have to change the movement of the act. However, low speed practice transformed to a greater speed demanded in competition requires a new movement; a change in body control.'

Therefore it is meaningless to undergo slow practice of tennis strokes, golf strokes or the hammer throw, because there would be no build up of momentum during such practice.

Recent studies have arrived at several conclusions:

- In skills where speed is the predominant factor for successful performance, the most efficient results are obtained by an early emphasis on speed.
- In skills where both speed and accuracy are important, emphasis on both speed and accuracy from the beginning gives the best results.

- The least desirable results are obtained where accuracy is emphasized first and speed is introduced later.

Levels of movement control

There are two main levels of movement control for the human body:
- Reflex movement
- Complex movement.

(1) Reflex movement

The human organism is able to perform an assorted array of movement patterns, ranging from the most elementary motor acts to the most complicated stunts. The simplest of responses to a stimulus, S-R, is a reflex.

Reflexes do not usually require the attention of the higher levels of the nervous system. Some reflexes are inborn (such as swallowing) and some are learned. Learned reflex movements include:
- Pulling your hand away from a hot surface
- Drawing back when someone pretends to strike you.

Figure 32.3 shows the processes involved in a reflex movement.

(2) Complex movement

Different areas of the brain control different functions of the body. The cerebrum contains motor,

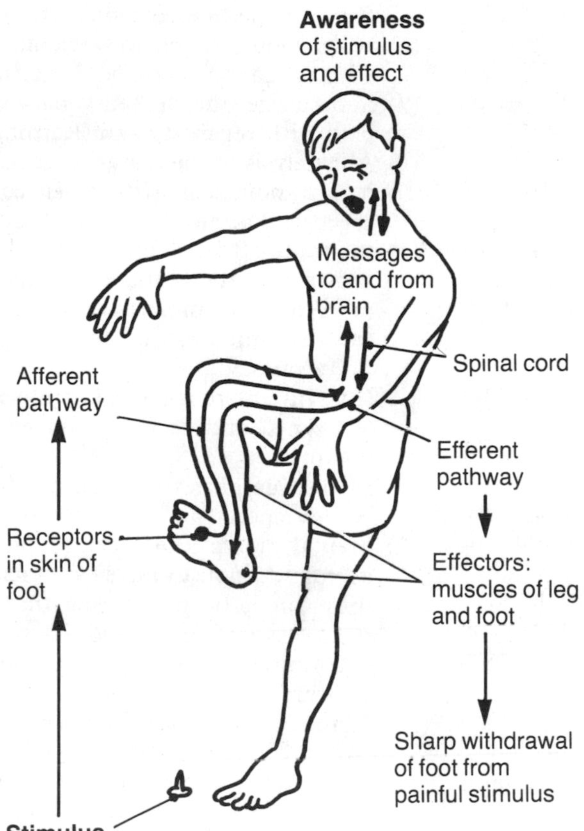

Figure 32.3 Reflex action demonstrating many reflex arcs.

sensory and association areas, which interact during the most complex of movements. For a skilled performer, many movements seem automatic or require no conscious control, but the pattern of these movements is a product of task familiarity, repeated experiences and refinement.

Learners move from crude and uneconomical behaviour, relying on external cues, to automatic smooth behaviours without the need to attend deliberately to the various components of the whole movment. The brain stores a number of movements from which a motor plan is selected.

Laboratory work 61: Dividing attention

Hypothesis
That skilled performers can divide their attention between different tasks, and this is made easier when one or more of the tasks is predictable.

Apparatus
- Soccer ball
- Basketballs.

Procedure
(1) (a) Take a soccer penalty kick when there is no goalkeeper.
(b) Repeat, but this time there should be a goalkeeper who attempts to save.
(c) Shoot a moving ball at the goal that is guarded by the goalkeeper.
(2) (a) Basketball dribble the length of the gym and shoot for goal. There are no opponents.
(b) Dribble around stationary players and shoot for goal.
(c) Dribble around players who are attempting to take the ball from you and shoot for goal.
(d) Six students dribble a ball inside the key. Each attempts to knock all the other balls out of the key while keeping his or her own ball under control.

Conclusions
(1) For each situation above, identify the stimuli that require attention.
(2) Which stimuli are predictable? Which are unpredictable?
(3) Compare each situation in relation to the hypothesis.
(4) How does the single channel theory fit in with your conclusions?

Worksheet 31: Motor control

(1) What are the major characteristics of movements made by skilled performers compared with those made by unskilled performers?
(2) Give an example of a ballistic response.
(3) Choose a skill. Draw a diagram to show the motor plan of that skill.
(4) What is the main difference between the attention that can be given by a skilled performer compared with that given by an unskilled performer?
(5) Briefly describe movement control under these headings:
(a) Reflex movement
(b) Complex movement.
(6) Why should some movements be practised with speed?
(7) Summarize the 'speed-versus-accuracy' debate with regard to skill learning.
(8) An analysis of the tennis serve has shown that it is a movement with equal components of speed and accuracy. Research into the area of the trade off between speed and accuracy has shown that the tennis coach should follow:
(a) An equal emphasis on speed and accuracy
(b) An emphasis on speed first, followed by accuracy
(c) An interchange of emphasis between speed and accuracy during the learning process
(d) An emphasis on accuracy first, followed by speed.
(9) Mental practice has been found to be a very useful addition to physical practice. To what uses can it be put during the normal competitive sporting situation? Use any sporting situation or situations to illustrate your answer.
(10) Name a 'whole' skill from a sport, and list the parts of it that could be taught separately.
(11) Note the difference in anticipation between skilled and unskilled performers.
(12) Effector anticipation:
(a) Involves the ability to predict the duration of some external event

(**b**) Involves predicting or anticipating the time a movement will take

(**c**) Involves the ability to order components

(**d**) Involves none of he above.

(**13**) Describe an example of anticipation using early signals in a sporting situation.

(**14**) Describe a sporting situation where past experience aids anticipation.

(**15**) What tactics could a skilled performer use to outwit an opponent with good anticipation?

33. Limitations of performance

Limitations of information processing

There are two main limitations to information processing within the human information processing system:

- Time limits
- Spatial limits.

These limitations to the information-processing system affect your ability to initiate and control movement and to process cues from the feedback mechanism.

Time limits

These include:

- The length of time that information can remain in the short-term sensory storage and the short-term memory.
- The time it takes to transfer information from the short-term memory to the long-term memory
- The time it takes to perform movements — that is, reaction time, movement time and response time
- The psychological refractory period
- The time during which you are exposed to stimuli
- The time it takes to retrieve information from the long-term memory
- The time it takes to receive feedback.

Limits of space

These include:

- Selective attention
- The number of items that can be stored in the short-term memory
- The single channel theory.

Spatial awareness limitations

Space is a concept developed in the brain. It is an essential perceptual component that must be interpreted by the visual mechanism. In order to learn, you must be able to relate your body kinesthetically in space and time to visual objects. If this does not happen, you will not be able to perform tasks requiring spatial relations.

For example, when playing baseball you might find yourself swinging at the ball too soon. This is an example of an inappropriate perception of space — you have not accurately interpreted the ball in space in relation to the bat, and so cannot hit the ball.

Time and space are inseparable qualities, but some motor activities — such as rhythmic exercises — are more highly loaded than others with the prediction of an event at a specific time relative to the person's position in space.

When playing soccer, if you are to kick to a receiver, you must be able to predict, with precision, the length of time it will take the ball to reach the specified spot, so that the receiver will not need to slow down in order to intercept the ball.

When performing gymnastics, you may not complete a somersault before landing because you have lost awareness of your body's position in relation to the floor.

Main aspects of spatial awareness

Spatial awareness involves two main aspects:

- **Kinesthesis** (body awareness or 'feel')

Kinesthesis is the **internal** awareness of the body and its parts in relation to each other — for example, are your legs straight in the handstand position?

- **Directionality**

Directionality is the ability to relate to **external** objects and space in relation to the body. For example, while playing a ball game you need to be aware of how far away the ball is, and how close you are to the goal.

Vision is our most efficient indicator of space. Vision can give us rapid estimates of space. We can look at a number of objects and locate them all simultaneously, but if we depended on kinesthesis we would have to locate them all independently.

Limitations imposed by motivational factors

The concept of motivation includes such ideas as:
- Innate drive
- Desire to achieve
- Level of aspiration.

You must have motivation before you can learn anything or perform well.

Motivational factors

Motivation limits performance, in that you are more likely to perform well if you are highly motivated, while your performance may be poor if you have no enthusiasm for it. Your level of motivation influences:
- Your selection of and preference for an activity
- Your persistence at an activity
- How much effort you put in
- How well you perform relative to your ability.

Effect of varying motivational levels

Many examples can be found to show that individuals perform differently when affected by different motivational levels. We've all heard stories of mothers performing incredible acts of strength to save their children, and of 'underdog' players who have shown incredible drive and skill on important sports days.

When identifying individual differences in motivation, consider the following:
- **The difference between under-, expected and over-achievers**

Motivation is only one factor in performance, and in order to find out how important it is, we need to ask questions such as:
— Is under-achievement caused by lack of ability or lack of interest?
— Can a person's motivation make up for lack of ability?
— Is the expected achievement based on ability or motivation?
- **The level of expectation**

If you expect to fail, you may not make the effort needed to succeed.
- **The need to achieve**
- **The need for social approval**
- **The level of anxiety**

The more anxious that you are, the more likely it is that your performance will suffer. (This is called over-motivation.)
- **The need to avoid failure or the limelight of success**
- **The individual goals of the person**

Desire or motivation can make a person of average skill excel.
- **The degree to which you feel that you are in control**

You are likely to put in a very different performance on the day you say 'It will happen anyway regardless of the effort I put in' than on the day you say 'If I really try I can succeed'.
- **Extrinsic and intrinsic sources**

(a) **Intrinsic motivation**
Intrinsic motivation occurs when you are motivated to indulge in an activity for the sake of the activity itself — for example, studying hard because you want to gain knowledge of a particular subject.

(b) **Extrinsic motivation**
Extrinsic motivation occurs when a person takes part in activity for the material gain to be received from it — for example, studying hard so that you will gain enough marks to gain a job or a place in a tertiary institution; or participation in sport for the money, honour or glory, rather than for comradeship, satisfaction and achievement. According to Singer, intrinsic motivation is more desirable and more mature than extrinsic motivation. It is also more effective.
- **Arousal level**

Tasks that are either too easy or too difficult are not motivational.
- **Past experience**

You are more motivated to perform well if you have had a recent string of successes than if you have failed so far.

Individual differences

Differences in age and sex

Performance varies from one individual to another. Age and sex are the most obvious differences between individuals. For example:
- Males perform better in some activities while females perform better in others.
- Children have a lower capacity than adults to process, store and remember information and they also have a lower level of motor control.
- Motor performance tends to deteriorate beyond the age of thirty. Some activities are best performed by people of a certain age. For example:
  — Female gymnasts and swimmers usually per-

form best in their teens
— Soccer players and basketballers perform best in their early to mid-twenties.

- Marathon runners and weightlifters tend to reach their peak in the late twenties and early thirties.

Sport	Age
Volleyball	26.2
Basketball	25.3
Foil fencing	27.5
Track: 100-metre	24.5
Marathon	28.3
Cycling	24.0
Weight lifting	27.2
Soccer	24.9

Figure 33.1

Figure 33.1 shows the average ages of competitors during the 1964 Oympic Games. **Note:** In addition, the average age of male swimmers was twenty, while male gymnasts had an average age in the late twenties, as did wrestlers. Figure 33.1 refers to male athletes.

Other differences between individuals

It is obvious that age and sex are not the only differences between people. Two boys of the same age are unlikely to perform identically, and indeed, the same boy may perform well in one activity but poorly in another. It is also true to say that an individual who fails in one activity will not necessarily fail in another.

Some other individual differences that contribute to different levels of performance include:

(1) Differences of ability
There is a wide difference between the abilities on which skills can be built. These include:

- **Physical abilities**, such as co-ordination, balance, kinesthesis and movement time
- **Mental abilities**, such as concentration, perception, reasoning and intelligence.

(2) Genetics
For many years, people have asked: 'Are great athletes born or made?' and 'Is there such a thing as a "natural" footballer?' No one would claim that anybody's ability or performance is caused purely by genetic factors or solely by environmental experiences. The end product is a combination of both heredity and environment. However, the relative contribution each makes to a person's level of attainment varies from one individual to another.

(3) Physical characteristics
Your performance is decided very much by such physical characteristics as:

- Body build
- Height
- Weight
- Strength
- Flexibility
- Endurance
- Vision
- Hearing
- Touch.

The part played by particular physical characteristics in particular sports is shown in Figure 33.2.

(4) Emotional stability
Your performance can be affected by high levels of tension, anxiety and stress, either permanent or temporary.

(5) Growth and development
People mature at differing rates of physical and mental growth, resulting in either late or early maturation. Chronological age is not an accurate indication of maturity.

It is important that activities taught suit the stage of development reached by the child. For example, because a child has limited information-processing capabilities, he or she is distracted easily and has a low concentration span.

Some children may have the physical ability to perform, but are given tasks beyond their information-processing ability at a particular stage of growth. Students affected in this way may feel frustration, loss of motivation and a low desire to continue learning. Similarly, if a taught activity is too simple, a student will feel only boredom and lack of motivation.

(6) Previous instruction and experience
The beginner is likely to have a lower level of performance than somebody who already has experience and knowledge of a given activity. Also, the quality and type of instruction experienced varies among individuals.

(7) Motivation
Performance may be said to equal learning plus motivation. An activity must be interesting and appealing to most students, but each student will have a different level of motivation and reason for learning the activity.

Sport	Morphology
Basketball	Tall and lean
Canoeing	Large and stout
Cycling	
• Long races	Short and lean
• Short races	Short and stout
Fencing	Lean
Gymnastics	Small and stout
Hockey	Small and a little stout
Rowing	Tall
Soccer	Small and a little stout
Swimming	
• Divers	Small
• Freestylers, back strokers	Large and lean
• Breast strokers, butterfly swimmers	Stout
Track and field	
• Hurdles	Large and lean
• Short dashes	Small
• Middle distances	Larger
• Long distance, marathon runners	Small and lean
• High jumpers	Large and lean
• Long jumpers	Lean and not so large
• Pole vaulters	Average
• Throwers	Large and stout
Volleyball	
• Forward players	Tall and lean
• Back players	Small and stout
Water polo	Large and stout
Weight lifting	Stout
Wrestling	Stout

Figure 33.2 Physical evaluation of competitors at the 1964 Olympics.

(8) Environmental conditions
Modifications to the environment influence the learning experience of individuals and, ultimately, the level of performance. These can include such factors as distractions, the standard equipment and weather conditions during performance, as well as the types of instruction, training and equipment used in the learning and preparation process.
(9) Sociocultural influences
Individuals are affected differently by varying social conditions, such as those involving competition, co-operation or performing in front of an audience.

In addition, cultural influences such as national tradition, family background, friends and economic position play a part in dtermining which activities an individual indulges in. For example:

- A southern European label might be pinned to soccer, so discouraging Australian students of Anglo-Saxon descent from playing soccer.
- Polo players and show jumpers are not usually expected to come from the same socioeconomic group as those who are involved in football or boxing.
- Very few Negroes are seen in US swimming or tennis teams. One reason given for this is that football or basketball are less costly to take up at the beginner's level.

Laboratory work 62: Short-term and long-term retention

Hypothesis
That retention of information in the short-term memory is affected by time and interference, but that this is not the case for long-term memory.

Apparatus
- Overhead projector
- Transparency
- Paper
- Pencil
- Storybook.

Procedure
(1) Randomly divide the class into two groups.
(2) Write down 10 numbers on the transparency, and position the overhead projector so that everyone can seen the numbers on the screen.
(3) Switch on the projector for 10 seconds.
(4) (a) Group A should immediately write down the numbers and practise learning the correct sequence.
(b) Group B will read a passage of a story for 60 seconds.
(5) After 60 seconds, both groups will write down the 10 numbers in the correct order.
(6) Both groups should write down the names of 10 colours.

Results

(1) Tabulate the number of correct responses for each individual.
(2) Work out the average number of correct responses in each group.

Conclusions

(1) What were the differences between the average scores of the two groups?
(2) Suggest reasons for these differences.
(3) Discuss the results in relation to the difference in the retention capacities of short-term and long-term memory.

Laboratory work 63: Limitations of short-term memory

Hypothesis

That short-term memory can cope with only limited amounts of information.

Procedure

(1) Write your phone number on a piece of paper. Don't let anyone see it.
(2) Show the number to your partner for five seconds only.
(3) Wait 30 seconds, and ask your partner if he or she remembers the number.
(4) Write down 20 letters of the alphabet in random order.
(5) Repeat (2) and (3) above. Note: The letters must be remembered in the correct order.
(6) What conclusions can you draw from your results?

Laboratory work 64: Anxiety and performance

Hypothesis

That levels of tension or anxiety affect performance.

Apparatus

Appropriate gymnastic equipment.

Procedure

(1) Select a gymnastic skill that each subject can perform well on the mats — for example, a handstand, headstand, cartwheel or forward roll.
(2) Have the subject perform the skill on top of a vaulting horse or balance beam.

Conclusions

Which of (1) or (2) was performed better or with greater ease? Why?

Worksheet 32: Summary of information processing

(1) Define:
  (a) Reaction time
  (b) Cognitive phase
  (c) Subroutine
  (d) Pacing
  (e) Open skill
  (f) Discrete skill
  (g) Signal detection
  (h) Reflex movement
  (i) Perception
  (j) Task vigilance
  (k) S-R compatibility
  (l) Knowledge of performance
  (m) Ballistic response
  (n) Recall schema
  (o) Distributed practice.
(2) Draw a model that represents the human as an information-processing system.
(3) Outline the differences between a skilled performer and an unskilled performer in terms of processing information.
(4) 'The processing of information is limited by time and space.' Discuss.
(5) Give two examples of extrinsic motives for participation in sport.
(6) Give two examples of intrinsic motives for participation in sport.

34. Overview of skill acquisition

Characteristics of skill learning

Definition
Learning
Motor performance
Executive programs
Subroutines
Types of skill
Phases of skill learning
Models of information processing

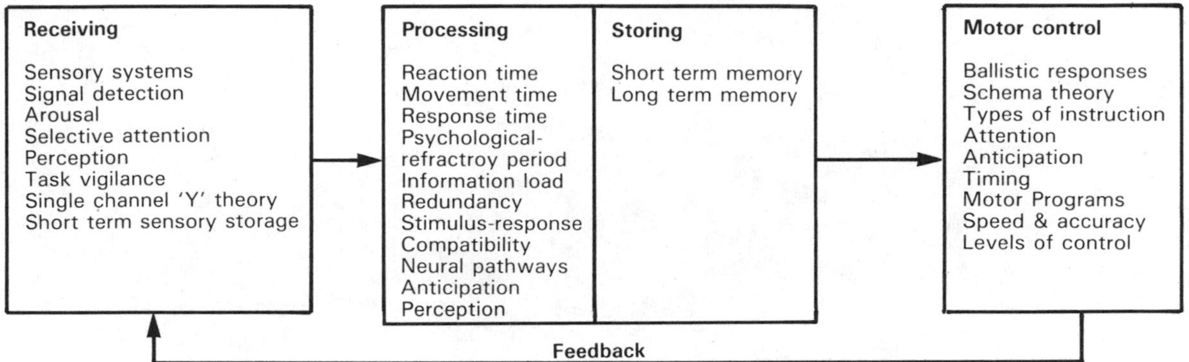

Limitations on Performance

Psychological refractory period
Time
Space
Attention
Motivation
Individual Differences

Part Five

Historical issues related to physical education

35. Why look at history?

History is much more than merely looking into the past. It is impossible to understand the complex issues of our world without an appreciation of how today's way of life has evolved through time. Furthermore, today's events are history in the making, determining what lies ahead.

History is, then, a look into the past, the present and the future.

There are many periods of history worth including in any investigation into the evolution of sport and physical education. There are also numerous issues in the current history of sport and physical education which deserve consideration.

The following section offers a sample of possible areas of investigation. This information should not be seen as comprehensive reference material, but as a basis for further research. Also, you do not need to research all the material. Instead, it is worth making a careful selection of areas that interest you, and investigating them. Some areas of interest are not included, but can be studied using parts of this resource as a model. For example, the information on lawn tennis can be adapted for studying other motor activities.

36. Education and sport in Ancient Greece: Outline

Education in Ancient Greece

As Figure 36.1 shows, Greece was divided into several city-states, the most famous of which were Athens and Sparta.

Athens

In Athens, formal education was mainly for boys. Girls stayed at home and learned domestic skills from their mothers.

Athenian parents had a legal obligation to send their children to primary school. The three main subjects that they learned were letters, music and gymnastics. There was also an apprenticeship system for learning trades.

The Athenians recognized that physical education benefited the spiritual and intellectual development of the child as well as his physical development. Physical education was also valued as an aid to military training.

Pupils were trained in physical education at a **gymnasium** or a **palaistra**. The main activities were wrestling, running, jumping, discus and javelin.

Sparta

In Sparta, boys underwent what is still called a 'Spartan education':

- They left home at an early age
- They were brought up by the State
- Almost all their education was physical education directed towards military training.

Spartan girls were encouraged to take part in formal education.

Activities taught in Ancient Greek physical education (gymnastics)

Wrestling

The Ancient Greeks taught wrestling in order to develop both mental and physical prowess. Greek boys wrestled in mud and dust, which made grasping and balancing very difficult.

The aim of Greek wrestling was to lay out one's opponent so that both his shoulders touched the ground. Doing this three times constituted a victory. Striking was not allowed.

There were two types of wrestling:

- **Rolling**, as described above
- **Standing:** the wrestler had to fell his opponent without losing his own balance.

Running

This was another traditional exercise, which the Ancient Greeks valued for leg strength and developing the lungs. Athletes ran in sand.

The main races were:

- The **stadium** (approximately 200 metres)
- The **double** (approximately 400 metres)
- The **dolic**, a long-distance race of up to 5 kilometres.

Jumping

Greek children leaped over pits of varying widths, according to their age. While jumping, they swung a lead weight in each hand.

Discus and javelin

The Ancient Greeks taught throwing of the discus to develop upper body strength, and throwing the javelin to increase visual acuity.

The **discus** was a bronze disc that could be thrown in two ways:

- For distance
- For height.

The **javelin** was also used in two ways:

- For throwing at a target
- For distance.

Other activities

Ancient Greek students also learned ball games, games with the hoop, military skills and riding. The teacher supervised all activities, coaching and demonstrating where required.

Black Sea
Epidamnus
Illyria
Thrace
Byzantium
Pangaeus
Maronea
Sea of Marmara
Pella
Pollonia
Amphipolis
Macedonia
Thasos
Khalkidhiki
Samothrace
Pidna
Olynthus
Dardanelles
Mt Olympus
Potidaea
Imbros
Phrygia
Troy
Epirus
Lemnos
Thessaly
Corfu
Larisa
Aegean Sea
Lesbos
Thermi
Pergamum
Pharsalus
Skyros
Cuma
Lydia
Leukas
Phocaea
Aetolia
Euboea
Phocis
Chalcis
Eretria
Chios
Izmir
Sardis
Delphi
Eretria
Clazomenos
Ithaca
Boeotia
Thebes
Marathon
Achaea
Eleusis
Megara
Ionia
Ephesus
Meander River
Sicyon
ATHENS
Andros
Elis
Corinth
Attica
Samos
Elis
Zakynthos
Pisa
Mycenae
Tenos
Icaria
Priene
Arcadia
Aegina
Caria
OLYMPIA
Argos
Epidaros
Sounion
Miletus
Peloponnesos
Argolid
Mykonos
Didyma
Laconia
Delos
Naxos
Messene
Paros
Halicarnassus
Messenia
SPARTA
Pylos
Syphnos
Kos
Melos
Amorgos
Lycia
Cnidos
Thera
Rhodes
Cythera
Karpathos
Crete
Kydonia
Kasos
Knossos
Mallia
Gortyna
Phaestos

Figure 36.1 The ancient Aegean world.

Figure 36.2 **Education at Athens** was less brutal than at Sparta. An Athenian boy practised athletics, but he also learned music and poetry. Here a boy is being heard reciting a piece of poetry that he has learned—probably Homer, whose works had to be known thoroughly. Written exercises were done on wooden tablets covered with wax. A pointed metal instrument was used. The man on the right is a slave, though you could not tell this from his dress. He escorts the boy to and from the lesson. Like other older men he is bearded and carries a long walking stick. All three of the group have fairly long hair, kept in place by a band, but not as elegantly plaited as the wrestler's or the banqueter's.

Research work 1: Physical education in Ancient Greece

The following assignments require you to conduct your own research, using a wide range of resources.

Research topics

(1) Compare the education systems of Athens and Sparta.
(2) Compare the education of boys and girls in Ancient Greece.
(3) What was the role of physical education in:
  (a) Athens?
  (b) Sparta?
(4) What was the political structure of Ancient Greece? How did it differ between Athens and Sparta?
(5) Find out about physical education programmes offered in schools today.

Possible influences on today

(1) The philosophy of educating the whole person
(2) The formal education system
(3) Our political structure
(4) The role of women in society and in sport
(5) The concept of leisure time
(6) The development of athletics
(7) The development of wrestling.

Essay suggestions

(1) Compare the type of physical education a boy would have received in one city-state of Ancient Greece with that experienced by a boy in modern Australia.
(2) Outline the influence that the philosophies of Plato and Aristotle have had on the development of modern physical education programmes.
(3) Discuss the place of physical education in Ancient Greek society, with special reference to any possible influences on modern physical education.
(4) The Ancient Greeks treated boys and girls differently with regard to physical education. Can the same be said of today's physical education?

37. The Olympic Games: Outline

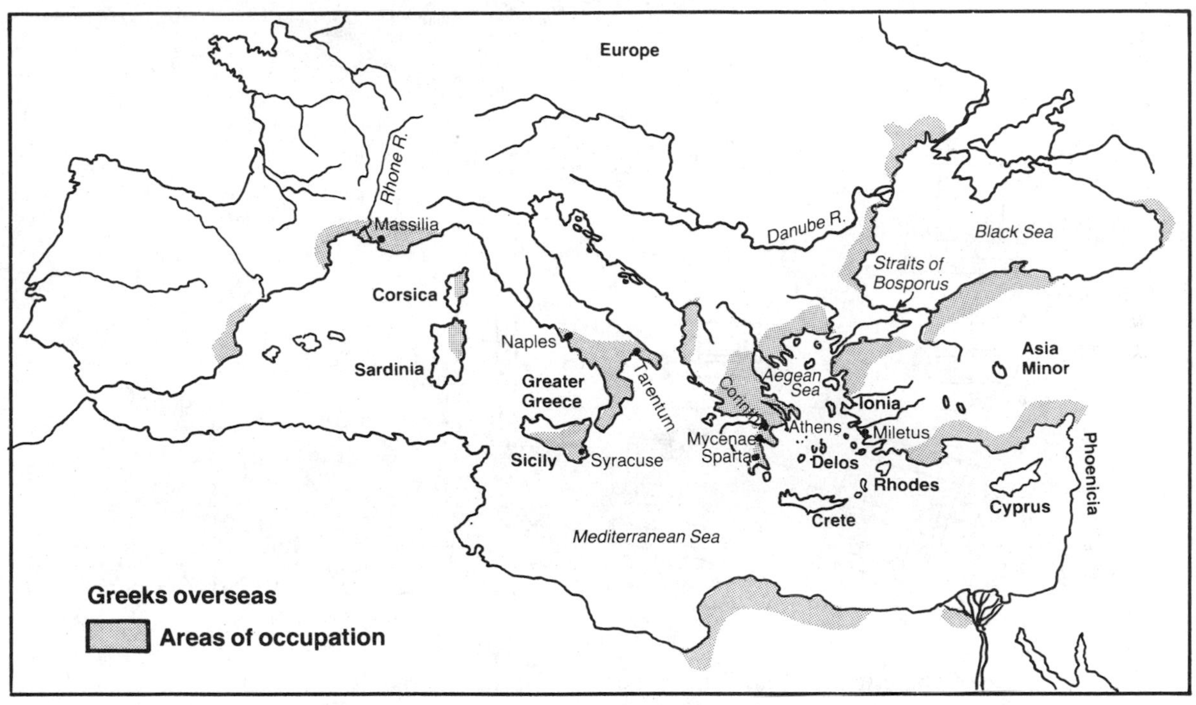

Figure 37.1 The Mediterranean and Black Seas in the classical period, showing Greek settlements.

The Ancient Olympic Games

In Ancient Greece, sporting fixtures took place regularly as part of religious festivals. These fixtures were held in a wide variety of locations, but the most famous one took place at Olympia — the Olympic Games.

The festival of Olympia was essentially a religious occasion, where people offered sacrifices to Zeus.

The first recorded Olympic Games were held in 776 BC. Their fame spread as Greeks emigrated to all corners of the world that surrounded the Mediterranean Sea (see Figure 37.1), and increased when Greece's Alexander the Great conquered most of the known world. The Olympic Games, which brought together athletes from all over the world, were seen as an opportunity to demonstrate Greek supremacy and as a means of promoting peace and co-operation among nations.

Organization of the Olympics

The Olympic Games operated under strict rules, which included a calling of a truce between warring nations. No weapons were allowed near Olympia,

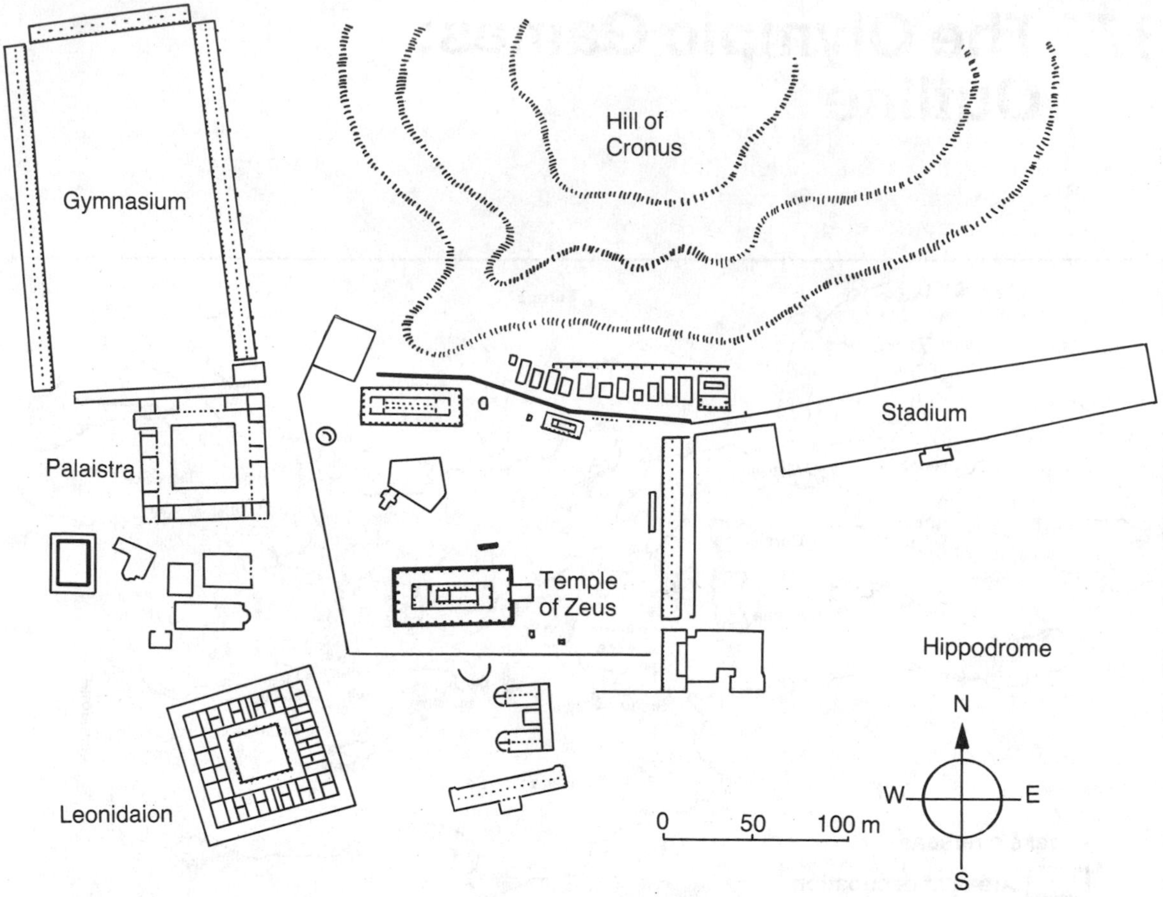

Figure 37.2 **Plan of ancient Olympia.** Centre: the Sacred Grove (Altis). Right: Stadium and Hippodrome, where the Games took place. Left: training and guest centre. The remaining buildings include baths, treasuries and council chambers.

and fines were imposed for violations of the truce.

The athletes themselves were bound by a code that included:

- The outlawing of slaves, barbarians and law-breakers
- The taking of an oath
- A prohibition against killing opponents
- A ban on unfair tactics
- A ban on bribery
- A ban against arguing with officials.

Athletes observed a strict training routine when preparing for the Games.

The capacity of the stadium of Olympia was 40 000 men. No women were allowed. The games opened and closed with great ceremony.

As the following article shows, Ancient Greek athletes and officials had many of the same problems faced by Olympians today, especially in the matter of amateurism and professionalism:

EVEN NAKED THEY WEREN'T LILY-WHITES

Los Angeles. — Amateur . . . the ancient Greeks actually did not have a word for it. But the French did, and it was and is commonly used to denote anyone doing anything for the love of it.

Athlete . . . aha, the Greeks certainly had a word for that and it identified, literally, a 'competition for a prize'.

And with those definitions as starting blocks, David Young, professor of classics at the University of California, Santa Barbara, is ready to publish proof that amateurism in ancient Greek athletics, including their Olympic Games, is the biggest myth since Achilles's heel.

'People have the notion that amateurism existed in the ancient games and professionalism came along as a corruption,' Young said.

'The upshot of what I'm going to say is that there was never the concept of amateur athletics in the original games, which flies in the face of the whole tradition.'

When Young's manuscript becomes 'The Myth of Greek Amateurism' (to be published shortly by Ares Publishers of Chicago), it also will claim:

- In Plato's time, the winner of the 200-metre sprint at an Athens meet would receive 100 amphoras (the 10-gallon size) of olive oil, which he could export tax-free. Translated into today's currency, that comes to $US67,800 — a purse fat enough to entice John McEnroe into two weeks of tournament tantrums.
- Like many modern competitors, Greek athletes followed rich, annual circuits. (In the early fifth century, boxer-wrestler Theogenes of Thasos claimed 1300 victories in a 22-year career.)
- Although ancient Olympic Games offered no prizes beyond the olive wreath, an athlete's home city made sure its heroes never were reduced to selling used chariots. The Athenian treasury, for example, paid its Olympic champions 500 drachmas — the equivalent of $US338,800 (tax free) — or the amount a skilled Greek craftsman might have earned in 14 years.
- Los Angeles's sense of loss at Steve Garvey's switch to San Diego apparently was nothing compared to the grieving in Croton in 484 BC. That's when their Olympic sprint champion Astylos went the way of every free agent since, changed franchises and in the 480 BC Games ran for Syracuse. It must be pointed out that Astylos did not switch uniforms because Greek athletes competed naked.
- There is ample evidence, Young said, to suggest that Greek medical schools (with much of their emphasis on health, diet and sports) recruited athletes in much the same way that colleges today scout high schools. Athletic purses included cash, leather coats or art objects in silver, gold or bronze, and many over-the-hill athletes pursued new careers as professional coaches.

And, Young insists, any belief that amateurism in today's Olympics is a tribute to the purity and non-professionalism of the ancient Olympics is misguided.

'Amateurism is a modern concept originating in 19th-century England to justify an elitist athletic system that sought to bar the working classes from competition,' Young says. 'Coubertin (Baron Pierre de Coubertin, the French educator who pioneered the 1896 restart of the Olympic Games) was a dyed-in-the-wool anglophile who loved the British school system, rugby in particular, and decided its way, where the intention of sports was to have the gilded youth gather, was the right way.

'And the reason it hasn't come out (before) is because the classical scholars who have written the books on ancient athletics were sympathetic to the goals of the 19th-century movement.'

What Young sees as the background for a 'calculated deception' by the 'idealistic, elitist and naive founders of the modern Olympics,' intent on keeping working-class types in the bleachers, is supported by two examples.

There were, he notes, the 1866 by-laws of the Amateur Athletic Club in England, which said that the organisation existed 'to afford gentlemen amateurs the means of practising and competing versus one another without being compelled to mix with professional runners'.

Later, in 1879, the ostracism reached beyond paid athletes. The rule book for towing at the Henley regatta in England decided that 'no person shall be considered an amateur, who is or has been by trade or employment for wages a mechanic, artisan or laborer'.

In all fairness, however, Young emphasises that ancient Greek athletes were not total mercenaries of track and field.

'What spurred them on was common to all Greeks — a love of competition and a desire to be first, to rise above ordinary human limitations and achieve what other men cannot,' he explained. 'So they competed for both — accomplishment and loot.

'The major impetus was to achieve something nobody else could — and the fact that they earned some money doing it didn't hurt.'

Young, 45, who holds a Ph.D. from the University of Iowa and was a high-jump champion in his home State of Nebraska, has translated ancient stones and documents, including lists of winners and their purses, during visits to Greek museums and ruins.

It has taken him almost 10 years to research and write his manuscript. He acknowledges that not every contemporary classicist agrees with his findings and, in particular, the amount of purses awarded.

'In actual fact, I think that my figures are on the conservative side,' he says, 'but whether it was $100,000 or $500,000 isn't important. The point is, it was money and a lot of money.

'I hope the book will help and promote the Olympic movement, not harm it,' he said. 'The reason I'm publishing my research is with a good will to the Olympics and the Olympic movement, not to put them in a dark light. For if we understand the past history as it is, we'll be able to take it from there much better.'

— Paul Dean, *Los Angeles Times*, reprinted in *The Age*, Melbourne

Events of the ancient Olympics

Track events in the stadium opened the first day of the ancient Olympic Games. Competitors were announced by name and nationality, and the crowd was asked if anyone challenged the athletes' status as citizens or honest men.

The athletes took off their clothes and rubbed themselves down with oil. Lots were drawn from the urn of Zeus for positions in each event.

After each event, the winner, his father, and the home country were announced. The winner's return to his home country was a brilliantly triumphant occasion. Large numbers of people welcomed him and, after he was dedicated at the temple of Zeus, there was a great banquet.

Figure 37.3 **Wrestlers.** Athletes wore no clothes. These two have rubbed themselves with oil and with fine sand, to give a better grip. Their long hair has been plaited and the plaits are arranged round their heads, giving the effect of a cap.

Running

Races were run in heats, with winners qualifying for the final. A starting gate, similar to that used in modern bike races, was used, and athletes had to run up to a post, run around it, and come back again. Changes in speed and bunching at the turn were features of these races.

The most prestigious event was the 200 metres, the winner of which had the Olympiad named after him.

The armed race involved running wearing full battle-dress.

Wrestling

Both types of wrestling were included: rolling and standing (see Chapter 36). They were knockout competitions, with the winner being the last competitor left.

Boxing

Boxers trained with a punch ball. The athletes wore leather gloves and bronze caps. A fight continued until one fighter gave in. There were very few rules, and competitors were usually badly hurt, or even died. Those who broke any of the few rules were flogged by the referees.

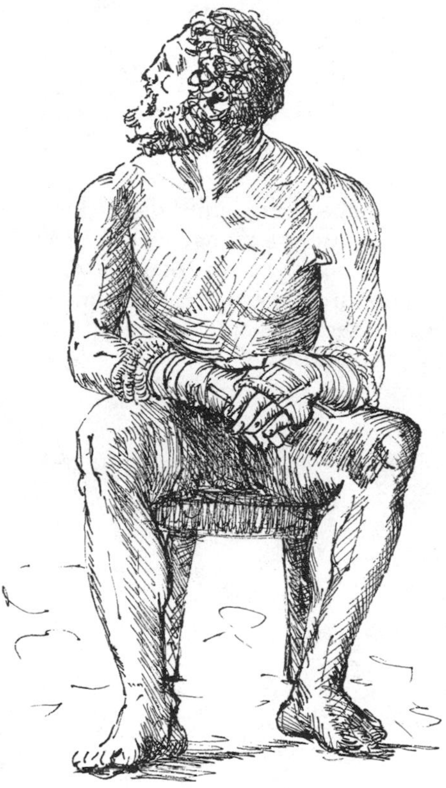

Figure 37.4 For **boxing**, the toughest of the Olympic sports, gloves consisting of leather thongs, and sometimes sheepskin, protected the hands and lower forearm. This type was popular in later times.

Pankration

The **pankration** was a combination of boxing, wrestling and judo, with very strict rules. It was a very violent sport, where such tactics as throttling and crushing the fingers of an opponent were allowed.

Figure 37.5 Not allowed—though much else was. In this all in wrestling match (**pankration**), one of the contestants is trying to gouge out his opponent's eyes.

The pentathlon

The pentathlon event comprised:

- Jumping
- Discus
- Javelin
- 200-metres run
- Wrestling.

Although this event did not have the status of other events, it was the event for the all-rounder.

The evidence seems to show that, in order to win the whole event, an athlete had to win at least one of the field events. There is also some evidence that the first three events were used as qualifying rounds, and that only the finalists performed in the running and the wrestling.

Jumping

There is considerable debate about the Ancient Greek long jump. The Greeks always held weights while jumping, and held on to them until they landed. We do not know why they did this. They certainly would not have obtained any assistance from the weights. One theory is that they simply wanted to make the event more difficult. Certainly there has been no move to start a modern jumping event using weights.

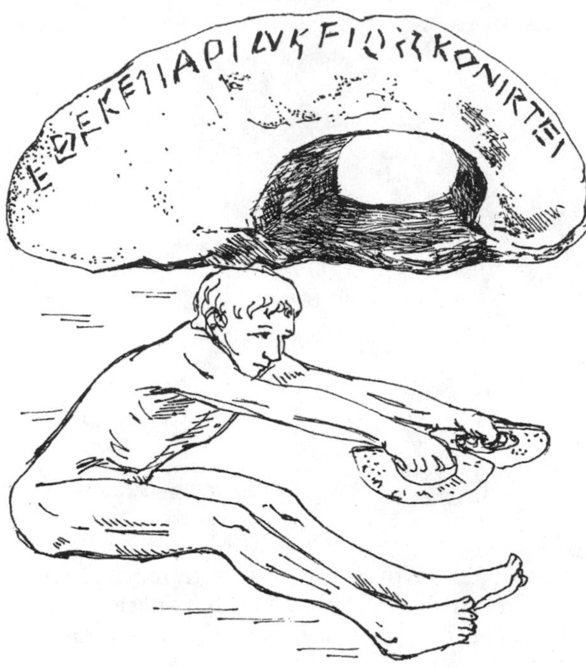

Figure 37.6 This **long jumper** is holding stone or lead weights, of which an inscribed example is shown above. He is shown in mid-air: in order to lengthen his jump and make a clean landing, he swings the weights forward and then back.

The only two jumps for which we have figures are 17 metres and 18 metres, so it must have been a multiple jump — perhaps double or triple.

Javelin

The javelin was a weapon of war, so this event came directly from military training. In other competitions, the javelin was aimed at a target, but in the Olympics it was thrown for distance.

The athlete wrapped a leather thong around the javelin, and then looped it over the fingers. The thong unwound during the throw, causing the javelin to spin.

Discus

Originally a valuable copper disc was awarded to the athlete who could throw it the furthest. The Greeks may have spun around before throwing the

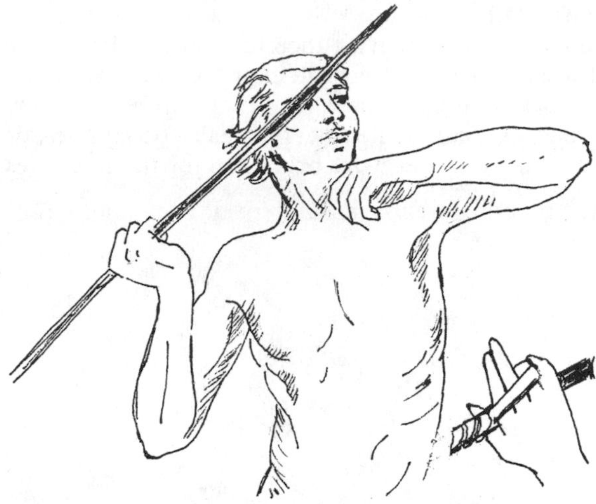

Figure 37.7 The inset picture shows how **javelin-throwers** made use of a thong, about half a metre long, wound the centre of the javelin, leaving a loop through which the first and middle fingers were inserted. As the javelin left the hand, the thong unwound.

Figure 37.8 **Discus-throwing** was one of the five events of the pentathlon. Vase-paintings and statues, including copies of the famous Discobolus of Myron, illustrate the techniques that were used. The athlete swung the heavy bronze discus back in his right hand, turned his body to the right, and then threw with an underarm motion. He had straightened his throwing arm for the back swing, but paintings show the elbow bent just before delivery. Special attention was paid to style and rhythm, and practice took place accompanied by flute music.

discus, but it seems to have been thrown with an underarm action, with the elbow bent just before release, and the fingers helping to create spin.

Chariot-racing and horse-racing

Chariot-racing and horse-riding were held at the Hippodrome, and these were the most popular events.

Research work 2: The Olympic Games

Research topics

(1) What were the origins of the athletic events of the ancient Olympic Games?
(2) What was the full significance of the Festival of Olympia to Ancient Greeks?
(3) Compare ancient and modern athletic techniques.
(4) Describe how the Olympic Games were run.
(5) Why did the ancient Olympics die out?
(6) What factors led to the revival of the Olympic Games during the nineteenth century?
(7) What significance has the Olympic Games in today's society?

Possible influences on today

(1) The development of athletics
(2) Values and ideals in sport
(3) The concept of the 'big event'
(4) The Olympic Games
(5) Politics in sport
(6) Professionalism in sport
(7) Violence in sport
(8) The status of women's sport
(9) Training in sport
(10) Athletic nutrition.

Essay suggestions

(1) To what extent has the attempt to model the modern Olympic Games on those of Ancient Greece been successful?
(2) 'Olympic competitors have never been amateurs.' Discuss.
(3) 'The modern Olympic Games are in danger of extinction for reasons similar to those that caused the ancient Olympics to die out.' Discuss.
(4) One of the aims of both the ancient and the modern Olympics is to bring about peace and co-operation among nations. To what extent has this been achieved?

Laboratory work 65: Ancient Greek athletics

Aim

To reconstruct and evaluate the methods used by the Ancient Greeks in the performance of athletic events.

Equipment

- A post
- Stop watch
- Dumbbells
- Discus
- Javelin
- Thong
- Target.

Running

- **Procedure**

(1) Run 50 metres in a straight line.
(2) Run 50 metres, by running 25 metres each way around a post.
(3) Run 20 metres in a straight line.
(4) Run 20 metres, by running 10 metres each way round a post.

- **Results**

Time all these runs.

- **Conclusions**

Discuss the influence of the two different pathways on the outcome of the event.

Jumping

- **Procedure**

(1) Perform some jumps using the modern styles for triple jump and long jump.
(2) Jump from a standing position.
(3) Try running jumps.
(4) Try triple jumping.

Note that (2), (3) and (4) must be performed while holding dumbbells in each hand.

- **Results**

Measure all jumps.

- **Conclusions**

Discuss how the use of weights affects each of the jumps with which you have experimented. What is your opinion of the most likely method of jumping used by the Ancient Greeks?

Discus

- **Procedure**

(1) Use the modern action of throwing the discus.
(2) Use the ancient Greek method of throwing the discus.

- **Results**

Measure both types of throw.

- **Conclusions**

Discuss the results of these two methods.

Javelin

- **Procedure**

(1) Use the modern method of throwing the javelin.
(2) Throw for distance.
(3) Throw at a target.
(4) Throw the javelin using a thong, in the style of the Ancient Greeks.

- **Results**

Measure all throws.

- **Conclusions**

Compare the different methods of throwing in relation to the level of skill required.

Presentation of results

When writing up this laboratory work

(1) Describe the aim of the practical work.
(2) Describe what was done during the practical work.
(3) Compare the Ancient Greek techniques of (**a**) sprinting, (**b**) jumping and (**c**) throwing the javelin and the discus with modern techniques, referring to the degree and types of skill involved, and the effects on the results.

Note: You will probably find it very useful to refer to modern books about athletics.

38. Ball games in Ancient Greece: Outline

Figure 38.1 Relief on a marble statue base showing a game of **'hockey'** in progress. This is the sole certain evidence for the use of clubs or bats in ancient ball games. The figures to the right and left appear to be individual players awaiting their turn, rather than competitiors participating in the game.

Ball games in Ancient Greece were very informal events that many Greeks took up in order to aid health and fitness. The Greek physician Galen was one who recognized the virtues of ball games in promoting physical health and social skills.

Two types of ball were used:

- **Large balls**, which were made of inflated ox or pig bladder
- **Small balls**, which were stuffed with animal hair or feathers.

There is little evidence that the Greeks used a club or stick to hit the ball. One exception is illustrated in Figure 38.1. The skill of kicking was not used by the Greeks, but was introduced later by the Romans.

An area called a **sphairisterion** was set aside for ball games.

Alexander the Great's preference for ball games helped to make them popular throughout his empire. An annual knockout competition for teams of boys in a ball game took place in Sparta in the second century AD.

The most popular ball games

Some of the most popular ball games played in Ancient Greece were:

Ourania

One player threw the ball in the air while the other leapt to catch it.

Figure 38.2 A scene on a red-figure hydria showing a girl playing **aporrhaxis**, a game entailing the continuous bouncing of a ball.

Apporrhaxis

(See Figure 38.2.) One player bounced a ball and counted the bounces. There is evidence to suggest that this game was also played against a wall.

Episkuros

Two teams of equal numbers stood opposite each other. A line was marked between them and behind each team. One team threw the ball over the opponents, who returned the ball from where they retrieved it. The aim was to push the opponents over the end line.

Donkey

(See Figure 38.3.) The person who dropped the ball was labelled 'donkey' and was 'out'. There was also a version where the donkey had to carry another player on his shoulders.

Trigon

There were two versions of trigon:

- **Harpastum**, with only three players (as below).
- Three men stood in a triangle and simultaneously hit the ball to the next player, who tried to catch it. The ball was struck with the hand.

Harpastum

This was a very popular game. It was very rigorous and competitive, and attracted spectators.

A player stood between two teams and tried to intercept their passes. The passer could not allow the ball to touch the ground.

It is possible that another version was played where the two teams tried to hit the player in the middle, and he fended the ball away with his hands. Some historians even say that a club may have been used to fend the ball, but there seems to be no evidence for this.

Figure 38.3 **This catching game** is depicted on several surviving vases, but is otherwise unknown. It has been suggested that the boy who was called 'donkey' because he had dropped a catch had to carry another boy on his back in this version of the game, but there is no evidence for this.

Figure 38.4 A scene in coloured marble inlay from a wall in the secular Basilica of Junius Bassus in Rome, built about AD 330. The magistrate in the **biga** is about to throw down the **mappa**, not to start a race but more probably a game of polo.

Research work 3: Ball games in Ancient Greece

Research topics

(1) Which ball games were played by the Ancient Greeks?
(2) What values did they see in these ball games?
(3) What influence did Alexander the Great have on the growth of ball games?
(4) How did the status of ball games compare to that of athletics?

Possible influences on today

(1) The concept of fitness related to activity
(2) The concept of therapeutic exercise
(3) The development of modern ball games
(4) The development of children's ball games
(5) The concept of activity as a social medium.

Essay suggestions

(1) Compare the role of ball games in Ancient Greek society with their role in modern society.
(2) Outline the influence that Galen or Alexander the Great might have had, directly or indirectly, on modern physical education programmes.
(3) 'The role of physical activity in developing physical fitness and social skills was as much appreciated by the Ancient Greeks as it is by modern Australians.' Discuss.

Laboratory work 66: Ancient Greek ball games

Aim

To experience the ball games played by the Ancient Greeks.

Equipment

Various sizes of balls.

Procedure

From the rules outlined in this chapter, reconstruct the following games:

(1) Ourania
(2) Apporrhaxis (both versions)
(3) Episkuros
(4) Donkey (both versions)
(5) Trigon (both versions)
(6) Harpastum (both versions).

Results

(1) Report on your findings, paying particular attention to:
  (a) Your impressions of these games
  (b) The type of people who probably played them
  (c) Their usefulness as a means of exercise
  (d) The degree of skill required for each
  (e) Their use as a means of socializing
  (f) The ways in which the games could be improved or added to in order to make them more interesting, vigorous or skilful.
(2) Also provide an outline of:
  (a) Aim
  (b) Equipment used
  (c) Procedure
  (d) Your findings.

39. Sport and physical education in the Middle Ages: Outline

Figure 39.1 The joust.

Main features of the Middle Ages

The Middle Ages — or Medieval era — is usually thought of as extending from about 800 AD to about 1300 AD. This was the era when people began living in towns, although most people worked in the country around the castles of the nobles. The influence of the Church was strong, and Sundays and holy days were kept free from work.

Girls were expected to stay at home until they were married. Most ordinary people apprenticed

Figure 39.2 The quintain.

their sons to trades or had them help with farmwork. Formal education was available only to monks or rich nobles. The rich sent their sons to Church schools, the castles of the nobles, or to grammar schools for their education. A few boys were sent to the newly opened universities, or were trained to be monks.

Within the newly developing towns, conditions were primitive. The values of hygiene were almost unknown, and houses were crowded together and very vulnerable to fires.

Figure 39.3 At basic practice, two pages fence with toy swords and shields. The would-be knight also sharpened his skills by using lance, sword and battle-axe on the quintain, a post or life-sized dummy.

Sports of the Middle Ages

(1) Aristocratic sports

• **The tournament**

(See Figures 39.1, 39.2 and 39.3.) The tournament was the centre of sporting activity. Military skills were displayed in **jousting**, tilting at the **quintain**, as well as in **hunting** and **fencing**.

• **Tennis**

Tennis was very popular with the nobles (see later in this chapter).

• **Games**

The nobles also played many card and board games.

Figure 39.4 **Bear-baiting**. Many sports in the Middle Ages seem cruel to us now. Bear-baiting was one such sport. A bear was chained to a post and dogs were made to attack it. The bear often killed a few dogs at first. But finally the bear became so tired that the dogs killed it.

(2) Pastimes among the peasants

• **Blood sports**

(See Figures 39.4, 39.5 and 39.6.) Blood sports were popular among ordinary people. They included:

— Bear-baiting
— Cock-fighting
— Goose- or pig-clubbing
— Foot-fighting
— Wrestling.

Figures 39.5 and 39.6 **Wrestling** matches were a highlight of every holiday. Clerkenwell, just outside the walls of London, was famous for its wrestling. The crowds were so large that they trampled all the crops in nearby fields. The head of the nunnery that owned the fields complained to King Edward I about it. Foot-fighting was less common, but people enjoyed it. They put bets on who would win.

Figure 39.7 Skates.

• **Quoits, skittles and bowls**
(See Figure 39.9.) Quoits, skittles and bowls were played by older people.

• **Ice sports**
(See Figure 39.7.) Ice sports, such as skating, were popular.

• **Military skills**
Every working man owed military allegiance to a noble, and was required by the king to practise military skills, such as archery.

• **Ball games**
See next section.

Ball games of the Middle Ages

Handball

(See Figure 39.9.) Handball was a Roman game, played by striking an inflated leather ball with the arms, which were protected by hollow wooden braces.

Figure 39.8 and 39.9 **Ball games.** As there are so many round things in nature, balls are probably the oldest toys in the world. Apples, oranges, and coconuts all make good balls. The schoolboys in Figure 39.8 are playing handball during a break from their lessons. In the background, two masters are having a game for chess. In Figure 39.9, a brother and sister are playing bowls in the garden.

Figures 39.10 and 39.11 **Bats and balls.** Children in the Middle Ages liked to play with bats and balls. Older boys and men played club ball, as you can see in Figure 39.10. Apprentices and students played a sort of hockey (**bandyball**) (Figure 39.11). There was no special pitch, and very few rules. The teams played out in the streets. The games were so rough and noisy that they were banned in Westminster when Parliament was sitting, because the noise disturbed the Members.

Football

Football was known as campball, and was an obvious progression from handball. It was a very rough game with few rules. Whole villages often joined battle against neighbouring villages, with the goals miles apart. Because of the terrible injuries that players often sustained, the Church condemned football and the English parliament declared it illegal.

Bandyball, or goff

(See Figure 39.11.) Bandyball was an ancester of hockey. It was played with a small, hard leather ball stuffed with feathers. The club was curved, with a piece of horn or metal on the end. The object of the game was to drive the ball between two sticks.

Club-ball

(See Figure 39.10.) Club-ball was similar to rounders. The batsman held a small club in one hand, the ball was pitched, and players formed a circle round the bat, waiting for a catch. We do not know whether or not the batsman had to run.

Figure 39.12 Trapball.

Stoolball

This game was particularly popular with girls and women, but was also played by men and boys.

Probably in pairs, players set up a three-legged milking stool, and one threw stones at it. Soon a ball was substituted for stones, and one player defended the stool with her fist. Later a club was used to hit the ball, with each hit counting as one point. If the bowler struck the stool or caught the ball after it was hit, the two players changed places. The pitch was probably about 16 metres long.

Trapball

(See Figure 39.12.) Trapball was one of the most popular medieval games. The ball rested in a hollow at one end of a short seesaw. The batsman hit the other end sharply with his bat, sending the ball into the air. He then tried to hit it as far as possible.

Wrestling

(See Figure 39.5.) This is the only popular activity from the Middle Ages to survive from Ancient Greece. Wrestling was very popular during holiday celebrations, and it attracted large crowds.

Figure 39.13 A tennis court.

KING-SIZED CHAMP IN A RIGHT ROYAL SPORT

It was only appropriate that Ogden Phipps should win the Australian Open doubles title in Royal tennis at Royal Melbourne Tennis Club, Richmond, yesterday. With a reputed fortune that ranks him fifth among America's wealthy, the New York banker truly is one of the kings of capitalism.

He teamed up with Tasmanian professional Graham Hyland to win the title carrying about 120 kg in weight. The secret of his success, he admitted later, was picking a quick partner.

Phipps, six times winner of the United States amateur doubles title and three times winner of the Professional title, is chairman of the Bessemer Trust Corporation and the New York Racing Association, and a horse breeder of some distinction . . .

Phipps, 41, does not like too much emphasis placed on the sport's royal past, but it is hard to avoid comparisons with Henry VIII, another lover of Royal tennis. A gallery of past French and English kings, no doubt, would enthusiastically applaud this New World scion's continued domination of doubles competition.

Royal tennis is thought to have its origins in the monastery cloisters of the 12th century. An indoors sport, it retains all the hazards of 'doors', galleries, a protruding wall and a 'monk's grille' in the walls. Tactics seem to blend squash and tennis, and allow an experienced player with cunning to hold his own against younger, quicker opponents.

That was obvious yesterday, when Phipps and Hyland edged out Melbourne pair Colin Lumely, 24, and Paul Tabley, 18, three sets to one. The win confirmed them as world's best Royal tennis doubles team.

— Andrew Bolt,
The Age, Melbourne, 17 May 1982

Foot-fighting

(See Figure 39.6.) This was another popular activity.

The Middle Ages and the origins of tennis

There are many claims about the origins of tennis, but it is generally accepted that the game owes its beginnings to medieval French monks. Their game, Le Jeu de Paume, is still played today. When proper courts were built, they still looked rather like monastic cloisters. The game spread to the nobles, but enthusiasm remained greatest among the monks (see Figure 39.13).

At first players used a bare hand when playing. Later a glove was introduced, and later still, a racquet. The game was called 'Royal tennis' because it became popular with French kings, and spread throughout the aristocracy of Europe.

There were two forms of the game:

- **'Longue paume'**, which was played outdoors
- **'Courte paume'**, which was played indoors.

Research work 4: Sport in the Middle Ages

Research topics

(1) The social structure of the Middle Ages.
(2) The Church's role in society during the Middle Ages.
(3) Formal education during the Middle Ages
(4) The early history of:
  (a) Tennis
  (b) Football
  (c) Cricket
  (d) Hockey.

Possible influences on today

(1) The role of women in society
(2) The role of the Church in society
(3) Violence in sport
(4) Class distinction
(5) The development of tennis, football, cricket and hockey
(6) Holidays and leisure time.

Essay suggestions

(1) 'The people of the Middle Ages spent their leisure time in many pursuits, some of which have had an influence on the development of modern sports.' Discuss.

(2) 'Class distinction in sport is a a feature of today that has its origins in the Middle Ages.' Discuss.

Laboratory work 67: Games played during the Middle Ages

Aim

To reconstruct and experience some of the games played during the Middle Ages.

Equipment

- Hockey stick
- Goal posts
- Cricket bat
- Rounders bat
- Baseball bat
- Softball
- Cricket ball
- Tennis ball
- Stool.

Procedure

(1) From the limited knowledge you have of these games, try to organize games of:
   (a) Bandyball
   (b) Club-ball
   (c) Stoolball.

(2) When writing up your results, include the following items:
   (a) A description of how you set about reconstructing the medieval games.
   (b) Your impressions of these games.
   (c) The reasons why these games developed.
   (d) Relationships between these and modern games.
   (e) Your opinions on the claim that cricket is derived from stoolball and club-ball.

40. Sport and physical education during the Renaissance: Outline

Figure 40.1 A football being inflated.

Figure 40.2 Tournaments, jousting and public games were spectacular events, brilliantly organized and attended by masses of people. This illustration shows a typical scene of this sort in Florence.

The Renaissance: a time of change

The Renaissance is usually considered to be the period of time between 1300 and 1600 AD. It was an age of political upheaval and a great religious change. Explorers from Europe roamed the world, discovering North and South America, and opening up new trade routes to Africa, Asia and the Americas. There was great economic growth and an upsurge in art, literature and science. Most of the initial growth was in France and Italy.

One of the major changes during the Renaissance was a movement of people and power from the country areas, ruled by the barons, to the cities, ruled by the merchants. These merchants, and the people who worked for them, formed a new middle class, filling a gap between the aristocracy and the peasants, and facilitating social mobility.

Educational changes during the Renaissance

Since schools were run by the Church, educational practices underwent great change during the Reformation. With the invention of the printing press came the dispersal of information among a wide group of people. Members of the new middle class wanted their children educated in professional skills, and not only the narrow academic skills that had been taught by the Church.

Figure 40.3 The fencing school.

A new emphasis on physical education

Although physical education was based on military training at first (see Figure 40.3), Renaissance thinkers rediscovered Greek and Roman literature, which emphasized the harmony between the well-educated mind and the well-trained body. As a result, the military emphasis in physical education declined, and the wider values of physical culture became appreciated.

People in the cities had more leisure time than anybody had had since Ancient Greek and Roman times. Festivals were celebrated and games developed (see Figure 40.2):

- Tournaments were still popular with the nobles
- In Florence, a highly organized game of football was played by the nobility (see Figure 40.1)
- A new concern for hygiene led to the development of swimming and water sports
- Homes became larger, allowing more space for family recreations
- Archery, kite-flying, horse-riding and racing, and boxing were all popular sports
- A game called **giuco della palla**, in which a ball was hit with a club, was played by Italian nobles
- People continued to play various forms of bowls and skittles.

However, women were excluded from games of skill, although they were encouraged in riding and dancing.

Hunting became less important than it had been during medieval times, mainly because of the clearing of the forests for agriculture.

Physical education in England

The new concepts in physical education did not reach England until about the sixteenth century, and they were acknowledged mainly because of the new emphasis on Greek literature.

During the Middle Ages, the teachers (mainly monks) had emphasized the importance of the soul and had neglected the body. Physical education had not been a part of formal education.

However, the Tudor kings (1500s) had embraced Protestanism, dismissed the monks, and placed a great deal of importance on sport and physical education. Henry VIII, the most famous Tudor king, was a renowned sportsman.

In England, as elsewhere, class distinction tended to decide which sports people took up. For instance, football was not considered a sport for gentlemen. It was considered such a rough game that at one time playing football earned up to six days' imprisonment.

Golf, a new game, was considered a 'sport of kings'. It was established in Scotland, and enjoyed by Mary Queen of Scots.

Among the ordinary people, the most popular sports and recreations were:

- The medieval ball games, which remained popular
- 'Fishing with an angle', which appealed to all classes
- Bear-baiting and cock-fighting, which developed into major spectator sports.
- A game called barley break.

LEONARDO ON HIS WAY DOWN UNDER

Figure 40.4 Leonardo da Vinci: 'The Muscles of the Shoulder' (*circa* 1510): impressively illustrating the mechanics of movement.

An exhibition drown from the Queen's own unparalleled collection of Leonardo da Vinci's anatomical drawings is coming to Melbourne.

The exhibition comprises 90 of the finest of the 200 anatomical drawings in the Queen's collection. It opens at Melbourne's National Gallery on 28 August [1982] after an initial showing in Adelaide.

This will be the first exhibition in Australia devoted entirely to the work of da Vinci.

The anatomical drawings reveal both facets of da Vinci's character — his remarkable gifts as an artist, and his ceaseless inquiry into scientific matters often far removed from the province of art. His drawings in this exhibition reveal a knowledge of human anatomy far deeper than that possessed by medical men of the time. His work in this area was not surpassed for another 200 to 300 years.

Among the most striking of his anatomical drawings are those of the infant in the womb, dating from 1510 to 1512.

When, in 1489, da Vinci first proposed a book on anatomy, he said: 'This book should begin with the conception of man, and describe the form of the womb and how the child lives in it, and to what stage it resides in it and in what way it is given life and food . . .'

The errors of anatomy that we can find today in da Vinci's drawings in no way detracts from the extraordinary achievement they represent. Human bodies of either sex were difficult to obtain and efforts to procure them were viewed with a good deal of suspicion.

Leonardo da Vinci used a variety of materials for his drawings, making the studies far richer in appearance than just pen-and-ink would achieve. In his 'Infant in the Womb' he used three shades of brown ink, with wash modelling over traces of black chalk, and red chalk.

— Anthony Clarke,
The Age, Melbourne, 17 April 1982

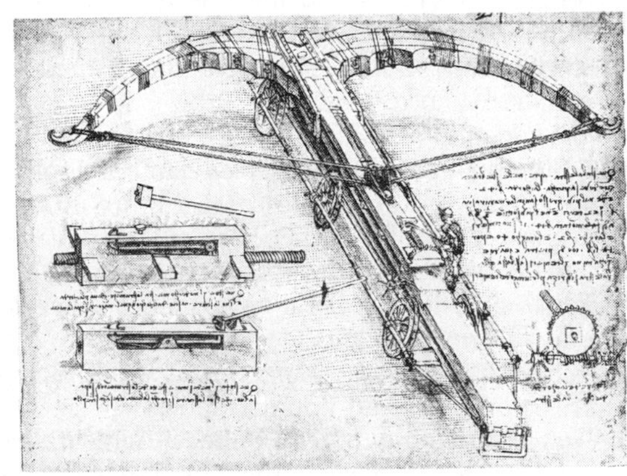

Figure 40.5 Leonardo's siege engine.

LEONARDO'S MAPPING OF AN UNKNOWN WORLD

Perhaps no smaller exhibition has ever come to Melbourne than Leonardo da Vinci's anatomical drawings from the Royal collection at Windsor; just 50 sheets of paper, about 23 cm by 12 or 14.

They are not 'works of art' in the traditional sense of the term; they were never commissioned, never 'hung'; they often overlap — many sketches on a single page, with more sketches on the back. In Leonardo's lifetime, they were never even bound into a respectable volume. Just 50 bits of paper filled with notes (written *backwards* — right to left, like Arabic!) and minute sketches of the human body. Even the figures are incomplete: arms, legs, vertebrae, skulls; intestines, hearts, livers, lungs; kidneys, bladders, reproductive organs . . . a long way from the Mona Lisa!

And yet, my guess is that this exhibition at the National Gallery . . . will arouse more wonder and silent applause than perhaps any other exhibition we have seen.

But why the sketches? Why not the paintings — the Mona Lisa or the Virgin of the Rocks? True, the paintings would be more spectacular: they are bigger, they are in color, and they are 'works of art' — commissioned, 'hung' and all the rest. And yet, the paintings would make an even smaller exhibition!

You would have to search far and wide to find works by Leonardo in his native Italy. Two in Florence — a long-disputed Anunciation (an early work anyway), and a Magi which is so unfinished that it's more a plan than a painting. A St Jerome in the Vatican which is said to have been found in two separate pieces — one being used as a table top!

In Milan, the Last Supper; but that has been restored four times in the past 300 years and was probably restored several times before that — so that only the outlines and positions, not the actual paint, are Leonardo's . . . a couple in London — a cartoon for a St Anne that was apparently never painted; and a Virgin of the Rocks which many critics regard as a copy. A couple in Russia, in the United States, and elsewhere.

The majority of Leonardo's paintings are of course in Paris, with Mona Lisa; but even the better preserved ones — like the Virgin of the Rocks — are 'buried under layer upon layer of yellow varnish (so that) we can form no real conception of the color, the values or the general tone of the originals', according to one expert. Even the Mona Lisa, for all her feline fascination, is submerged in a sea of varnish. 'The rosy tints around the eyes . . . and nose', described by Vasari in the mid-16th century, are no longer visible today. Neither are the 'red of the lips' or 'the flesh tones of the face'. Mona Lisa today has a pallor that is almost clinical — which is why Kenneth Cark dubs her 'the Submarine Goddess of the Louvre'.

If Leonardo has suffered, as a painter, more than any of his contemporaries, he fared little better as a scientist. His submarines never took to water; his flying machines never really flew; the churches he designed were never built; neither were the idyllic cities he planned, with split-level streets — the upper one for pedestrians, the lower one for the peasants and their carts and noise. The great bronze horseman, monument to Duke Francesco Sforza of Milan, was never cast — only a marvellous clay model, which was promptly used for target practice by invading French soldiers, and fell to pieces in Ferrara a few years later. . . .

Most surprising of all perhaps, he devoted a great deal of time to designing brilliant sets and costumes and some of the acts for the tournaments, masquerades and pageants of the brilliant Renaissance court of Milan. It is one of the supreme ironies of history that none of these ingenious projects or inventions — as far as we know — ever contributed significantly to the progress of science.

Most poignant of all, in the context of the exhibition, even his endless nights and days poring over decomposing human carcasses never as far as we know, yielded enough knowledge of human anatomy to heal one poor suffering soul.

So, what does it all amount to? About a dozen finished paintings, in worse repair than those of any other major Renaissance artist — infinitely worse than many of the the paintings of ancient Egypt which are 3000 years older; a couple of treasured bronzes, which were never cast; and some 5000 'bits of paper' covered with feverish sketches and observations on every conceivable topic, which he never found time (or never *made* time) to put together into something resembling a book. 'Tell me', he scribbled on page after page of his later notebooks, 'if anything at all has been achieved.'

And yet I maintain the exhibition will be a stunning success. Why?

First, because the sketches have an immediacy and an intensity which the studied paintings never had; they are fresh, natural, unposed, unidealised; dashed off in the heat of the moment of discovery, they breathe and vibrate; the ink is scarcely dry.

Second, they are unique because artist and scientist are one man. No more skilled hand ever put pen to paper, no sharper eye ever probed the human body for its secrets; and perhaps no other artist — or scientist either, for that matter — ever worked with such feverish intensity to expose the anatomy of the world he lived in.

The age of Leonardo has been called the Age of Discovery. Leonardo was 40 when Vasco da Gama sailed round the Cape of Good Hope, 45 when Columbus discovered the Americas. But no explorer was ever more excited by what he discovered in distant lands than was Leonardo in his progressive discovery of *man*. The body, not the soul — visible man, created master of the universe but still a mystery to himself.

Most of the time he is working beneath the skin. Inside the bones — the skull is like an onion, he says; make a cross-cut section and you can peel it off in layers. Or he is threading his way through a raw labyrinth of muscles, nerves, veins and arteries — which he draws with the delicacy of flowers. He draws everything he sees; a single sketch, he insists, reveals more than a mass of words: but every series of sketches demands a new series of fresh dissections.

'You will need three (dissections) in order to have a complete knowledge of the veins and arteries; three others for a knowledge of the membranes; three for the nerves, muscles and ligaments; three for the bones and cartilages, and three for anatomy of the bones, for these have to be sawn through in order to show which are hollow and which are not . . . three also must be devoted to the female body, and in this there is great mystery by reason of the womb and its foetus . . .'

Having discovered what we might call the geography of the human body (what's there) and, to a certain extent, its mechanics also (how do the joints, muscles, nerves and veins 'work'), he records what he finds in the notebooks, again in triplicate — seen from the front, from the back and from the side; sometimes he gives a succession of 'shots' that are like movie 'stills' — the subject remaining stationary while the 'camera' moves systematically round it.

Faces are unimportant in this jungle of human anatomy. The flesh he moulded in light in his paintings is of no account here: neither are backdrops or scenery — there are no rocks or blue hills disappearing in the distance. Instead of Mona Lisa we have 'the anatomy of a smile' — that is, the muscular machinery that pulls the corners of the mouth sideways to make that famous smile possible.

In his paintings, he pursued ideal beauty; not in the sketches. There are no 'Greek gods' in the sketches: he prefers the lean and the old to the graceful and the young, because they expose the machinery more clearly.

Is he an artist or a scientist? Obviously both, as he moves with equal dexterity from scalpel to pen and back again, searching for the make-up and mechanics of the human body and noting down all his findings on his precious 'bits of paper'.

He made mistakes at times, which he sometimes (not always) corrected in later studies; he failed to see or saw wrongly what any medical student must see today; and yet he saw more and revealed more of human anatomy than any man had ever seen before him, and more than most of us have seen to this day. And he did it all without microscopes or X-rays or tracer elements — without any of the formidable equipment of modern science.

It's a curious mixture — artist and scientist: there's little room for such a combination today. But, in Leonardo's case, art drove him to science, and science perfected his art. For how can you paint the human body in action unless you know how it is put together; you paint what you *know*; and you need to know not only the make-up of man, but also how to represent this three-dimensional figure and his world on a surface that is perfectly flat.

— Ian Guthridge,
The Age, 28 August 1982

Figure 40.6 A crude game of tennis played in England in the eighteenth century.

Tennis during the Renaissance

Royal tennis became popular among all classes during the Renaissance. However, the cost of building a court (see Figure 40.8), soon restricted the sport to the nobles. Later, outdoor versions of the game (see Figure 40.6) were invented in order to cut down costs.

Because of their political links with France, the Scots were introduced to the game before the English, and soon the monarchs of both countries were enthusiasts. Henry VIII of England built a court at Hampton Court.

Every European royal family, particularly the French, supported the game — to such an extent that by 1500 tennis had become the national pastime of France, and in 1571, the trade of 'tennis professional' (racquet-maker) was recognized.

At first the ball was struck with the bare hand, then with a glove, then a wooden bat, and eventually with a primitive racquet.

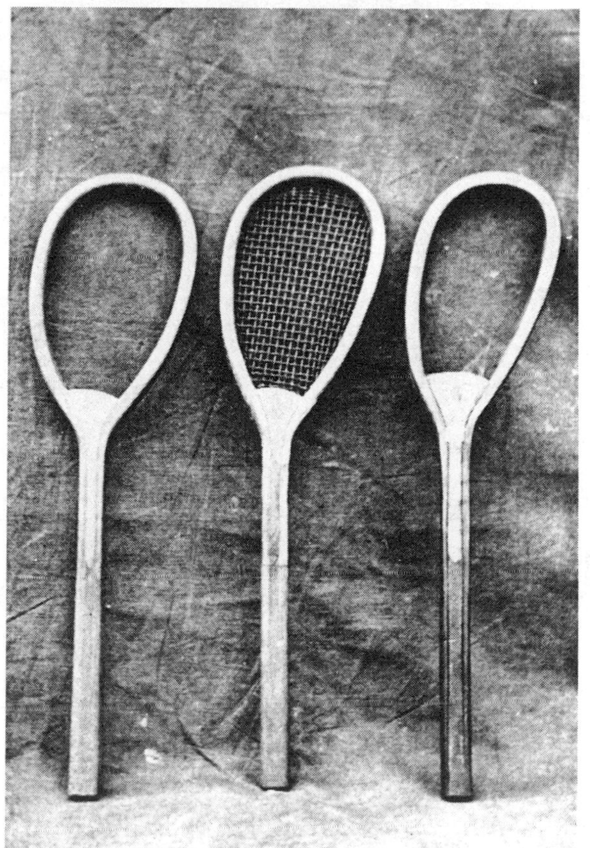

Figure 40.7 A display of old racquets. The modern racquet shape did not evolve until after World War I.

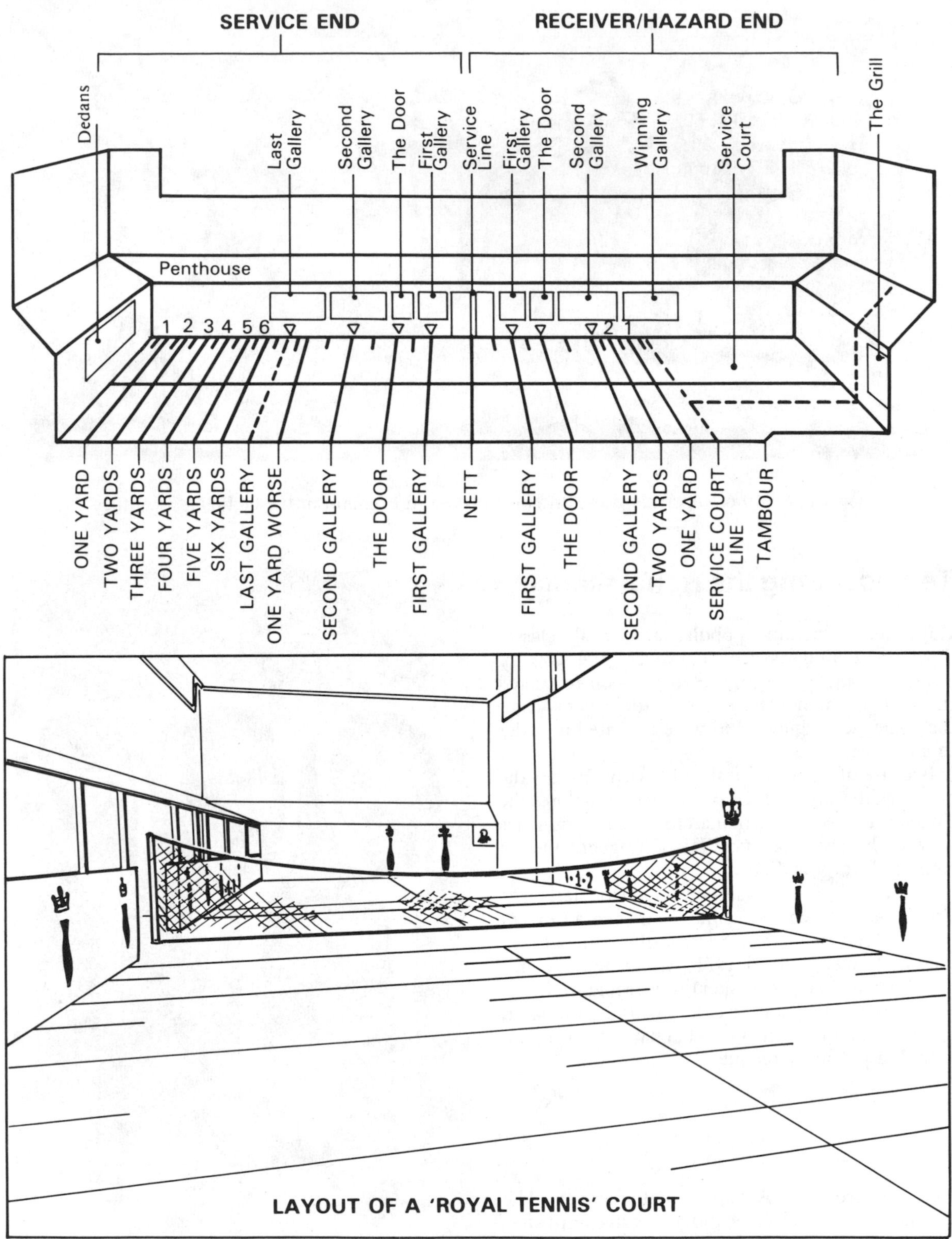

Figure 40.8 Royal tennis.

INTRODUCTION TO ROYAL TENNIS FOR THE VISITOR

The game is about 800 years old and is called Royal tennis in Australia, Réal Tennis, or just Tennis in UK, Court Tennis in USA, and Jeu de Paume in France. To distinguish it from the other game of tennis, the latter is called lawn tennis.

There are 17 playable courts in UK, eight in USA, two in France and three in Australia. We play more tennis than any other country. On average, our courts are booked for 10½ hours per court, per day, 365 days a year.

It is a game of spin and cut, tactics and strategy. It has been likened to a mixture of squash, lawn tennis and chess, but mainly chess. It is therefore an exercise for the mind as well as the body.

It is one of the few games where, at any time, you do not face the same set of circumstances as your opponent. To win you must spend a lot of time on the service side of the court. The other side is called the hazard side, because of all the hazards it has for the player on that side of the net; namely, the tambour, the grille, the winning gallery and the winning area, which is the only part of the floor of the court where you can win a point outright.

The service does not play the part it does in lawn tennis and hence the service does not change with each game. Nevertheless, there are about 50 different services you can do, and if the receiver does not read what is being done to the ball by his opponent, he will probably not be able to return it, and may not even reach it. Rarely does a server serve an 'ace', and if he does, it is usually a fluke. . . .

In lower grades of play, however, the serve can be all important and will throw the opponent into confusion. In top class tennis there is no serve which will trick the opponent, except of course the lucky one. The best that a server in top grades can hope for is to reduce his opponent's ability to return a winning shot. It is therefore the receiver who has the chance with his first shot of assuming command of the rally (called a 'rest'). Nevertheless, if you want to win, you must try and be the server most of the time, because of all the hazards you have to play at.

Unlike squash or lawn tennis, the Royal tennis ball reacts to spin a great deal. So different is Royal tennis to lawn tennis that a top class lawn tennis player would be no match for even a lesser class Royal tennis player, unless he was well practised in both.

It takes many months to understand the game, and many years to play it well. No matter for how long you play it, there will always be something else you can learn, and another way of playing it.

It is said that: 'Once a man becomes familiar with Royal tennis, he seldom drops it in favour of another pastime.'

— The Royal Melbourne Tennis Club, May 1981

Figure 40.9

THE GAME OF ROYAL TENNIS

Tennis, as distinct from lawn tennis, is one of the few games where you do not face the same set of circumstances as your opponent. Cricket is another such game. This is probably one of the reasons why Royal tennis is superior to all other ball games.

A ball is said to drop when it hits the floor on the first bounce. A ball is said to fall when it hits the floor a second time.

Service is always from the same end (the service end), and does not change with each game. To be a good service the ball, whatever else it does, must touch the service penthouse (between the net and the grille penthouse) at least once before it drops in the service court. A change of service is only brought about by the laying of a chase. This is done by the striker returning a ball in such a way that his opponent either does not wish to, or cannot, touch the ball before it bounces a second time. A chase is then laid down at the point where the ball falls (second bounce).

The floor on the service side is marked throughout, and the floor on the other side, the hazard side, is marked in part only, with lines parallel to the net called chase lines. When a player, either by accident or design, does not touch a ball which then falls on a particular part of the floor, he does not lose the point, but a chase is made on that part of the floor, and the point is held in abeyance until the players change ends. Chases are also made when a ball enters any of the galleries except the winning gallery or the dedans.

When two points are thus in abeyance, or one point at 40-love, 40–15, 40–30, or advantage, the players change ends, and the player against whom the chase was laid now attacks the chase by trying to make the ball fall closer to the appropriate back wall than the chase set. If he succeeds he wins the point; if he equals it, it is called chase off and the point is annulled; if he fails to do a good shot, or if the ball falls further away from the back wall than the chase set, he loses the point.

The perfect chase is 'better than half a yard', which is one where the ball falls closer to the back wall than 18 inches, at the service end. It cannot be beaten by a stroke on the floor, and the only way of winning the point is to force for the dedans.

At more than 6 yards from the back wall, the chases are named after the side galleries: last gallery, second gallery, the door, first gallery, the line, etc. These, being a long way from the back wall, are bad chases and are easy to beat when you change ends.

A ball falling just nearer the back wall than, say, chase 3 is called 'better than 3'. One which falls further from the back wall than chase 3 is called 'worse than 3'. One which falls exactly halfway between, say, 3 and 5 is called '3 and 4'.

When a chase is not being played for, points are won or lost as in lawn tennis, except that the score of the player who won the last point is called first. Thus, if the server wins the point and the score is 40-love, and the receiver wins the next point, the score is called 15–40, not 40–15.

Points can therefore only be won outright as follows:

- If the ball is not returned
- If you put the ball into the dedans from the hazard end
- If you put it into the grille or winning gallery from the service end
- If it falls (bounces the second time) in the winning area. The winning area is that part of the hazard court which is not marked with chase lines, and includes a ball falling on the winning gallery line
- If the ball falls anywhere else on the floor or enters a chase gallery, a chase is laid down.

You now have enough of the rules to get started on playing Royal tennis. The rest takes ten years hard labour.

— Royal Melbourne Tennis Club,
May 1981

THE OTHER SPORT OF KINGS IS GROWING EVEN STRONGER

Anyone for tennis? You will be hard pushed to find a free court at the Royal Melbourne Tennis Club. There is a match on now, as usual: for it is the most active club in the world — the two courts are in use 10 hours a day, 365 days a year.

If you presume this is tennis as you know it, you are mistaken: RMTC members will tell you that's 'the other game'. The game played here you might recognise if you had seen the film 'The French Lieutenant's Woman'. It is the ancient game of royal tennis — or réal, court, or Lord's tennis as it is variously known. The father of all ball games, in France it is 'jeu de paume' (the ball in the hand), which was how it was probably first played.

The difference between this and lawn tennis is said to be like the difference between chess and Chinese checkers. The fastest games in the world, racquets, jai-alai and pelota, all derived from this game, as did lawn tennis, squash, fives, badminton; plus team games like baseball and cricket.

The court could be used as a mediaeval room for a movie set: an enclosed room about 29 metres long with soaring galleries, intersected by a series of brightly painted lines and Alice-in-Wonderland sized symbols of crowns, divided by a high net which sags in the middle.

Breaking with tradition, the Melbourne courts are painted a pleasant green, not gloomy black, and have concrete floors in place of stone. But there are no two courts in the world alike — which adds to the complexities of this eccentric game — and gives permanent advantage to those playing on their home ground.

It is the complexity of the game that makes it attractive to people normally bored by sport: it has fascinated kings and commoners for over five centuries, since it spread from the church. Starting in open fields about 1000 years ago, it was first played in monastery cloisters during the 11th centry.

The RMTC president, Mr Bill Hepworth, says that it is the most skilful game in the world. 'People become absolutely hypnotised by it. Do you know another sport where the facility is in use that number of hours a day?' A game of spin-and-cut tactics, of strategy and intellectual challenge — perhaps it is best explained as a cross between squash and chess.

The sport is undergoing a worldwide renaissance, and it is the RMTC which is seen as the catalyst by the rest of the royal tennis world. Only two other clubs anywhere have two playing courts left — most have turned one over to squash if it has not fallen into disrepair. Not ▶

only is it extraordinary that a new country like Australia should be a cradle of the ancient game, but that with the court at the club in Hobart, we have three of the 30 courts still played on in the world — the only three existing in the Southern Hemisphere.

They are hardly some new phenomenon, but are interwoven with the history of the country. Royal tennis was first introduced to Hobart in 1875, then to Melbourne in 1882.

On 23 April [1982] the RMTC celebrated its centenary. . . .

The celebration of the sport he championed could cause Henry VIII to change his dour expression in the lithograph on the club wall. Dressed ready for play in Dunlop sneakers, he clutches the odd, pear-shaped racquet and handmade ball that are peculiar to the game.

Perhaps his expression is caused by the heavy losses he suffered from the gambling associated with the game. Despite taking his personal marker with him to matches, Henry lost often — as records of his privy purse show.

Eventually the game was banned to the common people, condemned for the gambling stakes and for keeping commoners from archery practice — essential in the defence of the nation.

The distinctive layout of the royal tennis court gives a clue that the game originated in the monasteries before it became widespread across Europe. There are cloisters round two sides, high galleries, and grille at one end, and a roped-off spectators' gallery at the other. The terms used — tambour, dedans — indicate its popularity in France, where it became the national pastime with more than 1000 courts (mostly outdoor) during the 17th century. It crossed the channel in the 14th century.

The aura of antiquity on court contrasts strongly with RMTC's modern club building, built in 1974, when members took the unconventional step of moving from the original Exhibition Street building out of the central city.

Building the court itself was a big challenge because it was the first new one for more than 60 years, and the builder of the last took the secret of its composition to the grave. Modelled on Henry VIII's court at Hampton Court (still one of the main courts in use) as there were virtually no other guidelines, the result is due, mostly, to the ingenuity of architect Daryl Jackson in collaboration with the RMTC.

The marriage of old and new maxims brought royal tennis into the 20th century, with a jolt that reverberated around the world, inspiring a resurgence of interest that has brought parallels in other countries. Bourdeaux has followed Melbourne in moving out of the city to build a new club; there is talk of reopening the historic clubs at Versailles and Fontainebleau, closed by the French Revolution. . . .

When the president spoke at the recent reopening of the stately Georgian Club at Lakewood, New Jersey, he acknowledged the contribution of the Melbourne Club. 'The tennis world was set afire by their efforts,' he said.

Playing the game

Even with the same scoring as lawn tennis, and the bewildering addition of chases, royal tennis can take months to understand, years to play well.

'You have to have the right kind of mind for the sport,' says Ted Cockram, Australian No. 1 player, who has just returned from winning the Tuxedo Cup in New York and was eliminated in the American semi-finals by the eventual winner. 'I've seen so many A-grade lawn tennis players who come here and can't make it past B grade.'

The racquet is a strange implement with a square wooden handle about 25 centimetres long, and a lopsided head about 25 centimetres wide. It is held halfway up the handle.

A quaint touch is the wooden basket for stacking the 100 balls used in a game, but their weight of about 60 grams each, plus the fact that they are not pressurised, makes them far from easy to hit.

The court is forbiddingly long and marked differently at each end. The Friar Tuck head in the grille is an added Antipodean adornment, based on the Hobart president's theory that errant monks may have once been required to stand in the grille opening, both for the spice of the game and for the good of their souls.

— Jill Rivers,
The Age, Melbourne, 3 May 1982

Research work 5: Sport in the Renaissance

Research topics

(1) The Reformation
(2) Influence of the Church
(3) Medical and scientific discoveries
(4) Voyages of discovery
(5) Social structure of Renaissance Europe
(6) Sports and games of the Renaissance.

Possible influences on today

(1) The non-military value of physical education
(2) Leisure time
(3) Class structure
(4) Knowledge of human body functions
(5) Knowledge of hygiene and nutrition
(6) Reinforcement of Greek ideals
(7) Forerunners of modern sports.

Essay suggestions

(1) Compare the role of the Church in Renaissance education with its role in education today. Particular emphasis should be given to factors that have influenced the development of physical education.
(2) 'The social, scientific, cultural, economic, political and religious revolutions of the Renaissance brought with them a revolution in physical education and sport. The values and attitudes that developed then, with regard to physical education, have remained with us ever since.' Discuss.
(3) To what extent have modern physical education programmes been directly or indirectly influenced by:
  (a) Leonardo da Vinci?
  (b) Henry VIII?

Laboratory work 68: Historical excursion

(1) Select some places of historical significance to visit. They could include such places as:
- The Royal Melbourne Tennis Club
- Kooyong Tennis Stadium
- Albert Park Tennis Courts
- Royal Ballarat Tennis Club
- Melbourne Cricket Ground
- Royal Melbourne Golf Club
- Site of the proposed National Tennis Centre.

(2) Describe:
  (a) The physical appearance of the place
  (b) The type of atmosphere you experienced there
  (c) The relevant information you received from your tour guide or teacher
  (d) Any other observations you made about the historical qualities of the place.

41. Nineteenth-century influences on sport and physical education: Outline

It is difficult to look at *all* the ways in which nineteenth-century developments in sport and education have affected us. Instead, three main areas will be considered:

- P. H. Ling and gymnastics in Sweden
- J. Jahn and physical education in Germany
- The development of organized games in Britain.

P. H. Ling and the development of gymnastics in Sweden

Several main factors influenced the development of physical education in Sweden during the early nineteenth century:

- The initial reason for participating in physical education was a military one. Following the wars of the eighteenth century, Swedes had a strong sense of patriotism and eagerness to be well trained in physical education in case of later wars.
- Physical education was popular with the monarchy and the government, and was encouraged in schools. Many teachers practised methods that they had learned from Germany.
- Sweden's harsh, cold climate was conducive to the development of indoor activities.

The efforts of P. H. Ling

However, the single most important influence on the development of physical education and, in particular, gymnastics, in Sweden after 1814 was P. H. Ling. His main aim was to make physical education available to the whole population. Gymnastics, to him, included many games and sports. Ling's system is described in the next section. In brief, Ling divided gymnastics into four groups, and he developed a system of exercises with seven advantages to students.

Ling insisted that physical education and medicine should be closely allied. He was very interested in the therapeutic value of exercise, and his system of medical gymnastics became widely accepted.

Ling's influence spread so widely that, after his death, gymnastics became the basis of physical education in Sweden. Military gymnastics flourished in secondary schools.

Later, Ling's system was adapted to a more graceful form for women and children.

By 1900, the influence of Swedish methods was being felt in Britain.

P. H. Ling's system of physical education

Ling divided gymnastics into four groups:

- Educational
- Aesthetic
- Medical
- Military.

He devoted most of his attention to the latter two groups. For his system of free-standing exercises he claimed the following seven advantages:

(1) More students can exercise at one time under one teacher.
(2) The movements can be performed in a variety of places — for example, on the march, in barracks, and in the schoolroom or schoolyard.
(3) His system eliminated the trouble and expense of keeping and maintaining apparatus.
(4) The entire class had to take the exercises at the same moment. Ling claimed that this practice promotes strength and agility and the rapid attainment of body control.
(5) The carrying out of gymnastics at the word of command reinforced the effects of strict military drill.
(6) Free movements are more easily adapted to the body peculiarities of individuals.

(7) His system seemed better than apparatus gymnastics for overcoming awkwardness and stiffness.

There appear to be contradictions between (**4**) and (**5**), and (**6**).

Physical education in nineteenth-century Germany

As in Sweden, physical education was developed because of a combination of political and military factors. The direction of development was guided mainly by two educationalists:

- Johann Gutsmuths
- Johann Jahn.

Johann Gutsmuths (1759–1839)

Gutsmuths wrote extensively on physical education, and many of his theories are still the basis of modern physical education. He developed an extensive physical education system for children.

Johann Jahn (1778–1852)

During the early nineteenth century, the small states of Germany still formed a very unstable alliance. They were under threat from the Napoleon, the French emperor.

Jahn was a soldier and an enthusiastic teacher of physical education. He became a national hero with the publication of his very patriotic book, *The German Way of Life*. He wanted to make German youth strong for the struggle against France and the unification of Germany.

He introduced such gymnastic aids as the horizontal bar and the parallel bars. His gymnastic clubs spread all over Germany, and he envisaged physical education for the whole population. He upheld the value of educating the 'whole man'.

Jahn's political views earned him enemies within Germany. About 1820 his gymnasiums were closed down and he spent six years in prison. In 1840 the bans were lifted by the new king, and Jahn's movement flourished, although he himself retired from public life.

By the mid-1800s, medical practitioners began to support the value of physical education and as a result it was introduced to schools.

By the late 1800s, new threats of war encouraged more and more people to join gymnastic clubs.

The influence of Speiss

In the late 1860s a man called Speiss challenged Jahn's methods. Speiss's system of 'order exercises' was designed to promote automatic obedience. He wanted to steer away from military objectives towards subject matter designed for the individual student's development. Jahn's methods, however, prevailed.

English influence

By the 1880s, team sports from England were having a marked influence on German physical education, and this led to a decline in the popularity of gymnastics.

The development of organized games in Britain

Because of influence of class distinction in England, two distinct systems of physical education developed:

- The public school system
- The government school system.

Physical education in the public schools

Because of the Industrial Revolution, a whole new group of wealthy people emerged in England. These people did not believe in educating their sons at home, but sent them to the large boarding schools which were set up especially to educate the children of the 'new rich'.

Here a system of sports and games was the basis of physical education. At first, the administrators of these schools placed little importance on physical education. However, during the mid-nineteenth century, the new system of sports and games become more accepted. Many of the public schools developed their own games — for example, Eton Fives. Perhaps the most famous example was the brand of football played at, and named after, the Rugby School. Some critics claimed that sport interfered with schoolwork. Some games were more important than others, and sportsmanship and fair play were significant features of all of them. Also, the need for military training was not overlooked in public school physical education.

Physical education in government schools

Compulsory primary education for all children did not become law in England until 1880. Until then, the main educating bodies for poor and middle-class children were church schools. They were overcrowded and understaffed, and taught only the 'Three Rs' — reading, writing and 'rithmetic.

When the government took over primary schooling, at first it took a keen interest in physical education. However, this interest declined because:

- Available finance had to be channelled into more urgent areas
- There was a lack of playground space in most schools.

Physical education, especially games, became known as an unnecessary luxury.

Meanwhile, schools became interested in gymnastics. Within the small playground space available, teachers could teach 'drill'. When, in the early twentieth century, the education department drafted an official physical education policy, it adopted Ling's system.

The demand for secondary schools for girls was high. However, qualified physical education staff were hard to acquire.

By the late 1800s, team games had become very popular with the masses, and the concept of the professional player had emerged.

Also, the new pastime of going to the beach led to the inclusion of swimming and other water activities in physical education and sports programmes.

Sport in nineteenth-century Australia

During the nineteenth century, class differences seem to have been less important for the development of sport than they were in England. Playing space was more freely available than in England, and people soon became interested in team games, especially the newly invented 'Australian Rules football'. A popular form of physical exercise in summer was swimming, although, as the following article shows, swimmers often ran into trouble with the law because of their bathing costumes.

WAVES AND WOWSERS: THE LIBERATION OF AUSTRALIA'S BEACHES

Australians have one love in common — the seaside. It's there, with socio-economic skins peeled away, that each is as good as the next man or woman baking on the sand. The beach is the headquarters of the country's egalitarianism and a barometer of its social thinking.

It's been that way since the first settlers stripped off their English worsteds and dived in together — butchers, bakers, candlestick makers and gentlemen of independent means. In an age before women were allowed to vote, they could at least enjoy the democracy of the seaside.

More than any other influence, the sea has shaped our character. Like life itself, its ebb and flow has imbued us with a rather fatalistic outlook; a 'she'll be right' and 'fair go' feeling.

Figure 41.1 Ladies a the Victorian seaside at the turn of the century trailed their dresses through the water rather than lift them and reveal an ankle.

Figure 41.2 Elwood beach. Gymnastics were the best way to keep fit without breaking the law.

The sea has shaped our laws, our language, our fashions, and our freedom. A few drops of it flow in the veins of most Australians, as LANA WELLS reports in this extract adapted from a new book.

Four English judges, sitting on the King's Bench Division in London in 1821, found that: 'Bathing in the sea, if done with decency, is not only lawful but proper and often necessary for many of the inhabitants of this country. Bathing promotes health.'

Bathing in the open sea for Australia's early settlers was considered not only unlawful and improper but dangerous. Whether or not it was necessary for the inhabitants of the new colony — with its hot climate and total lack of plumbing — was a matter not discussed by respectable people and not noticed by the others. Most of the settlers, convict or free, regarded any kind of water with well-founded suspicion after long and dreadful sea voyages that ended with their landing on the burning summer sands of deserted beaches. . . .

In Australia's early days, a few intrepid souls did try swimming, spurred by desperation, not delight. Tasmania's history is dotted with the names of convicts who 'disappeared' or drowned while trying to struggle through the icy waters lapping the penal settlement of Port Arthur. Bearing in mind that very few settlers had even the remotest idea of how to stay afloat in the water, it was probably fortunate that they looked on it as an exotic evil.

The laws of the sand have nearly all been moralistic, and were at first based on those back home in the Old Country, where for centuries there had been rules governing the shedding of one's clothes for purposes of bathing in public. For example, Cambridge undergraduates of 1571 knew that if they bathed in the river, they risked a public flogging or a spell in the stocks.

In Australia, many beaches were posted with official signs, making it hard for law breakers to plead ignorance. A notice at South Australia's Brighton beach in 1883 read: 'It is requested that all males bathe north and females south of this notice.'

Victoria's Flinders Shire — which covers some of the best beaches near Melbourne — posted 'Regulation No. 4', an act passed in 1903 and confirmed again in 1913. In effect, it made it hard for anyone over the age of 10 to go for a swim. If they did bother, they had to wear a neck-to-knee costume and 'proceed in a direct line to and from the dressing place'.

One of the problems with another law, which banned swimming during daylight hours, was that people kept drowning in the dark. This absurd law was based purely on the morals of another country far away, where the temptations of sand and surf close to the cities did not exist.

At Sydney's Manly beach in 1902, a couple of yachtsmen were arrested for leaping into the surf after beaching their craft, and two lads walking along The Corso in shorts and singlets heading for 'a joyous plunge in the cool Pacific' were also arrested.

In Victoria, bathers of both sexes were creeping into the water together at Williamstown and Hobsons Bay in 1908, and there was fear that news of this evil habit would

▶

float across Port Phillip Bay to the more popular beaches. It did. In 1911, Councillor Scudd of Moorabbin, shocked to discover mixed bathing going on at beaches under his control, reminded perpetrators it was against the law.

For many years, Sunday bathing was against the law in Melbourne, where the city's first church service had been a Methodist one. The Sabbath was the day of rest, when good clothes were worn and no work was done — at least not by those citizens in a position to make laws. The Sunday bathing ban was first challenged by members of the Open Sea Bathers' League on a Sunday afternoon about 1912. They entered the water at St Kilda, trembling (from the icy day, not fear), but were not arrested. Still no legal action was taken on future well-advertised occasions when the same performance was repeated. Despite pressure, St Kilda Council did not change the Sunday bathing law until about 1922 and by then thousands of bathers, including Methodists, had broken it.

If beach inspectors couldn't cope, 'Vesta', who wrote a column in the Melbourne 'Argus' in 1912, suggested 'vigilance' committees could be formed to control beach behaviour. What was needed were men 'young enough to administer a thrashing, and old enough to be respected'. Women could be punished by 'men's ostracism' and 'cold-shouldering'. The suggestion was never taken up.

Beach laws made in most States around 1912 stood virtually unchanged — although often broken — until the early 1930s. A world war had intervened and there were more important matters on people's minds.

In August 1932 the South Melbourne Council passed a regulation that bathers would have to wear Canadian or skirted costumes and 'no person in a bathing suit may sit, lie, loiter or run along the beach or sea shore and no games (particularly cricket and football) may be played. Sun basking on the beach is permitted only if the bathing costume is covered by short knickers, overcoat, kimono or other suitable covering'. It was all a bit hot!

Three years later, New South Wales swimmers received a nasty shock. The Minister for Local Government, the Honorable E. S. Spooner, 'updated' the antiquated neck-to-knee ordinance (which everyone had forgotten) and announced that, from 1 October 1935, bathers would have to wear costumes with legs at least three inches long, covering the body in front up to the armpits and on the back up to the waist. There was to be a half skirt from the waist down.

But it didn't survive for long. Seaside communities were half-hearted in fining those who broke the fashion code. In October 1936 a Manly magistrate fined a bather for having removed the top half of his costume. The penalty was one shilling.

The trouble with knitted wool or cotton was that it either shrank or stretched when wet. Bathing costumes had an embarrassing tendency to cling to the figure in much the same way as today's cotton T-shirts reveal all when wet.

But — aha! — some swimming and life saving clubs hit on a way to preserve their male members' modesty. Rules were passed that V-shorts (loose versions of modern jockettes) were to be worn over the bathing costumes. The result was eye-catching, accentuating rather than disguising the men's anatomy. The Vs went.

Men were the real law-breakers in those days. They insisted on doing awful things such as rolling their one-piece suits down to the waist, or wearing them over only one shoulder. No one would have believed that half a century later, women would do the same.

The 1930s saw decadence creep on to the beaches. Men began wearing waist-high woollen trunks — not always with a singlet. These trunks were anchored at the waist with a webbing belt and a chrome-plated buckle (which soon rusted).

Speedo sold them in 1936 for 15s 6d [$1.55], promoted with the catchy slogan: 'Next to your figure, Speedo looks best!'

Flappers began wearing backless suits with bare midriffs. All that skin! At Point Lonsdale young Paula Robertson shocked everyone by cutting her one-piece bathing suit in half. 'It was uncomfortable,' she said. Just as locals predicted, Paula went on to create further sensations. She moved to Queensland, married an ex-soldier, Beverley Stafford, and launched a hot number known as the bikini.

In 1952, this obscene fashion began showing signs of 'catching on'. Concerned citizens cried 'ban it!' Headlines were made, opinion polls conducted, and beach inspectors suddenly became arbiters of what was and was not acceptable beach attire.

Bondi beach's chief inspector Aub Laidlaw (who became nearly as famous as the beach itself) said in a report in the 'Sydney Morning Herald' of 4 October 1961: 'I think a lot more girls are trying to get away with daring costumes. I sent three off the beach today. Another fortnight and we'll have them weeded out.'

So great is the influence of the seaside on the Australia way of life that it wasn't long before doctors began using the 'bikini cut' — defined even further in Melbourne as the 'Portsea back beach bikini cut' — for abdominal surgery.

Victoria and South Australia seem to have had a kind of jetty-building competition. Each State felt it was without peer in this respect, and each construction was grander than the next.

Esplanades, jetties and sea walls were built for families to take the sea air rather than go for 'a dip in the briny'. Dipping one's person in the briny was claimed by the 'Popular Encyclopedia' in 1890 to be 'very salutary in several complaints, as diseases of the glands of all kinds, and of the skin in scrofula and a scrofulous predisposition'. It was also said to be good for calming 'hysteric attacks, epilepsy, and St Vitus's Dance.'

The 'Encyclopedia' advised those in doubt that 'ordinary sea bathing is, of course, cold', and warned that it was not suited for everyone and was 'taken much too indiscriminately'. It also emphasised that children 'because of the little resisting power of their young bodies are very readily depressed by sea bathing and are not to be subjected to it as a matter of course'.

Children, for this reason as much as propriety, were usually only allowed to remove their boots and wade. Little girls, trussed up in bloomers and frilly white cottons, clutching huge hats on their heads, paddled in the shallows while their alert mothers watched (fully dressed, including boots) from the sand. Boys were slightly luckier in as much as they didn't wear dresses.

Women who took sea baths in the mid-1800s were few and privileged. The well-to-do, such as Mrs Thomas Anne Ward Cole, who lived at Brighton, Victoria, in a now-demolished mansion called 'St Ninian's', would occasionally indicate her wish to bathe in the sea to her butler, who would give the nod to the gardener, who would then clear the beach for his mistress.

Only 50 years ago, sun bathing or sun 'basking' in a state of semi-undress on the beach was illegal. Anyone sitting or lying on the sand had to be 'suitably covered' with shorts, a beach robe or a kimono. The absurdity of 'sun basking in overcoats' became a major issue, especially in Melbourne, where Victorian morals were strongly defended.

Running in a bathing suit on the beach was also banned. But careful scrutiny of the rules and regulations revealed that the law-makers had forgotten to ban gymnastics on the beach. Young men and women quickly realised it was a way to kept fit, get a tan, and not get into trouble. It was, of course, the very kind of exhibitionism the wowsers had sought to prevent.

— Lana Wells, from *Sunny Memories, Australians at the Seaside* (Greenhouse), quoted in *The Age*, Melbourne, 20 November 1982

FOOTBALL B.C. (BEFORE COLLINGWOOD)

[Collingwood Football Club did not come into existence until 1892; this article gives some idea of what Australian Rules football was like before then.]

> The mellow glow of autumn is yet upon the scene, but lengthening shadows and fast deepening tints betoken winter's near approach while the oval's heavy thud is heard on many a grassy turf as leather once again rebounds from kindred hide, and the football season of this year of grace gives forth its stirring notes of warning.
>
> Peter Pindar, *The Australian*, 22 April 1882.

Nearly a hundred years ago, a spirited crowd of Australian Rules fans met the English team at Spencer Street and escorted them as they were driven in a pair of drays to the Town Hall, where the mayor and other worthies waited. The team, sponsored by those great cricket entrepreneurs Lillywhite and Shrewsbury, went on to the balcony, where cheers rang out from the assembled crowd.

The city organist, Mr David Lee, played a selection of selected English airs, the Coronation March, Forget Me Not (Macbeth) and the National Anthem. The Englishmen were royally entertained by the mayor in his private rooms, and toasted with champagne. Mr Seddon, the English captain, rose in response.

So far, he said, his team had been so absorbed in their rugby matches that they had had few opportunities to practise the Australian game. But the more they saw of it, the better they liked it. (Cheers.) Some of their players had gone so far as to say already that they liked it better than their own game. (Cheers.) He was certain that Victorians would be much pleased if his team took kindly to the Australian Rules and introduced the game to England upon their return, so that in a few years they might expect to see an Australian team of footballers meeting the best teams of England as the cricketers were now doing. (Loud cheers.)

The Englishmen were then conveyed to South Melbourne for further hospitality and a view of a game in progress at the Lake Oval.

This was Thursday, 14 June 1888, and the first international game of Australian football was set down for Saturday. It's an indication of the confidence and flexibility of Marvellous Melbourne that such a thing could not only be conceived of, but actually against all odds happened. A Maori team also travelled to the colonies in 1888.

Football is still trying to make an indentation in Sydney, let alone host not one but two international tours. Football had, from the first, seen itself as an international game, one with equal rights to rugby and British Association football, and even American football. . . .

Great excitement gripped the football public of Melbourne on that Saturday, 16 June 1888, and 29,355 fans paid £723 to watch the handsomely accoutred Englishmen play the previous season's premiers, Carlton, at the MCG.

The sporting crowd applauded every act of smart play by England, and only moderately cheered the doings of the Old Blues, partly, one supposed, because most supporters at the MCG barracked for the other 15 teams in the competition that year.

'It was thought they [the English] would exhibit no aptitude whatever for our style of play, but this was the opinion of only the extremists amongst our native population, and it was more than counterbalanced by the absurd idea entertained in quarters where everything Australian is despised, namely, that the visitors would have no difficulty in putting our men through. Neither prediction was verified in the encounter.

'England kicked very well indeed; they also dribbled the ball neatly and effectively, though the hand-play of the Carlton team more than outshone this feature of England's play. England were quite as fast and every bit as active as the Dark Blues, but their speed and activity were in many instances misdirected.

'One of their more noticeable weak spots was that England's placed men frequently lost sight

Figure 41.3

of Carlton's placed men and allowed them to wander off by themselves, so that when the ball was kicked forward the latter had no difficulty securing and getting away with it.

'Then again, the Englishman, when he gave chase to a colonial who had got a start with the ball, as a rule clapped on full sail; and when the downy native stopped suddenly and dodged with his customary adroitness to the left or the right his bewildered pursuer continued on his headlong course for several yards before he could get his brake to act.'

The one feature of the Englishmen's play which was least satisfactory was their very indifferent marking. Instead of taking a mark when it was offered they simply knocked it away in front of them, thus time after time they lost golden opportunities.

Carlton gave a splendid exhibition of the various points of the game. Their marking and kicking were magnificent, and their dodging and shepherding were perfect. Carlton players must have astonished the visitors, around and among whom they glided, eluding with apparent ease the vigorous efforts of the latter to overhaul them.

Carlton won 14 goals 17 behinds to England 2 goals 7 behinds. . . .

It was in the 1880s that Australian football became the game we would immediately recognise today, becoming less a bruising game of packs of players fighting over the ball, with big men ploughing through scattering the opposition. Geelong, the dominant club with Carlton and South Melbourne at this time, introduced a thing that was called 'team work'. It was accused by traditionalists of shirking the tough game by having players 'hanging out' from the packs. This was plainly such a sensible innovation, because it won matches, that it caught on.

It was Essendon's 'Commotion' Pearson who invented our game's most distinctive feature, the high mark. He would sail over the heads of his earthbound opponents, arms outstretched in great feats of acrobatics, to the dismay of old timers, and the fears of the public.

'At East Melbourne ground on Saturday Mr Pearson, who was the outstanding player for Essendon, gave spectators many thrilling moments with his phenomenal leaps skyward. Ladies in the pavilion screamed for fear Mr Pearson would cause some serious injury to himself when he caught the ball high above the others but toppled down head first among the bunch.' The 'Argus' said: 'While Mr Pearson takes risks with his rocket-like leaps into the air, who knows but that this may be a new revolution in high marking. What a thrill the game would become as spectacle if all players tried out this new idea. Perhaps in years to come we will see players all over the field sailing up in the air in this Pearson-like fashion.' . . .

The business of clubs trading in players is 100 years old as well. Wrote Peter Pindar: 'And in this connection a very good joke came recently under my notice in relation to a rising Northern player, who was regarded with longing looks by a rival concern over the river, and who, moreover, was fully determined his wares should bring their highest market value.

'The club with which he was identified and in which he had become known to fame, went out of its way to find him constant employment last season, and all went merry as a marriage bell until the preliminary canters this year, when the enticing rival decided to go one better.

'They not only found him work, but also a house, rent free, and a reasonable prospect of a fair fee per match. The bargain was then struck, and he shifted his camp, but whether he was dissatisfied with his surroundings, or whether he felt himself "a stranger in a strange land", or whether his old club agreed to improve his conditions, history does not disclose.

'At any rate, he resolved on abandoning his new quarters, and the other night a number of his former comrades, to make sure of him, hired a van, and carted him bag and baggage, household goods and belongings, back to where he came from, to the great disgust of his more recent friends.'

The moral of this story was 'football will soon be confined to two or three clubs whose financial resources enable them to monopolise the best talent, and what is now a mere manly recreation will speedily become but a money-making game, with all its attendant evils.'

— Garrie Hutchinson,
The Age, 27 March 1982

The development of lawn tennis

During the nineteenth century, Royal tennis had declined in popularity mainly because:

- The game was too costly for most people to play
- The type of ball used did not encourage exciting play.

Sphairistike

In the mid-1800s, the india-rubber ball was invented. In 1858 Major Harry Gem marked out a court on his lawn, based on the Royal tennis court.

Major Walter Wingfield devised the modern version of tennis, which he called **sphairistike** (see Figure 41.5). Soon it was popularly known as lawn tennis. Wingfield's game, which was introduced in 1873, was played on an hourglass-shaped court.

Spreading popularity of lawn tennis

Croquet lawns were suitable for the game of lawn tennis, and its popularity spread quickly through the upper classes of England, and in just over a year it was being played in the USA. The MCC met to standardize the rules in 1875.

In 1877 the All England Croquet Club was in financial difficulty. It was decided that the new game of tennis might attract spectators, so the name was changed to the All England Croquet and Lawn Tennis Club.

The All England Club drew up its own rules for

Figure 41.4 Sporting dress.

the game of lawn tennis. The first fund-raising venture was to stage a Gentlemen's Singles Championship in 1877.

The first US championship was held in 1881, the first French championship in 1891, and the first German championship in 1893.

In 1899 Dwight Filley Davis and his partner won the US doubles. In 1900 he donated a silver bowl for competition between the US and Britain. This was the Davis Cup. Within the next 20 years, many other countries, such as Australia, joined the Davis Cup competition.

Early changes in rules and tactics

Spencer Gore was the first lawn tennis player to advance towards the net and volley the ball before it crossed the net. There was a demand to outlaw the volley, but the resulting rule change was to stop the racquet from crossing the net.

Soon Gore's opponents realized that his tactics could be beaten by the lob. Later players devised ways of using the serve for attack.

Research work 6: Sport and education during the nineteenth century

Research topics

(1) Compare the ideals of Jahn with those of German society during the 1930s.
(2) Physical activity in the armed forces.
(3) Evaluate Ling's 'seven advantages' of his method of physical education.
(4) The main types of gymnastics.
(5) The English public school system.

Figure 41.5 Lawn tennis, or sphairistike.

(6) Games devised at particular English public schools.
(7) The development of major sports.
(8) Physical education in nineteenth-century Australia.

Possible influences on today

(1) Therapeutic exercise
(2) Nationalism and sport
(3) The concept of 'sport for all'
(4) Gymnastics, of all types
(5) Major sports
(6) Professionalism
(7) Spectatorism
(8) Sport and the military (especially as found in Eastern Europe)
(9) Sportsmanship
(10) Physical education in schools
(11) The variety of football codes
(12) Training of physical education teachers
(13) Sports associations.

Essay suggestions

(1) 'The modern system of Australian physical education has its roots in developments which took place in nineteenth-century Europe.' Discuss.
(2) Discuss reasons why the team games that originated in nineteenth-century Britain have survived to become the basis of today's major sports.

Oral history research

Interview some people of your grandparents' generation and write a report that includes such topics as:

(1) The way of life in their youth
(2) Their experiences in their youth
(3) Their experience, when young, of formal physical education
(4) The physical activities in which they indulged
(5) The major spectator sports when they were young
(6) The main issues related to sport when they were young
(7) Their perceptions of how physical education and sport have changed since they were young.

42. The development of twentieth-century Australian sport

Rather than trying to trace the development of all the major sports that have developed in Australia during the twentieth century, the first part of this chapter will concentrate on one sport: tennis.

This section provides the outlines of possible directions you might take while carrying out your own research into other motor activities.

The beginnings of Australian tennis during the nineteenth century

In Australia, as in America and England, lawn tennis found its first home on the private lawns of the rich.

By the late 1870s, the game had become more competitive, and the Melbourne Cricket Club was responsible for early developments in tennis. In 1878 an asphalt court was built at the Melbourne Cricket Ground (MCG). In 1879 a lawn court was put down. In 1880 the MCC was responsible for organizing Australia's first tournament: the Victorian Championships.

In 1884, women's events were introduced to the Victorian Championships. 1884 also saw the start of men's pennant competition between suburban clubs. Throughout the 1890s the Victorian Championships were played at the Albert Cricket Ground (now the Junction Oval).

In 1885 the Sydney Lawn Tennis Club inaugurated the NSW titles, and the first intercolonial match betwen NSW and Victoria was held at the Sydney Cricket Ground (SCG).

By 1892 NSW, Queensland and South Australia had formed tennis associations.

Developments in tennis during the twentieth century

In 1904 Australia and New Zealand combined and entered the Davis Cup competition in 1905 as Australasia. The two countries remained a combined force until 1921. Australasia won the Davis Cup in 1907, and held it for five years. In 1908 the first Davis Cup Challenge Round was held in Australia, at the Albert Ground.

In 1901 in Melbourne, women's pennant competition tennis began. In 1905 the first Australian National Men's titles were held, but competition was not open to women until 1922.

In 1907 Norman Brookes won the Wimbledon Championship for Australia.

In 1908 the first Victorian schoolboys' and schoolgirls' tournaments began.

On 20 December 1919 the Lawn Tennis Association of Victoria (LTAV) purchased an area of 17.5 acres (7 ha) of freehold land at Kooyong for £3080. The Kooyong Tennis Stadium was completed in 1922.

Australia's domination of world tennis since 1938

From 1938 until 1959, Australia and the US dominated the Davis Cup competition. In the 1950s and 1960s, world championship tennis was dominated by Australian players such as Lew Hoad and Neale Fraser.

Traditionally, champion tennis players remained amateurs. In the early 1950s, the American player Jack Kramer began to encourage top players to turn professional. The professional movement became important during the 1960s, and 1968 saw the first Open Championship (including both amateurs and professionals) at Wimbledon.

In 1970, the tie-breaker — virtually the only modern innovation to the game — was introduced.

The position of tennis in today's Australia

Tennis has become one of the most popular sports

of this century. Modern tennis players are among the highest paid sportsmen and women in the world. The game is booming in Australia. Youngsters are encouraged to take up the sport, and many facilities have been developed. Competition tennis in Victoria is organized by the Victorian Tennis Association (VTA). There are plenty of opportunities for young people to have professional coaching.

Perhaps Australia will again become *the* major force in world tennis.

THE VICTORIAN TENNIS ASSOCIATION

The Victorian Tennis Association is the state body controlling tennis in Victoria. We are recognized as such by the Victorian Government and the LTAA (Lawn Tennis Association of Australia), the parent body of tennis in Australia.

Approximately 1350 clubs and associations throughout Victoria are affiliated with us, either directly or indirectly. This represents around 25,000–30,000 tennis players, approximately 90 per cent of all tennis players in the state.

The VTA runs a number of annual tournaments and competitions for both adult and junior players. Of the senior competitions, Winter Pennant is the largest. In this competition, teams from clubs all over the metropolitan area are entered in various grade events, ranging from 'D' to 'A', and play every weekend from April to September. A similar competition for junior players belonging to clubs affiliated with associations is run from mid-September to the end of November. This competition is sponsored by the Shell Co. of Australia, and is known as the Association's Junior Competition.

In February each year the VTA organizes a Country Carnival. This is a mammoth event which runs for a week; literally hundreds of top players from the country converge on Melbourne for five or six days' tennis and festivities. A similar event is run for metropolitan associations over the Labour Day weekend.

The VTA also administers such traditional events as Victorian Hardcourt Championships for seniors and the Johnson Wax, Victorian Junior Lawn and Schoolboys/Schoolgirls Championships for juniors. In addition, the VTA runs junior fitness squads and coaching programmes for a number of the more promising juniors. These are run early in the morning and at weekends during term time. From these training squads boys and girls are selected for such interstate events as the Linton, Wilson and Reid Cups.

Nearly all tournaments run by Victorian clubs and associations are approved by the VTA, which produces an annual tournament calendar listing details of each tournament and giving contact names and numbers. Clubs usually forward copies of their entry forms to the VTA, and members of the public are welcome to pick these up at any time during office hours.

In order to assist clubs and associations to make money, and save time for honorary officials, the VTA administers fund-raising schemes. These include computerization of club membership records and VTA Insurance. Under the latter scheme, clubs or their members canb take out insurances through the VTA; the resulting commission is shared between the club concerned and the VTA.

All these activities require a tremendous amount of administration. Think of it — planning events, designing entry forms, distributing same, doing draws, organizing courts, issuing press releases and obtaining trophies, to name but a few.

Of particular interest to young people is the Schoolboys/Schoolgirls Championships, sponsored by Hooker Rex. This is open to all schoolchildren in Victoria, and is run early in December. Each country region is encouraged to select four (boys and girls) of its more promising juniors, who are then brought to Melbourne and accommodated and entertained, free of charge, for the week. This tournament is a great opportunity for any young person in Victoria to demonstrate his or her tennis ability. The next Newcombe or Cawley could even start this way!

—Victorian Tennis Association

OUR TENNIS TRADITION BEGAN WHEN THE GAME WAS ALL GOOD FUN

Jack Hawkes is old enough to be John McEnroe's grandfather, and that just about sums up the generation gap between tennis as it was played in 1926 — when Hawkes was Australian champion — and the McEnroe era. . . .

Where did the Australian teenis tradition begin? With Norman Brookes, winning Wimbledon in 1907 and combining with the New Zealander Anthony Wilding the same year to win the Davis Cup for Australasia. With Gerald Patterson, who won Wimbledon in 1919 and 1922. And with Patterson's doubles partner, J. B. (Jack) Hawkes, who won the Australian Open in 1926, reached the Wimbledon doubles final in 1928, and played Davis Cup between 1921 and 1925.

Sir Norman Brookes and Gerald Patterson are no longer alive, but Jack Hawkes is 83, active, and full of reminiscences which return to him as he stares out to sea from his home at Ocean Grove. He features prominently in a book

Figure 42.1 Jack Hawkes in 1932 and 1982: 'Nobody ever threw a racquet down. There was no money, and no bad behaviour.'

written . . . to mark [the] centenary of Geelong Lawn Tennis Club. It is called 'The Sweet Spot' and is written by Graeme Kinross-Smith, a senior lecturer in Australian studies at Deakin University.

Hawkes was, and is, a gentleman. At the time he was born, 1899, the only people who played tennis were those families wealthy enough to have their own courts. The Hawkes family had a prosperous hardware business and tennis courts at home in Geelong and at their holiday house in Ocean Grove.

Nobody had ever heard of coaching then. People had a serve, a forehand, and in some cases a volley. But nobody, according to Hawkes, had a backhand. Just like today's social tennis player.

It was the era of dances and great social occasions. The highlight of the Geelong tennis season was the Easter tournament, and the ball at the end of it.

Tennis was fun. Jack Hawkes used to fit in a couple of hours when he could after work during the week and then he would play at weekends.

For reasons of finance, he would travel to only a couple of big tournaments a year, the Australian (which up until 1972 used to move around the States) and perhaps the New South Wales. During World War I the only big championship was the Public Schools title, which Hawkes won from 1914 to 1918.

The year's highlight was the Challenge Round of the Davis Cup, held each year in the US around the end of August. It was the gracious era of travel, when passengers experienced ocean liner timelessness rather than Jumbo jet-lag. Hawkes used to set sail from Melbourne in May and he would arrive in Vancouver three weeks later.

Hawkes's first stop was Vancouver because Australia used to play off against Canada for the right to meet the US in the Challenge Round. It was Hawkes's misfortune to be playing the Americans at a time when Bill Tilden, considered by many judges to be the finest player of all time, was their No. 1. Hawkes lost to Tilden in straight sets, but ran him much closer in the doubles, his specialty.

Hawkes used to be away from Australia between May and September. The Lawn Tennis Association paid his expenses, but the only reason he could afford to be away from work for so long was because his brother used to run the family business for him.

Eventually Hawkes decided he could no longer afford the three-month trips away from the family firm, so he made 1928 his last. This time he purposely included Wimbledon in his itinerary. 'Then, as always, Wimbledon stood out above everything,' he says. 'That and the Davis Cup.' He and Patterson reached the doubles final, losing to Brignon and Cochet, two of the four French Musketeers. But on the way they beat the other two Musketeers, Lacoste and Barotra, as well as Tilden and Hunter.

Hawkes played no serious tournament tennis after that. When we went to visit him recently he had not picked up a racquet for 20 years. He has kept in touch with tennis though, through newspapers and television.

The thought of playing Connors or Lendl or McEnroe frankly alarms him. 'I wouldn't get a game off them,' he says. 'Their game is so complete. They have no weakness. In our time very few players had strong backhands. There was always a weakness you could play to.'

It is sometimes said Jack Kramer, the 1947 Wimbledon champion, invented the serve-and-volley game. Untrue; according to Hawkes, it was perfected by Norman Brookes and later followed by Gerald Patterson and himself.

Hawkes has a bit of trouble seeing the ball from the baseline these days, but put him at the net and the old volleying touch is still there.

Bringing out the racquet also brought out the memories and the scrapbook, and the 'Daily Mirror' picture of the 1928 doubles final at Wimbledon. Patterson was a great fighter, he said. 'H had a manner that did not endear him to everybody. He was outspoken, on and off court.'

'Did he throw his racquet down?'

'Good Heavens, no,' Hawkes said in horror. 'Nobody ever did that.

'There was no bad behavior. There was no money attached, you see. Big difference between winning $100,000 and nothing. It was all good fun in those days. It was serious but there was no animosity towards people. It was not like McEnroe's habits.'

— Richard Yallop,
The Age, Melbourne, 2 October 1982

Current history research: A major issue in sport

(1) Choose a currently important issue in the sport you have chosen as your main study. Exploration of this issue could take the form of various information-collection methods, such as:
- Reviews of books, videos, films, and magazine and news articles
- Interviews, surveys and questionnaires.

(2) Care should be taken to give a balanced view of the issue in question. Surveys, interviews and questionnaires should be directed at a broad sample of people. Where appropriate, sample populations should include:
- A variety of age groups
- Both sexes
- A variety of socio-economic groups
- Professionals and amateurs
- Participants and non-participants
- Students from state, Catholic and independent schools.

Why do people play sport?

FOR THE PRINCE OF ANTIGUA, WINNING IS ALL

Isaac Vivian Alexander Richards does not object to being called the world's greatest batsman.

But he has no liking for the popular Press tag of 'Black Bradman'. He appreciates that such a bracketing is the ultimate accolade for any cricketer, but nevertheless, he can do without it.

'I don't like that title really. I prefer to be called Viv, rather than Black Bradman. Bradman is Bradman. Viv is Viv,' says Richards.

'If there has to be a title, I'm happier with the Prince of Antigua.

'I get to live with being called the greatest batsman in the world. It doesn't worry me because I know there are two sides to the coin, man. If you don't have a particularly good season, people say it looks as though you're finished.

'But there's no pressure. I just like to do what Viv is capable of. Viv goes out to do what Viv can do,' he says smiling, his big brown eyes dancing.

Richards is consistently capable of the exceptional. Next to Sir Donald Bradman, he is the most successful Test batsman in history. In 44 Tests since 1974, he has scored 3969 runs at 62.01.

In 228 first-class matches since 1972, he has gathered 17,004 runs — with 49 centuries — at 48.30.

Figure 42.2 Viv Richards: 'gone cool'.

For an athlete with an imposing body to provide much of the impetus for his savage stroke-play, Richards is subdued, sensitive and self-effacing.

He is, in fact, the antithesis of what you expect. Warm and softly spoken, he is passionate about McEnroe and Frazier, and talks with some animation about their meanness and ruthless competitiveness.

'Joe Frazier is my idol; my complete idol,' he says with the fervor of many a schoolboy talking of Richards himself.

'I really admire him so much. He's so professional in his asttitude to sport, and he's so mean. I've only met him once, but would love to spend more time with him. I just like to look at him.

'John McEnroe is mean too. I like McEnroe. He has a certain way about him. He's competitive and wants to win at all cost. I like that. These are my kind of people'. . .

Richards believes in total competitiveness. He subscribes to the theory of American football coach, Vince Lombardi: 'Winning is not everything, it is the only thing'. However, he strongly objects to disputes being taken off the field.

'Obviously you get bad tempered people out on the field. Everyone wants to win. Some people would kill their own mother to win. I see nothing wrong with a desperate will to win, as long as it's not prolonged after the game.'. . .

Like Bjorn Borg, who as a schoolboy had his racquets taken away by parents irked by his unruly court demeanor, Richards has learned the hard way. As a teenager, he was suspended for two years for disputing a decision and abusing an umpire.

'I've certainly learned by my mistakes. I get mixed up in the odd thing now and again, but nothing to compare with when I was younger. Then I was a bit fiery and all that.'. . .

Richards, who admits to being a more responsible person following marriage and fatherhood. . . is irked by feelings of stress.

'You're going to get things that upset you. But I try not to get too upset because when I'm upset I get a headache and feel uncomfortable. I want to feel happy within myself. If I get upset I try and sleep it off.'

— Mike Coward,
The Age, Melbourne, 18 November 1981

Research work 7: Why do people play sport?

(1) Compile a list of reasons why people play sport.
(2) Select a few of those reasons, and study them in depth.
(3) Give examples to illustrate each of these reasons.
(4) Give your own opinions about the value of these reasons given for playing sport. Are there any positive or negative aspects to the playing of sport for these reasons?

Suggested research project titles

(1) 'Win at all costs' is a common saying. What arguments can be put forward to agree or disagree with this saying?
(2) 'People indulge in physical activity for many reasons — some good, some bad.' Discuss.

Society's attitudes to sport

THE SOCCER TRIBE

The human animal is an extraordinary species. Of all the events in human history, the one to attract the largest audience was not a great political occasion, nor a special celebration of some complex achievement in the arts or sciences, but a simple ball-game — a soccer match. On a June day in 1978, it is claimed that more than a thousand million people tuned in to the World Cup Final between Argentina and Holland. This means that something like one-quarter of the entire world population stopped whatever they were doing and focused their attention on a small patch of grass in South America where twenty-two brightly clad figures were kicking a ball about in a frenzy of effort and concentration.

If this occurrence was monitored by aliens on a cruising UFO, how would they explain it? What would they record in their ship's log? A sacred dance of some kind? A ritual battle? A religious ceremony, perhaps? If their curiosity was aroused and they carried out a survey of human cities around the globe, they would quickly discover that almost every major settlement boasted at least one large, hollow building with a green hole in the middle on which similar ball-kicking rituals could be observed at regular intervals. Clearly, ball-kicking has some special significance for the human species — a unique obsession not shared by any of the hundreds of thousands of other life forms visible on the planet earth.

The biggest problem for the puzzled aliens would be discovering the function of this strange activity. Why do thousands of people do it and why do millions of other people watch them doing it? What possible fulfilment can it bring? On the surface it appears to be little more than a child's playground game, a harmless pleasure gained from the realization that striking a spherical object produces a much more spectacular movement than hitting any other shape. For children, this is merely an amusing pastime, part of the business of exploring the physical properties of the environment, like skipping, jumping, rolling a hoop or spinning a top. But unlike these other juvenile actions, ball-kicking, for some strange reason, persists into adulthood and acquires the trappings of a major industry. It is no longer accompanied by high-pitched laughter, but by deep groans, shouts and roars from manly throats. It is now a serious endeavour, with every move dissected and debated in earnest tones, the whole ritual elevated to the level of a dramatic social event. There must be more to it than meets the eye. Since the actions themselves are so simple, the true explanation must be that they have somehow become loaded with a symbolic significance.

Hardly anyone seems to query the importance attached to the game. For those who do the kicking and those who watch it so avidly, the whole matter is taken for granted. Football is football, and of course it is fascinating, so what is there to question? For those who ignore it, it is plainly a stupid waste of time, so why bother with it? It is not worth discussing. Both sides overlook the fact that, viewed objectively, it is one of the strangest patterns of human behaviour to be seen in the whole of modern society.

With this in mind I decided to carry out my own investigation. It soon became clear that each centre of football activity — each football club — was organized like a small tribe, complete with a tribal territory, tribal elders, witch-doctors, heroes, camp-followers, and other assorted tribesmen. Entering their domain I felt like an early explorer penetrating for the first time some remote native culture. I understood little of their echoing war-chants or their colourful displays, their primitive superstitions or their weird customs. It occurred to me that the best course of action was to behave as if I really *were* an anthropologist making an unbiased field-study, and I set about a systematic analysis of this strange and often savage 'Soccer Tribe'.

— Desmond Morris,
Introduction, *The Soccer Tribe*,
Jonathan Cape, 1981

Research work 8: Society's attitudes to sport

(1) What are the differing attitudes to sport prevalent in today's society:
   (a) Are these attitudes related directly to sport? — for example, 'Football is a violent sport because many injuries result from it.'

   or

   (b) Are these attitudes related indirectly to sport? — for example, 'Football is a violent sport because the spectators often brawl.'

(2) How justified are these attitudes?
(3) How do these attitudes affect sports?
(4) Which attitudes are good for sport?
(5) In what ways would sport benefit if some of these attitudes were to disappear?

Suggested research project titles

(1) 'Fanaticism is just as unhealthy as being an "armchair athlete".' Discuss.
(2) 'Society needs sporting heroes.' Discuss.
(3) 'The sub-culture of English soccer, as described by Desmond Morris in *The Soccer Tribe* (see above), could easily be applied to Australian sport.' Discuss.
(4) Heather McKay was 19 times World Women's Squash Champion, but is unknown by most Australians. Ken Rosewall never won Wimbledon, but is a household name to most Australians. Why do some sports create more interest in society than others?
(5) There are many different attitudes to sport in our society. Discuss some of these, with particular reference to how they affect support for, and the organization of sport in Australia.

The economics of sport

STRETCHING FOR THE ALMIGHTY TENNIS DOLLAR

The annual meeting of Tracy Austin Enterprises took place in London last Sunday. The officers of the corporation — Austin, her mother, Jeanne, her father, George, and two of the partners of the Washington law firm which handles her affairs, Donald Dell and Frank Craighill, met to discuss her 1981–82 earning and investment performance.

The 19-year-old, currently ranked No. 3 in the world, has so far amassed $1.6 million in prize-money in her five-year career, and that figure would have been considerably surpassed by additional income raised from endorsement contracts of tennis equipment and other products.

Dell, described by 'World Tennis' magazine as the most powerful man in tennis, likes to put his clients into oil and gas. 'Not exploratory drilling in the middle of the desert, that's too risky,' he says, 'but developmental drilling, on proven fields,' He favors drilling because the US Government allows tax concessions on it. 'I tell my clients it's not how much you're paid, but how much you keep that matters.'

It is now 13 years since tennis went 'open', in the sense that payments to players which had been previously made under the counter became above board and players were allowed to increase their earnings as tennis professionals.

The sport has exploded beyong anyone's comprehension. Next year there will be a Grand Prix circuit with prize money worth $18 million, a rival WCT circuit of 15 tournaments worth $300,000 each run by Texan oil millionaire Lamar Hunt, and exhibitions and private promotions worth as much as the entire tournament programme.

Then there is the Davis Cup, sponsored to the tune of $2 million, the ladies' team equivalent, the Federation Cup, other minor team competitions, junior competitions, and so the list goes on.

'In 13 years, tennis has swallowed golf commercially,' Dell said. 'The top 100 players in tennis would earn three times as much as the top 100 in golf.' . . .

Dell's background is tennis, politics and law, which is a perfect indication of the direction the sport is currently facing. He played Davis Cup five times for the US between 1961 and 1963, went into law, and then campaigned for Bobby Kennedy in 1968.

Kennedy's assassination, and the offer of the US Davis Cup captaincy in 1968 and 1969, caused him to turn away from mainstream politics into the politics of tennis. He was a founding member of the Association of Tennis Professionals — the players' union — and then helped establish the Men's Council, which runs the Grand Prix.

His main platform now is his law firm, Dell, Craghill, Fentress and Benton, which is one of the two major player management companies in the world, the other being Mark McCormack's International Management Group. Another company, Proserv, handles marketing and merchandising for Dell's clients.

Roughly speaking, Dell controls half the tennis players in the world, and McCormack has the other half, and competition between the two is ferocious. They fight for players, for television rights, for the best endorsement deals, for the biggest piece of the action. . . .

The agents are an immensely powerful group, characterised by the arrogance of knowing they have a product to sell that everyone — media, manufacturers, and tournament directors — wants to buy. If you leave a telephone message asking them to ring back, there is an 80 per cent chance they won't return the call. . . .

Dell started his player management business with Arthur Ashe and Stan Smith . . . , Bob Lutz and Charlie Pasarell. His prize possession now is Ivan Lendl . . . . He also has Gene Mayer, Roscoe Tanner, and nine of the 16 men's seeds at Wimbledon. His personal fee is $200 an hour on contract negotiations, or 20 per cent on endorsement contracts. . . .

'My first responsibility is to look after my clients and maximise their earnings and career opportunities,' Dell said. 'No, I don't think the players are screwing the game.

'And what the hell does the good of the game mean anyway? Before tennis went open the players got screwed. A player could not even afford to take his wife with him on the plane. Now 15-year-olds can afford to take three or four people with them. I am a product of the sport. We're businessmen first.'

Tennis may be a business, but would he put his daughters — who are just taking up the game at a coaching camp in Florida — on the tour? His wife Carole says she would like them to be club players but no more. 'I am 60–40 in favor of them becoming pros,' Dell said. 'It would be fun to see them play at Wimbledon, but I won't push them.'

— Richard Yallop,
The Age, Melbourne, 3 July 1982

Research work 9: Economics of sport

Research of this subject could cover any of the following topics:

(1) Sponsorship of sport
(2) Government funding of sport
(3) Sport on television
(4) Professionalism and amateurism
(5) Gambling and sport
(6) Sport: the industry.

Suggested research project titles

(1) 'Different socio-economic groups relate differently to particular sports.' Discuss.

(2) 'An amateur is one who competes for the love of sport and as a means of recreation without any motive of securing material gain for such competition.' Discuss.

(3) (a) In what ways is sport supported by governments or the business community?

(b) How does this sponsorship aid the development of sport?

(c) To what extent is sponsorship in sport a positive or negative aspect of our society?

(4) To what extent do the mass media influence the development of sport in Australia?

(5) Would sport survive without gambling?

Women in sport

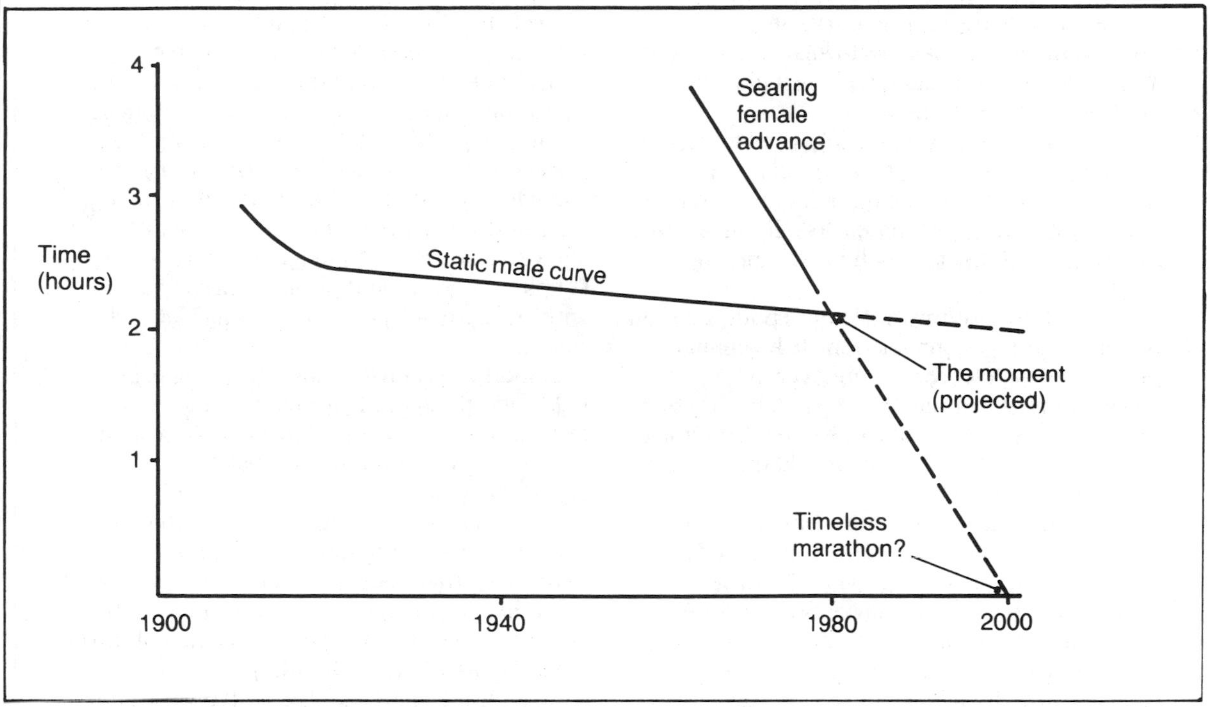

Figure 42.3 Marathon progress.

Strength: Women have 30 per cent less upper body strength

Fat: Women have 20 per cent fat; men have 15 per cent fat

Heart/lung: Women have 10 per cent less haemoglobin — pump less oxygen

Menstruation: Premenstrual tension affects performance; female distance runners often suffer amenorrhea (absence of periods).

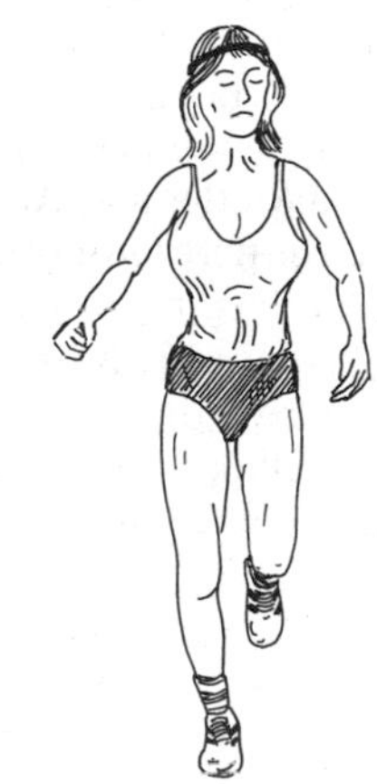

NO, WOMEN JUST CANNOT WIN

'Women in Sport — the Irresistible Advance', trumpet the fashionable headlines that women will soon run faster, jump further and throw things longer than men. In the Open Olympics of the future we are told to expect women to stand alone on the winner's podium.

Part of the hype comes from recent improvements in marathon performance. No matter that women run the 42.2 kilometres some 17 minutes (12 per cent) slower than men, optimists draw the searing curve of improvement in female performance and predict that, in a couple of years, women will be fighting out the finishes with men.

The same logic, by extension, can be used to predict that before the end of the century women will have run the marathon in zero time. They will, as the sporting hacks tell, 'make no race of it!' and 'the race will be over before it began!'

So much for optimism. Realists point up the radical differences in male/female hormonal make-up which leave women severely disadvantaged in athletic comparison with men. Because of inferior strength, women lag some 66 years in high jump, 80 years in 100 metres and 90 years in long jump.

These are huge crosses for women to bear, and they show up when women compete on equal terms with men. In the Melbourne Marathon, for example, survey evidence shows that women train *harder* than men — but they perform worse — some 15 per cent slower. And an analysis of 39 marathons held in Australia, Europe and the US sees women trailing some 30 minutes (21 per cent) behind men.

These are top marathons with Grete Waitz, Lorraine Moller and Allison Roe competing — all elite runners with training inputs around the 200-kilometre-per-week mark. All runners who have dramatically improved their upper body and leg strengths and reduced their fat contents to below 10 per cent. Yet they can't foot it with top men and, as seen from age-group records, the top women actually fight their races against the teenagers and pensioners.

The answer to why women can't beat men, despite identical devotion to training, is easy — just run behind a woman and observe the difference in fat content and distribution compared with men. The extra load on hips, thighs and breasts which has to be carried 42.2 kilometres.

Forget the popular idea that fat is energy, that women have more fat and *ergo*, more energy — you don't use fat in a marathon but, rather, the carbohydrate source, glycogen. It's just a question of useless weight which must be carried. For the average man to run with a woman's fat content he would have to carry a housebrick strapped to the top of each thigh.

On the other hand, female characteristics are advantageous in some sports. In swimming, a high fat content gives a better ride in the water and added insulation. The record for crossing the English Channel is held by a woman. Women also have advantages in sports where suppleness, grace and poise are needed along with strength — sports like gymnastics and skating.

Nonetheless, no woman can ever expect to hold a world record in athletics. The reason is testosterone — the male hormone associated with leanness, strength and 'male' characteristics.

Testosterone is not normally available to the woman athlete, although it is common knowledge that many top women athletes use it, and other steroids, to boost performance. In so doing they are directing their body metabolism towards 'maleness' — building lean muscle which, with weight training, will give strength approaching male potential.

As well as profound physical disadvantages, women have also to fight the Dickensian attitude of sports administrators towards sex. Women have been required to prove their gender, at first by degrading internal examination, and later by chromosome tests. Sports administrators, seeing sex in straight male or female terms, have forced a number of women out of sport because of chromosome abnormalities. Taiwan's Lily Yao, the first woman to fail a chromosome test, was later reported to have given birth.

Males, in contrast, have not been required to prove their physical or chromosomal masculinity in order to compete in sports. Yet we know that sex is, in fact, a sliding genetic scale, and it may be that certain female traits are advantageous in male sports.

Could it be that male ice skaters of great poise, power, grace and, incidentally, of effete disposition are favored genetically ? We will never know because men don't have to pass sex tests.

— John Sumner,
The Age, 25 September 1982

Research work 10: Women in sport

Research of this subject could cover any of the following topics:

(1) Comparisons with men:
  (a) Physical
  (b) Psychological
  (c) Social
(2) Competition between women and men
(3) Women's sports
(4) History of women in sport
(5) The development of sport and physical education in girls' schools.

Suggested research project titles

(1) 'The trend is for women to succeed in traditionally male sports.' Discuss.
(2) 'The role of women in society is reflected in the role of women's sport in society.' Discuss.
(3) 'Women's sport is secondary to men's sport.' Discuss.
(4) Compare the status of women's tennis with that of other women's sports.

Politics and sport

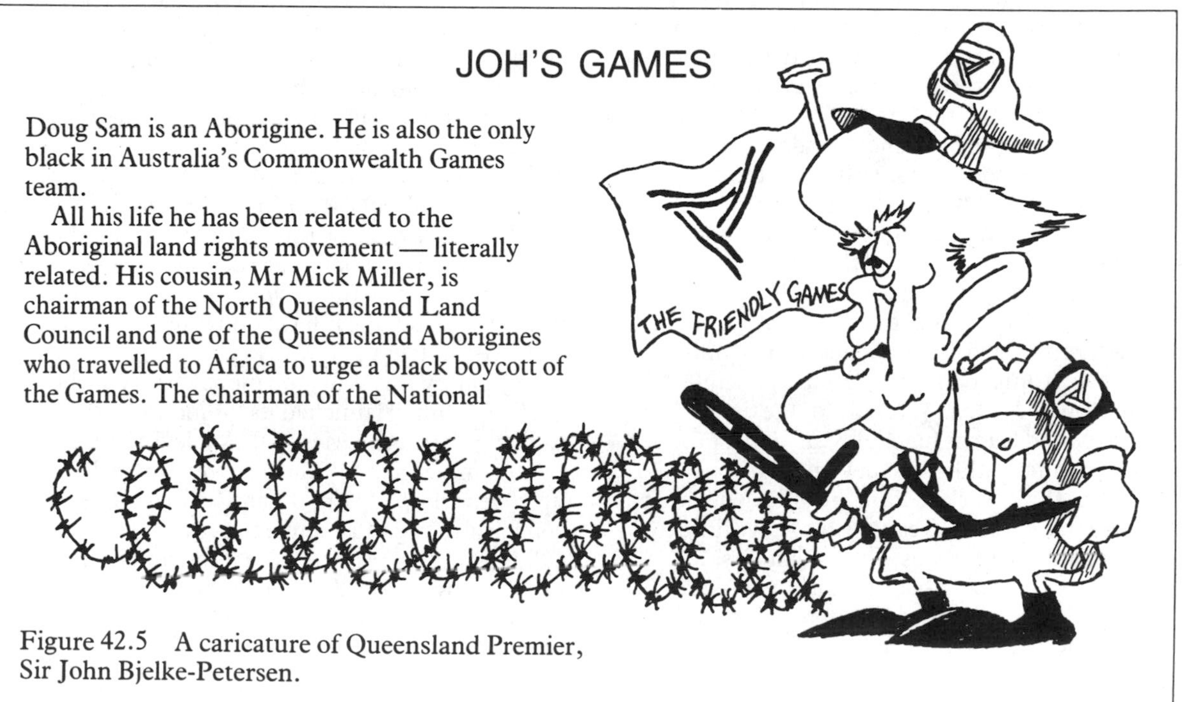

JOH'S GAMES

Doug Sam is an Aborigine. He is also the only black in Australia's Commonwealth Games team.

All his life he has been related to the Aboriginal land rights movement — literally related. His cousin, Mr Mick Miller, is chairman of the North Queensland Land Council and one of the Queensland Aborigines who travelled to Africa to urge a black boycott of the Games. The chairman of the National

Figure 42.5 A caricature of Queensland Premier, Sir John Bjelke-Petersen.

Aboriginal Conference, Mr Steve Mam, is such a close friend that Sam calls him 'Uncle' Steve.

So where does that put the middleweight boxer in the issue of Aboriginal land rights and the Commonwealth Games? 'I guess you could say right in the middle,' he said, as he emerged from his shower at the Railway Insitutute gym in Brisbane's Roma Street.

'It is impossible for me not to sympathise with the land rights movement, but I have trained for 10 years for this chance and I believe I am a good medal prospect. I have to think like a sportsman.'

If anybody thinks he should not be taking part in the Games they have not told him. 'I don't want my relatives and friends to think of me as a turncoat, but boxing is a way for me to get somewhere in life and I think they realise how hard it is to get into the Games. Actually, a lot of people in north Queensland are quite proud of me.'

A lot of white Australians will also be proud of him if he wins a medal. They might be quite proud of him now if they have heard of him, but with only three weeks to go very few Australians could list any or all of our Games team.

With all threats of an African boycott safely behind them, Games organizers are almost ready for the arrival of a record 2500 athletes and officials from 56 nations. Only two members of the Commonwealth Games Federation, Bangladesh and the Seychelles, are not sending a team. Even the Falkland Islands are sending two competitors, large-bore rifle-shooters.

More than 1400 sports reporters, commentators and cameramen are ready to descend on Brisbane and the ABC is setting up a $25 million operation to allow 380 specialists to broadcast the feats of the athletes to an estimated radio and television audience of 1000 million.

According to the foundation's general manager, Mr Dan Whitehead, the first un-boycotted Games for eight years must produce outstanding athletic achievements.

But three weeks before the official opening ceremony, the Games appear to have little to do with athletics for most Queenslanders.

Reports of possible African boycotts and violent protests by land rights groups, and anyone else who thinks the racial policies of Mr Bjelke-Petersen should disqualify Brisbane as host city, have buried the fact that for many Queenslanders the Games are looming as a festival of statehood; proof that the State has come of age and is ready to play host to thousands of foreign visitors who will leave sharing the Queenslanders' conviction that this is the best part of Australia, where the best people live.

When the Games begin, Doug Sam will be in the middle of 50,000 Aborigines from all parts of Australia and the Queensland police force. He will also be in the middle of one huge white land rights festival.

Like the people of Melbourne preparing for the 1956 Olympics, most Queenslanders will become excited only by the exertions, achievements and heartbreak of the people for whom the Games are really held only after the first shot from the starter's gun and the first shot from the television cameras. Like the people of Melbourne, Queenslanders have gone through different moods about the Games and will go through a few more before they start.

Eighteen months ago, the official and commercial mood was the good old-fashioned cringe. Commercial radio commentators and newspaper writers wondered what all those foreign visitors would think of Brisbane. They exhorted Brisbane people to remember that the stranger they might treat in their normal friendly, but probably off-hand and casual way might be a foreigner ready to judge them and take their judgement home with them.

The Tourism Minister, Mr Tony Elliot, inspired talk about casual Brisbane dress standards by saying he thought people should smarten up a bit. There were newspaper articles on the 'ugliness' of the drive the foreign visitors would take from the international airport to any of the city hotels. . . .

In January this year, the mood changed when the City Council launched its 'Shine on Brisbane' campaign, using a series of slick television and radio commercials to exhort citizens to 'pick it up', 'clean it up', 'paint it', and 'trim it'. The council also began a campaign to give away 100,000 trees to replace those its own workers had cut down in the days when the sign of progress in a sub-tropical climate was cleared ground.

The radio and television recordings of the 'Shine on Brisbane' tune were catchy enough for most stations to run many of them free. While the words — 'Now it's true I'll tell you mate, We're from Brisbane and it's great' — might not overstimulate readers, anyone who listend to 'Up There Cazaly' the whole way through would be forced to admit they are infectious.

The campaign had a dramatic impact. According to Brisbane's Labor Lord Mayor, Mr Roy Harvey, a survey taken last month showed 86 per cent of the population said the Games had prompted them to do something to improve the city. More than 51 per cent felt more involved in the Commonwealth Games, 25 per cent had planted trees, and 10 per cent had painted their houses in time for the Games. Overall, 41 per cent 'felt better' about living in Brisbane. . . .

Meanwhile, somewhere in Queensland a large group of the State's fittest and toughest policemen are taking a crash course in using a devastatingly effective weapon called the Monadnock PR24. The PR24 is the unusually long baton with a pistol grip with which New Zealand police inflicted extraordinary injuries on demonstrators during the Springbok rugby tour.

Some of the New Zealand police who put those batons to such telling use are understood to be in Queensland showing police how to use them against Aboriginal protesters who might attempt to disrupt the Games.

'Understood' is the correct word because nobody really seems to know for certain, and for a good reason. The Police Minister, Mr Russ Hinze, who last year told Parliament it was a 'fact that terrorism would be a threat during the Brisbane Games', has imposed a 'blackout' on information about police preparations.

The blackout was imposed after a series of newspaper attacks on the threat to Queensland civil liberties posed by the wide-ranging Commonwealth Games security legislation, passed by Parliament early this year.

It also followed a series of Government-fuelled fear stories which reached an hysterical climax in March with reports quoting unidentified Government and police sources claiming Aborigines were receiving terror training in Libya and guerilla training from a Maori terrorist holed up in the jungles of far north Queensland.

Mr Hinze's officials began drafting the Games Act about the time the chairman of the Aboriginal Development Commission, Mr Charles Pekins, declared as fact that there would be no games without land rights for Queensland Aborigines. Mr Perkins spoke of Aborigines' willingness to shed their blood on Brisbane streets whatever Mr Hinze's 'police thugs' did to them.

When the bill became law early this year, it gave the Government and the police unprecedented powers to effectively suspend several civil rights from 17 September to 10 October. According to the president of the Civil Liberties Council, Mr Terry O'Gorman, the act indicated 'a determination to crush any attempt by Aborigines to peacefully draw world attention to their claims'. . . .

Since the formation of the Black Protest Committee in January there has been a steady procession of Queensland black leaders saying Aborigines do not want violence and are sick of being beaten up.

The co-ordinator of the committee, Mr Budger Davidson, is co-ordinating Aboriginal protest plans from a basement of the office of the Builders' Laborers Federation. He says he is not worried about Mr Hinze's legislation and does not believe there will be Aboriginal violence.

'The Games Act is getting a few white civil libertarians excited, but blacks have lived under that sort of law for ever,' he said. 'We are going to stage the most important peaceful protests in Aboriginal history. We expect at least 50,000 Aborigines, including most of the important elders, to come from all States.

'There will not be any violence, because ratbags who want to cause trouble will be reminded that they are guests of Queensland blacks and will be dealth with under tribal law. If they upset any of the elders they will get a spear in the leg.'

The protest programme includes a mass march from the New South Wales border to Brisbane, a cultural festival, rock concerts by black bands, and traditional dancing, painting and weapon displays.

— David Broadbent,
The Age, Melbourne, 4 September 1982

Research work 11: Politics and sport

Investigation of this subject could include any of the following topics:

(1) Racial discrimination
(2) Patriotism and national prestige
(3) The history of politics in sport
(4) Government policies and sport
(5) International politics.

Suggested titles for research projects

(1) Sporting links with South Africa.

(2) Discuss the role of international sport in developing patriotism and national prestige in Australia. Do you consider this to be a legitimate, or illegitimate, role for sport in society?

(3) 'The image of sport is often damaged by the internal arguments of administrators.' Discuss.

(4) 'The course of international sport is inseparable from that of international politics.' Discuss.

(5) Politics and the Olympic Games.

(6) In recent years the number of black people succeeding in sport in predominantly white societies has increased markedly. Discuss possible reasons for this.

Part Six: Selected issues in the sociology of sport

43. The sociology of sport: Introduction

The following section follows a slightly different pattern from other sections. Some chapters, for instance, follow a question-and-answer pattern that is designed to set you thinking.

This section is designed to encourage you to examine your own collection of current newspaper articles in order to question, identify and begin to explain the sociological patterns that emerge.

Definitions

Before discussing the sociology of sport, we need to define the terms that set the framework for this section. They are:

- Play
- Sport
- Socialization
- Sociology.

Play

Play is 'an enjoyable experience derived from behaviour which is self-initiated in accordance with personal goals or expressive impulses; it tolerates all ranges of movement abilities; its rules are spontaneous; it has a temporal sequence but no predetermined ending; it results in no tangible outcome, victor or reward' (Singer, *Physical Education: Foundations*, p. 32).

PLAY	SPORT
simple spontaneous	complex formulated

Sport

Sport is a 'human activity that involves specific administration, organization and an historical background of rules which define the object and limit the pattern of human behaviour; it involves competition or challenge and a definite outcome primarily determined by physical skill' (Singer, p. 28).

Theoretically, because of its insistence upon rules and equality (disregarding the prejudice that can exist within the framework of sport), sport 'provides an egalitarian utopia in which rich and poor, white and black, can subject themselves to a symbolic test unhampered by the accumulation of wealth or poverty, looks or skin colour' (Ashworth, in *Readings in Sports Psychology*, p. 171).

Socialization

Socialization is 'the (dynamic) process by which one inherits the culture of one's society, learning its norms, roles, values and expectations' (that is, education for life) (Singer, p. 278).

Sociology

Sociology is 'a science concerned with the study of society, social institutions and all human relationships. Sociology attempts to isolate the underlying regularities of human social behaviour' (Singer, p. 269).

44. Determining Australia's sporting identity

Who is the Australian sportsperson?

How his brown strength drove through the hollow and coil of green — through weirs of water!
Muscle of arm thrust down long muscle of water.
And swimming so, went out of sight. . . .

— Judith Wright, 'The Surfer'

or

'Norm' carving a suitable depression in the lounge suite and footy stand?

OUR UGLY HEROES

Australia is basking in the glory of recent sporting achievements, but THOMAS KENEALLY is disappointed by the ugly side of modern sporting heroes. This article by Keneally, the prize-winning author of 'Schindler's Ark', is reprinted from 'The Great Australian Annual' . . .

Some years ago, writing in 'The Age', I made the claim that all Australians of whatever eminence see themselves as failed sportsmen.

I cite the case of David Williamson, who as a lofty three-year-old was patted on the head by relatives and assured: 'You'll be jake for

Figure 44.1 Don Bradman batting during the 1930s.

Collingwood in the ruck, little Dave,' but who was never jake for Collingwood and had to compensate by writing 'The Club'....

The point of all this is that even now, when Australians dream, they dream of themselves as sportsmen. Most Australians would rather be Tracey Wickham and Robert de Castella than Patrick White and Judith Wright. On the edge of sleep they do not turn a good image, but instead take the ball from the base of the scrum, shrug off the hands of the opposing lock forward, beat the five-eighth and score under the posts.

It is interesting to look at what the fathers of Australians of my generation told us about the great sportsmen of the previous Depression. Every five-year-old in 1941, say, was told that Don Bradman was Cootamundra-born and Bowral-raised, but he had put a fine edge on his talents at an early age by whacking a ball against a brick wall for hours on end. We were also told that, like Ponsford, he had in the end triumphed over Larwood's bodyline bowling in the only area that counted — by scoring runs.

The story our fathers told us then was of elements we were all familiar with — the country town, the brick wall, the fence paling bat. The Aussie-battler pertinacity of driving the ball for all those childhood hours was an exercise which led as a matter of course to the quiet moral grandeur which enabled Don to surmount Larwood and Voce in the end, particularly in the Fifth Test at The Oval in 1934, when he joined in a partnership of 451 with Ponsford.

If, behind the grandeur, there were profanity and threats during the close-in work, we did not hear about it — partly because there were fewer facilities for focusing on behavioral intimacies of great sportsmen and women, but also partly because things were different, because cricket was not only cricket, it was also 'cricket', a body of civilised conventions which governed the public conduct of all sports.

Of course you can argue that we needed stainless sporting heroes then, both because we were mere innocents and because our very education told us that Australians could excel only in war, wool-breeding and sport. The history we learned was largely British and European, the poetry, except for a few bush ballads, came from the English Romantics. None of us could be Wordsworth or Coleridge, but any one of us could be Bradman, because we were familiar with the tools of Bradman's genius — a length of paling, a tennis ball, and a garage wall whether of brick or fibro.

It was not simply, however, that in the 70s we became more worldly. A sort of pathology appeared in our sport. In the same decade, significantly, we saw the destruction of the 'cricket' of the Constitution — of that body of conventions which, our founding fathers believed, any gentleman bred in the British sporting tradition would observe....

In this decade the tradition is of Chappell bowling underarm, of Lawson pointing dismissed English batsmen to the pavilion, of Lillee baiting Miandad, of the Poms themselves outrageously whingeing, of the ruthless urging of umpires, of Australian batsmen who have just saved a one-day match leaving the field scything with their bats to keep children away. These men cannot exalt us, because they are as mean as we are. Our sportsmen now bring out in us that which is most destructive, especially in hard times — rootless aggression, callow xenophobia, immature Pom-bashing. (Surely if our nationalism had more than a childish base, we would signify it by becoming in a mature and constitutional sense our own people.)

And now that there is no 'cricket' left in cricket, it seems there is no cricket left anywhere. Take the case of an athletic meeting at Canberra on Australia Day, 1982. At Bruce Station, in the midst of a day of relay events, the Australian Institute of Sport men's 4 × 100 metre team — virtually an Australian Olympic team — intended to make an attempt on the Australian record. Seven other men's teams would also be racing in the event, but they would merely be proficient club teams, adequate for giving an edge to the running of the big-timers.

Starting in lane 2, the first Institute runner was ahead at the first change, but the change was not a good one, and immediately the record was in doubt. The second change was excellent, but the third poor — there was even some chance that the last runner, a Commonwealth Games 100 metre grand finalist, had overrun his mark and therefore been disqualified. But this would not be known until the race was over. The

Institute athlete did not bother finishing, however. He went 10 metres at half pace, and then hurled his baton across the track into centre field. In so doing he risked clouting the athlete in lane 1 with the baton.

This tantrum was seen by hundreds of young athletes from Victoria, New South Wales and the Australian Capital Territory. Some spectators were disgusted, but it is significant that others said: 'It's because of the stress they are under.'

But wasn't the women's Australian 4 × 100 metre team at the Olympics in 1956 under similar stress when they were disqualified and lost not just a national record but an Olympic Gold medal? Did they mouth hatred and hurl equipment? Weren't Bradman and Ponsford under stress facing Larwood and Voce? Wasn't Betty Cuthbert under stress in the women's 400 metre final in 1964, having qualified for the Olympic final with the second slowest time of anyone in the field, yet taking the medal against all expectations?

The question is not talent. Some of our cricketers, athletes, footballers are superb. What disappoints people is that they do not enlarge life as the old players did — that too many of them are storm troopers and not gods.

— Thomas Keneally,
The Age, Melbourne, 10 October 1983

(1) From the above article, 'Our Ugly Heroes':
   (a) Identify the reasons for our obsession with sport.
   (b) Identify the main characteristics of our current sporting image.
(2) Do you believe that these characteristics can be found in all sports? Cite examples.

How Australia's sporting identity was shaped

A wide variety of Australian authors have offered many reasons why a strong sporting awareness emerged in Australia during the nineteenth century.

In its early years, Australia offered a fine climate, good food, and an abundance of room and time to play sport. Also, the early settlers brought a sporting heritage from Britain, and developed a surly, confident attitude that probably came from the convict era, and developed as Australians learned to 'take on the world'.

The early settlers needed such qualities as mateship and the 'have-a-go' attitude. Pioneers in the bush could not survive in the bush without relying on their mates. In turn, these mates could be relied on for a game of cricket or football. Settlers had to 'have a go' to solve the problems of battling fire, flood and drought. They discovered their own physical skills, which they used in sport.

There were many social reasons for being interested in sport in early Australia. Prize-fighting, horseracing, hunting, rowing and cricket were sports that gathered together crowds of people. Australians were always fond of gambling; Keith Dunstan calls compulsive gambling among all classes of Australians 'the most powerful of all formative forces in the Australian lifestyle', except, perhaps, poverty.

Sporting prowess made successes of people in Australia who would otherwise have been unknown. They included migrants who had been exiled from their home countries because of poverty and political suppression, and groups such as women and minority racial groups who were excluded from other social activities.

By the end of the nineteenth century, it was true to say that 'You're somebody in Australia if you're a sportsperson'. The sporting type fitted Australians' image of themselves: people of toughness and 'manliness' who never gave in; tall, suntanned, resourceful and independent. This attitude is summed up in such Australian national sayings as: 'Run, and get rid of excess energies' and 'Sport is wholesome. It can do no harm.'

In 1889, it was commented that 'Colonial governors, if they wished to be popular with Australians, simply have to be good sportsmen. They still do' (Keith Dunstan, *Sports*, p. 11).

Today, politicians continually link themselves with sports activities and sportspeople. Harold Holt made sure pictures were taken of him wearing spearfishing gear; John Gorton was shown swimming; Billy Macmahon played squash; and Bob Hawke linked himself and his Government with the America's Cup victory of the Australia II.

You should easily be able to list current examples of this phenomenon.

Research work 12: 'Laconically Australian'

And there was Lukin, so laconically Australian. Just as Australia II proved a whole nation could become 'expert' about the exotic sport of 12 metre sailing, there was proof that the same nation was thoroughly versed in the everyday business of the clean-and-jerk.

— *Sport Report*, September 1984

(1) What is it about Dean Lukin that can so efficiently, as suggested, describe Australia?

(2) What is Australia's sporting identity:
- **(a)** For the Australian?
- **(b)** For the outsider?

(3) Is it true that Australia's strong sporting identity has largely been upheld and perpetrated by a few individuals who have been prominently displayed? Has the larger community increased its sporting involvement as a result?

(4) What is meant by Australia being a 'sporting nation'?

(5) What aspects of sport are highlighted by the mass media to help create an 'Australian sporting identity'?

(6) What do current statistics suggest about our sporting image?
- **(a)** Our sporting participation
- **(b)** Our level of spectatorship
- **(c)** Our level of fitness and health — are we truly a sporting nation?
- **(d)** The number of sportspeople who have received the title of 'Australian of the year' compared to other groups represented in society
- **(d)** Are we 'good sports' in dealing with each other, or with minority groups within our society, such as Aborigines?

(7) What does the Minister for Sport and Recreation say about our sporting identity?

(8) Why was John Sumegi, Olympic Silver Medallist canoeist and Australian title-holder, forced to retire because of general apathy and lack of sponsorship?

(9) Name the specialized area to which the following people have contributed. Which are the easiest to identify? Why?
- **(a)** Don Bradman
- **(b)** Robert Helpmann
- **(c)** David Williamson
- **(d)** John Curtin
- **(e)** Phar Lap
- **(f)** John Landy
- **(g)** Sir Arthur Streeton
- **(h)** Manning Clark
- **(i)** Marilyn Rowe
- **(j)** Patrick White
- **(k)** Ron Clarke
- **(l)** Edmond Barton
- **(m)** Frederick McCubbin
- **(n)** Geoff Hunt
- **(o)** Eileen Joyce
- **(p)** Ric Charlesworth
- **(q)** Sidney Nolan
- **(r)** Keith Walker
- **(s)** Ron Barassi
- **(t)** Norman Kaye
- **(u)** Wendy Turnbull
- **(v)** William Dobell
- **(w)** Bev Francis
- **(x)** Judith Wright.

(10) 'Australia is sporting mad!' To what extent do you believe this is true, giving reference to our heroes and anti-heroes?

45. Political involvement and sport

. . . But sport was susceptible to political interference because of its competitive and representative structure, the identification of athletes with their nation and the 'ideological innocence' of sport. Victory has a political significance as an example of national superiority and prestige. Conversely, defeat may be seen as an example of national inferiority and shame.

— Bob Paddick, 1981

Figure 45.1 Black September attack, 1972.

HOW SPORT HAS BECOME A POLITICAL WEAPON

When Black September's *fedayeen* smashed into the Olympic village on 5 September 1972, sport, a once sacrosanct social institution, became for shocked millions an integral part of the Arab-Israeli conflict.

For those people, sport had become 'political'. Television mostly caused this mass connection between sport and politics (or, more precisely, international relations). Olympic television coverage began in 1936 but until 1968 technical limitations restricted it to local broadcasts and delayed reports. The first live international telecasts came in 1968. By 1972 the largest-ever live television audience provided an obvious political target for the *fedayeen*.

Hundreds of millions of people saw the terrorists make their political point. So the Munich Massacre did more than bring 'sport in international relations' to greater numbers of people. It also marked a shift in the political use of sport internationally. Before Munich, sport was usually directed to *constructive* ends, to demonstrate the social strengths and merits of nations or political systems. From 1972 on it became increasingly common for sport to be *destructive*, to reveal the flaws of a system or to force acceptance of an unwanted view.

The constructive or positive use of sport in politics began with the ancient Greeks. Leading athletes were paid the equivalent of thousands of dollars to enhance the prestige of their city-States.

In Rome, political groups used charioteers to parade their political causes. During the Middle Ages, both in East and West, jousting and other ritualised sports tested the administrative strengths and loyalties of court retainers.

Throughout 19th century Europe, sports and games were used to encourage desirable social characteristics. 'Tom Brown's Schooldays' and 'the playing fields of Eton' are the most vivid reminders of that.

And administrators in African and Asian colonies used games like cricket and football to promote social change among their subjects.

In the 20th century, the post-World War I sports carnivals run by the Allies celebrated the victory of one way of life over another, the superiority of a political and social system. Hitler then used the 1936 Berlin Olympics to proclaim the emergence of his new social order.

At the first Asian Games in 1951, too, post-colonial States like India and Indonesia used sport to display their new political and cultural independence. After World War II, though, the constructive use of sport was most developed by the superpowers.

The United States decided early in the life of the modern Olympics that sport brilliantly demonstrated capitalist power and efficiency. Games like American football, basketball and baseball were believed to symbolise the strength of American life.

In the USSR, too, sport was a major contributor to the new social order following the 1917 Revolution. Sport's role was effectively laid down in a 1925 official party manifesto. It was to promote health, form character, back up military training, promote State objectives and to display internationally Russian political and social superiority.

But the most spectacular recent use of sport's constructive power has been in the German Democratic Republic. Despite post-war political and reconstruction difficulties, the East Germans emphasised the social importance of sport.

Beginning its Olympic career in 1896, by 1976 Australia was ranked 12th in the world with 178 medals. After just three Olympic Games, East Germany was already in 13th position with 181 medals. The 1980 Games merely widened the gap. The difference between the two countries was that the GDR regarded sport as a serious social issue with a positive international advertising function. . . .

The bloody Black September attack in 1972, using international satellite cover, set the scene for the 1970s and 1980s. International sports events might be used to convey any political grievance, whether or not it had a sports connection. . . .

The most concerted use of this aggressively negative power has been against South Africa's racial policies. By the mid-1970s there was scarcely an international sport not affected by the campaign.

South Africa was eased out of Olympic competition by 1968, followed by Rhodesia in 1972. One reason was that their racial policies had become increasingly unacceptable internationally. But a main reason was the post-colonial strength of those black African countries which had won independence by the mid-1960s.

Those countries had two valuable international resources. First, they had numbers in the United Nations, the so-called 'Third World' bloc. The great powers still had the veto, but black Africa still could command substantial influence.

The second African resource was the quality of its athletes at a time when international sporting prestige and diplomacy were becoming increasingly important. From the 1960s on, athletes like Bikila, Temu, Biwott, Gammoudi, Yifter, Keino, Akii-Bua, Romo and Bayi became political as well as athletic resources and symbols, whether or not they liked it as individuals. If their absence could be engineered to protest against some policy or other, it would have far more impact internationally than would their countries' meagre economic or political protests.

This was first recognised in 1976 when more than 20 countries (mostly African) boycotted the Montreal Olympics to protest against New Zealand's rugby union contacts with South Africa.

The subsequently renewed debate about whether politics should 'be allowed' in sport was irrelevant. It missed the point that superpower emphasis on international sport and the telecommunications revolution had made international sport inevitably 'political'. Many countries with an international point of view had discovered that sport was their only powerful means of expressing that view.

During the early 1970s, for example, India forfeited Davis Cup ties because South Africa was not excluded. Indian political or economic sanctions would not have had the same international impact. In 1977, Spain put its view on the China question by denying visas to Taiwanese judo competitors. The world championships were cancelled.

It is against this misunderstood and complex background that Australia has approached the 1982 Brisbane Commonwealth Games. . . . When Queensland's Premier, Mr Bjelke-Petersen, and his Ministers like Russell Hinze call for the politics to be 'taken out', they ask the impossible and ignore the evidence. They also underestimate the powerful effect a black athlete absence would have.

The Queensland Government has recognised far less than its Federal counterpart the changed function of international sport. While 'British Empire Games' meant obedience to one authority, 'Commonwealth Games' mean a free-flowing political relationship, involving *both* approval and criticism between member States. . . .

Ten years after Munich, then, the role of politics in sport is at a new stage. The constructive advertising of a social system's superiority remains (and, possibly, the creation of international friendship), but the destructive element is dominant.

Sport is a strong lever, along with political or economic resources, to be employed against any disputed political or ideological viewpoint. Importantly, the operation of that level is no longer dominated by the international powers. For many otherwise powerless groups, sport is the one source of influence.

While that situation remains, sport will become only more 'political', not less. And Brisbane will be no exception.

— Brian Stoddart,
The Age, Melbourne, 3 September 1982

International politics and Australian sport

Today it seems unrealistic to say that 'politics and sport do not mix' or 'should not mix', as sporting grants from national, state and local levels of government have enabled the construction and functioning of many sports complexes, and the funding of teams and sporting efforts. The government, spending the taxpayers' money, sees itself with a duty to say how that money is spent to ensure that public interests are served.

Many people, however, dislike the connection between sport and politics because of the display, manipulation and, sometimes, violence of nationalistic fervour. The involvement of 'politics' itself is not the core issue, but rather the methods that have been used. Indeed, the modern Olympic Games, as one of the most important sporting events in the world, was founded for political reasons. Baron de Coubertin, founder of the Olympics, saw them as a way to improve understanding and goodwill between nations.

The above article, 'How Sport Has Become a Political Weapon', gives examples of international conflict in the sporting arena. Recently, the issue of Australian cricketers playing in South Africa has demonstrated that politicians can verbally express their disapproval of the policies of another government, but that the individual player makes the final commitment. Under the Gleneagles (international) Agreement, the governments decided to withhold any form of support for, and to take every practical step to discourage contact or competitions by their nations with sporting organizations, teams or sportsmen from South Africa. The Brisbane Code of Conduct is also designed to deter *apartheid* (the South African official name for its policy of separating the races) in sport. Despite some moves by the South African Government to involve blacks in South Africa in sport, the new policy of dismantling sporting apartheid is not complete, and continued active discouragement of sporting associations with South Africa by sporting bodies still exists.

Is Graham Yallop naive to believe that 'mixing sport and politics' has only recently 'reared its ugly head' in Australia, particularly in the light of extensive government support of sporting bodies? See the next article 'To Play or Not'.

Figure 45.2 Tom Carroll, surfer.

Figure 45.3 Graham Yallop, cricketer (far left).

TO PLAY OR NOT

Tom Carroll, the current world champion surfer, may lose his title after deciding to stage a personal protest against apartheid by not competing in South Africa. Graham Yallop, a former Australian cricket captain, has decided to tour South Africa as part of the 'rebel' team. He says sport and politics should not be mixed. Here they explain their opposing views . . .

The best surfing wave in the world is, according to Tom Carroll, in South Africa, at Jeffreys Beach near Port Elizabeth. There are plenty of other good waves there too and a significant chunk of the points for a world championship are on the South African leg of the circuit.

But for Carroll, the waves, winnings and world rankings are well behind 'moral obligations' and he has decided not to go back to South Africa. To do so would be, for him, breaching that moral obligation. It is his personal protest against apartheid and is a protest which will cost him all three of the attractions above.

His decision not to return was made this year. 'I came to the decision slowly. The situation slowly came to light over the four times. I don't like that sort of situation and never have and it really just dawned on me that I could do something really solid about it,' he says.

'As world champion (for the past two years) I could make a point. It is a bad government over there.'

Carroll is making his own protest by withdrawing his undoubted skills as a surfer. His vast following among the surfing youth of Australia and the world have had their attention drawn to the question of apartheid because he feels so strongly about it.

'I just didn't want to go back and be looked upon as a supporter of the regime over there. The blacks look upon you as supporters because you are there and the whites are very happy that you are there,' he says.

He has found reactions among whites in South Africa about the question of apartheid extremely interesting. 'It is hard for people going over there to ask whites about it and for them to come out honestly and say they agree with the racist system and say "Yeah, I'm a filthy racist",' he says. . . .

While agreeing that 'to go or not to go' is a strictly personal decision (he has not been criticisng the cricketers) he does not believe the proposition that no South African Government money is behind the tour. 'They say the money is not coming directly from the Government. If there is no direct finance, there is sure plenty of indirect,' he says.

He saw South Africa as a country with 'a helluva lot of scares. . . . They have kept very suspicious of the communists coming in from Angola and the country is fiercely independent and very strong militarily. The whites, of course, have a very high standard of living, but also a lot of scares.

'So they are pleased to see people from overseas coming in and enjoying their country and playing for the people there. They are pleased when people don't mind going. It is a bit like when the "Rand Daily Mail" incurred heavy losses and was forced to close. It was about the only multi-racial voice and the Government seemed pretty pleased about that.'

He has some sympathy for cricketers going to South Africa, as they have 'got so many other things to think about' and sees the difference in the sports. There are other surfing spots and surfing countries, but cricketers really have only a few countries to go to. 'But I don't agree with them going at all. That is not to say I have just said "No" and not taken into account a poor person's circumstances and the heavy media cricketers have been hit by. Especially if you have gone from Australian captain to what he (Hughes) was made out to be last season. He has decided to make a future elsewhere,' he says. . . .

The talk about the big money on offer for the cricketers holds little water for Carroll. He says he has proved wrong suggestions by commentators that anyone would accept such a big offer to set himself and his family up for life. 'You look at people like Allan Border. It has been said that Allan Border would have a price of about $500,000. I don't see it as that sort of thing. It is quite a heavy situation over there and you make a stand or you don't. The situation goes beyond money.'

When a cricketer is peppered with short-pitched, intimidatory deliveries, he is liable to go on the offensive. Graham Yallop is now being hit with bouncers over his decision to go to South Africa and is defending grimly.

The former Test captain is still firm in his belief that he has done nothing wrong and wishes discussion about the tour would return to 'what it is all about' — cricket.

When an ABC reporter showed Yallop film of anti-apartheid demonstrations in South Africa and a clip of two policemen beating a black citizen, the cricketer did not quibble about saying apartheid was an 'evil system' and he was against 'all racist regimes'.

He is now almost impossible to draw on the political side of the matter, saying only: 'That happened back in 1960 anyway . . . they don't give a fair indication of what the society is like nowadays.'

When asked if he was going over there to see for himself, he gave an affirmative mumble, but then quickly added: 'Well, no. I've been contracted by the South African Cricket Union to play cricket there. It's not political . . . the media has got it all wrong. We are not concerned with politics. We want to play cricket, that's all. That is all we are, that is all that we want to do. It has become a political issue which we want no part of.'

The problem, as he sees it, of mixing sport and politics has 'reared its ugly head' in Australia. 'Hopefully it goes no further.' He says the politicians have done the mixing of sport and politics in this case and wonders why.

Certainly, it is not to get public support. 'Public support is definitely on our side. Maybe the politicians see it as conforming to the Gleneagles Agreement in the eyes of other Commonwealth countries. It has become so much of a political issue, that the sport itself is being forgotten,' he says.

Does he see it as an attempt by South Africa to have an Australian team over there to bring themselves back into the cricketing fold? 'That is their general aim, of course.'

He sees himself as an individual playing cricket over there. 'I am a professional cricketer. I am an individual. We were approached on an individual basis, therefore we should be able to play cricket over there, like individuals in other sports.

'Numerous other sports are associated with South Africa, like tennis, golf, surfing and car racing. Why are we being singled out? . . . there have been 92 countries in the past two years that have had sporting links with South Africa. Turning a blind eye to the problems of South Africa is certainly not going to help end apartheid.

'If you haven't been over there, you really don't know what the situation is. And most of the media and people I've spoken to haven't been there, particularly the media, and they present one side and they say, "You are against apartheid, why go?" and show me clips . . . it has become a political issue which we want no part of.'

He agrees that the huge money being outlaid in South Africa for the players is a sign that the South Africans desperately want to be part of the International Cricket Conference again. 'They want international cricket. They are prepared to pay. Obviously it is the only way to do it.'

He says that cricket has become integrated in South Africa, that other big changes have taken place and that the Prime Minister should look at his own responsibility regarding the huge trade with South Africa. . . .

'It is the right of an individual to make a decision like this,' he says.

'Now, the political side of it has been flogged to death. We want to talk about the cricket side of South Africa and that only. I am a professional cricketer. I want to play international cricket. I am an individual. That's why I am going.'

— Simon Balderstone,
The Age, Melbourne, 23 May 1985

The Australian Institute of Sport

In 1981 Dr Maureen O'Bryan, the vice-president of the International Assembly of National Sports Confederations, criticized governments for exploiting sport for political aims. She said that world sport today stands as a highly desirable commodity for profiteers, political activists and governments. She sees sportspeople who are victims of boycotts as 'trying to achieve the true spirit of international play, and bearing the brunt of superpower confrontation' (*The Age*, 25 March 1981). Governments should continue 'to support sport for the development of national health, participation and enjoyment. It can be a vital factor in the provision of incentives for the less glamorous but broadly based mass participation programmes'.

Figure 45.4 Australian Institute of Sport, Canberra.

The main criticism of the AIS is that it is a centralized concept and elitist. Are the two concepts, 'Sport for the elite' and 'Sport for all' mutually exclusive?

AIS — SHOWPLACE '85

The transformation that has taken place at the Australian Institute of Sport in the last four years is nothing short of fantastic.

A showplace, which is attracting world-wide interest, the institute has become more functional with the opening of the $5 million sports science and medicine centre and the imminent opening of the $11 million residential-administration complex.

When the institute commenced, the sports science and medicine unit worked in cramped space underneath the National Athletics stadium. The athletes were accommodated off campus at various halls of residence attached to the Australian National University and Canberra College of Advanced Education. The administrative staff and coaches overflowed from limited office space in the National Indoor Sports Stadium and some had to use space in several pre-fab buildings.

Now it is all coming together.

The sports science and medicine complex was opened officially by the Minister for Sport, Recreation and Tourism, Mr Brown, on July 22 [1985].

Already it is being acclaimed as the most modern facility of its type anywhere in the world and it is to be visited by scientists, coaches and athletes from all parts of the world as part of an exchange of the latest technology.

Dr Dick Telford, co-ordinator sports sciences and a physiologist, and Dr Peter Fricker, co-ordinator of sports medicine, and their staff, undertook years of planning and research into the most advanced technology and techniques at the leading institutions around the world to ensure that the institute's complex would be a world leader in design and function.

The unit will carry out precise analysis of an athlete's progress so that his coach can be advised what dietary developments are necessary for maximum efficiency. In addition, the unit will be a pioneer in the field of research, this being aided by a grant of $14,900 to the physiology department to study the micro-nutrient status of Australian sports people and the effect of vitamin and mineral supplementation on performance.

This grant was made by the Australian Sports Commission under the Applied Sports Research Program.

Working as a close-knit team, the physiologists, medical team and physiotherapists provide comprehensive testing designed to prevent injuries, as well as treat sports injuries.

Psychologists tend to the emotional and motivational problems that may affect performance. . . .

A unique biomechanics department will provide a wealth of knowledge as regards the athlete's technique. . . .

The huge area allows an athlete to be studied while performing a triple jump, a pole vault, sprinting over a straight course or curve, a tennis player serving, a gymnast as he tumbles, a javelin thrower in action or a weightlifter.

Digitised computer analysis of, say, a long jumper in action will reveal any variation in speed of approach to the board, direction of force at take-off and style flaws.

Once again this department will engage in research, initially with the aid of another Commission grant of $12,000, for a biomechanics analysis and technical intervention program to enhance the spiking skills of volleyball players. . . .

The residential buildings include 250 single bedrooms for institute athletes, 20 married or VIP quarters and 52 units for the use of people involved in the National Training Centre program. . . .

These latter units are fully accessible to, and have facilities for, disabled athletes.

Ken Merry, the principal of Wesley College, Melbourne, [took] up his appointment as manager of the residence late [in 1985]. His support staff . . . include tutors to look after athletes' study commitments and house parents, to ensure a home environment for the younger athletes. . . .

The institute's Board of Management['s] new chairman [is] deputy chairman, Professor John Bloomfield, [who] takes over from foundation chairman, Kevan Gosper.

— John Hourigan,
Sports World, September 1985

After the disappointing performance of Australian athletes at the Montreal Olympics in 1976, athletes and government officials alike saw the need to rethink Australia's sporting policies. The AIS was opened in 1981 by the Fraser Liberal-National Party Government with the aim of returning Australia to an important position in international sport. Promised government and private funding would be $3 million per year. The aim of the Institute was to help both individual athletes and Australian sport as a whole to win. 'It must produce winners or the financial tap will be turned off,' reported the ABC.

Research work 13: Government involvement with sport

(1) The commentator Kevin Giles suggests that past champions like Herb Elliot and Raelene Boyle were the product of natural reproduction, whereas athletes today are made successful by development.

How do other nations cater for their elite sportspeople? Look at activity in one country — for example:

- 'Sporting scholarships in the USA.'
- 'Sporting institutes in the USSR.'

(2) The material in this chapter has discussed political intervention at an international and national level:

(a) What are current examples of political involvement at a state and local level?

(b) Do politicians primarily support the interests of sport, or do they use sport as a political tool — for example, for the elevation of a politician or party?

46. Physical activity and the elderly

'You are old, Father William,' the young man said,
'And your hair has become very white;
And yet you incessantly stand on your head —
Do you think, at your age, it is right?'

— Lewis Carroll

We have some odd ideas about how older people, even those barely in their forties, ought to behave. They should like Lawrence Welk, not Bob Dylan; it is more seeming if they eat porridge not pizza; and they ought to be dozing in a Barca-Lounger rather than working up a sweat on the road from Hopkinson to Boston.

— James F. Fixx,
The Complete Book of Running

VETERAN SPORTS IN SOCIETY

Providing for the sporting needs of older people has, up to recently, had a low priority. The need for a quality social and physical recreation program is essential.

The consciousness of maintaining appropriate levels of health led to legislative amendment of the Older Americans Act in 1975 (Moran, 1979) to include 'services designed to enable older persons to obtain and maintain physical and mental well-being through programs of regular activity and exercise.' These sentiments were also echoed recently at the World Assembly on Ageing (1982) in Vienna. It was recommended that 'social, cultural and leisure activities . . . are necessary for the elderly . . . and should be provided by each country. . . .'

The general policy recommendation of the Conference indicates that one way older people find personal satisfaction was through 'participation in community organisations . . . and recreation'. The assembly confirmed a need, at both government and non-government level, to further develop policies and programs for elderly people.

In WA it is estimated by the year 2011, the population would be between 2.13 and 2.19 million. The number of over 65s is estimated between 234,000 and 262,000 persons (Peter, 1983). The implications of these growing numbers on the health and social service institutions and agencies would be enormous if the elderly were made dependent on them. Such strains would be reduced if older individuals led more independent and healthy lifestyles through recreational activity. Unfortunately certain prejudices and myths exist about the capabilities and capacities of older people.

The term ageism was referred to by Butler and Lewis (1973) as a process of systematic stereotyping; of a discrimination against people because they are old. There is a common but erroneous belief that age is synonymous with disability. The fact is that a vast proportion of old Australians have the capacity and willingness to be fit and active.

The growing trend of middle-aged to older people is their greater confidence in themselves, their capabilities and capacities. This is reflected in the numerous veteran sports groups and associations that have sprung up.

Sport in life-cycle

The beneficial effects of physical activity experiences in a wide variety of individual and team pursuits is important. . . . De Carlo (1974) found a positive relationship between 'continued participation in recreative activities, particularly after 60, offered substantial rewards to ageing subjects'. . .

The essential necessity of keeping fit has been aptly described by MacCallum (1982):

> Fitness is more than just a good idea, a current fad, an enjoyable leisure-time pursuit, or a basis for scientific study. It is fundamental to modern life.

It is clearly important at the age of eight as it is at eighty.

The health significance of physical activity through sport is noted in the following observations (Skoll, 1982):

1. Several studies suggest improved health status (measured in terms of reduced hospital admission and medical consultations) for older people following good health practices.
2. A number of well-known authorities on ageing believe that a substantial part of the degenerative process attributed to ageing may be due to habitual inactivity rather than to true disease or any irreversible ageing process. The term 'hypokinetic disease' is now used to describe diseases brought on, in part, by insufficient movement.
3. Exercise affects not only the size and strength of our muscles, but is also the trigger mechanism for activating our metabolism. While older people do not need to exercise particularly hard, their bodies do need (and they benefit from) an active way of life.
4. Regular physical activity helps reduce the likelihood of illness and accidents.
5. The great benefit of maintaining physical fitness is the degree of independence it affords through improved cardio-respiratory functioning, strength and flexibility.

Some of the socio-psychological benefits arising from physical activity are:

- Increasing self-worth and self-esteem through participation for enjoyment, entertainment and friendship.
- Decreased level of anxiety, enhanced body image and improved overall mood (Sidney and Shepard, 1976).
- Internal focus of highly skilled senior tennis players indicated the older player's belief that he was in control of his own destiny, rather than a victim of fate (Rotella and Bunker, 1978).
- Heinzelman and Bagley (1970) studied men aged 45–49 and noted improved self-image, increased ability to cope with stress, improved attitude towards work and work performance and a positive effect on healthy behaviour.
- Bennett et al. (1982) found significant improvement in depression levels of 38 adults in ages ranging 58 to 98 (M = 75.7).
- Hattlestad (1979) observed participants in exercise programs and found increased social interaction.

The socio-psychological benefits help to perform physical skills; interact with friends; increase one's feeling of self-worth; and manage stress more effectively.

Veteran sports associations

Though several associations cater for older people, I will concentrate on swimming and athletics.

Swimming

The Aussie Masters Swimming Association promotes health and fitness, regardless of ability. Membership is open to anybody over 20. Most members are 30 to 50 while many are between 50 and the late 70s. The oldest member is 82. WA's

19 clubs have 930 members and is one of the most active in Australia. There are 3500 members in Australia.

The Association concentrates on:

- competition
- fitness maintenance
- coaching and stroke correction
- sociability.

Competition ranges from club and State level to national and international level. Fitness is one of the major objects of the Association. Incentives such as the State National Aerobic Trophy are awarded where swimmers gather points for distances in specific times.

Coaching and correction reflects the willingness and confidence of participants to learn or re-learn the proper swimming techniques despite advancing age.

Sociability, pleasurable experiences of swimming, are enhanced with the variety of friends and associates. Social group swimming sessions are programmed as frequently as three times a week.

Athletics

The Western Australian Veterans Athletic Club has 232 members. Eligibility is based on age; 30 for women and 35 for men. The club operates in two sectors — track and field and distance running. Participants in the distance running run from 8 kilometres to a marathon and include variations in terrain from flat to cross-country. Competition running includes local, State, national and world competition. Though training for competitive programs is serious it is leisure-based. Examples of outstanding achievements include multiple world record-holder John Gilmore and Sydney-to-Melbourne super-champion, Cliff Young. The social aspect is emphasised, and often after the Sunday morning session a barbecue is arranged.

Planning veteran sport

Older players can play a big part in helping youngsters' role models, especially in sports such as hockey, and quite often father-son or mother-daughter members play in the same sport. It is a refreshing thought that the mutual relationship helps to bridge the generation gap.

Tennis veterans helped coach young players in training clinics in schools and voluntary agencies where money is a problem.

The survival of active sports involvement is dependent on the readiness of sport planners to adapt. Indoor cricket is an example; participation by every member, some degree of physical skill, management within a limited period and space. It is available to the adult as well as the young players of either sex.

— Francis Lobo,
Sports Coach, Vol. 9, No. 1

Research work 14: Veteran sports in society

Refer to the article 'Veteran Sports in Society' as well as all other possible sources when conducting the following projects:

(1) What have researchers discovered about the types of relationships that exist between ageing and activity levels? List the benefits of physical activity for older people.

(2) In your locality, what recreational provisions have been made for the elderly? (Possible examples: on-site facilities at retirement villages; information from shire offices.)

(3) Obtain a copy of *Prime Time* magazine, whose readers are mainly aged 50 or more. What attitude does this periodical have to physical activity?

(4) Which factors might inhibit the elderly from participating in physical activity? Conduct your research using interviews or questionnaires.

The 'Life. Be In It' organization suggests the following reasons:

(a) Too busy. (Time.)	Attitude
(b) Not important enough. (Priorities.)	Attitude
(c) Too embarrassed. (Fear.)	Attitude

(d)	Not skilled enough. (Too slow.)	Skill
(e)	Poor body image. (Too fat, too short.)	Attitude Physical limitation
(f)	History. (Remember school...)	Attitude
(g)	See sport as elitist.	Attitude
(h)	Lack opportunities. (Lack facilities, etc.)	Community opportunities
(i)	Too old, handicapped...	Attitude Physical limitations
(j)	Language and other barriers.	Community opportunity
(k)	Over-emphasis on competition.	Attitude.

(5) Determine the levels of physical activity experienced by the elderly:

(a) Do they believe that their present exercise patterns support good health?

(b) Is economics a limiting, or influential factor in the decisions the elderly make about physical activity?

(c) Does the medical profession encourage recreational activity among the elderly?

47. Competition in sport

To compete: to be one of a number striving against each other for a thing desired, i.e. rivals.

— *Pocket Oxford Dictionary*

I can still remember the Alexandra State School Athletics Sports when I was in Grade 6 (Under 12s). I was lined up in the 100 yard dash against the bearded and hot favourite, Peter Parker. He had already won the javelin, discus, long jump, shot put, and probably a few others by a country kilometre and now he stood between myself and glory. Somehow I managed to win that day (I believe he fell over at the start); and from that moment on I pursued a satisfying and enjoyable time in sports.

— C. Field

Research work 15: The competitive spirit in sport

(1) What are the socializing influences that can engender a competitive spirit within an individual during his or her early years? (Possible examples: sibling, parent, coach.)

(2) What is meant by being competitive? Does a sense of competition depend on extrinsic rewards or intrinsic rewards?

(3) Competitiveness may be regarded as a continuum, as shown in this diagram:

INDIFFERENT ←——————————→ AGGRESSIVELY COMPETITIVE

Determine, by means of graded questions, how competitive are you, your fellow students or your family. An example of the type of question to ask:

'Your peers have approved and encouraged aggression.
(a) Often **(b)** Sometimes **(c)** Rarely
(d) Never.'

(4) Two Melbourne boys, after returning from scholarship visits to Louisiana State University, made such comments as: 'The only way of upholding your rights on court is by using John McEnroe tactics. The system is so competitive that it breeds that kind of aggressiveness. . . . They say, "I'll see you outside the locker room afterwards." . . . Cheating is very common. . . . They want to win all the time. . . . That's all he's [the coach] interested in . . . if you lose he doesn't want to know you.'

What do you think are the criteria for determining whether or not competition is healthy?

Children and competitive sport

In play situations, children are psychologically safe to expose themselves to socio-emotional situations, and to practise different elements of skill, chance and strategy. Children thereby gain experience and confidence in differing cognitive and emotional processes. If play becomes constricted because of adult imposition (as in organized sports), there is therefore a restriction of the child's basic experiences, and his or her future adult responses can suffer.

Opie goes so far as to say that: 'If children are given the idea that they cannot enjoy themselves without being provided with the "proper" equipment, we need blame only ourselves when we produce a generation who have lost their dignity, who are ever dissatisfied, and who descend for their sport to the easy excitement of rioting, pilfering or vandalism' (*The Impoverishment of Children's Games*, p. 16).

Therefore there is a tension between introducing sports to children and discontinuing their play activity. When considering a child's moral development, the tension continues. Obviously, very young children who have parent-organized play and competitive activities will be unable to internalize reactions, feelings and motivations. Even those who are not actually involved in sports will have difficulty in participating freely in 'kids' stuff' because of the pressure exerted by 'little leagues' and other forms of children's organized sport.

Not only will they suffer from peer pressure but they will also be subjected to their own and their parents' expectations that arise from watching television coverages of games. They may well become part of the 'nation of spectators' at a very early age.

For the competitors, early playing of sports can introduce an unhealthy problem of competition. Children's self-image during their primary and secondary years is fragile, and so failure of any type might cause an inferiority complex that could have been avoided. Competition can increase stress levels and encourage aggression and the violation of rules. (Catharsis theories say much the opposite.)

The following incident suggests the problems that competitive sports-playing in childhood may cause for the maturing person are cultural.

Louis Alley (head of the Department of Physical Education for Men at the University of Iowa, USA) was to organize school track and basketball competitions for students in Burma. In that locality there were no interscholastic competitions, school teams or sports pages. Over 3000 competitors played, with no spectators! What is more, in the finals of the basketball match (which probably would have been televised in the USA), the score was tied, and only three minutes of play were left. One of the players suddenly left the field, his reason being that he was 'just tired!'

Perhaps it is not the sports that are at fault, but the social context within which they operate!

The 'win emphasis' in club sport and the 'ugly parent syndrome'

SAVE OUR CHILDREN BY STAMPING OUT SPORT

I'm puzzled about sport. How does it keep escaping the attention of people who worry about the corruption of youth? It's not good enough to say these people have their hands full fighting drugs, pornography and television violence. Sure, those things are terrible for the young, and I wouldn't want my children exposed to them. But neither would I want them exposed to sport as now practised in the United States.

Consider a few of the traditional high-minded excuses for athletics:

- A sound mind in a sound body: That was the classic reason for sport. No sensible child who has been subjected to the sports news can hear it nowadays without curling his lips in a sneer.

He has heard too much about the importance of 'playing with pain' and multi-million-dollar contracts. It is not 'a sound mind in a sound body' that he contemplates when he thinks of sport — it is an avaricious mind in a crippled body.

- Sports build character: Old-timers used to say that. Football coaches were especially fond of it. 'Football builds character', they used to say. But

show me a child whose parents have mindlessly let him follow football, and I'll show you a child who knows that what football really does is fire coaches who lose.

• It's not whether you win or lose, but how you play the game: Try this one on an American youngster some time if you want to see a kid roll on the floor with laughter.

Unless he's been sheltered against sports, he knows the great Vince Lomabardi's dictum — 'Winning is the only thing' — and applauds the latest tennis brat for the swinishness of his winning game.

For the young, the lesson from the field is that rotten manners, greed and determination to win at any cost to body and soul are virtues. Is it really worse having a child hooked on pornography or drugs? Pornography eventually gets boring, a drug habit can be broken, but a child trained to admire loutishness will remain a lout all his life.

For a really bright child, a child who lifts his eyes from the locker room and looks at sport as an institution, the results are even more devastating. Do you want to bring up a child who looks on other people as so much tax-deductible meat?

That's what a kid sees nowadays if you let him read about the owners of professional teams who depreciate their players to cut tax bills. . . .

It's time we set better goals, at least for our kids. If we're not willing to start somewhere, we ought to quit whining about the loss of those wonderful old values that everybody laments.

A good way to start would be to stop children from being exposed to sports, and especially news about the people who own and operate the country's sports system. A child who has been marinated in such stuff in recent years won't even respect his elders.

If the kid has half a brain, he can't help realising that 'fan' is just another word for 'sap'. . . . If the kid had grown up on sports, he knows a fan is nothing but a dumbbell who's paying taxes to keep the owner in residence until he can locate another town with an even bigger bunch of saps. . . .

Imagine the child of higher ambition who yearns to become an educator. What does he dream of after exposure to the sports world? Surely not of running an academy where everyone will be conversant with Ovid and quantum theory.

No, he dreams of presiding over a campus operated as a profitable minor-league training camp for professional sports, whose products can be shipped off to the big time before commencement day creates the embarrassment of having to give them degrees.

Save the children. Stamp out sports.

— Russell Baker,
The Age, 30 April 1984

PARENTS PROTEST OVER TENNIS BRATS

A group of Melbourne parents will protest to the LTAA and Victorian tennis officials about the misconduct of junior players at the recent 16-and-under tournaments in Canberra.

'The behavior was appalling,' said one parent who had a child competing in Canberra. 'There was bad language, throwing of racquets, abuse of opponents, and cheating on the calls. Not everyone was involved, but the general standard was terrible.'

One boy had dropped his pants on court during a match.

The parent, and another contacted by 'The Age', both asked not to be named for fear that their children would be victimised and their tennis careers affected.

'I've played tennis since I was 10, and I've been to all the junior tournaments in the last few years, but this was the worst behavior I've ever seen,' the parent said. 'I was completely disillusioned.' She said she had also seen girls using bad language and throwing racquets.

The tournament director for the junior events, Leon Braslin, said he would be submitting a report to the LTAA about the lead-in tournaments, but he would not comment further.

Another parent who accompanied her son to

the championships said the on-court behavior was disgusting. 'It generally is with boys who think they are top players. Their language is disgusting. You try to tell your own child not to do it and then they see everyone else doing it.'

She said that on one occasion she had seen two juniors go on arguing despite the efforts of the umpire to continue play. 'From what I can see the officials do nothing about it,' she said. . .

'Parents who have been up here told me how bad it was in the first two weeks,' Brian Connor (manager of the Victorian boys' team) said. 'I think it's fashionable. They see how some of the professional players go on, and they copy it.'

Connor said that the Victorian Tennis Association was about to run a course for officials telling them how to write reports on misconduct which would enable the association to take action against offenders. He said there had been talk of disqualifying boys from the Canberra tournament, but in the end no action was taken.

— Richard Yallop,
The Age, 21 January 1985

WINNING ISN'T EVERYTHING

Once upon a time, children learnt that 'John can run' and 'Betty can jump'. Today it sometimes seems that the primers have been rewritten to convey a different message: 'John and Betty can win'.

The introduction of competitive sport for children seemed like a good idea at the time. Miniaturised versions of premiership tussles would add glamor, enable the kids to get the same kick out of sport as their sporting heroes enjoyed. Encouraged by the rewards of winning, more kids would play the game.

It didn't turn out that way. Sporting participation rates, particularly among adolescents, dropped. General game skills declined. The ugly side of competitive sport — the on and off the field violence, spectator abuse and player stress — became endemic in children's sport.

One sports analyst, Geoffrey Watson, from Western Australia, went so far as to write, in 1979, that children's sport constituted 'one of the most severe forms of child abuse known yet (it is) publicly sanctioned by the community'.

A few incidents from the darker side of junior sport occasionally make headlines, like the recent episode in which a goal umpire in an under-12 football match had part of his ear bitten off while trying to break up a brawl between parents.

Figure 47.1 David Parkin, VFL football coach.

Sports authorities know that such bizarre events are isolated. They are more troubled by the dozens of examples of minor physical abuse and hostile barracking which happen every weekend at junior sporting fixtures.

Spectator misbehavior is only part of the problem. Many sports authorities are concerned that, by trying to make kids play like adults, organisers are turning children off sport altogether and harming the nation's long-term sporting future. . . .

A number of sporting authorities are working hard to undo some of the damage that untimely competition does to children's love of play. . . .

For seven years the Junior Football Council has espoused the non-competitive approach. It has introduced clinic training and tabloid sports where the emphasis is on skills acquisition. Coaches are coached in the delicate art of teaching children and now 25,000 Victorian primary school children play football under the tutelage of accredited coaches.

The council's approach is typical of many sports organisations which have recently developed modified rules and equipment for young players. But changing the play is only a start. The real modification has to be in attitudes. . . .

David Parkin, lecturer in health, physical education and recreation at Victoria State College, Burwood, has done a deal of research on children's attitudes to sport. 'The number one motive from all the studies is to get better at the game,' he says. Other motives are participation, approval and companionship. Winning is low in a child's priorities. . . .

Mr Parkin, one of the VFL's most successful coaches, has replicated the work of other American researchers who asked whether young football players would rather play in a losing side or be a substitute player for a winning team. The results show the Australian children agree with their American peers. They would prefer to play.

It is the same desire for participation and skill-testing that makes playing in the ruck a preferred position because that is where the ball, and the action, is, Mr Parkin says.

Yet research among boys playing standard Australian Rules shows that one-third of the players get 90 per cent of the kicks. Adult rules clearly do not meet the children's needs. The answer is to change the rules.

If reducing competition and increasing participation are two aims of modified sports, the reduction of stress and enhancement of enjoyment are equally important. Modification of equipment and rules takes into account the psychological and physical development of the participants.

In some cases, David Parkin points out, modification has actually restored the essence of the game. Netball, a high-scoring game when played by adults, has not been so when played by kids. 'They are only little tackers and can't shoot for goal successfully with a regulation 15-foot (4.57 metre) net,' he says. A year ago, the net height was lowered and children's netball has become a high-scoring game.

Sports organisers in the past have failed to take account of vastly differing maturation rates of children. Streaming of young competitors by age alone, instead of an appropriate combination of age, weight, height and skill levels, has had adverse effects. Bigger children dominate play, leaving the smaller ones frustrated and unable to improve their skills.

Modifications are now addressing that problem. In collision sports like Australian Rules, hockey and rugby, weight is a factor as well as age. In all sports, skill tests are being used to stream players.

Not everyone is in favor of modified sports. The Tasmanian report noted that some adults were hostile to changes because the result was not a 'proper game'. A few sports administrators who believe sport is a battle of survival are opposed to any adaptations. And the parents who pressure their kids to win at all costs certainly find the gentler form of play less satisfying. American experience has shown that modified hockey attracts lower parental participation because it is less interesting to watch.

But while the grown-ups are arguing the merits of modifications and just how, and how far, games should be adapted, it is a fair bet that a lot of kids are getting on with the game and playing for the sheer pleasure of it.

— Sally White,
The Age, 15 June 1983

Research work 16: The 'win emphasis'

(1) Using the above article, 'Winning Isn't Everything', as a starting point for your research, examine what is being done to overcome constructively the negative aspects of competition in junior sport.
(2) What are the merits and disadvantages of modified games?

Research work 17: Modification of adult games for children

Assumptions to be tested

(1) That organized sport has great potential for enjoyment, success, character development, relationships and co-operation.
(2) That adult games can be modified for children.
(3) That modified games lead to the following results:
 (a) Provide fun, physical activity and an increase in skill level
 (b) Give 'a fair go' to some children who would be disadvantaged by adult games
 (c) Provide increased participation for all children and increases in team effort and co-operation
 (d) Decrease the importance of dominant performers
 (e) Generally increase the self-esteem of each child.

Procedure

Construct a research project that will yield clear evidence on each of the following questions:
(1) To what degree are these objectives being met?
(2) Are the following criticisms of modified games valid?
 (a) Better performers are disadvantaged by modified games
 (b) Children do not regard modified games as 'the real thing'
 (c) Modified games lose competitiveness and importance.
(3) To what extent are modified games being used in schools?

Aggression and violence in sports

A hot-tempered man stirs up strife, but the slow to anger pacifies contention. . . . A gentle answer turns away wrath, but a harsh word stirs up anger.

— Proverbs 15

SPORT: THE UNPROFESSIONALS

'The Australian's' admirable London man, Murray Hedgcock, asks why modern tennis has, and endures, McEnroe behavior.

Until the 1960s, tennis didn't suffer the ugly tantrums, so why now? Hedgcock posits two theories and asks one important question.

Firstly, a universal notion that sport, professional or amateur, will always reflect the age and the society in which it exists. So if society is more violent and less gracious, less responsive to authority, less disciplined (as in the 1980s), then its sport will reflect those characteristics.

Secondly, there is the view that tennis (or anything else) isn't played for fun, but to win — and winning means millions of dollars. If we live in a violent, undisciplined, money-grubbing age, how (he asks) do we explain the graciousness and gentility of an Arthur Ashe amid the greed and grot of McEnroe and Connors?

Hedgcock has touched on three key elements in modern sport: violence, professionalism (for which substitute the words commercialism or avarice), and personality (for which don't substitute that dreadful word 'charisma').

▶

Sport is doubtless a barometer of the age in which it exists. But the sad truth is that most of western society has been violent from the start. In old Rome, Colosseum Productions promoted Christians versus lions, and assorted other gladiatorial contests to the death. . . .

There is a whole genre of death as a spectator sport: cockfighting, dog fighting, bear baiting, bull fighting and modern rodeo — which, if not death, is as close as one gets to the real thing. . . .

The common factor, says [writer, Don] Atyeo, is that 'violence makes for delicious entertainment'. The brutal truth is that 'brutality thrills, violence is mesmerizing and bloodshed fascinating' — so long as it's someone else's blood being shed.

Novelist Irwin Shaw put it this way: 'If the players were armed with guns there wouldn't be stadiums large enough to hold the crowds.'

Atyeo concludes that we have the sports we have because they are what we like. Perhaps: but they are also what we're told we want by, in the main, commercial television . . . .

Today we have instant Channel 9 gladiators: helmeted, padded, cock-boxed, gauntleted, be-weaponed, ready to crunch ribs, fingers, temples. We have slow-motion replay-replay-replay glorification of such physical giants as Snow, Lillee and Thomson.

They bear their own testimony. Snow: 'I'm not ashamed of leaving a trail of fractures . . . a finger, a thumb, a whole right hand and one foot on the latest count . . . after all, that's what I'm there for. Not to inflict deliberate injuries, of course . . .'

Lillee: 'I try to hit a batsman in the rib cage when I bowl a purposeful bouncer. I want it to hurt so much that the batsman doesn't want to face me any more . . .'

Thomson: 'The sound of the ball hitting the batsman's skull was music to my ears.'

Tennis? The blood is missing but the verbal mayhem is there for all to see and hear. The verbal violence is brutal and often borders on criminal libel. Shorts advertising coming bouts have actually called attention to McEnroe's behavior as a spectator attraction in itself.

In what other venue can one hear someone call an official a stream of four-letter words in front of a million viewers — and be hailed, approvingly, as a personality?

— Professor Colin Tatz,
Macquarie University,
Weekend Australian, 3–4 April 1982

AGGRESSION IN SPORT

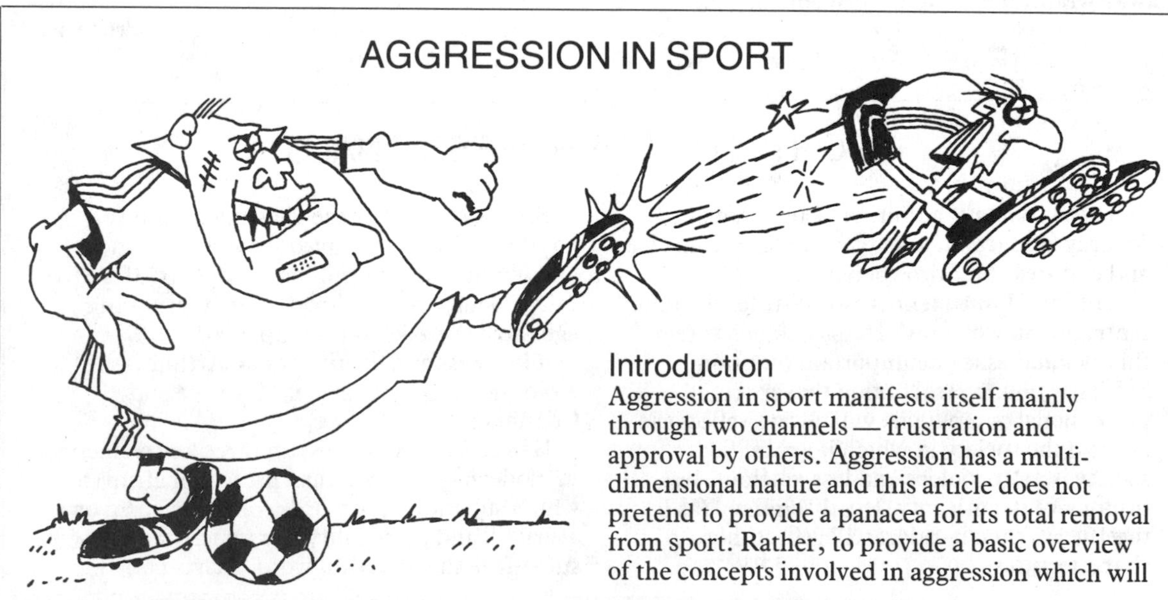

Introduction

Aggression in sport manifests itself mainly through two channels — frustration and approval by others. Aggression has a multi-dimensional nature and this article does not pretend to provide a panacea for its total removal from sport. Rather, to provide a basic overview of the concepts involved in aggression which will then allow coaches to recognise situations likely to give rise to aggressive behaviour.

Aggressive styles of play often affect the outcome of games, decrease their quality, heighten crowd reaction and cause unnecessary injury. Athletic aggression is defined as the 'initiation of an attack with the intent to injure'.

Despite the increasing occurrence of violence, sport is still popularly regarded as being both socially and psychologically beneficial. The central ideology of the Olympic movement, for example, is that sport leads to the development of peace, understanding and goodwill between nations and individuals. However, the 86-year history of the modern Games, disrupted by two world wars, terrorist attacks and political boycotts, contrasts sharply with the 1200 years of uninterrupted competition in the ancient Olympic Games.

Two types of aggression

There are basically two psychological descriptions of aggression with which coaches should become familiar:

1. **Reactive aggression** is an emotional response to an individual perceived as an enemy or a frustrating rival. The aim of reactive aggression is the infliction of injury, either physical or verbal, on another person. It involves anger.

2. **Instrumental aggression** is where the primary goal is not injury to an enemy, but an attainment of a reward. Instrumental aggression does not involve anger and it is not a response to frustration. Sport, for the majority of athletes, involves mainly instrumental aggression as they try to beat their rivals for the satisfaction of proving their own competence, for praise and approval or for other extrinsic rewards. For some athletes, however, anger is a necessary part of the generation of competitive arousal and, for these people, winning probably has to be interpreted in terms of psychologically injuring the opponent in order to maximise performance.

The modern coach must realise both of these may be determined by personality traits and situational states. One of the major instigators of athletic aggression is frustration. . . .

Most aggression in sport results from frustration, although not all frustration in sport results in aggression.

The coach may help by suggesting to the athlete new techniques to deal with frustrating circumstances. . . .

Retaliation

A great deal of aggression in sport can be attributed to retaliation or revenge. In a study of schoolboy basketball players (Harrell, 1980) it was found that the most significant predictor of aggression and fouls was the amount of aggression directed by opponents towards a player. The players' level of aggression matched the aggressive level of the players on the opposing team.

Figures 47.2 and 47.3 give a list of tribunal hearings between 1977 and 1982 detailing aggressive charges associated with basketball at one Victorian metropolitan venue (Albert Park).

Figure 47.2 Albert Park basketball tribunal charges, 1977–82

Brought before the tribunal	**No.**	**Percentage of total hearings**
Male players	368	95%
Female players	18	5%
Male teams	18	86%
Female teams	3	14%

Figure 47.3 The nature of the tribunal charges 1977–82

Charges heard	**Number**
Striking	174
Assault	62
Assaulting referee	55
Fighting	38
Threatening language	33
Striking referee	25
Putting referee in fear of impending violence	19
Kicking	18
Unduly rough play	18
Attempting to strike	7
Elbowing	5
Pushing	3
Head butting	1
Tunnelling	1

Another reason given for the prevalence of aggression in sport is the possibility that athletes and non-athletes vary in the degree of inherent aggression which they possess. Sport by natural selection attracts individuals who are best able to meet the psychological and physical demands of the task. In contact sports, highly aggressive individuals with talent should theoretically become the best performers. . . .

It seems that much aggression on our sports fields is not a result of any theory of aggression but a reflection of the dirty tactics and strategies which some teams and individuals use . . .

The influence on juniors

Australian tennis officials last year introduced a junior code of conduct where juniors who refused to take heed of official warnings were suspended from the tournament.

'The Herald' newspaper ran an article titled, 'Kids' Footy: Umps' Fear', in which it was reported that umpires throughout the State are worried about the increasing incidence of abuse — sometimes physical — of umpires in junior football matches. Bill Deller, VFL umpires' adviser, said: 'The physical danger for umpires is really quite alarming and it's becoming extremely difficult to recruit umpires because of this attitude which has been built up over the years. . . the real crunch of the matter is the future of the game, the game is suffering. That's the tragedy of it all.'

Overt aggression is apparent in the verbal language of sport. In order to express frustration, anger, or disgust, swearing is a common form of venting hostility though it may not be particularly acceptable. However swearing has become relatively common behaviour at sports events that generate high tension and a high level of competition.

On the other side of the coin, one newspaper printed an article by Don Scott, an ex-VFL player, demanding 'Let's get physical and not hysterical!' In the article of June 7, 1983, he said: 'Don't let's get to the stage where you can't even use your body to knock someone over. Already the trend is moving away from genuine physical courage.'

However, most coaches who demonstrate genuine concern for the sport with which they are associated, and that naturally includes the welfare of the players, realise that *channelled* aggression increases the quality of the game, provides more satisfaction for the players, coaches, spectators, referees and sports-journalists.

There have been many suggestions to control the increase of violent aggression in sport:

1. Aversive control on coaches and players
Loss of selection; suspensions for a fixed period; monetary fines.

2. Control on media
Media legislation against highlighting aggressive sporting occurrences.

3. Greater recognition for non-aggressive skilful playing styles
Trophies 'All Clean Team'; best and fairest; Brownlow Medal; TV replay of skilful performances.

4. Psychological development of athletes
Assessment guidance and support by sport psychologists or trained professionals — a useful tool is the positive reinforcement system.

Fundamental changes are needed

Much as these measures are needed, they will only scratch the surface of the problem. What is really needed is a fundamental change in our sporting values and attitudes.

The deification of top teams and individuals in sport has led to an increasing tendency to emphasise excellence at the expense of participation as the sports themselves have become commercialised, professionalised and institutionalised.

The benefits of physical activity are concerned with providing the participants with the opportunity for vigorous physical activity, improvement of skill, co-operation with others, competition in controlled situations and enjoyment and satisfaction. These benefits are made less effective by too much emphasis on winning and the undesirable forms of behaviour, including hostile aggression which such an emphasis precipitates.

— Peter Meaney
Lecturer, Phillip Institute of Technology,
Sports Coach, Vol. 7, No. 4 (No. 27),
March 1984

Aggression

Aggression, as outlined in *Beneath the Surface of Sport*, is:

- The act of initiating an attack
- Behaviour causing harm or pain, not necessarily physical pain
- Not dependent on the result of an action, but on the behaviour itself
- A form of energy, either innate or rising in response to (or intensified by) frustration.

Why is there aggressive behaviour in sport?

Aggression in sport is theoretically explained in two opposing ways:

- It operates according to the cathartic principle — that is, sport provides a socially suitable outlet for pent-up aggression.

or

- It is socially learned behaviour, developed by external environmental inputs such as:
  - — Models of behaviour (from such people as parents and teachers)
  - — Media exposure to the exploitation of violence
  - — Reinforcement (from coaches, the media, etc.)
  - — Situational stimuli (for instance, injustice shown by an umpire)
  - — Social anomie (deterioration of social constraints and norms).

In current articles, writers discuss reasons why there are aggressive and violent sporting scenes. From the articles you have just read, and from your own collection of newspaper articles, summarize your reading under the following headings, to add to the list given:

- Why are sports participants aggressive?
- Why are spectators aggressive?
- What possible solutions can we offer to reduce violent behaviour in sports?

(1) Why are sports participants aggressive?

Here is a preliminary list of explanations that have been offered. Add to the list, if possible.

- The need to win, to gain the victory
- Personal retaliation or revenge
- Letting out pent-up frustrations
- To gain attention
- To 'cause a scene' deliberately
- As an 'ego trip', a response to the increasing emphasis on 'toughness', as projected by the media and society at large
- Pressure from crowds, coaches or friends
- Examples set by sports hero(es) who are habitually aggressive
- Parental prompting and upbringing
- Monetary gain
- Influence of films
- Specific dirty tactics
- Stimulation by the high level of physical contact inherent in the game
- Lack of respect for umpires, players, rules and other people's decisions
- An emotional response to an individual perceived as an enemy
- Self-defence against blunt aggravation by other players
- As a tactic to 'slow up' a talented player (because of jealousy, or as instructed)
- Oppressive environmental conditions, such as heat.

(2) Why are sports spectators aggressive?

Here is a preliminary list of suggestions. Provide your own items for the list as well.

- Alcohol (alone, or in combination with other reasons)
- Defeat of the spectator's team — a blow to the pride
- Fanatical allegiance to a team, identifying with its successes and losses, because the team confers esteem and recognition on the supporters; the team is seen as extension of one's own potential performance
- Sports events providing an escape from the routine and monotony of daily living
- Increased unemployment, leading to increased restlessness and search for identity
- Deliberate orchestration by an antagonist (or to serve the purposes of political terrorism)
- Desensitization to violence by the mass media
- A natural consequence of urban living
- Reaction to sport as an entertainment, a spectacle
- Awareness of violence as a part of the heritage of a particular sport
- Reaction by emotionally immature people, especially 'poor losers'

- Bringing out the innate violence in human nature
- Increased acceptance of violence as a valid expression of emotions in fields other than sport
- Industrial and political tensions' expression in physical force, leading to a pattern that is shown in other tense situations, especially around the sporting field.

(3) Possible solutions to help reduce aggression

Here are some of the solutions that have been suggested recently. Add to the list, if possible.

- The removal of alcohol from sports spectators, either by banning its availability all together or by strictly limiting its presence
- Consciously changing people's attitudes and character so that they will make deliberate decisions to avoid confrontations — that is, helping people to mature emotionally
- Altering standards so that tribunals will deal with aggressive behaviour much more strictly than they do at present
- Improving umpiring standards, where necessary, to ensure that rules are enforced
- Banning notoriously aggressive supporters from attending matches — that is, legislating against agitators
- Improving models of behaviour, especially models presented by the mass media
- Enforcing parental control of television and film viewing (this involves educating parents as well as children)
- Educating young athletes, parents and coaches against aggressive behaviour
- Making a concerted effort, through the media, to warn against aggressive behaviour or highlight non-aggressive behaviour.

Drug abuse in sport

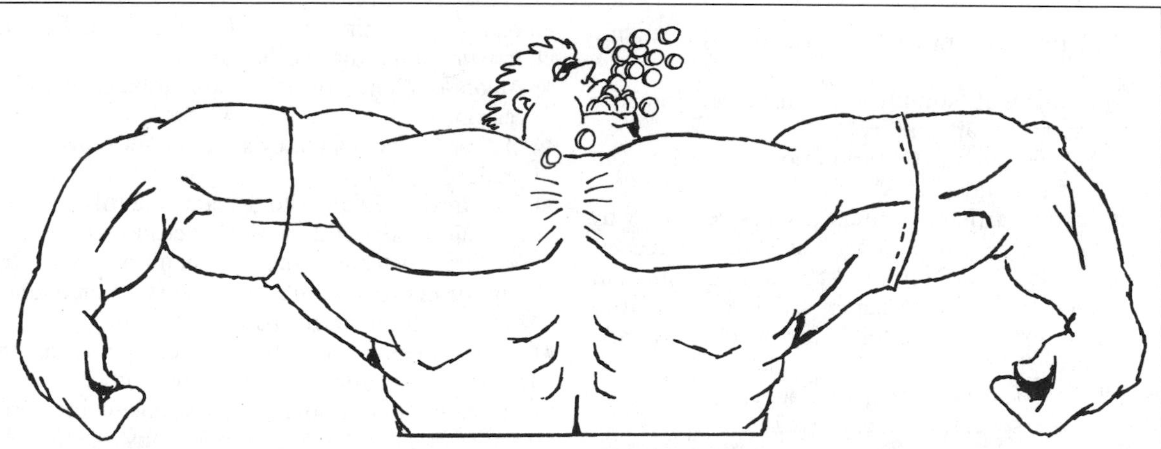

WHEN THE LOCKER ROOM BECOMES A DISPENSARY

[The increasing use of anabolic steroids by athletes, especially female athletes, has been condemned by sports administrators. In this excerpt from his book *Death in the Locker Room*, Bob Goldman, a champion bodybuilder, details the dangers of drug abuse in sports.]

Steroids scare me for what they can do over the long term. And for what they can do to women.

— Professor Arnold Beckett,
University of London

You've seen her standing on the blocks at the end of a pool waiting for the starting gun, or running down the field, or into the spin that hurls her discus further than the others, or standing at rest at the side of a track with a javelin in her hand, or walking away from you in her running shoes and warm-up suit. And you've said to yourself, 'My god, is that a woman? Look at those great hulking shoulders and those arms. Why, she looks more like a man than half the men I know.'

If you had seen her earlier — a month, six months, a year, three or four years, or more — in the privacy of her locker room at her home gym, you would have seen her drinking a white powder mixed in juice or swallowing tablets or taken an injection in her behind.

If you had asked her what she was taking, she might have been able to tell you, but she was more likely to answer, 'Oh, just some powder to make me stronger. All the girls take it.'

'Just some vitamins that the coach gave me.'

'Some growth stuff that all the East German girls are taking.'

If you had suggested that she was taking a drug that might be harmful, she would probably have dismissed your concern.

'I know that, but I need it so I can break the record', or 'win in Mexico', or in wherever the next major competition was scheduled, or,

'Well, maybe. But I'm going to stop taking it when I retire and then I'll be OK,' or,

'I don't think my coach would give me anything that would really hurt me, and besides, it's worth it. Do you know I've taken nearly three seconds off my time since I started taking those drugs?' or,

'I get a lot of exercise and I don't drink or smoke or take birth-control pills, so I don't think I'll get any bad effects from this stuff. It's only helping me get stronger like steak or supervitamins or something', or,

'Listen, when everybody gives up booze and Valium, come back and tell me about it.'

— *Sydney Morning Herald*, 23 February 1985

DRUG ABUSE IN SPORT

Although an ancient problem, the tragic consequences of drug use in sport have been regularly highlighted since the 1960s. The use of a variety of substances by some athletes to modify sports performance has become commonplace. As a consequence, the Australian Sports Medicine Federation (ASMF), in a spirit of international co-operation, is formulating a series of programs and policies to deal with this issue.

The general community may assume that the drugs in sport problem only exists in elite sporting programs, but this is not the case. As indicated by the ASMF 'Survey of Drug Use in Australian Sport', drug use or doping is a problem which permeates all levels of sport.

Doping can be defined as 'the deliberate or inadvertent use of substances by an athlete to modify athletic performance'. The ASMF and other international organisations consider those who provide or administer such substances to be involved in doping practices. This has obvious implications for coaches, trainers and health care professionals.

The Australian sporting community must acknowledge the escalating drug abuse in sport. Self-deceiving arguments such as 'everyone else is involved in it' or 'it is only a problem in the Eastern Bloc' have too often been used.

The use of drugs in sport cannot be condoned. Sport should reflect competition between athletes, not between pharmacologists. Ethical considerations, concerns about health and legal ramifications of drug abuse and transport are sufficient reason to end doping practices in sport. To be involved in doping practices is cheating! This jeopardises the integrity of the sporting community and erodes public support and trust.

A fundamental concern in this issue is the health risk to athletes through the indiscriminate use of large doses of a variety of compounds. Medals or championships are not worth the sacrifice of an individual's health. It is ironic that athletes who exemplify the ultimate in human

▶

performance and fitness are jeopardising those qualities in their search for victories. The delayed complications from the abuse of certain drugs are still unknown and may take decades to emerge.

The control, custody and transportation of certain drugs are under civil and criminal statute both in Australia and overseas. Thus an athlete risks various legal repercussions through involvement in doping practices. All lists of banned substances group the drugs concerned into various categories. The International Olympic Committee, for example, has listed banned drugs into the following five categories:

- Narcotic analgesics (e.g. morphine)
- Anabolic androgenic steroids (e.g. testosterone)
- Psychomotor stimulants (e.g. amphetamines)
- Sympathomimetic amines (e.g. adrenalin-like substances often found in decongestants)
- Central nervous system stimulants (e.g. high doses of caffeine). . . .

In some shooting sports alcohol is banned and specific tests are carried out for its detection. Beta-blockers, a cardiac medication which reduces heart rate, is also banned in many shooting events because of its ability to lessen tremor and reduce subsequent vibrations of the arm.

Diuretics are drugs which cause the kidneys to excrete large volumes of urine. Participants in sport where competition is controlled by weight, such as boxing and weightlifting, may use this medication, even though the disruption of body chemistry following the use of diuretics can lead to heart and kidney failure. Diuretics have also been used to wash out other banned drugs prior to drug testing.

During the 1950s anabolic steroids found their way from medicine into sport. These are synthetic chemical modifications of the male sex hormone testosterone. Their use can increase weight, appetite, and possibly muscular strength, and may aid recovery following intense exercise. But anabolic steroids and related compounds have also been associated with adverse effects on the liver, cardiovascular system, reproductive system and psychological status.

The use of numerous dietary and nutritional supplements by athletes should also be considered with respect to doping practices. An individual who consumes these supplements becomes convinced of his or her power and thus relies on an external source for success and improved performance.

No drug is an adequate substitute for a well-conceived and thoughtfully implemented training program.

As drug abuse has grown in sport, technologies have emerged to combat it. At major international games and many Australian national events, sophisticated technology is used to combat the doping problem. Competitors are selected for drug testing randomly and/or by virtue of their position of finish.

The ASMF is initiating a set of policies and developing programs designed to discourage the use of drugs in sport. These programs are comprehensive and need to involve all national sporting organisations as they apply to the entire sporting community, including athletes, coaches, and health care professionals.

(Further information on the issue of drugs in sport is available from: Mr Steve Haynes, Drugs in Sport Co-ordinator, ASMF, PO Box 243, Kingston, ACT 2604; phone: (062) 95 0032).

— Steve Haynes, Drugs in Sport Co-ordinator, *Sport Report*, December 1984

Sport: What is its real importance?

Sport can be used as a pleasurable test of supremacy, and demands discipline and expertise to be developed, to ensure maximum performance. This is absent in play. The role of sport can also be important for the adolescent as a specific means for adjustment and acceptance, and expression of identity. As self-concept or identity may be one of the most important motivators of behaviour, it must be regarded highly. After childhood, one's self-attitude can change, but one's self-concept is not changed so easily. Sports coaches, then, must not be overkeen to inflict the sporting experience, if it is inappropriate for the readiness of the child.

Movement should be explored and not just consist of the mimicking of a skill, and the coach should never create the sporting context where one's self-image is totally tied to winning or losing. Any emphasis should be on effort and not results.

Sports can compensate for psychological problems, and provide identity (cf. academic failure) and even the possibility for success and an increase in status.

The sporting environment should ideally be one where 'children (and adults) are able to risk being "last" and "first", so that all can be realistically successful' (US Medical Association, *Exercise and Recreation*).

48. The mass media and sport

Just as television has forced politicians to fluff up their hair, clean their teeth, change their clothes and develop speech patterns appropriate to the medium, so sportsmen have been forced to adapt and change their skills to meet the demands of those who package and market their games for the box.

— Michael Gawenda,
The Age, 5 April 1982

Beneath the surface of sport

Assumptions (held by some individuals about sport and the media)

(1) The more a sport is televised, the more it is likely to encourage people to play.
(2) The more a particular sport is promoted by the mass media, the more it changes or is changed to suit the mass media.
(3) The mass media reinforce the dominant political ideology in Australian society, i.e., the values of success, hard work and dedication.
(4) Television and its sponsors are more interested in profit than promoting sports for sport's sake.
(5) Commercial television treats sport differently and for different reasons than government-sponsored television (ABC).

Issues

(1) Do the media actually influence sporting behaviour? (Does the creation of cult heroes breed behavioural phenomena?)
(2) What is/has been the role of the mass media and their influence on sport? Do they change sport unnecessarily?
(3) Do the media distort and/or exaggerate reality? (What are the media aiming for in their packaging of sport?)
(4) Does sport rely more on the mass media than the mass media on sport? (Which needs which most?)
(5) Does the promotion associated with the mass media affect athletes, especially those who are the centre of attention? (Are excessive pressures being applied?)

(Based on Rob Sands (ed.), *Beneath the Surface of Sports: Sociology of Sports for Teachers*, Victoria College, Rusden Campus.)

FORGET THE GAME — RAZZAMATAZZ IS THE WINNER

There are now more sports viewers than there are spectators. Television has put sport firmly in the arena of entertainment, where replays and commentaries play as great a role in thrilling viewers as the action. NEIL ADMUR of the 'New York Times' reports.

The sports and business officials from South Korea listened intently to the presentation from the American Cable Television executives — $750 million for the exclusive American rights to the 1988 Summer Olympics was a realistic figure to expect from a network, they were told.

They were also told that a pay-television package, offering 19 straight days and 24 hours of Olympic activity for $200 a household, might generate as much as $1.8 billion just from the US. No decision has been reached on how the Seoul Olympics will be sold or packaged, but there is no doubt that the final figures will be large and that television, as never before, is the most powerful force in sports.

In addition to bankrolling established leagues and sports organisations and new ventures such as the United States Football League, television has altered the texture, perceptions and images of American athletics. . . .

What the viewer actually sees, however, according to Dr Jennings Bryant, is 'packaged reality'. Dr Bryant, who is the chairman of the communications department at the University of Evansville, says 'packaged reality is not the reality of the stadium or arena. It's what the producer and director, by their shot selection and pictures and the addition of commentary, create. It's a sports entertainment event.'

Several studies by Dr Bryant and Dolf Zillman, the director of the Institute for Communications Research at Indiana University, have confirmed the visual and auditory impact television can have.

In one study, published earlier this year in the 'Journal of Communication', a group of about 100 college students listened to dubbed commentary of a routine tennis match between two veteran players, Torben Ulrich and Sven Davidson.

The students were asked to watch as they normally would. Then they were asked to evaluate the event by reporting their feelings about the match in terms of how they enjoyed it and how intense the competition was. One third of the group listened to commentary in which the players were reported to be good friends. One third heard commentary describing the players as bitter enemies. A third group heard commentary in which the relationship between the two players was not specified.

The results of the study, Dr Bryant wrote, showed that viewers who perceived the competitors as hostile found the telecast more interesting, exciting and enjoyable.

'Although the play was unaltered,' Dr Bryant said, during a recent interview, 'altering the commentary was sufficient to alter fans' perception of the event.'

'The more you integrate drama and the more you attribute personal rivalry to two sides,' says Elihu Katz, a professor of Sociology and Communications at the University of South California, 'the more involvement you get from the viewer.'

In a recently completed study, Dr Bryant compared the descriptive, dramatic and humorous commentary during six randomly selected National Football League (NFL) telecasts on the three networks from the 1976 season with six games from the last season. The conclusion: descriptive commentary had decreased slightly and dramatic commentary had increased 30 per cent with a clear trend toward more 'player-versus-player conflict'.

'Viewers' expectations of sporting events have changed because of television,' Dr Bryant said. 'Because TV has to rely on dramatic elements that often have to do with giving all and violence, the event on television is different from what is unfolding on the field.'

Edwin Diamond, the director of a new study group in the department of political science at Massachusetts Institute of Technology, points to the switch to more attractive, tighter-fitting uniforms, the liberalising of rules in many sports and the focusing on Olga Korbut and Nadia Comaneci in Olympic gymnastics, a relatively obscure sport, as further examples of television's

▶

ability to rearrange reality.

'Television does not portray sports as they are,' said Dr George Gerbner, the Dean of the Annenberg School of Communications at the University of Pennsylvania. 'It integrates sports into its own system.' Using sports figures as analysts and personalities on other programs reflects this integration, Gerbner says.

The proliferation of sports has also changed the way television has done its job. In pursuit of technical innovations, networks have recruited the Goodyear Blimp, installed television cameras in stock cars and used wireless microphones on football and basketball coaches, runners and outriders at thoroughbred race tracks. Refinements in editing, relays from a variety of camera positions, slick graphics and lighter, more mobile cameras have resulted in additional technical improvements. The public's fascination with replays is one reason why many arenas and stadiums have installed large scoreboards equipped with slow-motion and re-run capabilities.

'It clearly produces a different kind of expectancy in the event itself for the viewer,' says Dr Bryant. 'The spectator who goes to the stadium now may not find it as thrilling because the production is less satisfying than television.'

Roone Arledge, the president of ABC News ... says 'exclusivity' and the ability to 'mass-market' is what has expanded television's horizons. Simply tying up the television rights to a specific sports event heightens its appeal....

Bob Wussler, a former president of the CBS Television network...who is now executive vice-president of Turner Broadcasting Systems Inc., said survey operators see the '80s as a 'decade of stay-at-homes', with television playing the major part in sports.

'Ultimately', Wussler said, 'we're heading for a situation where most professional sports will be available for some form of pay television. This will have to affect the future of sports and televised sport.'

— Neil Admur,
New York Times

THE SPORTS FAN'S CHANGING FACE

We are seeing is a major shift in Australian sports crowd behavior. Like overseas sport, the Australian product has changed in character very quickly in a short time as it becomes entertainment and a spectacle.

Take alcohol, for example. It is now common to blame sports trouble on drunkenness, with the natural attempt being to eliminate alcohol from the sports area....

But the changed circumstances in which the drinking occurs have been ignored. 'A beer at the game' has had a long and fairly honorable history in Australian sport. Drunkenness did occur, but on a small and controllable scale in areas unofficially recognised as the grog spots. The Sydney Hill was like that for a lot of its history.

But a lot of that tradition has broken down recently. Many problems have been encountered in Australian tennis spectacles, for example, where spectators have been inspired to get involved verbally with players. In that sense, the sports arena has almost become an extension of the suburban pub. Because of that, the popular attitudes towards drinking at games has begun to change....

Removing alcohol might reduce, but will not eliminate the real underlying problem....

Another important consideration is that the community now is far more aware of crowd behavior than it was 30 years ago. The reason is simply television. For the past few years Australian sports groups and television authorities have been well aware of the sharp debate about whether TV violence helps create real violence.

Again, the Perth events highlight the central problem. Should television have: not shown nor commented about the violence; shown it, but not commented on it; or focused on it as a major event?

Perhaps the violence was not so great as was imagined. Had we seen recent Pakistan cricket or British football riots we might not have been so shocked. This is not to underrate, let alone sympathise with, what happened in Perth. It is to point out that with television a one-sided view is obtained easily. . . .

Some English cricket writers noted a few seasons ago that Australian night games provided the first working-class cricket crowds. They were making connections between English soccer crowds and night cricket spectators. That comparison resurfaced at the weekend.

The reasons were obvious enough: the flags, banners, chanting, singing and general noise. But the real importance of this apparent soccer connection is that it shows how changes to the traditions and character of cricket can also change crowd expectations.

One-day cricket promises color, excitement, constant action and instant results. The fans for that will have their expectations shattered in a Test where survival like Tavare's, skill like Yardley's, finesse like Gower's, and inconclusion like a draw are foremost.

If that is the case then no amount of liquor control or police activity will remove the frustration of unfulfilled expectations.

Modern entertainment sport has changed the nature of crowd involvement with games. We are now witnessing Australia's first experiences of dealing with that change.

Any punishment will be effective only if we confront the causes rather than the symptoms of behavior.

Let us try to determine what those people were doing at the ground, what their expectations were, how they related to the rest of the crowd and the game, and what motivated their ultimate action.

If we do not at least try to understand these things, then our slide towards the overseas behavior pit will be unchecked.

— Brian Stoddart,
Lecturer in Sports Studies, Canberra CAE,
The Age, 16 November 1982

Research work 18: Television and our changing perception of sport

Using the two articles, 'Forget the Game — Razzmatazz is the Winner' and 'The Sports Fan's Changing Face', your own collection of articles, general knowledge, and class discussion, supplement the following lists of answers.

(1) What are the motives or responsibilities of a television sports broadcaster?
- (a) Provide information that is representative of what is happening in the sport world
- (b) Provide a community service
- (c) Entertain viewers
- (d) Make money by selling advertising time
- (e) Gain recognition and status for the television station
- (f) Assist promotion of sports
- (g) . . . .
- (h) . . . .

etc.

(2) What are the differences between the way commercial and government stations provide a coverage of sport?

(a) **Presentation on commercial stations**
- (i) More professional male sport and major sports teams in prime time
- (ii) More international and live broadcasting of sport
- (iii) Less variety of individual and team sports
- (iv) Image presented: male, dynamic and aggressive sports that fit the active 15–25 age group
- (v) . . . .

etc.

(b) **Why do commercial stations present sports this way?**

Commercial TV:
- (i) Needs to entertain large numbers of viewers
- (ii) Needs to make as much profit as possible
- (iii) Needs to pay creditors; profit is gained through advertising and this is in turn related to the success of individual programmes; the more interest, the more profit
- (iv) . . . .

etc.

(c) **Presentation of government-financed — that is, Australian Broadcasting Commission (ABC) stations leads to:**
  (i) More minor sports, shown on a wide variety of time slots
  (ii) Less total airtime devoted to sports
  (iii) More female sport than on commercial stations
  (iv) An image that relates to people who both active and passive, and who cover a wide range of ages
  (v) More emphasis on 'educating' the public about sports that are not well known
  (vi) ....
  etc.

(d) **Why do ABC stations present sports this way?**
  (i) To inform viewers as well as entertain them
  (ii) Because profit is an unimportant consideration when deciding presentation policy
  (iii) The ABC's charter is to cater for a wide variety of interests that might not necessarily be covered by private enterprise stations
  (iv) ....
  etc.

(3) The main methods used by commercial stations to increase the entertainment value of sports on television include:
  (a) The production of 'stirring' football songs
  (b) The establishment of people as media stars as well as stars on the sports fields, and the promotion of these stars in such events as panels and interviews
  (c) Making sports stars seem glamorous, especially by giving them prizes and trophies
  (d) Involving sports people in presenting competitions for viewers
  (e) Involving sports stars in slick and expensive pre-event advertising and promotion
  (f) ....
  etc.

Note: The promotion of sports stars on television usually takes the following path:
  (a) The person becomes a 'star' — very popular because of his or her success at sport
  (b) Viewer numbers increase for any sports programme featuring that star — this shows in increased ratings for the television station
  (c) Advertisers pay for extra advertising time on sports programmes that have high ratings, and they pay higher rates for the time they've taken already
  (d) The station's profits increase.

(4) Why are some sports programmes on television more popular than others?

The television popularity of a game does not seem to be decided by the number of people who actually play it — that is, the game's participation rate. After all, some sports, such as netball, lawn bowls, soccer and basketball are very widely played, but they are not extensively televised.

Instead, the most liked (not necessarily most played) sports are usually the most sponsored and most telecast. Sports associations develop a marketing approach, and concentrate on sponsorship contracts.

The popularity of sports programmes on television seem to be determined by such factors as:
  (a) The 'thrill' component
  (b) Dramatic content of the game being televised
  (c) Uncertainty about results, especially when large amounts of prize money are awarded
  (d) Emotional aura surrounding large-crowd events
  (e) Crowd attendance, and simultaneous radio and newspaper publicity
  (f) The participation by highly skilled 'hero' figures
  (g) Aggression level shown by opposing sides
  (h) Levels of strength and speed that can actually be shown on screen
  (i) ....
  etc.

(5) How has television coverage of sport changed over the last few years?
  (a) Increased use of music
  (b) Increased use of complex camera work — for instance, switching rapidly between crowd scenes and close-ups of play
  (c) Introduction of slow-motion replays
  (d) Changing style of commentary
  (e) ....
  etc.

(6) How do sponsors involve themselves with the televising of sport?

(a) The use of players or scenes from games in commercials — for example: ....
(b) Advertising during the sports event, using the appeal of the sport to sell the product — for example: ....
(c) ....
etc.

(7) Which images and atmosphere does television itself create during a sports event?
(a) Athletes are shown as 'superhuman'
(b) Creation of an atmosphere of hostility between opponents, although actually there is mutual respect
(c) Microphones placed near, say, a cricket's wicket in such a way as to destroy the image of cricket as a 'gentleman's game'; courtside microphones used to pick up insults during international tennis games
(d) ....
etc.

(8) What changes to the nature, rules and presentation of sports have occurred because of the presentation of those sports on television?
(a) **Basketball:** bonus three-point basket from outside a set boundary; ....
(b) **Football:** a free kick awarded for a ball out on the full (to encourage accuracy on the part of players); payments to players have escalated by more than 1800 per cent in League football during the 1970s and 1980s, so that now a National League may be needed because there is not enough money available among Melbourne clubs to support the game; ....
(c) **Soccer:** the rules are different in America and in Europe, largely because soccer is much more widely televised in Europe than in America; ....
(d) **Cricket:** Since 1977, when cricket was first marketed as a commercial game, there has been increased interest by many people, but also the introduction of a new style of clothing (helmets, coloured clothing, etc.), field behaviour (a great increase in aggressive behaviour), and style of playing (introduction of one-day matches); ......
(e) **Increased power of sponsors**, who can now dictate where games will be held, at what times, and with which gear and clothing; ....
(f) ....
etc.

(9) Construct laboratory exercises to test the truth of the patterns and trends outlined above — for example, conduct a close analysis of dialogue used by commentators reporting from a live sporting event.

49. Sponsorship in sport

The days of funding being provided by someone assuming the obligations of the sporting body or simply as patronage are past. Sporting organizations that accept funds provided as an investment must become business organizations to handle them.

— G. Day,
Executive Director, Confederation of Australian Sport

SPONSORSHIP — GETTING IT ... AND KEEPING IT

This article by Doug Stewart explains how a minor sport, namely table tennis, can obtain sponsorship and maintain it. 'Sports Coach' believes that the principles described in attaining and keeping sponsorship in the case of table tennis can be transferred to many minor sports.

Sponsorship has contributed greatly to the growth and success of many sporting organisations in the last 20 years. With sponsorship, the tournament organisers are, to a great extent, free from the worry of possibly incurring large losses which could bankrupt their association, and they can also offer reasonable money prizes to attract good players.

In some sports, including tennis and golf, the sponsorship and prize money business has gone completely crazy, and a few players of ability (and some without much ability) are making vast sums of money.

Sports such as tennis, golf, the various codes of football, cricket and motor sports do not seem to have any trouble in attracting sponsors, and others such as athletics, volleyball, boxing and swimming also have their occasional major successes in attracting big money.

Table tennis is in the minor leagues as far as this sort of activity is concerned. There are few sponsors who see table tennis as an effective way of promoting their products or services. The table tennis equipment manufacturers and importers do put some money into sponsorship but, in my opinion, not enough. However, that is another story — the fact is that there are very few sponsors for table tennis.

Motives for sponsorship

Let's face it — there are very few sponsors who will put up a substantial amount of money merely as a charitable gesture. If you have a businessman who will back table tennis to the hilt — who is a personal enthusiast for the game — then your association is indeed in a fortunate position, and also in a minority position. There just aren't many such patrons around, especially in these times of belt-tightening for business all over Australia.

Kerry Packer can afford to put up a few hundred thousand. He says he is doing it 'because he is proud to be an Australian and because Australia has been good to him' but unfortunately he isn't putting it into table tennis and in any case there aren't many like that around.

Commercial sponsorship of sports in Australia started to boom when colour television was introduced to this country, and that's no coincidence. The big companies are flocking to put money into the sports which attract a big television coverage, with their banners and logos strategically placed for the camera. Unfortunately that doesn't help table tennis.

Table tennis very rarely makes the television screen. A notable exception was the Wills tournament of three and four years ago. Matches of the calibre of the famed Javor v. Tasaka clash drew praise from everybody who viewed them, whether they knew anything about table tennis or not. But the Wills tournament is no more, and the other two nationally sponsored events — by Ansett and Samboy — also ceased two years ago.

However, we lack a generous benefactor or patron who is table-tennis-mad enough to pour money into the game. Our only chance of obtaining significant sponsorship is by convincing the potential sponsor that his investment of money is a sound business proposition.

A business proposition

So, we are looking at sponsorship as a carefully planned commercial exercise with returns in exposure, advertising and promotion to such an extent that the sponsor will say 'Yes, we got value for our money'. And just as importantly 'Yes, we'll do it again'.

Getting them to do it again may not be so difficult if you can demonstrate value-for-money the first time, but how do you go about signing up a substantial (to us, anything from $300 onwards is substantial) sponsor for the first time?

The nitty gritty concept is 'public exposure', and the extent of public exposure available to a potential sponsor is influenced by the following factors:

- the level of public interest in the sport.
- the likelihood of heavy radio and newspaper publicity.
- the likely attendance at the meet.
- the likelihood of television coverage.
- the estimated TV audience (i.e. the probable rating figure).

As we have already agreed, the last two of these factors don't have much application to table tennis, so we have to concentrate on the first three. The level of public interest and the likely attendance at the meet are both not as high as we think that they should be, and they certainly wouldn't produce any firm and reliable figures which would get a sponsor really excited. Radio? Well, this medium is I think a bit limited in its potential for table tennis and, I think that print media publicity is really the only one of these factors that we table tennis people can successfully exploit. . . .

Evaluation

Some sponsors try to evaluate, in advance, what they might get for their money. Ampol sponsored our closed championships in 1980 and our open event in 1981, and before making a firm commitment they sent us the following questionnaire to complete.

'If Ampol takes up this sponsorship, do you propose to:

- Include Ampol's name in the official title of the promotion?
- In the name of a particular event?
- What will the titles be?
- Acknowledge Ampol's sponsorship with our logo and all printed matter for the event?
- Ensure that all news releases acknowledge Ampol's sponsorship?
- Use your best endeavours to persuade media representatives to cover sponsorship in news reports?
- Briefly describe what printed matter is planned?
- Invite Ampol to be represented at all receptions associated with the event, including trophy presentations?
- Allow a reasonable number of Ampol promotional signs to be erected in the club house and games area?
- Ensure that minor sponsors are restricted to a lesser amount of promotional material?
- Collate and forward progressively to this office all club printed matter and details of media coverage of the event?
- Provide a schedule of paid advertising (if any)?
- Provide assistance under the direction of our representative for the erection, removing and packing of promotional material used?'

The questionnaire concludes:

'Please advise at which committee meeting the above items were discussed and which officials have agreed to the answers above.'

All this is a part of the sponsor's legitimate attempt to ensure that his money will not go down the drain. There have been some monumental flops in the past, for example:

- Non-appearance of expected sports stars — several recent Australian men's tennis titles would be an example of this.
- Bungling by the organisers — the much-publicised air race across Australia in 1976 ended at Bankstown Airport with the first official arriving at the airport two hours after the first competitor touched down, and 10,000 spectators wondering what was going on.

To get your initial sponsorship you will obviously have to convince the potential sponsors that your organisers are capable of running the event to everybody's satisfaction, and that they are capable of 'doing the right thing' as far as promotion of the event and the sponsor's product are concerned.

You don't want your event to be a complete shambles and people remembering the sponsor for that reason!

Sponsorship is business and obviously you have to be business like to sign up a sponsor for the first time. . . .

A case study

The Wagga Wagga Table Tennis Association has enjoyed reasonable success in obtaining sponsorship for table tennis in this city of about 50,000 population. In each of the last two years we have been able to obtain a total of around $2500 to run four or five tournaments with a different sponsor for each. . . .

Print media use

Out promotional efforts on behalf of our sponsors have been mainly concentrated on the print media, of which there are a number available:

- a local daily newspaper
- a regional weekly newspaper
- a monthly journal which circulates around the local clubs
- daily, bi-weekly or tri-weekly newspapers of varying sizes in the other towns in the Riverina region
- our own table tennis association's occasional newsletter
- the ATTA Newsletter.

Readers in all areas can recognise these sorts of print media vehicles which could be available to them.

Natural we try to get as many mentions for our sponsor as possible, and there are a number of ways of doing this. . . .

Doing it yourself

Of course, your own association is most likely in the same situation as the vast majority — trying to promote a sport that doesn't already have an enthusiast on the local newspaper — and having to concoct and provide all the media material and having to convince the football and racing orientated sports staff that it is worth printing.

So, you organise press releases and submit them in the hope of having them printed. How can you maximise your chances of success?...

The news release is one of the main links in the chain of communication from organisations to the general public, but the communication of many organisations suffers because the function of the news release is not properly realised and the technique is not properly applied.

What is news?

The following effective treatment of this complex topic has been given by Michael King in his book 'Make It News':

'Fundamentally, news is something that interests a general audience. Or, more accurately, it is something that journalists believe will interest a general audience.

'It is rarely something that concerns only a few individuals or a single special interest group.

'No one has been able to devise a single comprehensive definition of news. It is often as subjective as the journalists who select it. But some common ingredients can be identified and agreed upon. The most important are:

- **Human interest:** Who cares about this topic? People are most interested in people, e.g., 'A 10-year-old Malaysian boy is to be brought to this country by the Combined Service Clubs for an operation that may save his life.'
- **Novelty and immediacy:** Is this new, fresh? 'The Government is considering making Crown Land available for young people to run settlements on similar lines to the kibbutz system in Israel.'
- **Proximity:** Does this touch upon the lives of my readers? Can I make it do so? e.g. 'All Australians will be affected by the Government's proposed citizens' tax.'
- **Freakishness:** News is often the silhouette against a background of normality. The 99 people out of 100 who lead a normal daily life are less interesting than the one who doesn't. e.g. 'A three foot six dwarf from Phoenix has been accused of a $500 bank robbery. Although the bank's cameras were working, no usable picture resulted because the man's head did not come up to the counter level.'
- **People in high places:** The person who says or does something may be more important than what is said or done, e.g. 'Prince Philip camps under stars in Australian outback.'
- **Dramatic use of language:** It is more newsworthy to call a lake an 'unflushed toilet' than to say it 'is polluted'. The language used can be newsworthy in itself.

Other news elements include: sex, security, survival, conflict, entertainment, suspense or 'local boy makes good' (or bad).

If your readers find your story dull, commonplace, repetitive, self-evident or of narrow concern, it's not news....

The 'strengths' of table tennis

Every sport or other activity has its 'strengths' as far as publicity appeal is concerned. What are the strengths of table tennis? Some of these include:

- it is a family sport where all the members of the family can enjoy it together, at the competitive as well as at the social level
- it is a lifetime sport
- it is an international sport with more than 130 associations affiliated to the international body
- it is a non-contact, non-violent sport
- it is a sport in which Australia does enjoy some international standing
- it is a sport that anyone can play — anyone has played.

Try to exploit these strengths in your media publicity attempts....

What our sponsors want

We have found that the people who are willing to sponsor table tennis at this regional level want publicity for their product and publicity for the local people who are involved....

►

On-site displays

Displays of the sponsor's products can usually be easily arranged at the site of the tournament, but in general we have not found sponsors to be much interested in this publicity. On one occasion we obtained a sponsorship from a local sports store and an effective display of sports clothing and equipment was arranged on a couple of old table tennis tables.

We have always offered our sponsors the opportunity to erect their own displays, banners and posters, but in the absence of significant television attention, the sponsors do not seem to see much advantage in this. . . .

We try to give our sponsors continuing publicity at every opportunity. For example, at a Leisure Expo organised by the local sport and recreation people we put on a table tennis display and publicly acknowledge all our major sponsors of the past few years.

— Doug Stewart,
Sports Coach, Vol. 8, No. 2, October 1984

THE MARKETING AND SPONSORSHIP OF SPORT IN AUSTRALIA

Sports marketing in Australia

Sports marketing in Australia is relatively new. It was once looked on with disdain by sporting administrators who often pointed to a successful past and assumed that what was good enough then was good enough for the future.

Cricket is an intensely competitive Australian marketplace which has to fight and justify its place as the No. 1 national summer sport. Marketing methodology and techniques need to be constantly reviewed to ensure the maximum impact is made. It is necessary to communicate clearly the excitement and attraction of the sport to the public, to turn casual interest into support.

Marketing is defined as having the right product, in the right place, at the right time, in the right quantities and at the right price.

The trick is getting these elements right. The place to start is with research, not just in the technical sense with its doctorate consultants, university trained interviewers and computer based statistical techniques. There is a wealth of information from newspaper reports, television and radio surveys, gate information, advance ticket sales and government registers.

Marketing of cricket in Australia

Marketing firms need to be closely attuned to their market. When it was confirmed that a substantial proportion of cricket attendance is still a spontaneous decision PBL introduced a radio campaign into our media mix to reach people in the throws of making up their minds.

It's best not to assume public taste, feelings, views or reactions. Research was needed in the rule changes, the coloured clothing, the advertising, the sponsorship, the ticket prices, the itinerary, the teams and the players.

Getting the message across

Each cricket season mass communication gets across the single vibrant message that cricket is exciting entertainment. Cricket television commercials have worked well. The advertising agency, Mojo, who created the 'C'mon Aussie' jingle, commences work around Christmas each year on the style of next season's commercials.

Cricket exposure includes television and an extensive commercial radio campaign and newspaper advertisements prior to the start of international cricket in each market. This campaign is supported by a promotional program involving sponsors, licensees, commercial radio stations and newspapers.

Five years ago the Australian Cricket Board did not have a published program. PBL looked upon publishing as an element in our overall marketing to have a say in the way cricket is seen by the public.

Last year more than 300,000 copies of Australian Cricket Board publications were sold, and this year almost 20 titles will be on sale. . . .

Work has also been put into the merchandising area. . . . It has taken five years to develop 29 licensees, but this season we expect cricket merchandise to top $5 million in retail turnover and to start producing a satisfactory level of return.

We have ensured that the position of the major sponsor, The Benson and Hedges Company, is supported through all PBL activities. Gaining full benefits for the company is our problem. No sport can afford to lose the support of major companies — they are too hard to get in the first place.

After a major sponsor has been found, other companies become involved. The McDonald's Family Restaurants became the sponsor of the interstate one-day series and Ansett became the official carrier. Various competitions, such as the Sidchrome Supertest team and Australia's most popular sports competition, the Nissan Classic Catches, were introduced.

A great deal of time, money and effort was spent on media relations. A comprehensive press handbook was published.

Working on the premise that most journalists are lazy, well-researched and well-written material will be used if it is provided to them. It encourages editorial exposure. . . .

Sport and the media

Media has looked to sport as a valuable source of stories.

Sport looks to the media to publicise its activities, explain its rules, inform its supporters, and attract new devotees. From this very strong base of mutual interest a closer working relationship should exist between the media and sporting organisations.

Sporting management in Australia is handled by unpaid, or poorly paid enthusiasts who give vast amounts of time to their sports. But, for the most part, they can't handle the requirements of today, either in the media or player relations. . . .

Do not underestimate the importance of the interaction between a sport and the media. The media can, and have been the creators of a broad support base of many sports. The management of this relationship is what sets certain sports apart as public attractions. The most obvious and keenly sought after media aspect is television coverage. However, many administrators ignore the major function of building their sport to attract audiences independent of television coverage.

Every sporting association with a television contract is guaranteed x number of dollars before a single ticket is sold. If a guaranteed income is assured before the doors are open, it takes away the risk. . . .

The trends of the USA are already evident in Australia where, fortunately for the local sport administrators, four television networks all chase attractive sporting events.

Television is constantly re-examining the public arena to discover formats which will satisfy demands for sporting events.

As an example, the BBC found a new sport which was ideally suited to television, but was not popular. The sport was snooker, and the show 'Pot Black'. Suddenly snooker had a whole new supportive base which greatly accelerated the game's development.

Television development of match-play golf between the two top players allowed the game to be explained.

In the United States, tennis was a minor sport as recently as the mid-1960s. It was played mainly in select clubs but it did not capture the interest of the populace. When it was taken up by the three American networks, spotlighted ▶

and explained, tennis boomed. The scoring pattern was changed temporarily to be more understandable to a mass audience who had never been near a tennis court, much less on one.

Tennis is now the boom sport in the US. The number of players has increased dramatically and the support has become almost fanatical.

The media, particularly television, are a vital ingredient to the development of sport and can, given the correct circumstances, accelerate that sport's growth at a rate not possible by any other method.

Some critics are concerned that television exploits major sports such as cricket, with the result that people become watchers rather than participants. One of the outstanding achievements of cricket's television coverage is that the spectator base, particularly among females, has been widened.

Conclusion

In a dynamic market it is the responsibility of marketers and administrators to continually re-appraise their techniques and methods and to provide media, particularly radio and television, with innovative concepts and ideas for the promotion and marketing of the game.

In summary:

1. **Research** — potential audience; perception of sport; intention; demographics; pricing. To promote the game as attractive to the widest possible audience, which is achieved through advertising, promotion, merchandising, marketing.
2. **Advertising** — television; radio; press. To create public awareness and achieve maximum attendance and maximise gate receipts to return the greatest revenue to the game for its development.
3. **Promotions and marketing concepts** — give-aways, itinerary cards, competitions, personal appearances. Purpose — to create audience involvement.
4. **Merchandising** — to achieve the maximum return from merchandising and marketing. Be aware at all times that there are promotional aspects which may override the level of return in order to achieve the full promotional benefit.
5. **Publications** — to educate and reflect on all aspects of the sport.
6. **Media relations** — to achieve a harmonious relationship with radio, press and television networks in order to maximise TV rights fees. Use this relationship to communicate with your audience, which ensures promotion for the sport.

— Lynton Taylor,
Marketing Director, PBL Marketing,
Sports Coach, Vol. 8, No. 2, October 1984

Find the facts: Sponsorship and sport

From 'Sponsorship — Getting It . . . and Keeping It'

(1) What is the role of sponsorship in sport today in Australia?
(2) What are the motives of sponsors?
(3) Which sports, other than table tennis, are neglected by sponsors?
(4) What is public exposure of a sport dependent upon?
(5) What might a sponsor require from a sports association?
(6) What are some examples of print media?
(7) What makes a sports article newsworthy? Find a current sports article and identify its important ingredients.
(8) For a sport of your choice:
- **(a)** Identify the most important aspects of its public appeal — that is, its strengths.
- **(b)** List any special events, known to you, that have obviously been well publicized.
- **(c)** List the ways in which which the sponsor's name and/or products have been utilized or displayed during the sports promotion.

From 'The Marketing and Sponsorship of Sport in Australia'

(9) How do marketing companies obtain their information?
(10) What techniques are used by PBL Marketing to turn casual interest in cricket into wide-spread support?

(11) Who are the major sponsors of cricket?
(12) What is the relationship between sport and the media?
(13) What is the effect of television coverage of a given sport?
(14) List the methods used for advertising, promoting and advertising by a sport known to you.

Figure 49.1 Top money-earners Greg Norman, Robert de Castella, Peter Brock and Pat Cash.

WHAT THE TOP AUSTRALIANS EARN IN SPORT

Australia's international cricketers are now by a clear margin the country's highest-paid team of sportsmen, but their earnings are still small compared with champions in individual sports.

Under new contracts announced by the Australian Cricket Board this week, 16 players in the international squad are guaranteed payments of $65,000 per year. This probably means that the celebrities among them, including captain Kim Hughes, will earn altogether about $100,000 each from he game when payments for commercials and endorsements are taken into account.

But leading golfers, tennis players, racing drivers — even professional cyclists — earn much more. Tennis player Pat Cash is well above this, with about $225,000, as is multiple Bathurst winner, racing driver Peter Brock, with about $160,000. Each would do much better were he to win Wimbledon. Just behind Brock, at $150,000, is cyclist Phil Anderson, now competing in the Tour de France.

Golfer Graham Marsh probably earned three times as much from sport last year as his brother Rod, the cricketer.

Greg Norman earns most of all — about $550,000 a year, according to an informed estimate. These days he is said to make $25,000 a tournament in appearance fees alone, yet his really lucrative days in golf are probably still ahead of him.

Robert de Castella is already doing nicely, with about $150,000, but would do better by far if he won the Olympic marathon. De Castella's manager, Mr Graeme Hannan, has estimated that de Castella stands to gain $400,000 by winning at Los Angeles.

Terry Gale, the Perth golfer, provides an interesting point of comparison. Cricket was his favourite game, and in the late 1960s he was once chosen as 12th man for Western Australia. Today, he thanks his stars he was not in the XI.

'If I had made 30 or 40 and kept my place in the team I would have concentrated on cricket because cricket was my first love,' he said. 'I might have become a cricketer instead of a golfer.'

Gale is one of Australia's most consistent players, but he is hardly a golfing star. 'I'm a low-key player,' he said. 'People don't jump up and down about me,' Yet Gale earns more than $200,000 a year as a golfer — at least twice as much as he would had he become a Test cricketer.

Still, there is no doubt that Test cricketers fare better on the whole than other team sportsmen. Although Peter Daicos, the Collingwood Victorian Football League player, and Wally Lewis, the Australian Rugby League captain, are reckoned to earn about $100,000 each from their games, the fact is that nearly all first-grade Rugby League and VFL footballers earn much less than this. Most have incomes ranging from $20,000 to $30,000.

Soccer players do not do so handsomely, with the Australian captain, John Kosmina, thought to make about $12,000, including wages reimbursement.

The present earning power of cricketers has several interesting implications. First, it means that umpires' decisions can have a profound effect on players financially. It is not hard to imagine a situation in which, say, an lbw ruling against a batsman could eventually cost him tens of thousands of dollars if he lost his place in the team because of it.

Second, it means that selectors' decisions, too, can make or break a player financially. Phil Ridings, the retiring chairman of selectors, says this never occurred to him when he was selecting Australian teams. 'I'm rather pleased it didn't,' he says.

— Philip Derriman,
The Age, 16 July 1984

TOBACCO SPONSORSHIP OF SPORT

[Excerpt from *The Way We P(l)ay*, a report of the House of Representatives Standing Committee on Expenditure, November, 1983.]

Tobacco company sponsorship of sport is a sensitive issue in the sports community. The Anti-Cancer Council of Victoria claimed to the Committee that tobacco company sponsorship of sport helped to defeat a major purpose of Commonwealth assistance to sport and recreation, namely the encouragement of more healthy lifestyles among Australians.

The Council recommended that Commonwealth financial assistance be denied to sporting organisations which accepted tobacco company sponsorship. There was some dissension of opinion on this matter among sporting organisations who gave evidence to the Committee. A number of sporting organisations took the view that they should be able to accept sponsorship from any legitimate source and that any restrictions on this source of assistance would prove detrimental to sport in general. Other sporting organisations had adopted a policy of either not accepting or not seeking tobacco company sponsorship. Some organisations extended this policy to cover other so-called health risk products such as alcohol.

Public health objectives are one set of a number of policy objectives for sport and recreation. Other objectives such as the improvement of the administration of sporting organisations may be served well by tobacco company sponsorship. The question facing government is whether the harm to public health or other policy objectives caused by continued tobacco company sport sponsorship outweighs these benefits to sporting organisations.

Commonwealth and State Health Ministers have recommended that tobacco company sponsorship of sport be restricted by disallowing so-called 'indirect advertising' at sporting fixtures. The Commonwealth Department of Health, in a submission to the Committee, recommended that the Committee heed the recommendation of the Senate Standing Committee on Social Welfare in its report on 'Drug Problems in Australia — An Intoxicated Society' (1977):

> That the Commonwealth Government make any grants to sporting and cultural bodies conditional on their not accepting money from manufacturers and retailers of tobacco products and investigate the possibility of indemnifying such bodies for loss of revenue, at least in the short term....

The Committee considered that, to be effective, any eventual Commonwealth policy on tobacco company sponsorship of sport would need to address four questions:

- Does tobacco company sports sponsorship constitute a deliberate advertising campaign in response to a loss of public image or government action?
- Would the removal of tobacco comapny sponsorship have a significant effect wholly or in part on the level of tobacco consumption?
- What would be the consequences for sporting organisations and sport generally of the withdrawal of tobacco company sponsorship?
- Why should tobacco products, out of a number of alleged health risk products, be singled out for special attention? The Committee felt that the sponsorship of sporting organisations by tobacco companies did amount, at least, to indirect product advertising....

The second question addressed the heart of the policy issue. The Committee considered three possible answers to the question:

- Advertising does not influence the level of consumption of tobacco but the market share of the advertised product. The overall level of consumption is determined by other, less tractable factors.
- Advertising does influence the level of consumption, but only marginally. Banning advertising will have only an insignificant effect. Reliance should be placed on other measures.
- Advertising influences the level of consumption significantly, and banning advertising, provided it is total, can have a significant effect. Education programs may be a necessary adjunct of the ban.

The evidence available to the Committee suggested that a total ban may have some effect, but it was not conclusive. In Norway a total ban on tobacco advertising since 1975 has been associated with a significant reduction in tobacco consumption. On the other hand, the evidence of a more recent total ban in Singapore was not supportive.

— From *The Way We P(l)ay*, AGPS, 1983, extracted in *The ACHPER National Journal*, December 1984

WHO BENEFITS ANYWAY FROM SPONSORSHIP?

When you have two billion dollars riding on the result (that, roughly, is the amount Government collects from smoking and drinking) it is not surprising that morality gets mixed up with money — and that the latter somehow influences the former.

Hence the equivocal outcome to last week's debate about what to do with that hot potato, or burning issue: sports sponsorships by tobacco companies.

Health Ministers couldn't quite bring themselves to ban those signs around fences even though the Federal Minister, Dr Blewett, was concerned about suggestions that TV cameras remained 'lovingly on cigarette billboards and people smoking' — as if this were some dastardly plot by the stations, hatched by the manufacturers.

In truth, the camera follows the action, nothing more. Indeed, stations bend over backwards to prevent any free advertising.

The funny part about it all is that as an advertising medium signs around sports grounds are probably not worth the paper or tin or whatever it is they are written on. It is virtually impossible to trace any results and little research has been conducted to measure recall.

However, one English study in 1981 said flatly 'the substantial costs of sports ground advertising were unlikely to be justified by the benefits'.

For while 53 per cent of a 2000-plus sample could remember 'seeing sports ground advertising via television', less than two per cent were able to recall a coded list of actual advertisers. The highest registration for any one advertiser was eight per cent.

So, while cigarette manufacturers might quite legitimately insist on their sovereign right to advertise a product which it is quite legal to manufacture (and in that is wrapped the real argument) it probably wouldn't amount to a puff of smoke if ads around the pickets were banned.

Except those indigent footballers, cricketers, tennis players, golfers et al. might suffer some horrible withdrawal symptoms. They would have to get by on less.

— R. R. Walker, 'Advertising' column, *The Age*, 4 May 1983

Figure 49.2 Sports ground advertising: effective or not?

Debate: Sponsorship and health risk products

Using the articles reprinted above, and your own research among newspaper and magazine articles and other sources, set up a class debate on either of these topics:

(1) That the sponsorship of sporting associations by companies producing alleged health-risk products, such as alcohol and tobacco, is important for the maintenance of sporting events in Australia.

or

(2) That the sponsorship of sporting associations by companies producing alleged health-risk products, such as alcohol and tobacco, is hypocritical and, in the long term, detrimental to the livelihood of Australians.

Research work 19: Effects of large-scale sponsorship of sport

(1) From your reading of current newspapers, find out the most important examples of massive sponsorship of sport by large companies.

(2) What are the main consequences of large-scale sponsorship of sport?
  (a) **Positive** — for example, increased participation in a particular sport
  (b) **Negative** — for example, the neglect of minor sports that cannot gain sponsorship
  (c) **Other consequences** — for example, changes made to the nature of a particular game.

50. Women in sport

Boys *will* be boys. But even that wouldn't matter if only we could prevent girls from being girls.
— Anonymous

DO WOMEN GET A SPORTING CHANCE?

Responses to the Commonwealth Government's recently appointed working group on women in sport show decisively that media coverage of women's sport is inadequate, says the group's convener, Senator Rosemary Crowley.

More than 100 submissions received so far from associations and interested individuals indicate a widespread awareness and dissatisfaction, says Senator Crowley, who is herself a marathon runner.

'We understand that media executives have to operate within given guidelines. We are not trying to divide, but to extend,' she says. 'But the more women's sports are covered, the more women will read their papers, watch their television and listen to their radio.'

Male sports like football, cricket, golf and racing get big coverage and have access to the best facilities and grants, she says. 'For instance, in Victoria, junior football got about $150,000; yet netball, which has about as many juniors involved as football, got $28,000.

'We don't intend to give a litany of how bad things are but we do want to find out how best to deal with them. We have to look closely at sports issues for migrant and Aboriginal women and for handicapped people.'

One frequently voiced concern was over the lack of professionalism in women's sports associations. Another was over virtually compulsory merging of their groups with the men's, because of the Government's insistence on payment of grants to one 'parent' body.

'Perhaps a lot of any shortcoming in professionalism has something to do with women's own lack of self-esteem. They often go out of sporting activities at child-bearing age. This is the time when men are athletically at their peak. We have made adjustments in our society for such men, but we have not given the same consideration to women in their child-bearing age,' Senator Crowley says.

Figure 50.1 Gail Van bowls for Victoria.

The group will examine television cover (mostly overseas) of high-profile women's sports like tennis, swimming, ice skating, athletics, gymnastics and golf. It will look for options to increase coverage through features on less popular sports and historical angles on women's involvement in sports traditionally dominated by men, such as the Olympics, cricket, athletics and rowing.

One member of the group is Joyce Brown,

former captain and more recently coach of three world champion Australian netball teams. 'The Jack High television bowls series could just as easily be the Jill High,' she says. 'Women are just as heavily committed and as interested and as skilful.

'Women are believed to read far more sports magazines than men do. I believe they are sick and tired of watching men's sports on television and reading newspapers full of men's sport,' she suggests.

'The lack of coverage of women's sport means there is no role model for young girls to see that they could be successful, that they should have expectations.

'For a long time women have had to apologise for their activities in sport. Women can be proud of their sporting achievements and it is important that they can parade their egos to each other. Girls don't get to see that role. And after all, women pay half the taxes of this country,' she says.

'Let's see the Prime Minister and top level women at the woemen's events, saying, "Yes, women have done well in sport". With Betty Cuthbert, we didn't say "Yes, but she didn't run against men". And did we say Dawn Fraser was great but she didn't swim against men?'

Joyce Brown sounds a note of warning to women, however. 'When women want media coverage, they must be prepared. It's a tough world out there. How many women would want to cope with what Kim Hughes has had to take? We must take the good with the bad.'

— Peg McMahon,
The Age, 7 December 1984

WOMEN'S SPORT AND THE MEDIA

From 16 years' reporting women's sport at grass roots, State, national and international level, I must concur with most of the criticism about coverage. The situation is improving, but slowly.

'The Age', for instance, has recently appointed a female cadet to cover sport generally, which is a good trend since women's achievements ought not be treated differently from men's. The ABC, too, has recently appointed a female sports reporter.

Sadly, however, there seems still to remain a sea of male conditioning, even among the best-intentioned males, who fail to recognise many quite superb skills of women. Generally, to make the back page pictures, a woman athlete needs to look like Jan Stephenson, Raelene Boyle in poetic motion or the elfin Nadia Comaneci. Not so with male footballers or cricketers. They may look like a tin of worms and still make the pictures.

But the problem is almost equally with the women's sports themselves. Experience has taught that trying to get news from many of them is akin to drawing a tooth. And then they carefully hide anything they don't want exposed, regardless of public interest. They seem to regard the media as some kind of publicity machine for them.

Perhaps decades of doing their own thing — making decisions over kitchen tables and coming out, regardless, with an efficient operation in the sports arena — has led them to believe they could get along without the help of the media.

That tactic may have operated successfully in many cases in the past, but no longer. This is an era when, like it or not, Government and sponsorship money is essential to their very existence.

Because sport is an acknowledged top-value goodwill platform, governments and sponsors are increasing their input but expecting their pound of flesh. This comes from maximum exposure. So the circle continues: women must win a segment of it, since their recognition is tied directly to it.

More women are in the work force — about 45 per cent — so fewer women now have the time it takes to devote in an honorary capacity to the running of a sport. Indeed, the very funding of paid sports organisers has itself created

▶

problems in many areas. Honorary workers over many years now ask 'Why should I?' The voluntary tea-maker or orange-cutter is almost as scarce as the dodo.

The group's findings on merging of men's and women's associations appear valid. In most cases merging has operated to the detriment of women, especially in robbing them of decision-making.

It has naturally been more convenient for governments — and both Liberal and Labor share the responsibility — to pay out one grant and hope, ostrich-like, that all will be neatly confined in stipulated boxes. It does not work like that.

Experts suggest that the dramatic fall in the number of women athletes competing is directly connected with merging. Joint programs have become too long and tedious and much of the fun has gone out of the sport.

— Peg McMahon, *The Age*, 7 December 1984

Figure 50.2 Deborah Towns and principal John McConville in the playground of Wembley Primary School, Yarraville.

DEBATE: CHILD'S PLAY, THE NOT SO EASY ISSUE

[Are girls losing out to boys in school sport because of regulations designed to prevent sex discrimination? According to critics of the Commonwealth Sex Discrimination Act, they are. This year, the Victorian Director-General of Education, Dr Norman Curry, told schools the act meant there could be no discrimination in school sport based solely on a child's sex for children under 12.

But sporting bodies claimed that instead of increasing opportunities for girls, the directive would mean they would miss out on the

chance to compete in inter-school and state championship events. . . . GEOFF MASLEN acted as moderator in a debate on the issue between the head of the Education Department's equal opportunity unit, DEBORAH TOWNS, and the president of the Victorian Primary Schools' Sports Association, JOHN McCONVILLE.]

As I understand it, your argument, John McConville, is that instead of increasing sporting opportunities for girls, the Education Department directive would lead to girls missing out on chances to compete in inter-school and state championships. Would you care to expand on that view?

McConville: In the field of athletics and swimming, the act meant that you could not have separate girls' and boys' events; children would be picked by their age — 10 years, 11 years and 12 years — and their ability to compete in whatever events were being held in the competition.

Over a large period of time we have monitored the performances and we could see girls would be lucky to get into many events at these championships. When choosing state teams, there would be very few girls with enough ability to be selected in state teams.

So your argument is that in the peak competitions, boys in the same age group are going to be superior to girls and therefore fewer or, in some cases, no girls in fact will have an opportunity to compete in events that at the moment they are able to?

McConville: That is so in the fields of athletics and swimming. We've got results to show that. . . .

Towns: I feel that there has to be a number of introductory things said about the issue of sport and about the spirit of the Sex Discrimination Act. It is important to realise that the Sex Discrimination Act comes from the United Nations convention for the elimination of discrimination against women. It is designed to ensure that the traditions and the inferences about girls' and boys' sport are looked at so that we encourage girls; we ask sports people to review the ways they organise themselves, especially to see that girls develop skills which traditionally have been those developed in boys and not necessarily developed in girls.

A school can start by developing programs which will give girls these skills, which boys have traditionally had from a very early age. You can't discuss how many girls would have been in, say, the Pacific Games or how many girls would qualify or how many girls would have won, without looking at the background to the issue.

We have to encourage schools to look at how they organise sport to ensure there is equality of outcomes for girls and boys in sport.

Are you saying that the conditioning and social attitudes of school teachers and parents, and the children themselves, has meant that girls are not as skilful at athletics or swimming as boys are?

Well, you could argue that some girls have been just as skilled as some of the better boys, but you can also argue that it is conditioning in many respects and, at the same time, social expectations. If you give girls different expectations in other areas of the curriculum, such as the use of computers, that is if girls understand there are career opportunities in computer areas, then they are more interested in developing computer skills. I think the same sort of thing can be applied to the issue of sport; because it's an education issue, it's just not dependent on the sport or who is going to win a gold medal. It's a real educational issue.

Do you accept the proposition that there is a conditioning effect and a lack of emphasis on girls being as active as boys, or being encouraged to gain skills the way boys are?

McConville: No, I wouldn't accept that. I've been heavily involved myself in girls' sport and in my 22 years of involvement in sport and primary schools, the girls have had as much skill development as the boys, yet the boys would still come across and be better than the girls at whatever sport they were participating in. . . .

Towns: I have to say two things immediately. If we talk about the expectations of men and women as far as sport is concerned we have to look at the way society addresses men's and women's sport. Now when the women's cricket team won the international final two years ago it was put on the back page of 'The Age', for example, yet if the men's Australian cricket team wins, it's televised for days on end. I mean, male sport is given a lot more prominence. So, women's and girls' attitudes about the importance of sport has to be different.

The other thing that's important is that this is an educational, not just a sport issue. Research has demonstrated that there are differences in the ways boys and girls learn in the classroom. So, as John said, boys and girls can have the same physical education program for six years and yet boys compete better after that program. You can look at the same issue with girls and boys in a primary school class taking mathematics. Although they are in the same classroom for six years, boys and girls don't learn the same skills and that's why we have to look at the dynamics of learning, the dynamics of relationships.

We're finding, in our work, that often when girls are learning on their own and in particular areas which have been seen as areas where girls don't do well, they improve their skills. Where girls are on their own for a short period of time, even for a few years, they can actually catch up, they can have the same sorts of skills taught to them as the boys, given the same expectations. . . .

John McConville, do you accept the proposition that schools have, unconsciously or otherwise, discriminated against girls — or inevitably, because of the behavior of the two groups of children, the more boisterous and active behavior of boys and the quieter one of girls, that girls are relegated to a smaller portion of the school yard, and that school teachers, themselves socially conditioned, are prone to give more time and more equipment to the more demanding males?

I think that's a very general statement. I don't know where the evidence came from, but I can look at primary school areas and I know that as much money has been spent in primary sport facilities and equipment for girls as for boys. I'd say that as much time is spent in teaching skills for girls as boys. And I don't agree with the argument that at the primary school level — which is the level we're looking at because it only affects children under 12 — that there are these differences at the moment.

I think the act ignores a lot of things. There are facts such as genetics and physiological differences in which there is evidence from America that boys can already outrun girls by the age of 2! These are facts that are ignored, even in America now where they have these co-ed sports — they are starting to look at them and say 'Are they right?' Such things as peer group pressure is coming on where boys or girls are failing against the opposite sex, and it's causing humiliation, causing confusion for the children in identifying themselves.

The other point I would like to make is what happens to the girls who are playing traditional boys' sports at age of 10, 11 and 12, when they get older and go to secondary school, if they haven't learnt the skills of some of the girls' sports, which they then have to move into. Football, rugby and so on are not catered for at the secondary level. Surely the school development we are looking at for these children is that which means they can be active in both community sport and other sport as they grow older.

Deborah, what's your reponse to that?

Well, I would hope that all of the students, as individuals, learn the skills that are going to be available to them as adults, not only in competitive sport but social sport. You can't argue that if girls learn about football they're not going to learn about basketball. I would like to think that if boys are learning about cricket and football . . . they'll also be learning about netball and rounders, for example.

Once again, we have to think about what's happening in our schools. Not all primary schools have competitive sports or compete against other schools. Many schools offer modified sports programs where competition or winning is not rated so highly. . . .

— *The Age*, 15 June 1985

Research work 20: Women in sport

Conduct your research on the following topics, using your own files of newspaper and magazine articles, books and other research materials, the articles printed above, and the article, 'No, Women Just Cannot Win' (in Chapter 42 of this book).

(1) What percentage of newspaper articles deal with females and their sports?

(2) How prevalent today is the image of males as shown in terms of strength, ruggedness, aggressiveness and competitiveness?

(3) What is the main type of person that 13-to-15-year-old males emulate?

(4) Is it still true that high-school girls 'drop out' of sport at 13 to 15 years of age? Why? Why not?

(5) Are school sporting programmes biased in favour or against males or females?

(6) Are physical educators biased in favour or against males or females?

(7) Because of the dominance of media coverage of male sports, are school-age children influenced in their attitude to women and female sports?

(8) Are female family members more passive than male members about becoming involved with sport?

(9) Do males place more emphasis than females on winning in sport?

51. Ideas for research projects

Research work 21: Media analysis

Rationale

> The influence of television on the lives of the young cannot be underestimated. Television, by its content alone, teaches children many of the ways of society ... the duties of the detective ... functions of hospitals ... behaviours in hotels ... the language of the football field.
>
> — D. Staniford, *Play and Physical Activity in Early Childhood Socialisation*, (1978), pp. 50–1

Procedure

An analysis of television programmes could include one or more of the following aspects (**Note:** Other media forms — for example, radio and magazines — can be subject to similar analyses):

(1) **Live or recorded?**

(2) **Production techniques**
- Close-up shots
- Crowd shots
- Slow motion
- Camera angles.

(3) **Intended audience**
- Small sectional
- Large sectional
- National interest.

(4) **Commentary style**
- Descriptive
- Sensationalized
- Analytical
- Discussion of plays, tactics, events, etc.

Is it assumed that viewers are initiated into rules and procedures of a particular sport?

(5) **Make a breakdown of programming in relation to total broadcasting time, using the following categories:**

(**a**) Total sports broadcasting time
(**b**) Percentage of sports programming during peak viewing period — that is, 6 p.m.–9 p.m.
(**c**) Percentage of sports programming during non-peak viewing period
(**d**) Broadcasts of Australian sports vs. overseas sports
(**e**) Broadcast of male sport vs. female sport
(**f**) Age groups represented in the sports broadcast
(**g**) Type of sport broadcast by commercial stations cf. those broadcast by national (ABC) network
(**h**) Sports during children's viewing time — 4 p.m.–6 p.m.
(**i**) Amount of time given to contact sports cf. non-contact sports
(**j**) Social values highlighted by camerawork and commentary — for example, comments on skill, misdemeanours, personalities, etc.
(**k**) Sporting component of advertisements — relevant to the product?; use of sporting personalities?

Research work 22: Sport and mass culture

Aims

(1) To determine the percentage of advertisements in a glossy magazine (such as *The Australian Women's Weekly*) which have a sporting component.
(2) To determine what types of sport are projected and their relevance to the products being sold.

Hypothesis and procedure

From wide-ranging research of available magazines and newspapers, work out:

(1) **Your hypothesis**
Your theory about mass culture and sport that you want to test.

(2) **Your procedure**
The series of steps by which you can test the hypothesis, using the assembled evidence.

Research work 23: Sport and migrant students

Read the following extract, and investigate the two questions asked below it:

SPORT AND MIGRANT STUDENTS

School sport often has little relevance to migrant students, according to a secondary teacher who conducted a survey of 134 schoolgirls in Sydney.

Ms Aura Levin told a recent conference at La Trobe University, on The Making of Sporting Traditions, that many migrant students were not socially equipped to understand the Australian sports values of individuality, aggressiveness, competitiveness, teamwork and sportsmanship.

Ms Levin said she had noticed differences between Anglo-Australian and non-English-speaking students in their attitudes towards school sport.

'It seemed to me that there were marked differences in their enthusiasm about sport, their appreciation of its place in school life and their desire to participate in it,' she said.

The survey was conducted at an inner city secondary school in a largely industrial area of Sydney. The girls, aged between 13 and 16, were divided into five groups: Anglo-Australians, Greeks, European and Middle Eastern, Asian and South American. About two-thirds of the girls were from non-English-speaking backgrounds, with Greek students as the biggest single ethnic group.

The survey tried to identify what link, if any, existed between the mothers' interest and experience in sport and their daughters' attitudes towards sport.

Ms Levin said the survey found that only 10 per cent of migrant mothers played sport, compared to 50 per cent of English-speaking mothers. Australian mothers played 12 different sports while migrant mothers only played tennis and table tennis. About the same number of women from English and non-English-speaking backgrounds were employed.

All girls said their mothers saw school sport as important. 'Migrant daughters, however, stressed that compared to their academic subjects their mothers saw sport as mostly irrelevant,' Ms Levin said.

'The migrant girls tended to play less competitive sports and choose more individual sports such as tennis, table tennis and squash rather than team sports such as hockey and softball,' she said.

The survey found that few migrant girls wanted to play sport with boys. Mixed sports were favored by 68 per cent of Australian girls whose mothers played sport and half the Australian girls whose mothers did not participate in any sport.

The only exception among migrant girls were those from Arabic-speaking backgrounds, all of whom favored mixed sport. Ms Levin said these girls were 'extremely shy' and all were Moslem. Many were forbidden to sit next to a boy in their classrooms.

'Therefore mixed sport could possibly be seen for them as a rare opportunity for normal socialising with the opposite sex under relaxed conditions,' Ms Levin said.

Ms Levin said the results of the survey indicated that sport seemed to be more of an exercise for leisure for migrant girls rather than a disciplined, systematic form of physical education.

'While most girls seemed to think that sport was a necessary means of keeping fit and healthy, the predominant view among migrants was that competitive sport was the domain of males,' she said.

'One of the most important issues raised during this study was the lack of relevance of much school sport for students from migrant backgrounds.'

Ms Levin said sports teachers, despite good intentions, were often ill-informed about the problems migrant students faced with sport at school. Moslem girls, for instance, faced barriers participating in school swimming events because of their cultural background. Many migrant students feared ridicule if they tried to explain their values to a teacher.

There were problems with the types of sports played at Australian schools. 'While many schools offer a wide variety of competitive and non-competitive sports, it seems that these are often chosen by "pot luck" depending on the interests of the available teachers and the availability of ground space,' Ms Levin said.

Volleyball, for example, was very popular among Asian girls but ranked low in priority when playground space was tight.

'Teachers in multi-ethnic schools therefore have a responsibility to become aware of the not always apparent barriers that exist for migrant girls in school sport,' Ms Levin said.

'Having become aware, they have a responsibility to encourage them to try to participate more actively and make them feel at ease in their attempts to do so.'

— Mark Brolly,
The Age, 13 October 1981

(1) Investigate the hypothesis presented in the above article that sports teachers, despite good intentions, are often ill-informed about the problems that migrant students face with sport at school.

(2) Can sport be used as a social vehicle for migrant and other minority groups, such as Aborigines? Or could the effort needed to attain acceptable proficiency in one of the major games be better used to learn other vital social skills?

Research ideas

Choose from among the following research ideas those which interest you most. In each case the aim and hypothesis of the research project has been given to you. For each project, you will need to work out a method of investigating the hypothesis.

(1) (a) **Aim**
To determine the sporting preferences of Year 7 and Year 10 students.
(b) **Hypotheses**
(i) Year 7 students are more active than Year 10 students.
(ii) Males are more active than females in school sports.

(2) (a) **Hypothesis**
'In competitive sport, parents place an unnecessary mental strain on children, which detracts from their participation and enjoyment of the game' (R. Matheson)
(b) **Aims**
(i) To determine to what extent children enjoy participating in competitive sport.
(ii) To find out some of the effects of mental strain on children in competitive sport.

(3) (a) **Aims**
(i) To investigate the differences in sports participation between males and females aged between 12 and 21.
(ii) To determine whether socio-economic factors restrict sports participation in this age bracket.
(b) **Hypothesis**
Males aged between 12 and 21 participate:
— In a greater variety of sports
— More frequently
— In more competitive situations
than do females of the same age bracket.

(4) **Hypothesis**
Physical activity, in and out of schools, encourages the development of sex roles in sport.

(5) (a) **Aim**
To ascertain reasons why some elderly people are active and some are inactive.
(b) **Hypothesis**
A lack of facilities is preventing people from playing sports they want to.

(6) (a) **Hypothesis**
Physical activity for adults declines with age because of age stereotyping within society.
(b) **Aims**
(i) To determine whether physical activity declines with age.
(ii) To determine whether age stereotyping causes older people to be less active than younger people.
(iii) To determine the main causes of the decline of physical activity with age.
(iv) To discover possible remedies to the problem of the decline of physical activity with age.

(7) **Aims**
(i) To investigate how physical activity and sport in schools has changed over past generation(s).
(ii) To determine whether males and females differ in the amount of sport offered to them.
(iii) To establish whether or not attending a public or a private school is an advantage as far as the amount of sport offered.

Bibliography

The following texts are referred to in the Parts given as headings. They are also useful references for extending your knowledge of particular areas of the course.

Note: Once a book has been listed, it will not be listed again. Many of the following books can be used for each Part of the book.

Parts 1 and 2

Anthony, C. P., and Thibodeau, G. A., *Anatomy and Physiology Laboratory Manual*, C. V. Mosby, St Louis, 1979

Anthony, C. P., and Thibodeau, G. A, *Structure and Function of the Body*, sixth edition, C. V. Mosby, St Louis, 1980

Astrand, P., and Rodahl, K., *Textbook of Work Physiology*, second edition, McGraw Hill, New York, 1977

Beckett, B. S., *Illustrated Human and Social Biology*, Oxford University Press, Oxford, 1981

Bevan, J., *A Pictorial Handbook of Anatomy and Physiology*, Beazley, London, 1978

Burke, E. J., *Towards an Understanding of Human Performance*, second edition, Mouvement, Ithaca, New York, 1980

Corbin, C. B. (ed.), *Concepts in Physical Education*, second edition, W. Brown, Dubuque, Iowa, 1974

De Vries, H., *Physiology of Exercise for Physical Education and Athletics*, W. C. Brown, Dubuque, Iowa, 1972

De Coursey, R. M., and Renfro, J. L., *The Human Organism*, fifth edition, McGraw Hill, New York, 1980

Edington, D. W., and Cunningham, L., *Biological Awareness: Statements of Self-discovery*, Prentice Hall, Englewood Cliffs, 1975

Edington, D. W., and Edgerton, V. R., *The Biology of Physical Activity*, Houghton Mifflin, 1976

Fox, E., *Sports Physiology*, second edition, W. B. Saunders, Philadelphia, 1979

Getchell, Bud, *Physical Fitness: A Way of Life*, second edition, John Wiley and Sons, 1979

Gibbs, R., *Sports Injuries*, Macmillan, Melbourne, 1977

Hockey, R., *Physical Fitness: The Pathway to Healthy Living*, fourth edition, C. V. Mosby, St Louis, 1981

Jacob, S., and Francone, C., *Structure and Function in Man*, fifth edition, W. B. Saunders, Philadelphia, 1982

Mathews, D., and Fox, E., *The Physiological Basis of Physical Education and Athletics*, third edition, W. B. Saunders, Philadelphia, 1981

Morehouse, L. E., and Miller, A. T., *Physiology of Exercise*, seventh edition, C. V. Mosby, St Louis, 1976

Pyke, F., *Towards Better Coaching*, Australian Government Publishing Service, Canberra, 1980

Pyke, F., and Watson, G., *Focus on Running*, Harper and Row, Sydney, 1979

Robinson, C. H., *Fundamentals of Normal Nutrition*, third edition, Macmillan, New York, 1978

Russo, P., *Aussie Robics*, Paul Hamlyn, Sydney, 1978

Thompson, C., *Manual of Structural Kinesiology*, ninth edition, C. V. Mosby, St Louis, 1981

Tudor, E. R., Tudor, E. McL., Brown, E. H., and Dick, P. G., *Understanding the Human Body: Resource Manual*, Pitman, Melbourne, 1983

Watson, A. W. S., *Physical Fitness and Athletic Performance*, Longman, London, 1983

Part 3

Auty, M. G., *Compendium of Biomechanical Material*, 1984, available from 12 Olympic Avenue, Montmorency, Victoria 3094

Baley, J. A., and Piscopo, J., *Kinesiology: The Science of Movement*, John Wiley, New York, 1981

Barthels, K. M., and Kreighbaum, E., *Biomechanics: A Qualitative Approach*, Burgess, Minneapolis, 1981

Barthels, K. M., and Kreighbaum, E., *Studying Human Movement*, Burgess, Minneapolis, 1981

Broer, M. R., and Zernicke, R. F., *Efficiency of Human Movement*, W. B. Saunders, Philadelphia, 1979

Burke, R. K., and Rasch, P. J., *Kinesiology and Applied Anatomy*, sixth edition, Lea and Febiger, Philadelphia, 1978

Camione, D. N., and Groves, R., *Concepts in Kinesiology*, Saunders, Philadelphia, 1983

Daish, C. B., *The Physics of Ball Games*, second edition, Hodder and Stoughton, London, 1981

Dyson, G. H. G., *The Mechanics of Athletics*, seventh edition, Hodder and Stoughton, London, 1978

Harmer, J. C., and Hosford, G. T., *Biomechanics in Physical Education Slide Teaching Kit*, Victoria College, Burwood, Victoria, 1984

Hay, J. G., *The Biomechanics of Sport Techniques*, second edition, Prentice Hall, Englewood Cliffs, 1978

Hay, J. G., and Reid, G. J., *The Anatomical and Mechanical Bases of Human Motion*, Prentice Hall, Englewood Cliffs, 1982

ISIS (ed.), *Physics of Sport*, Ginn, Lexington, Massachusetts, 1980

Jensen, C. R., and Schultz, G. W., *Applied Kinesiology: The Scientific Study of Human Performance*, McGraw-Hill, New York, 1970

Krause, J. V., and Barham, J. N., *The Mechanical Foundations of Human Motion*, C. V. Mosby, St Louis, 1975

Howell, R., and Howell, M., *Foundations of Physical Education*, W. Brooks, Brisbane, 1984

Logan, G. A., McKinney, W. C., and Northrip, J. W., *Introduction to Biomechanical Analysis of Sport*, second edition, W. C. Brown, Toronto, 1974

Page, R. L., *The Physics of Human Movement*, A. Wheaton, London, 1978

Payne, H., and Payne, R., *The Science of Track and Field Athletics*, Pelham, London, 1981

Pyke, F. S. (ed.), *Towards Better Coaching: The Art and Science of Sports Coaching*, AGPS, Canberra, 1970

Pyke, F. S., and Watson, G., *Focus on Running: An Introduction to Human Movement*, Harper and Row, Sydney, 1978

Part 4

Boulton, A., and Duncan, N., *Reaction Timer: Skill Acquisition Computer Package*, 1984, available from 35 Essex Road, Surrey Hills, Victoria 3127

Cratty, B. J., *Teaching Motor Skills*, Prentice Hall, Englewood Cliffs, 1973

Drowatzky, J. N., *Motor Learning Principles and Practices*, Burgess, Minneapolis, 1981

Harris, J., *Principles Underlying Skill Acquisition*, Reading Guide B13, Physical Education Curriculum Committee, Melbourne, 1982

Knapp, B., *Skill in Sport*, Routledge, London, 1963

Lawther, J. D., *The Learning and Performance of Physical Skills*, Prentice Hall, Englewood Cliffs, 1977

Magill, R. A., *Motor Learning Concepts and Applications*, second edition, W. C. Brown, Dubuque, Iowa, 1985

Martenuik, R. G., *Information Processing in Motor Skills*, Holt, New York, 1976

Nettleton, B., *You're the Coach*, AGPS, Canberra, 1980

Robb, M., *The Dynamics of Skill Acquisition*, Prentice Hall, Englewood Cliffs, 1972

Schmidt, R. A., *Motor Control and Learning*, Human Kinetics Publishers, Illinois, 1982

Singer, R. N., *Motor Learning and Human Performance*, second edition, 1975, third edition, 1980, Macmillan, New York

Whiting, H. T. A., *Acquiring Ball Skill*, G. Bell, London, 1976

Part 5

Historical investigation

Barber, R., *Tournaments*, Penguin, London, 1978

Brailsford, D., *Sport in Society: Elizabeth to Anne*, Routledge, London, 1969

Cashman, R., and McKernan, M. (eds.), *Sport in History*, University of Queensland Press, St Lucia, 1979

Comte, S., *Everyday Life in the Middle Ages*, Editions Minerva, Geneva, 1978

D'Agostino, B., *Greece*, Cassell, London, 1974

Education Department of Victoria, *Physical Education for Post Primary Schools*, 1975

Education Department of Victoria, *Physical Education — Technical Schools, Program Guidelines, Years 10–11*, 1980

Education Department of Victoria, *Program Guidelines for Victorian Secondary Schools*, 1979

Glanville, B., *The Puffin Book of Tennis*, Penguin, Harmondsworth, 1981
Grant, M., *The Olympic Games*, Penguin, London, 1980
Harris, H. A., *Greek Athletes and Athletics*, Greenwood Press, Connecticut, 1979
Harris, H. A., *Sport in Greece and Rome*, Thames and Hudson, London, 1972
Howell, R. (ed.), *Her Story in Sport*, Leisure Press, New York, 1982
Jeffreys, S., *Tourney and Joust*, Wayland, London, 1973
Kinross Smith, G., *The Sweet Spot*, Hyland House, Melbourne, 1983
Lawn Tennis Association of Victoria, *A Journey into the Past: The Story of Tennis*, Melbourne, 1976
McIntosh, P. C. et al., *Landmarks in the History of Physical Education*, revised edition, Routledge, London, 1981
Moss, P., *Sports and Pastimes through the Ages*, Argo, New York, 1962
Mountfield, D., *Everyday life in Elizabethan England*, Editions Minerva, Geneva, 1978
Pierroti-cei, Luisa, *Life in Italy during the Renaissance*, Editions Minerva, Geneva, 1977
Ricker, J., and Saywell, J., *Greece: The Greatness of Man*, Clarke Irwin, Toronto, 1973
Van Dalen, D. B., and Bennett, B. L., *A World History of Physical Education*, second edition, Prentice Hall, Englewood Cliffs, 1971

Investigation of current issues

Boutilier, M. A. and San Giovanni, L., *The Sporting Woman*, Human Kinetics, Illinois, 1983
Cashman, R., and McKernan, M. (eds.), *Sport: Morality and the Media*, University of New South Wales, Sydney, 1981
Cashmore, E., *Black Sportsmen*, Routledge, London, 1982
Cratty, B. J., *Children and Youth in Competitive Sports*, Educational Activities, New York, 1974
Dyer, K. F., *Challenging the Men: Women in Sport*, University of Queensland Press, St Lucia, 1982
Gillett, C., *All in the Game*, Penguin, London, 1971
Jacques, T. D., and Pavia, G. R., *Sport in Australia*, McGraw-Hill, Sydney, 1976
Jenkin, D., et al., *Beneath the Surface of Sport*, Victoria College, Rusden, 1983
Leonard, W. M., *A Sociological Perspective of Sport*, Burgess, Minneapolis, 1980
McNab, T., *The Complete Book of Athletics*, Ward Lock, London, 1980
Mandle, B., *Winners Can Laugh*, Penguin, Ringwood, 1974
Mitchell, S., and Dyer, K., *Winning Women*, Penguin, Ringwood, 1985
Morris, D., *The Soccer Tribe*, Cape, London, 1981
Oglesby, C. A., *Women and Sport: From Myth to Reality*, Lea and Febiger, Philadelphia, 1978
Royal Melbourne Tennis Club, Richmond, Victoria — information
Sands, R. (ed.), *Beneath the Surface of Sport*, Laboratory Manual, VICTRACC, Melbourne, 1985
Schickel, R., *The World of Tennis*, Random House, Toronto, 1975
Shneidman, N. N., *The Soviet Road to Olympus*, Routledge, London, 1979
Snyder, E., and Spreitzner, E., *Social Aspects of Sport*, Prentice Hall, Englewood Cliffs, 1978
Tilmanis, G. A., *Advanced Tennis for Coaches, Teachers and Players*, ANZ Book Co., Sydney, 1975
Victorian Tennis Assoication — information
Whittington, R. S., *An Illustrated History of Australian Tennis*, Macmillan, Melbourne, 1975

Part 6

Books

Singer, R. N. (ed.), *Physical Education: Foundations*, Holt, Rinehart, Winston, New York, 1975
Coakley, J., *Sport in Society*, C. V. Mosby, St Louis, 1978
Craig, T. T. (ed.), *The Humanistic and Health Aspects of Sports Exercise and Recreation*, sponsored by the Committee on the Medical Aspects of Sports, American Medical Association, Chicago, 1976
Dunstan, K., *Sports*, Cassell, Sydney, 1973
Hart, M., and Birrell, S., *Sport in the Sociocultural Process*, third edition, W. C. Brown, Dubuque, Iowa, 1981
Hoch, P., *Rip Off the Big Game*, Doubleday, New York, 1972
MacCallum, M., 'Get 'Em Moving', in *Fitness for Older Adults*, Ottawa, Canada, 1982

Peter, R., *Preparting for Retirement*, report prepared for the Department of Youth, Sport and Recreation, Western Australia, August 1983

Roberts, G., et al., *Social Science of Play, Games and Sport: Learning Experiences*, Human Kinetics, Champaign, Illinois, 1979

Saunders, E. D., and White, G. B., *Social Investigation in Physical Education and Sport*, State Mutual Books, New York, 1980

Skoll, L., 'Growing Fitter, Growing Older', in *Fitness for Older Adults*, Ottawa, Canada, 1982

Staniford, D., *Play and Physical Activity in Early Childhood Socialization*, Canadian Association for Health, Physical Education and Recreation, Vanier City, Ontario, 1978

Storey, D., *This Sporting Life*, Penguin, London, 1960

Wicks, B. M., *Whatever Happened to Australian Rules?*, Libra, Hobart, 1980

Yiannakis, et al., *Sport Sociology: Contemporary Thems*, Kendall Hunt, Iowa, 1976

Laboratory and field experiences

Sands, R. (ed.), *Beneath the Surface of Sport* (details — list for Part 5)

Smith, R., *HSC Physical Education Laboratory Book*, Londs Publishing, Melbourne, 1982

Films

The State Film Centre (Victoria) has the following relevant films at the time of writing, but it is advised that ongoing contact be established with the centre for advice concerning new releases:

Understanding Aggro: Hooliganism (UK, 1976), colour, 16 mm, 30 minutes (origins and forms of soccer hooliganism)

Women in Sports: An Informal History (US, 1976), 16 mm, 28 minutes

Sports for the Handicapped (The Other Olympics), three tracks, motion picture

Girls Sport: On the Right Track (1975), colour, 16 mm, 17 minutes (movement from limited to increasing opportunity for female sports)

The Other Olympians (Melbourne, 1980), colour, 16 mm, 23 minutes (training of two athletes for 1980 Olympics)

Children and Sports (US, 1980), colour, 16 mm, 27 minutes

Breaking Down the Barriers (Australia, 1981), colour, 16 mm, 30 minutes

A Sporting Chance (Australia, 1980), colour, 16 mm, 25 minutes (a view of female sex role conditioning).

Periodicals

Sport Report
Prime Time
Sports Coach Journal
AJPHER.

Index